Name	Symbol	Atomic Number	Atomic Mass[a]	Name	Sym[bol]	[Atomic Number]	[Atomic M]ass[a]
Actinium	Ac	89	(227)	Neodymium	N		
Aluminum	Al	13	26.98	Neon	Ne	10	20.18
Americium	Am	95	(243)	Neptunium	Np	93	(237)
Antimony	Sb	51	121.8	Nickel	Ni	28	58.69
Argon	Ar	18	39.95	Niobium	Nb	41	92.91
Arsenic	As	33	74.92	Nitrogen	N	7	14.01
Astatine	At	85	(210)	Nobelium	No	102	(259)
Barium	Ba	56	137.3	Osmium	Os	76	190.2
Berkelium	Bk	97	(247)	Oxygen	O	8	16.00
Beryllium	Be	4	9.012	Palladium	Pd	46	106.4
Bismuth	Bi	83	209.0	Phosphorus	P	15	30.97
Bohrium	Bh	107	(264)	Platinum	Pt	78	195.1
Boron	B	5	10.81	Plutonium	Pu	94	(244)
Bromine	Br	35	79.90	Polonium	Po	84	(209)
Cadmium	Cd	48	112.4	Potassium	K	19	39.10
Calcium	Ca	20	40.08	Praseodymium	Pr	59	140.9
Californium	Cf	98	(251)	Promethium	Pm	61	(145)
Carbon	C	6	12.01	Protactinium	Pa	91	231.0
Cerium	Ce	58	140.1	Radium	Ra	88	(226)
Cesium	Cs	55	132.9	Radon	Rn	86	(222)
Chlorine	Cl	17	35.45	Rhenium	Re	75	186.2
Chromium	Cr	24	52.00	Rhodium	Rh	45	102.9
Cobalt	Co	27	58.93	Roentgenium	Rg	111	(272)
Copper	Cu	29	63.55	Rubidium	Rb	37	85.47
Curium	Cm	96	(247)	Ruthenium	Ru	44	101.1
Darmstadtium	Ds	110	(271)	Rutherfordium	Rf	104	(261)
Dubnium	Db	105	(262)	Samarium	Sm	62	150.4
Dysprosium	Dy	66	162.5	Scandium	Sc	21	44.96
Einsteinium	Es	99	(252)	Seaborgium	Sg	106	(266)
Erbium	Er	68	167.3	Selenium	Se	34	78.96
Europium	Eu	63	152.0	Silicon	Si	14	28.09
Fermium	Fm	100	(257)	Silver	Ag	47	107.9
Fluorine	F	9	19.00	Sodium	Na	11	22.99
Francium	Fr	87	(223)	Strontium	Sr	38	87.62
Gadolinium	Gd	64	157.3	Sulfur	S	16	32.07
Gallium	Ga	31	69.72	Tantalum	Ta	73	180.9
Germanium	Ge	32	72.64	Technetium	Tc	43	(98)
Gold	Au	79	197.0	Tellurium	Te	52	127.6
Hafnium	Hf	72	178.5	Terbium	Tb	65	158.9
Hassium	Hs	108	(269)	Thallium	Tl	81	204.4
Helium	He	2	4.003	Thorium	Th	90	232.0
Holmium	Ho	67	164.9	Thulium	Tm	69	168.9
Hydrogen	H	1	1.008	Tin	Sn	50	118.7
Indium	In	49	114.8	Titanium	Ti	22	47.87
Iodine	I	53	126.9	Tungsten	W	74	183.8
Iridium	Ir	77	192.2	Uranium	U	92	238.0
Iron	Fe	26	55.85	Vanadium	V	23	50.94
Krypton	Kr	36	83.80	Xenon	Xe	54	131.3
Lanthanum	La	57	138.9	Ytterbium	Yb	70	173.0
Lawrencium	Lr	103	(260)	Yttrium	Y	39	88.91
Lead	Pb	82	207.2	Zinc	Zn	30	65.41
Lithium	Li	3	6.941	Zirconium	Zr	40	91.22
Lutetium	Lu	71	175.0	—	—	112	(285)
Magnesium	Mg	12	24.31	—	—	113	(284)
Manganese	Mn	25	54.94	—	—	114	(289)
Meitnerium	Mt	109	(268)	—	—	115	(288)
Mendelevium	Md	101	(258)	—	—	116	(292)
Mercury	Hg	80	200.6	—	—	118	(293)
Molybdenum	Mo	42	95.94				

[a]Values in parentheses are the mass number of the most stable isotope.

Improve Your Understanding!

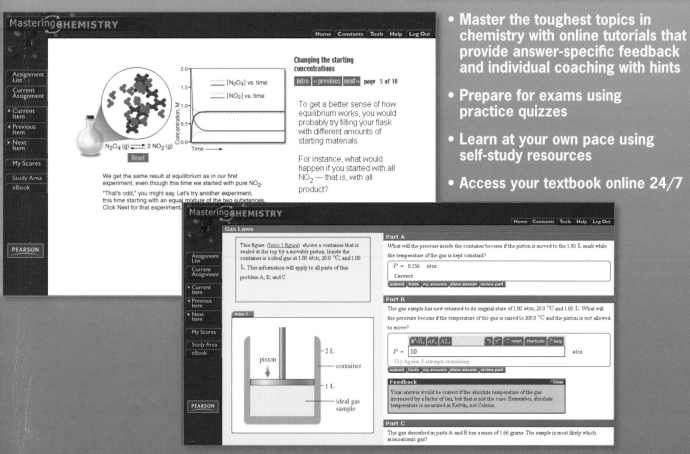

GENERAL, ORGANIC, AND BIOLOGICAL CHEMISTRY

STRUCTURES OF LIFE

VOLUME 2

KAREN C. TIMBERLAKE

GEORGIA PERIMETER COLLEGE EDITION - CHEM 1152

Taken from:
General, Organic, and Biological Chemistry: Structures of Life, Third Edition
by Karen C. Timberlake

Custom Publishing

New York Boston San Francisco
London Toronto Sydney Tokyo Singapore Madrid
Mexico City Munich Paris Cape Town Hong Kong Montreal

Cover Art: Courtesy of Photodisc/Getty Images

Taken from:

General, Organic, and Biological Chemistry: Structures of Life, Third Edition
by Karen C. Timberlake
Copyright © 2010 by Pearson Education, Inc.
Published by Prentice Hall
A Pearson Education Company
Upper Saddle River, New Jersey 07458

This special edition published in cooperation with Pearson Custom Publishing.

Printed in the United States of America

10 9 8 7 6 5 4

2009180022

DM

**Pearson
Custom Publishing**
is a division of

www.pearsonhighered.com

ISBN 10: 0-558-33161-0
ISBN 13: 978-0-558-33161-0

BRIEF CONTENTS

CONTENTS

11
Introduction to Organic Chemistry: Alkanes   415

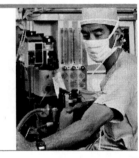

12
Alkenes, Alkynes, and Aromatic Compounds   446

15

Carbohydrates   542

16

Carboxylic Acids and Esters   575

17

Lipids   602

18
Amines and Amides   644

19
Amino Acids and Proteins   672

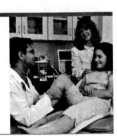

20
Enzymes and Vitamins   702

21

Nucleic Acids and Protein Synthesis   738

APPLICATIONS AND ACTIVITIES

ENVIRONMENTAL NOTE

GREEN CHEMISTRY NOTE

GUIDE TO PROBLEM SOLVING

ABOUT THE AUTHOR

Karen Timberlake is Professor Emerita of chemistry at Los Angeles Valley College, where she taught chemistry for allied health and preparatory chemistry for 36 years. She received her bachelor's degree in chemistry from the University of Washington and her master's degree in biochemistry from the University of California at Los Angeles.

Professor Timberlake has been writing chemistry textbooks for 33 years. During that time, her name has become associated with the strategic use of pedagogical tools that promote student success in chemistry and the application of chemistry to real-life situations. More than one million students have learned chemistry using texts, laboratory manuals, and study guides written by Karen Timberlake. In addition to *General, Organic, and Biological Chemistry: Structures of Life*, third edition, she is also the author of *Basic Chemistry*, second edition, and *Chemistry: An Introduction to General, Organic, and Biological Chemistry*, tenth edition with the accompanying *Study Guide, Selected Solutions Manual, Laboratory Manual*, and *Essential Laboratory Manual*.

Professor Timberlake belongs to numerous science and educational organizations including the American Chemical Society (ACS) and the National Science Teachers Association (NSTA). She was the Western Regional Winner of Excellence in College Chemistry Teaching Award given by Chemical Manufacturers Association. In 2004, she received the McGuffey Award in Physical Sciences from the Text and Academic Authors Association for her textbook *Chemistry: An Introduction to General, Organic, and Biological Chemistry*, eighth edition, which has demonstrated excellence over time. In 2006, she received the Textbook Excellence Award for the first edition of *Basic Chemistry*. She has participated in education grants for science teaching including the Los Angeles Collaborative for Teaching Excellence (LACTE) and a Title III grant at her college. She speaks at conferences and educational meetings on the use of student-centered teaching methods in chemistry to promote learning success of students.

Her husband, Bill, is also a chemistry professor and has contributed to writing this text. He taught preparatory and organic chemistry at Los Angeles Harbor College for 36 years. When the professors Timberlake are not writing textbooks, they relax by hiking, traveling, trying new restaurants, cooking, and playing tennis.

PREFACE

To the Student

Welcome to the third edition of *General, Organic, and Biological Chemistry: Structures of Life.* This chemistry text was written and designed to help you prepare for a career in a health-related profession, such as nursing, dietetics, respiratory therapy, and environmental and agricultural science. My main objective in writing this text is to make the study of chemistry an engaging and positive experience for you by relating the structure and behavior of matter to its functions in health and life. This new edition introduces rich problem-solving strategies, including new concept checks, more problem-solving guides, conceptual and challenge problems, and new sets of combined problems.

It is also my goal to help you become a critical thinker by connecting the scientific concepts with current issues concerning health and the environment. Thus, I have utilized materials that

- motivate you to learn and enjoy chemistry;
- relate chemistry to careers that interest you;
- develop problem-solving skills that lead to your success in your chemistry course; and
- promote learning and your success in your chosen career.

I hope that this textbook helps you discover exciting new ideas and gives you a rewarding experience as you develop an understanding and appreciation of the role of chemistry in your life.

Features of this Text

You may wonder why your career path includes a class in chemistry. A common view is that chemistry is just a lot of facts to be memorized. To change this perception, I have included many features to help you learn about chemistry in your life and career choice and to give you the skills to learn chemistry successfully. These features include connections to health, the environment, and green chemistry, visual guides to problem solving, and in-chapter problem sets to work immediately that reinforce the learning of new concepts. A successful learning program in this text provides you with many learning tools, which are discussed here.

Career Focus and Real-World Applications

This Text Was Designed to Help Students Attain Their Career Goals

Chapter Opening Interviews with Scientists and Health Care Professionals   Each chapter begins with an interview with a professional in a career such as nursing, forensic anthropology, nuclear medicine, dentistry, and oceanography. These professionals discuss the importance of chemistry in their careers.

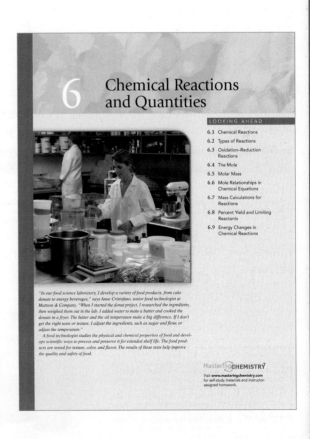

6 Chemical Reactions and Quantities

LOOKING AHEAD

6.1 Chemical Reactions
6.2 Types of Reactions
6.3 Oxidation–Reduction Reactions
6.4 The Mole
6.5 Molar Mass
6.6 Mole Relationships in Chemical Equations
6.7 Mass Calculations for Reactions
6.8 Percent Yield and Limiting Reactants
6.9 Energy Changes in Chemical Reactions

"In our food science laboratory, I develop a variety of food products, from cake donuts to energy beverages," says Anne Cristofano, senior food technologist at Mattson & Company. "When I started the donut project, I researched the ingredients, then weighed them out in the lab. I added water to make a batter and cooked the donuts in a fryer. The batter and the oil temperature make a big difference. If I don't get the right taste or texture, I adjust the ingredients, such as sugar and flour, or adjust the temperature."

A food technologist studies the physical and chemical properties of food and develops scientific ways to process and preserve it for extended shelf life. The food products are tested for texture, color, and flavor. The results of these tests help improve the quality and safety of food.

Mastering CHEMISTRY

Visit www.masteringchemistry.com for self-study materials and instructor-assigned homework.

Career Focus   Within the chapters are additional interviews with allied health professionals using chemistry.

On the Web   The **MasteringChemistry Study Area** features in-depth resources for each of the health professions featured in the book and takes students through interactive case studies.

Students Will Learn Chemistry Using Real-World Examples

NEW Green Chemistry Notes   The new **Green Chemistry Notes** highlight the practical applications of chemistry that are beneficial to human health and the environment. The new green chemistry approach that chemists, engineers, scientists, health professionals, and researchers are taking focuses on practices and products that are "benign by design" and that provide sustainability.

GREEN CHEMISTRY NOTE

Fuel Cells: Clean Energy for the Future

Fuel cells are of interest to scientists because they provide an alternative source of electrical energy that is more efficient, does not use up oil reserves, and generates products that do not pollute the atmosphere. Fuel cells are considered a clean way to produce energy.

Unlike a battery that runs down, fuel cells are provided continually with new reactants to generate an electrical current. One type of hydrogen–oxygen fuel cell has been used in automobile prototypes. In this hydrogen cell, gas enters the fuel cell, where it comes in contact with platinum embedded in a plastic membrane. The platinum assists in the oxidation of hydrogen atoms to hydrogen ions and electrons:

$$2H_2(g) \xrightarrow{Pt} 4H^+(aq) + 4e^- \quad \text{Oxidation}$$

The electrons produce an electric current as they travel through the wire. The hydrogen ions move through the plastic membrane to react with oxygen molecules. The oxygen is reduced to oxide ions that combine with the hydrogen ions to form water:

$$O_2(g) + 4H^+(aq) + 4e^- \longrightarrow 2H_2O(l) \quad \text{Reduction}$$

The overall hydrogen–oxygen fuel cell reaction can be written as

$$2H_2(g) + O_2(g) \longrightarrow 2H_2O(l)$$

Fuel cells have already been used to power the space shuttle and may soon be available to produce energy for cars and buses.

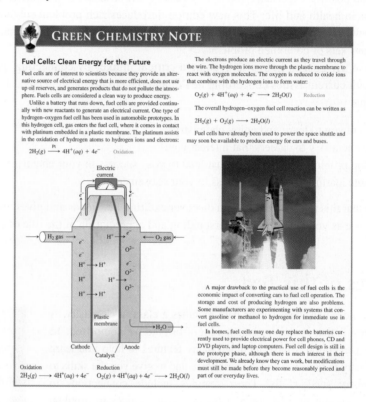

A major drawback to the practical use of fuel cells is the economic impact of converting cars to fuel cell operation. The storage and cost of producing hydrogen are also problems. Some manufacturers are experimenting with systems that convert gasoline or methanol to hydrogen for immediate use in fuel cells.

In homes, fuel cells may one day replace the batteries currently used to provide electrical power for cell phones, CD and DVD players, and laptop computers. Fuel cell design is still in the prototype phase, although there is much interest in their development. We already know they can work, but modifications must still be made before they become reasonably priced and part of our everyday lives.

Oxidation
$$2H_2(g) \longrightarrow 4H^+(aq) + 4e^-$$

Reduction
$$O_2(g) + 4H^+(aq) + 4e^- \longrightarrow 2H_2O(l)$$

ENVIRONMENTAL NOTE

Plastics

Terephthalic acid (an acid with two carboxyl groups) is produced in large quantities for the manufacture of polyesters such as Dacron and plastics.

When terephthalic acid reacts with ethylene glycol, ester bonds can form on both ends of the molecules, allowing many molecules to combine until they have formed a long polymer known as a *polyester*:

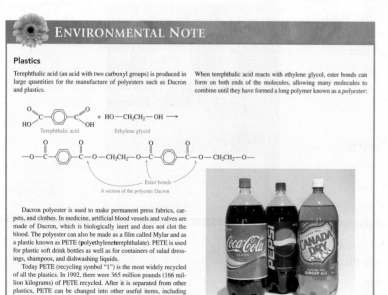

A section of the polyester Dacron

Dacron polyester is used to make permanent press fabrics, carpets, and clothes. In medicine, artificial blood vessels and valves are made of Dacron, which is biologically inert and does not clot the blood. The polyester can also be made as a film called Mylar and as a plastic known as PETE (**p**oly**e**thylene**te**r**e**phthalate). PETE is used for plastic soft drink bottles as well as for containers of salad dressings, shampoos, and dishwashing liquids.

Today PETE (recycling symbol "1") is the most widely recycled of all the plastics. In 1992, there were 365 million pounds (166 million kilograms) of PETE recycled. After it is separated from other plastics, PETE can be changed into other useful items, including polyester fabric for T-shirts and coats, fill for sleeping bags, doormats, and containers for tennis balls.

Environmental Notes   **Environmental Notes** throughout the text relate chemistry to real-life topics in science and medicine that are interesting and motivating and support the role of chemistry in the real world. They delve into issues such as global warming, biodiesel fuels, radon, acid rain, pheromones, ozone depletion, and toxicity of mercury.

HEALTH NOTE

Hot Packs and Cold Packs

In a hospital, at a first-aid station, or at an athletic event, an instant *cold pack* may be used to reduce swelling from an injury, remove heat from inflammation, or decrease capillary size to lessen the effect of hemorrhaging. Inside the plastic container of a cold pack, there is a compartment containing solid ammonium nitrate (NH_4NO_3) that is separated from a compartment containing water. The pack is activated when it is hit or squeezed hard enough to break the walls between the compartments and cause the ammonium nitrate to mix with the water (shown as H_2O over the reaction arrow). In an endothermic process, each gram of NH_4NO_3 that dissolves absorbs 79 cal of heat from the water. The temperature drops and the pack becomes cold and ready to use.

Endothermic Reaction in a Cold Pack

$$6.2 \text{ kcal} + NH_4NO_3(s) \xrightarrow{H_2O} NH_4NO_3(aq)$$

Hot packs are used to relax muscles, lessen aches and cramps, and increase circulation by expanding capillary size. Constructed in the same way as cold packs, a hot pack may contain the salt $CaCl_2$. The dissolving of the salt in water is exothermic and releases 160 cal per gram of salt. The temperature rises and the pack becomes hot and ready to use.

Exothermic Reaction in a Hot Pack

$$CaCl_2(s) \xrightarrow{H_2O} CaCl_2(aq) + 18 \text{ kcal}$$

Health Notes The many **Health Notes** in each chapter apply chemical concepts to relevant topics of health and medicine. These topics include weight loss and weight gain, artificial fats, sweeteners, anabolic steroids, alcohol, genetic diseases, viruses, and cancer.

EXPLORE YOUR WORLD

Using Gumdrops and Toothpicks to Model Chiral Objects

Part 1: Achiral Objects

Obtain some toothpicks and several orange, yellow, green, purple, and black gumdrops. Place four toothpicks into the black gumdrop, making the ends of toothpicks form a tetrahedron. Attach gumdrops to the toothpicks: two orange, one green, and one yellow.

Using another black gumdrop, make a second model that is the mirror image of the original model. Now rotate one of the models, and try to superimpose it on the other model. Are the models superimposable? If achiral objects have superimposable mirror images, are these models chiral or achiral?

Part 2: Chiral Objects

Using one of the original models, replace one orange gumdrop with a purple gumdrop. Now there are four different colors of gumdrops attached to the black gumdrop. Make its mirror image by replacing one orange gumdrop with a purple one. Now rotate one of the models, and try to superimpose it on the other model. Are the models superimposable? If chiral objects have nonsuperimposable mirror images, are these models chiral or achiral?

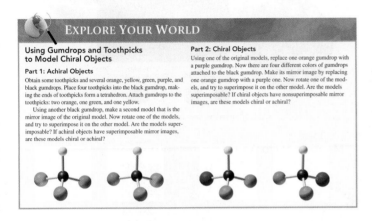

Explore Your World **Explore Your World** contains hands-on activities that use everyday materials to encourage students to actively explore selected chemistry topics, either individually or in group-learning environments. Each activity is followed by questions to encourage critical thinking.

Student-Friendly Approach

Keeping Students Engaged Is the Ultimate Goal

Student-Friendly Writing Style To enhance student understanding, I try to use an accessible writing style, based on a carefully paced and simple development of chemical ideas, suited to the background of allied health students. All terms are precisely defined, and clear goals are set for each section of the text. Clear analogies help students visualize and understand key chemical concepts.

Learning Goals At the beginning of each section, a **Learning Goal** clearly identifies the key concept of the section, providing a roadmap for studying. All information contained in that section relates back to the Learning Goal. The Learning Goals for each section are also repeated in the Chapter Review so students can make sure they have mastered the key concepts.

NEW Concept Checks The many **Concept Checks** throughout each chapter allow students to check their understanding of new concepts. The many new Concept Checks give students an opportunity to focus on their understanding of newly introduced chemical terms and ideas.

Concept Maps Each chapter ends with a **Concept Map** that reviews the key concepts of each chapter and how they fit together.

6.1 **Chemical Reactions**

As we discussed in Chapter 2, a *chemical change* occurs when a substance is converted into one or more new substances. For example, when silver tarnishes, the shiny silver metal (Ag) reacts with sulfur (S) to become the dull, black substance we call *tarnish* (Ag_2S). (See Figure 6.1.)

LEARNING GOAL

Write a balanced chemical equation from the formulas of the reactants and products for a chemical reaction.

CONCEPT CHECK 6.4

■ **Moles and Particles**

Explain why 0.20 mole of aluminum is a small number, but the number of atoms in 0.20 mole is a large number: 1.2×10^{23} atoms of aluminum.

ANSWER

The term *mole* is used as a collection term that represents 6.02×10^{23} particles. Because atoms are submicroscopic particles, a large number of atoms are in 1 mole of aluminum.

CONCEPT MAP

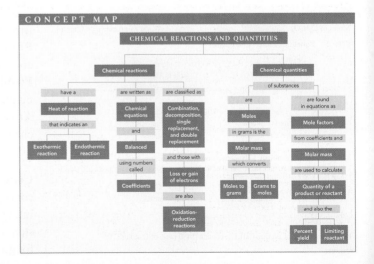

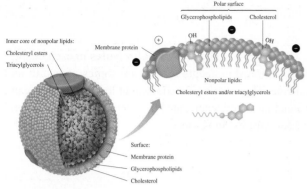

FIGURE 17.9 A spherical lipoprotein particle surrounds nonpolar lipids with polar lipids and protein for transport to body cells.
Q Why are the polar components on the surface of a lipoprotein particle and the nonpolar components at the center?

Clear Illustrations Help Students Visualize Chemistry
The **art program** is not only beautifully rendered, but pedagogically effective as well.

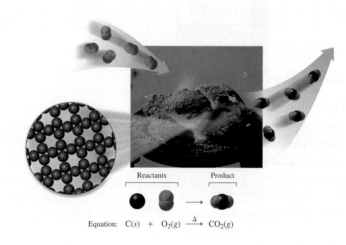

Equation: $C(s) + O_2(g) \xrightarrow{\Delta} CO_2(g)$

Macro-to-Micro Art

Macro-to-Micro Art **Macro-to-micro art** portrays the atomic structure of recognizable objects, putting chemistry in context and connecting the atomic world to the macroscopic world. A question with each figure challenges students to think critically about photos and illustrations. Many new photos expand visual connections.

Problem Solving

Many Tools Show Students How to Solve Problems

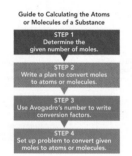

A Visual Guide to Problem Solving As part of a comprehensive learning program, the **Guides to Problem Solving** (GPS) illustrate the steps students need to solve problems. I clearly understand the learning challenges facing students in this course, so I walk students through the problem-solving process step by step. For each type of problem, I use a unique, color-coded flow chart that is coordinated with parallel worked examples as a visual guide for each problem-solving strategy.

Sample Problems with Study Checks Numerous **Sample Problems** appear throughout the text to demonstrate the application of each new concept. The worked-out solutions give step-by-step explanations, provide a problem-solving model, and illustrate required calculations. Each Sample Problem is followed by a **Study Check** question that allows students to test their understanding of the problem-solving strategy.

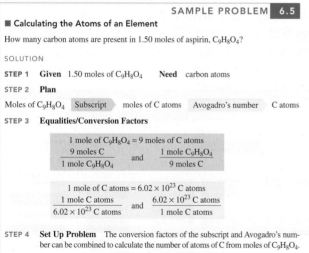

Integrated Questions and Problems **Questions and Problems** at the end of each section encourage students to apply concepts and begin problem solving after each section. **Paired Problems** of each even-numbered problem with a matching odd-numbered problem guide students through solving problems. **Answers** to odd-numbered problems are given at the end of each chapter.

End-of-Chapter Questions and Problems **Understanding the Concepts** questions encourage students to think about the concepts they have learned. **Additional Questions and Problems** integrate the topics from the entire chapter to promote understanding and critical thinking. **Challenge Questions** are designed for group work in cooperative learning environments.

NEW Combining Ideas Problem Sets   This **new feature** appears after every 2–4 chapters as a set of integrated problems designed to test students' cumulative understanding of the previous chapters.

The Most Advanced Chemistry Homework and Tutorial System

Mastering**CHEMISTRY**™

www.masteringchemistry.com

MasteringChemistry™ is the most advanced chemistry homework and tutorial system available. This online homework and tutoring system uses the Socratic Method to coach students through problem-solving techniques, offering hints and simpler questions on request. It tutors students individually with feedback specific to their errors. MasteringChemistry helps students learn, not just practice. (See the MasteringChemistry insert at the front of the book.)

Instructional Package

General, Organic, and Biological Chemistry: Structures of Life, third edition, is the nucleus of an integrated teaching and learning package of support material for both students and professors.

For Students

Study Guide   for *General, Organic, and Biological Chemistry*, third edition, by Karen Timberlake, is keyed to the learning goals in the text and designed to promote active learning through a variety of exercises with answers as well as practice tests. (ISBN 0321587553)

Selected Solutions Manual   for *General, Organic, and Biological Chemistry*, third edition, by Karen Timberlake, contains the complete solutions to the odd-numbered problems. (ISBN 0321616634)

Laboratory Manual for General, Organic, and Biological Chemistry   by Karen Timberlake. This best-selling lab manual coordinates 42 experiments with the topics in *General, Organic, and Biological Chemistry*, third edition; uses new terms during the lab; and explores chemical concepts. Laboratory investigations develop skills of manipulating equipment, reporting data, solving problems, making calculations, and drawing conclusions. (ISBN 0805349049)

Essential Laboratory Manual   by Karen Timberlake. This manual contains 25 experiments for the standard course sequence of topics in *General, Organic, and Biological Chemistry*, third edition. (ISBN 0805330232)

For Instructors

Instructor Resource Center on CD/DVD   This CD/DVD includes all the art and tables from the book in JPG format for use in classroom projection or creating study materials and tests. In addition, the instructor can access the PowerPoint™ lecture outlines, featuring over 2000 slides. Also available on the discs are downloadable files of the *Instructor Manual*, a set of "clicker questions" suitable for use with classroom-response systems, and the test bank. (ISBN 0321587561)

Transparency Pack   Contains 300 full-color transparency acetates. (ISBN 032158757X)

Instructor Solutions Manual   Prepared by Kathy Thrush Shaginaw and Karen Timberlake, this manual highlights chapter topics and includes suggestions for the laboratory. Contains complete solution setups and answers to all problems in the text. (ISBN 0321587596)

Printed Test Bank   Prepared by Kathy Thrush Shaginaw, Lynn Carlson, and Bill Timberlake, this test bank contains over 2000 questions in multiple-choice, matching, true-false, and short-answer format. (ISBN 0321587588)

Online Instructor Manual for Laboratory Manual   Contains answers to report pages for the Laboratory Manual and Essential Laboratory Manual. (ISBN 0321499670)

Course Management: Blackboard and WebCT   course management systems provide powerful course management capability. All of the content available in the Mastering-Chemistry Study Area is also available in **WebCT** and **Blackboard**. Pearson Prentice Hall offers content cartridges for these text-specific Classroom Management Systems. Visit **http://www.pearsonhighered.com** or contact your Prentice Hall sales representative for details.

Also visit the Prentice Hall catalog page for Timberlake's *General, Organic, and Biological Chemistry*, third edition, at **www.pearsonhighered.com** to download available instructor supplements.

New to This Edition

New features have been added throughout this third edition, including the following:

- A new Prologue introduces chemistry, the scientific method, and a study plan for learning chemistry.
- New Concept Checks with Answers build conceptual understanding.
- More Guides to Problem Solving (GPS) illustrate step-by-step problem-solving strategies.
- New Green Chemistry Notes include "Biodiesel as an Alternative Fuel," "Greenhouse Gases," and "Energy-Saving Light Bulbs."
- New Health Note "Brachytherapy" has been added.
- New Career interviews include Geologist and Conservator of Photographs.
- New molecular models in problem sets improve visual understanding of chemical reactions.
- New photos and updated diagrams improve clarity and provide visual connections to real life.
- New units of measurement include parts per million (ppm) and parts per billion (ppb).
- New Sample Problems and Study Checks model problem-solving strategies.
- New Understanding the Concepts problems add more visual examples to conceptual learning.
- New inter-chapter Combining Ideas problem sets provide problems with greater depth using concepts from several chapters.

Chapter Organization

Throughout this text, the structures of compounds and organic and biochemical molecules are related to their function. The discussion of bonding and shapes of molecules in Chapter 5 provides a foundation for understanding the structure of organic and biochemical molecules. The topic of stereochemistry and chiral organic molecules in Chapter 14 is revisited as an important concept in the understanding of structures of carbohydrates, amino acids, and chiral drugs.

The structures of molecules are related to their physical and chemical properties such as solubility in water, density, and boiling point. The structural levels of proteins are related to their function, while chemical processes that denature proteins emphasize the importance of structure to activity. Throughout the text, the atomic structure of matter is highlighted by macro-to-micro art that relates the atomic level to the macroscopic structures of real-life materials. In this way, the chemical concepts and structures of molecules are continuously related to the behavior and function of biomolecules in the body.

In each textbook I write, I consider it essential to relate every chemical concept to real-life issues of health and environment. In this text, I have added the theme of Structures of Life. All the material usually found in appendices has been integrated with the appropriate chapter material so that there are no longer any appendices at the end of the book. Because a course of chemistry for allied health may be taught in different time frames, it may be difficult to cover all the chapters in this text. However, each chapter is a complete package, which allows some chapters to be skipped or the order of presentation to be changed.

Prologue

The **Prologue**, a new feature, introduces students to the concepts of chemicals and chemistry, discusses the scientific method, and asks students to develop a study plan for learning chemistry. A *Health Note*, "Early Chemists: The Alchemists," was added.

Chapters 1 and 2

Chapter 1, "Measurements," looks at measurement and the need to understand numerical structures of the metric system in the sciences. The section on *Scientific Notation* is now a separate section. Items added include *peta* prefix to Metric and SI Prefixes, and parts per million (ppm) and parts per billion (ppb) to percentage conversion factors.

- A new feature called *Green Chemistry Note* discusses "Toxicology and Risk-Benefit Assessment."
- *Health Note*, "Bone Density," has been rewritten to discuss changes in bone density with age.
- New *Guides to Problem Solving*, "Calculating Density" and "Using Density," use color blocks as visual guides in the step-by-step solution pathway.
- The discussion of "Temperature" has been moved to Chapter 2.

Chapter 2, "Energy and Matter," now combines temperature, physical and chemical changes, energy, and matter into a single chapter that discusses energy and heat, nutritional energy values, temperature conversions, states of matter, and energy involved in changes of state. New energy problems use the SI unit of the joule (J).

- *Green Chemistry Note* updates the content of "Carbon Dioxide and Global Warming."
- New macro-to-micro art emphasizes the atomic level for changes of state.
- Many *Sample Problems* were reworked to utilize the Guide to Problem Solving strategy.

- New to this edition is an inter-chapter problem set, *Combining Ideas from Chapters 1 and 2*.

Chapters 3 and 4

Chapter 3, "Atoms and Elements," looks at elements, atoms, subatomic particles, and atomic mass. *The Periodic Table* emphasizes the numbering of groups from 1–18. Elements with atomic numbers 116 and 118 were added.

- New items include a discussion of the discovery of electrons by J. J. Thomson using the cathode ray tube. The calculation of the average atomic mass of an element uses percent abundance and isotope mass.
- Section 3.8, *Periodic Trends*, discusses periodic properties of elements including valence electrons, atomic size, and ionization energy.
- A new *Green Chemistry Note*, "Energy-Saving Lightbulbs," has been added.

Chapter 4, "Nuclear Chemistry," extends the concepts of subatomic particles, atomic number, and atomic mass to a discussion of radioisotopes including the positron. Nuclear equations are written and balanced for both naturally occurring and artificially produced radioactivity. The topic of biological effects of radiation is now part of the chapter content.

- Tables of radioisotopes were expanded.
- New *Health Note*, "Brachytherapy," was added.
- Update on "Radon in Our Homes."
- The half-lives of radioisotopes are discussed, and the amount of time for a sample to decay is calculated.
- Radioisotopes that are important in the field of nuclear medicine are emphasized.

Chapters 5 and 6

Chapter 5, "Compounds and Their Bonds," describes how atoms form ionic and covalent bonds in compounds. Chemical formulas are written, and ionic compounds—including those with polyatomic ions—and covalent compounds are named. An introduction to the three-dimensional shape of molecules provides a basis for the shape of organic and biochemical compounds. The discussion of polyatomic ions, which includes more polyatomic ions, follows the formation of ionic compounds. The concept of resonance is discussed for the electron-dot formulas for compounds with multiple bonds.

- New items include a discussion on the sizes of ions compared to the sizes of their corresponding atoms.
- New questions use the electron-dot formulas or electron configurations to determine chemical formulas and names. Electronegativity leads to a discussion of the polarity of bonds and molecules.
- The section *Attractive Forces in Compounds* now appears in Chapter 5.

Chapter 6, "Chemical Reactions and Quantities," includes the quantitative aspects of reactions such as the mole and molar mass (which are used in calculations of the number of particles in a quantity) and mass calculations in reactions. Equations for chemical reactions are balanced and organized into combination, decomposition, single replacement, and double replacement reactions.

- Section 6.3, *Oxidation–Reduction Reactions*, was rewritten to include oxidation–reduction in biological systems.
- A new *Green Chemistry Note*, "Fuel Cells: Clean Energy for the Future," has been added.
- Mole and mass relationships among the reactants and products are examined along with calculations of percent yield and limiting reactants.
- The material on limiting reactants has been expanded to give more examples.
- Section 6.9, *Energy Changes in Chemical Reactions*, is now included with Chapter 6.
- New to this edition is an inter-chapter problem set, *Combining Ideas from Chapters 3 to 6*.

Chapters 7 and 8

Chapter 7, "Gases," discusses the properties of a gas and calculates changes in gases using the gas laws.

- New art was added on gas pressure at different altitudes.
- The chapter includes calculations of the amount of a gas required or produced in a chemical reaction.
- New items include predicting changes in gas variables, a *Guide to Problem Solving*, "Using Molar Volume," and a *Summary* of Gas Laws.
- A new *Green Chemistry Note*, "Greenhouse Gases," on the types and sources of greenhouse gases has been added.

Chapter 8, "Solutions," describes solutions, electrolytes, saturation and solubility, concentrations, osmosis, and dialysis. The volumes and molarities of solutions are used to calculate product quantities in chemical reactions.

- The topics of dilution and titration were updated and new problems on concentrations and dilution were added.
- New items include Table 8.3, *Possible Combinations of Solutes and Solvents*, and Section 8.6, *Physical Properties of Solutions*, which discusses the impact of solution particles on the lowering of freezing points and the elevation of boiling points.
- The material on electrolytes and nonelectrolytes, saturation, and osmosis has been rewritten and new questions added.

Chapters 9 and 10

Chapter 9, "Chemical Equilibrium," looks at the rates of reactions and the equilibrium condition when forward and reverse rates for a reaction become equal. Equilibrium expressions for reactions are written and equilibrium constants are calculated. Le Châtelier's principle is used to evaluate the impact on concentrations when a stress is placed on the system.

- A new Section 9.6, *Equilibrium in Saturated Solutions*, and a new Guide to Problem Solving, "Guide to Calculating K_{sp}," have been added.

Chapter 10, "Acids and Bases," discusses acids and bases and their strengths; conjugate acid–base pairs; pH; and buffers. Section 10.1, *Acids and Bases*, now includes Brønsted–Lowry Acids and Bases.

- The acids HCN, $HClO$, and $HClO_4$ have been added to Table 10.1, *Naming Common Acids*.
- A *Green Chemistry Note*, "Acid Rain," updates the topic of acid rain.
- New problems related to acid rain have been added. Acid–base titration uses the neutralization reaction between an acid and a base to calculate quantities of an acid in a sample.
- The chapter includes discussions of strengths of acids and bases, their dissociation constants, acid–base properties of salt solutions, and buffers.
- New to this edition is an inter-chapter problem set, *Combining Ideas from Chapters 7 to 10*.

Chapter 11, 12, and 13

Chapter 11, "Introduction to Organic Chemistry: Alkanes," discusses the structure, nomenclature, and reactions of alkanes. Guides to Problem Solving (GPS) clarify the rules for nomenclature. An overview of functional groups and isomers describes the structure of organic chemistry and forms a basis for understanding the biomolecules of living systems.

- The subsection *Halogenation of Alkanes (Substitution)* was deleted.
- The *Health Note* "Toxicity of Carbon Monoxide" describes the products of incomplete combustion and their toxicity.
- A new *Career Focus*, "Geologist," has been added.

Chapter 12, "Alkenes, Alkynes, and Aromatic Compounds," discusses alkenes and alkynes, cis–trans isomers, addition reactions, polymers of alkenes used in everyday items, and aromatic compounds.

- Section 12.2, *Cis–Trans Isomers*, has been rewritten for clarity.
- An *Explore Your World* feature, "Modeling Cis–Trans Isomers," now asks students to model cis and trans isomers using gumdrops and toothpicks.
- The discussion of addition reactions hydrogenation, halogenation, hydrohalogenation, and hydration illustrates reactions important in biological systems.
- The *Career Focus* "Laboratory Technologist" is now included in this chapter.

Chapter 13, "Alcohols, Phenols, Ethers, and Thiols," discusses structures, names, properties, and reactions of alcohols, phenols, thiols, and ethers.

- The *Health Note* "Some Important Alcohols and Phenols" now includes a discussion of bisphenol A (BPA).
- Section 13.3, *Physical Properties of Alcohols, Phenols, and Ethers*, was rewritten for clarity.
- The *Health Note* "Oxidation of Methanol" is now titled "Methanol Poisoning."
- The *Health Note* "Oxidation of Alcohol in the Body" has been updated to include current methods of determining blood alcohol.

Chapters 14 and 15

Chapter 14, "Aldehydes, Ketones, and Chiral Molecules," discusses the nomenclature and structures of aldehydes and ketones.

- The subsection *Some Important Aldehydes and Ketones* is now a *Health Note*.
- Section 14.5, *Chiral Molecules*, uses simple compounds to introduce chiral molecules and chirality early in the text in preparation for the next chapter.
- An *Explore Your World* feature, "Using Gumdrops and Toothpicks to Model Chiral Objects," constructs chiral and achiral molecules by using gumdrops and toothpicks.

Chapter 15, "Carbohydrates," applies the organic chemistry of alcohols, aldehydes, and ketones to biomolecules, which relates the study of chemistry to health and medicine.

- Section 15.2 is now *Fischer Projections of Monosaccharides*, and Section 15.3 is *Haworth Structures of Monosaccharides*.
- New art includes Fischer projections for all the carbohydrate structures.
- The section *Haworth Structures of Monosaccharides* is rewritten to provide clearer instructions for drawing the closed ring structures.
- The *Health Notes* "How Sweet Is My Sweetener?" and "Blood Types and Carbohydrates" have been updated with recently developed sweeteners and information on blood types.
- New to this edition is an inter-chapter problem set, *Combining Ideas from Chapters 11 to 15*.

Chapters 16, 17, and 18

Chapter 16, "Carboxylic Acids and Esters," discusses two organic families that are important in biochemical systems.

- In this new edition, there is more emphasis on the use of Le Châtelier's principle to explain direction of reactions such as esterification and acid hydrolysis of esters.

Chapter 17, "Lipids," contains the functional groups of alcohols, aldehydes, and ketones in larger molecules such as triacylglycerols, glycerophospholipids, and steroids.

- Table 17.1, *Structures and Melting Points of Common Fatty Acids*, now includes arachidonic acid. The differences in the structures of prostaglandins E and F are now explained. Structures for fatty acids now include the line-bond formula. *Health Notes* of interest to students include olestra, trans fatty acids, and lipoproteins.
- A new *Green Chemistry Note*, "Biodiesel as an Alternative Fuel," has been added.
- Section 17.6, *Sphingolipids*, has been rewritten to clarify the structural differences between a sphingomyelin, ceramide, glycosphingolipid, and ganglioside. The role of lipids and cholesterol in cell membranes is discussed along with lipids that function as bile salts and steroid hormones.

Chapter 18, "Amines and Amides," emphasizes the nitrogen atom in their functional groups and their names.

- New *Guides to Problem Solving* now include steps for naming amines and amides. *Health Notes* include amines and amides in health and medicine, as well as alkaloids, which are naturally occurring amines in plants.

Chapters 19, 20, and 21

Chapter 19, "Amino Acids and Proteins," connects the functional groups of amines and amides to their related biomolecules. The classification of amino acids has been rewritten to include their ionized structures.

- Table 19.2, *The 20 Amino Acids (Ionized) in Proteins*, compares the form of amino acids above, below, and at the isoelectric point (pI). The importance of the structure of proteins from primary to quaternary is related to the shapes and activity of proteins.

Chapter 20, "Enzymes and Vitamins," relates the importance of the three-dimensional shape of proteins to their function as enzymes. Table 20.1, *Classification of Enzymes*, was simplified. The students learn that the shape of an enzyme is a factor in enzyme regulation and how end products might change the shape of an enzyme to increase or decrease the rate of an enzyme-catalyzed reaction. We also see that proteins change shape and lose function when subjected to pH changes and high temperatures. The important role of water-soluble vitamins as coenzymes is related to enzyme function.

- New to this edition is an inter-chapter problem set, *Combining Ideas from Chapters 16 to 20*.

Chapter 21, "Nucleic Acids and Protein Synthesis," describes the nucleic acids and their importance as biomolecules that store and direct information for cellular components, growth, and reproduction. The role of complementary base pairing is highlighted in both DNA replication and the formation of mRNA during protein synthesis. Discussions include the genetic code, its relationship to the order of amino acids in a protein, and how mutations can occur when the nucleotide sequence is altered.

- The *Explore Your World* feature "A Model for DNA Replication and Mutation" is expanded to include formation of mRNA and dipeptide formation.
- The preparation and uses of recombinant DNA in forensic science and the discussion of the Human Genome Project have been updated.
- The role of DNA or RNA in viruses that utilize host cells to replicate is discussed.

Chapters 22, 23, and 24

Chapter 22, "Metabolic Pathways for Carbohydrates," describes the stages of metabolism and the digestion of carbohydrates, our most important fuel. The breakdown of glucose to pyruvate is described using the glycolytic pathway, which is followed under aerobic conditions by the decarboxylation of pyruvate to acetyl CoA. The synthesis of glycogen and the synthesis of glucose from noncarbohydrate sources are discussed.

Chapter 23, "Metabolic Pathways and Energy Production," looks at the entry of acetyl CoA into the citric acid cycle and the production of reduced coenzymes for the electron transport system and oxidative phosphorylation.

- The discussion of the reactions of the citric acid cycle has been expanded and now includes the enzymes that catalyze the reactions.
- Details on the structure and function of ATP synthase are included.

Chapter 24, "Metabolic Pathways for Lipids and Amino Acids," discusses the digestion of lipids and proteins and the metabolic pathways that convert fatty acids and amino acids into energy. Discussions include the conversion of excess carbohydrates to triacylglycerols in adipose tissue and how the intermediates of the citric acid cycle are converted to nonessential amino acids.

- The *Explore Your World* feature "Fat Storage and Blubber" has been updated and expanded to give clear instructions for the procedures.
- Finally, the relationships between the catabolic and anabolic pathways in metabolism are summarized.
- New to this edition is an inter-chapter problem set, *Combining Ideas from Chapters 21 to 24.*

ACKNOWLEDGMENTS

The preparation of a new edition is a continuous effort of many people. As in my work on other textbooks, I am thankful for the support, encouragement, and dedication of many people who put in hours of tireless effort to produce a high-quality book that provides an outstanding learning package. The editorial team at Pearson Publishing has done an exceptional job. I want to thank Nicole Folchetti, editor in chief, and acquisitions editor, Dawn Giovanniello, who supported my vision of this third edition and the addition of new *Concept Checks*, *Green Chemistry Notes*, *Combining Ideas*, problem sets, and an updated art program. I much appreciate all the wonderful work of Jessica Neumann, assistant editor, who was like an angel encouraging me at each step while skillfully coordinating reviews, art, website materials, and all the things it takes to make a book come together. I am grateful to Ray Mullaney, editor in chief of science book development, and Karen Nein, developmental editor, for their watchful eyes during the writing and development of this new edition. I appreciate the work of Beth Sweeten, project manager, and Lynn Lustberg of Macmillan Publishing Solutions, who brilliantly coordinated all phases of the manuscript to the final pages of a beautiful book. Thanks to Kathy Thrush Shaginaw, manuscript reviewer, and Richard Camp, copy editor, who precisely reviewed and edited the initial and final manuscripts to make sure the words and problems were correct to help students learn chemistry.

I am especially proud of the art program in this text, which lends beauty and understanding to chemistry. I would like to thank Suzanne Behnke, art director and book designer, and Travis Amos, photo editor, whose creative ideas provided the outstanding design for the cover and pages of the book. Eric Schrader, photo researcher, was invaluable in researching and selecting vivid photos for the text so that students can see the beauty of chemistry. Thanks also to *Bio-Rad Laboratories* for their courtesy and use of *KnowItAll ChemWindows Edition* drawing software that helped me produce chemical structures for the manuscript. The macro-to-micro illustrations designed by Production Solutions and Precision Graphics give students visual impressions of the atomic and molecular organization of everyday things and are a fantastic learning tool. I want to thank Michael Rossa for the hours of proofreading all the pages. I also appreciate all the hard work in the field put in by the marketing team and Elizabeth Averbeck, marketing manager.

This text also reflects the contributions of many professors who took the time to review and edit the manuscript and provide outstanding comments, help, and suggestions. A special thanks to Kathy Thrush Shaginaw, Mark Quirie, and Timothy Kreider for their outstanding accuracy reviews of the entire manuscript. Their keen eyes and thoughtful comments were extremely helpful in the development of this text.

I am extremely grateful to an incredible group of peers for their careful assessment of all the new ideas for the text; for their suggested additions, corrections, changes, and deletions; and for providing an incredible amount of feedback about improvements for the book. In addition, I appreciate the time scientists took to let us take photos and discuss their work with them. I admire and appreciate every one of you.

If you would like to share your experience with chemistry or have questions and comments about this text, I would appreciate hearing from you.

Karen Timberlake
E-mail: khemist@aol.com

REVIEWERS

PROLOGUE
Chemistry in Our Lives

San Francisco Museum of Art

"As a conservator of photographic materials, it is essential to have an understanding of the chemical reactions of many different photographic processes," says Theresa Andrews, Conservator of Photographs at the San Francisco Museum of Modern Art. "For example, the creation of the latent image in many photographs is based upon the light sensitivity of silver halides. Photolytic silver 'prints out' when exposed to a light source such as the sun and filamentary silver 'develops out' when an exposed photographic paper is placed in a bath with reducing agents. Photolytic silver particles are much smaller than filamentary silver particles making them more vulnerable to abrasion and image loss. This knowledge is critical when making recommendations for light levels and for the protection of photographs when they are on exhibition. Conservation treatments require informed decisions based on the reactivity of the materials within the photograph and also the compatibility of materials that might be required for repair or preservation of the photograph."

Mastering**CHEMISTRY**™

Visit **www.masteringchemistry.com** for self-study materials and instructor-assigned homework.

What are some questions in science you have been curious about? Perhaps you are interested in how smog is formed, what causes ozone depletion, how nails form rust, or how aspirin relieves a headache. Just like you, chemists are curious about the world we live in.

- How does car exhaust produce the smog that hangs over our cities? One component of car exhaust is nitrogen oxide (NO), which forms in car engines where high temperatures convert nitrogen gas (N_2) and oxygen gas (O_2) to NO. In chemistry, these reactions are written in the form of equations such as $N_2(g) + O_2(g) \longrightarrow 2NO(g)$. The reaction of NO with oxygen in the air produces NO_2, which gives smog its characteristic reddish-brown color.

- Why has the ozone layer been depleted in certain parts of the atmosphere? During the 1970s, scientists discovered that substances called *chlorofluorocarbons* (CFCs) were associated with the depletion of ozone (O_3) over Antarctica. As CFCs are broken down by ultraviolet (UV) light, chlorine (Cl) is released and acts rapidly with ozone in the atmosphere to form chlorine oxide gas (ClO) and oxygen: $Cl(g) + O_3(g) \longrightarrow ClO(g) + O_2(g)$. This reaction causes the breakdown of ozone molecules and the destruction of the ozone layer.

- Why does an iron nail rust when exposed to air and rain? When solid iron (Fe) in a nail reacts with oxygen gas in the air, the oxidation of iron forms rust (Fe_2O_3): $4Fe(s) + 3O_2(g) \longrightarrow 2Fe_2O_3(s)$.

- Why does aspirin relieve a headache? When a part of the body is injured, substances called *prostaglandins* are produced that cause inflammation and pain. Aspirin acts to block the production of prostaglandins, thereby reducing inflammation, pain, and fever.

Chemists perform many different kinds of research. Some design new fuels and more efficient ways to use them. Researchers in the medical field look for evidence that will help them understand and design new treatments for diabetes, genetic defects, cancer, AIDS, and other diseases. For the chemist in the laboratory, the physician in the dialysis unit, or the agricultural scientist, chemistry plays a central role in providing understanding, assessing solutions, and making important decisions.

P.1 Chemistry and Chemicals

Chemistry is the study of the composition, structure, properties, and reactions of matter. *Matter* is another word for all the substances that make up our world. Perhaps you imagine that chemistry is done only in a laboratory by a chemist wearing a lab coat and goggles. Actually, chemistry happens all around you every day and has a big impact on everything you use and do. You are doing chemistry when you cook food, add chlorine to a swimming pool, or start your car. A chemical reaction takes place when a nail rusts or an antacid tablet fizzes when dropped into water. Plants grow because chemical reactions convert carbon dioxide, water, and energy to carbohydrates and oxygen. Chemical reactions take place when you digest food and break it down into substances that you need for energy and health.

All the things you see around you are composed of one or more chemicals. A **chemical** is a substance that always has the same composition and properties wherever it is found. When a chemical undergoes a *chemical change*, a new substance with a new composition and properties is formed. Chemical changes take place in chemistry laboratories, manufacturing plants, and pharmaceutical labs as well as every day in nature and in our bodies. Often, the terms *chemical* and *substance* are used interchangeably to describe a specific type of matter.

TABLE P.1 Chemicals Commonly Used in Toothpaste

Chemical	Function
Calcium carbonate	Acts as an abrasive to remove plaque
Sorbitol	Prevents loss of water and hardening of toothpaste
Carrageenan (seaweed extract)	Keeps toothpaste from hardening or separating
Glycerin	Makes toothpaste foam in the mouth
Sodium lauryl sulfate	Acts as a detergent used to loosen plaque
Titanium dioxide	Makes toothpaste base white and opaque
Triclosan	Inhibits bacteria that cause plaque and gum disease
Sodium fluorophosphate	Prevents formation of cavities by strengthening tooth enamel with fluoride
Methyl salicylate	Gives a pleasant flavor of wintergreen

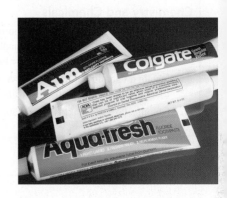

Each day you use products containing substances that were developed and prepared by chemists. Soaps and shampoos contain chemicals that combine with oils on your skin and scalp. When you shower in the morning, these oils are removed by rinsing with water. When you brush your teeth, the chemicals in toothpaste clean your teeth, prevent plaque formation, and prevent tooth decay. Some chemicals commonly contained in toothpaste are listed in Table P.1.

In cosmetics and lotions, chemicals are used to moisturize the skin, fight bacteria, prevent deterioration of the product, and thicken the product. Your clothes may be made of natural materials such as cotton, or synthetic substances such as nylon or polyester. Perhaps you wear a ring or watch made of gold, silver, or platinum. Your breakfast cereal is probably fortified with iron, calcium, and phosphorus, while the milk you drink is enriched with vitamins A and D. Antioxidants are chemicals added to your cereal to prevent it from spoiling. Some of the chemicals you may encounter when you cook in the kitchen are shown in Figure P.1.

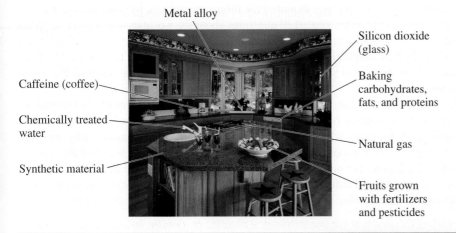

FIGURE P.1 Many of the items found in a kitchen are obtained using chemical reactions.

Q What are some other chemicals found in a kitchen?

CONCEPT CHECK P.1

■ Chemicals

Why is copper wire an example of a chemical, while sunlight is not?

ANSWER
Copper wire is a substance that has the same composition and properties wherever it is found. Sunlight is not a substance and does not contain matter.

SAMPLE PROBLEM P.1

■ Everyday Chemicals

Identify the chemical described by each of the following statements:

a. Aluminum is used to make cans.
b. Salt (sodium chloride) is used as a preservative.
c. Sugar (sucrose) is used as a sweetener.

SOLUTION

a. aluminum   **b.** salt (sodium chloride)   **c.** sugar (sucrose)

STUDY CHECK

Which of the following are chemicals?

a. iron   **b.** tin   **c.** a low temperature   **d.** water

The answers for all Study Checks are included at the end of each chapter.

QUESTIONS AND PROBLEMS

Chemistry and Chemicals

The answers for all the magenta, odd-numbered Questions and Problems are included at the end of each chapter. Checking your answers will let you know if you understand the material.

P.1 Obtain a vitamin bottle and observe the list of ingredients. List four. Which ones are chemicals?

P.2 Obtain a box of breakfast cereal and observe the list of ingredients. List four. Which ones are chemicals?

P.3 A "chemical-free" shampoo includes the following ingredients: water, cocomide, glycerin, and citric acid. Is the shampoo "chemical-free"?

P.4 A "chemical-free" sunscreen includes the following ingredients: titanium dioxide, vitamin E, and vitamin C. Is the sunscreen "chemical-free"?

P.5 Pesticides are chemicals. Give one advantage and one disadvantage of using pesticides.

P.6 Sugar is a chemical. Give one advantage and one disadvantage of eating sugar.

P.2 Scientific Method: Thinking Like a Scientist

LEARNING GOAL

Describe the activities that are part of the scientific method.

When you were very young, you explored the things around you by touching and tasting. When you grew a little older, you asked questions about the world in which you live. What is lightning? Where does a rainbow come from? Why is water blue? As an adult, you may have wondered how antibiotics work or why vitamins are important to your health. Each day you ask questions and seek answers as you organize and make sense of the world around you.

When the late Nobel Laureate Linus Pauling described his student life in Oregon, he recalled that he read many books on chemistry, mineralogy, and physics. "I mulled over the properties of materials: why are some substances colored and others not, why are some minerals or inorganic compounds hard and others soft?" He said, "I was building up this tremendous background of empirical knowledge and at the same time asking a great number of questions." Linus Pauling won two Nobel Prizes: the first, in 1954, was in chemistry for his work on the structure of proteins; the second, in 1962, was the Peace Prize.

Scientific Method

Although the process of trying to understand nature is unique to each scientist, a set of general principles called the **scientific method** helps to describe how a scientist thinks.

1. **Observations.** The first step in the scientific method is to observe, describe, and measure an event in nature. Observations based on measurements are called *data*.

2. **Hypothesis.** After sufficient data are collected, a *hypothesis* is proposed that states a possible interpretation of the observations. The hypothesis must be stated in a way that it can be tested by experiments.

3. **Experiments.** Experiments are tests that determine the validity of the hypothesis. Often many experiments are performed, and a large amount of data is collected. If the results of the experiments are different than those predicted by the hypothesis, then a new or modified hypothesis is proposed, and new experiments are performed.

4. **Theory.** When many scientists repeat the experiments with consistent results that confirm the hypothesis, the hypothesis becomes a *theory*. Each theory, however,

continues to be tested and, based on new data, sometimes needs to be modified or even replaced. Then a new hypothesis is proposed, and the process of experimentation takes place once again.

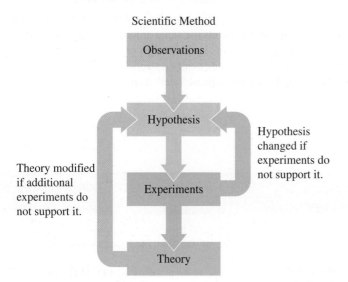

Using the Scientific Method in Everyday Life

You may be surprised to realize that you use the scientific method in your everyday life. Suppose you visit a friend in her home. Soon after you arrive, your eyes start to itch and you begin to sneeze. Then you observe that your friend has a new cat. Perhaps you ask yourself why you are sneezing and form the hypothesis that you are allergic to cats. To test your hypothesis, you leave your friend's home. If the sneezing stops, perhaps your hypothesis is correct. You test your hypothesis further by visiting another friend who also has a cat. If you start to sneeze again, then your experimental results support your hypothesis that you are allergic to cats. However, if you continue sneezing after you leave your friend's home, your hypothesis is not supported. Now you need to form a new hypothesis, which could be that you have a cold.

TUTORIAL
Scientific Method

CONCEPT CHECK P.2

■ Scientific Method

Label each of the following as an observation, hypothesis, or experiment:

a. Drinking coffee at night keeps me awake.
b. When I drink coffee only in the morning, I can sleep at night.
c. I will try drinking coffee only in the morning.

ANSWER
a. An observation describes what happens when I drink coffee.
b. An observation describes what happens if I drink coffee only in the morning.
c. Changing the time for drinking coffee is an experiment.

SAMPLE PROBLEM P.2

■ Scientific Method

Identify each of the following statements as an observation or a hypothesis:

a. A silver tray turns a dull gray color when left uncovered.
b. It is warmer in summer than in winter in the northern hemisphere.
c. Ice cubes float in water because they are less dense.

SOLUTION

a. observation   **b.** observation   **c.** hypothesis

STUDY CHECK

The following statements are found in a student's notebook. Identify each of the following as observation (O), hypothesis (H), or experiment (E):

a. "Today, I planted two tomato seedlings in the garden. I put two more tomato seedlings in a closet. I will give all the plants the same amount of water and fertilizer."

b. "After 50 days, the tomato plants in the garden are 3 feet high with green leaves. The plants in the closet are 8 inches tall and yellow."

c. "Tomato plants need sunlight to grow."

HEALTH NOTE

Early Chemists: The Alchemists

For many centuries, chemists have studied changes in matter. From the time of the Greeks to about the sixteenth century, alchemists, early chemists who studied matter, described matter in terms of four components of nature: earth, air, fire, and water. These components had the qualities of hot, cold, damp, or dry. By the eighth century, alchemists believed that they could rearrange these qualities to change metals such as copper and lead into gold and silver. They searched for an unknown substance called a *philosopher's stone* that they thought would turn metals into gold as well as prolong youth and postpone death. Although these efforts failed, the alchemists did provide information on the processes and chemical reactions involved in the extraction of metals from ores. The alchemists also designed some of the first laboratory equipment and developed early laboratory procedures. These early efforts were some of the first observations and experiments using the scientific method.

The alchemist Paracelsus (1493–1541) thought that alchemy should be about preparing new medicines, not about producing gold. Using observation and experiments, he viewed the body as a series of chemical processes that could be unbalanced by certain chemical compounds and rebalanced by using minerals and medicines. For example, he determined that inhaled dust, not underground spirits, caused the lung diseases of miners. He also thought that goiter was a problem caused by contaminated drinking water, and he treated syphilis with compounds of mercury. His opinion of medicines was that the right dose makes the difference between a poison and a cure. Today this idea is part of the risk analysis of medicines. Paracelsus changed alchemy in ways that helped to establish modern medicine and chemistry.

Science and Technology

When scientific information is applied to industrial and commercial uses, it is called *technology*. Such uses have made the chemical industry one of the largest industries in the United States. Every year, technology provides new materials or procedures that produce more energy, cure diseases, improve crops, and produce new kinds of synthetic materials. Table P.2 lists some of the important scientific discoveries, laws, theories, and technological innovations that have been made over the past 300 years.

TABLE P.2 Some Important Scientific Discoveries, Laws, Theories, and Technological Innovations

Discovery, Law, Theory, or Innovation	Date	Name	Country
Law of gravity	1687	Isaac Newton	England
Oxygen	1774	Joseph Priestley	England
Electric battery	1800	Alessandro Volta	Italy
Atomic theory	1803	John Dalton	England
Anesthesia, ether	1842	Crawford Long	United States
Nitroglycerin	1847	Ascanio Sobrero	Italy
Germ theory	1865	Louis Pasteur	France
Antiseptic surgery	1865	Joseph Lister	England
Discovery of nucleic acids	1869	Friedrich Miescher	Switzerland
Radioactivity	1896	Henri Becquerel	France
Discovery of radium	1898	Marie and Pierre Curie	France
Quantum theory	1900	Max Planck	Germany
Theory of relativity	1905	Albert Einstein	Germany
Identification of components of RNA and DNA	1909	Phoebus Theodore Levene	United States
Insulin	1922	Frederick Banting, Charles Best, John Macleod	Canada
Penicillin	1928	Alexander Fleming	England
Nylon	1937	Wallace Carothers	United States
Discovery of DNA as genetic material	1944	Oswald Avery	United States
Synthetic production of transuranium elements	1944	Glenn Seaborg, Arthur Wahl, Joseph Kennedy, Albert Ghiorso	United States
Determination of DNA structure	1953	Francis Crick, Rosalind Franklin, James Watson	England
Polio vaccine	1954	Jonas Salk	United States
	1957	Albert Sabin	United States
Laser	1958	Charles Townes	United States
	1960	Theodore Maiman	United States
Cellular phones	1973	Martin Cooper	United States
MRI (magnetic resonance imaging)	1980	Paul Lauterbur	United States
Prozac	1988	Ray Fuller	United States
HIV protease inhibitor	1995	Joseph Martin, Sally Redshaw	United States

Not all scientific discoveries, however, have been positive. The production of some substances has contributed to the development of hazardous conditions in our environment. We have become concerned about the energy requirements of new products and how some materials may cause changes in our oceans and atmosphere. We want to know if the new materials can be recycled, how they are broken down, and whether there are alternate and safer processes. The ways in which we continue to utilize scientific research will strongly affect our planet and its communities in the future. These decisions can best be made if every citizen has an understanding of science.

ENVIRONMENTAL NOTE

DDT: Good Pesticide, Bad Pesticide

DDT (dichlorodiphenyltrichloroethane) was once one of the most commonly used pesticides. Although DDT was first made in 1874, it was not used as an insecticide until 1939. Before DDT was widely used, insect-borne diseases such as malaria and typhus were rampant in many parts of the world. Paul Müller, who discovered that DDT was an effective pesticide, was recognized for saving many lives and received the Nobel Prize for medicine and physiology in 1948. At that time, DDT was considered the ideal pesticide because it was toxic to many insects, had a low toxicity to humans and animals, and was inexpensive to prepare.

In the United States, DDT was used extensively on home gardens as well as on farm crops, particularly cotton and soybeans. Because of its stable chemical structure, DDT did not break down quickly in the environment, which meant that it did not have to be reapplied frequently. At first, everyone was pleased with DDT—crop yields increased and diseases such as malaria and typhus were under control.

However, during the early 1950s, problems attributed to DDT began to arise. Insects were becoming more resistant to the pesticide. At the same time, the public was increasingly concerned about the long-term impact of a substance that could remain in the environment for many years. The metabolic systems of humans and animals cannot break down DDT, which is soluble in fats but not in water and is stored in the fatty tissues of the body. Although the concentrations of DDT applied to crops were extremely low, the concentrations of DDT found in fish and the birds that ate the fish were as much as

10 million times greater. Although the affected birds did not die immediately, the DDT in their bodies reduced the amount of calcium in their eggshells. As a result, the incubating eggs cracked open early, causing many offspring to die. Because of this difficulty with reproduction, the populations of birds such as bald eagles and brown pelicans dropped significantly.

By 1972, DDT was banned in the United States. The Environmental Protection Agency (EPA) reported that by 1978 DDT levels were reduced by 90% in fish in Lake Michigan. Today, new types of pesticides that are more water soluble and do not persist in the environment have replaced long-lasting pesticides such as DDT. However, these new pesticides are much more toxic to humans.

QUESTIONS AND PROBLEMS

Scientific Method: Thinking like a Scientist

P.7 Identify each of the following statements as an observation (O), a hypothesis (H), an experiment (E), or a theory (T): At a popular restaurant, where Chang is the head chef, the following occur:
  a. Chang determines that sales of the chef's salad have dropped.
  b. Chang decides that the chef's salad needs a new dressing.
  c. In a taste test, four bowls of lettuce are prepared with four new dressings: sesame seed, oil and vinegar, blue cheese, and anchovies.
  d. The tasters rate the dressing with sesame seeds the best.
  e. After two weeks, Chang notes that the orders for the chef's salad with the new sesame dressing have doubled.
  f. Chang decides that the sesame dressing improved the sales of the chef's salad because the sesame dressing improved the taste of the salad.

P.8 Identify each of the following statements as an observation (O), a hypothesis (H), an experiment (E), or a theory (T): Lucia wants to develop a process for dyeing shirts so that the color will not fade when the shirt is washed. She proceeds with the following activities:
  a. Lucia notices that the dye in a design on T-shirts fades when the shirt is washed.
  b. Lucia decides that the dye needs something to help it set in the T-shirt fabric.
  c. She places a spot of dye on each of four T-shirts and then places each one separately in water, salt water, vinegar, and baking soda and water.
  d. After 1 hour, all the T-shirts are removed and washed with a detergent.
  e. Lucia notices that the dye has faded on the T-shirts soaked in water, salt water, and baking soda, while the dye did not fade in the T-shirts soaked in vinegar.
  f. Lucia thinks that the vinegar binds with the dye so it does not fade when the shirt is washed.

P.3 A Study Plan for Learning Chemistry

Here you are taking chemistry, perhaps for the first time. Whatever your reasons are for choosing to study chemistry, you can look forward to learning many new and exciting ideas.

Features in This Text Help You Study Chemistry

This text has been designed with a variety of study aids to complement different learning styles. On the inside of the front cover is a periodic table of the elements that provides information about the elements. On the inside of the back cover are tables that summarize useful information needed throughout the study of chemistry. Each chapter begins with *Looking Ahead*, which outlines the topics in the chapter. A *Learning Goal* at the beginning of each section previews the concepts you are to learn. A comprehensive *Glossary/Index* is included at the end of the text.

Before you begin to read a chapter, obtain an overview of the topics by reviewing the list of topics in *Looking Ahead*. As you prepare to read a section of the chapter, look at the section title and turn it into a question. For example, for Section P.1, "Chemistry and Chemicals," you could write a question that asks "What is chemistry?" or "What are chemicals?" When you are ready to read that section, review the *Learning Goal*, which tells you what you need to accomplish. As you read, try to answer the question you wrote. Throughout the chapter, you will find *Concept Checks* that will help you understand key ideas. When you come to a *Sample Problem*, take the time to work it through, and try the associated *Study Check*. Then, check your answer at the end of the chapter. If your answer does not match, you may need to study the section again. When you finish each section, immediately work through the *Questions and Problems* for practice.

Throughout the chapters, boxes titled *Health Notes*, *Green Chemistry Notes*, and *Environmental Notes* connect the chemical concepts you are studying to real-life situations. Many of the figures and diagrams throughout the text use macro-to-micro illustrations to depict the atomic level of organization of ordinary objects. These visual models illustrate the concepts described in the text and allow you to "see" the world in a microscopic way.

At the end of each chapter, you will find several study aids that complete the chapter. *Chapter Reviews* and *Concept Maps* at the end of each chapter give a summary and show the connections between important concepts. The *Key Terms* are boldfaced in the text and listed again at the end of the chapter. *Understanding the Concepts* is a set of questions that use art and structures to help you visualize concepts. *Additional Questions and Problems* and *Challenge Problems* provide more problems to test your understanding of the topics in the chapter. Answers to all the *Study Checks* and *Answers to Selected Questions and Problems* are provided at the end of the chapter.

Using Active Learning to Learn Chemistry

A student who is an active learner continually interacts with the chemical ideas while reading the text and attending lectures. Let's see how this is done.

As you read and practice solving problems, you remain actively involved in studying, which enhances the learning process. In this way, you learn small bits of information at a time and establish the necessary foundation for understanding the next section. You may also note questions you have about the reading to discuss with your professor and laboratory instructor. Table P.3 summarizes these steps for active learning. The time you spend in lecture can also be useful as a learning time. By keeping track of the class schedule and reading the assigned material before lecture, you become aware of the new terms and concepts you need to learn. Some questions that occur during your reading may be answered during the lecture. If not, you can ask for further clarification from your professor.

TABLE P.3 Steps in Active Learning

1. Read the set of *Looking Ahead* topics and *Learning Goals* for an overview of the material.
2. Form a question from the title of the section you are going to read.
3. Read the section looking for answers to your question.
4. Self-test by working *Concept Checks*, *Sample Problems*, and *Study Checks* within each section.
5. Complete the *Questions and Problems* that follow each section and check the magenta odd-numbered answers.
6. Proceed to the next section and repeat the above steps.

Many students think that studying with a group can be beneficial to learning. In a group, students motivate each other to study, fill in gaps, and correct misunderstandings by teaching and learning together. Studying alone does not allow the process of peer correction that takes place when you work with a group of students in your class. In a group, you can cover the ideas more thoroughly as you discuss the reading and problem solving with other students. Waiting to study until the night before an exam does not give you time to understand concepts and practice problem solving. You may ignore or avoid ideas that turn out to be important on test day.

Thinking Scientifically About Your Study Plan

As you embark on your journey into the world of chemistry, think about your approach to studying and learning chemistry. You might consider some of the ideas in the following list. Check those ideas that will help you learn chemistry successfully. Commit to them now. Your success depends on you.

My study of chemistry will include the following:

_____ Reviewing the *Learning Goals*

_____ Keeping a problem notebook

_____ Reading the text as an active learner

_____ Self-testing by working the chapter problems and checking solutions in the text

_____ Reading the chapter before lecture

_____ Being an active learner in lecture

_____ Going to lecture

_____ Organizing a study group

_____ Seeing the professor during office hours

_____ Attending review sessions

_____ Organizing my own review sessions

_____ Studying a little bit as often as I can

CONCEPT CHECK P.3

■ A Study Plan for Chemistry

What are some advantages to studying in a group?

ANSWER

In a group, students motivate and support each other, fill in gaps, and correct misunderstandings. Ideas are discussed while reading and problem solving together.

SAMPLE PROBLEM   P.3

■ A Study Plan for Learning Chemistry

Which of the following activities would you include in a study plan for successfully learning chemistry?

a. skipping a lecture
b. forming a study group
c. keeping a problem notebook
d. waiting to study until the night before the exam
e. becoming an active learner

SOLUTION

Your success in chemistry can be helped if you include the following in your study plan:

b. forming a study group
c. keeping a problem notebook
e. becoming an active learner

STUDY CHECK

Which of the following would help you learn chemistry?

a. skipping review sessions
b. working assigned problems
c. attending the professor's office hours
d. staying up all night before an exam
e. reading the assignment before a lecture

QUESTIONS AND PROBLEMS

A Study Plan for Studying Chemistry

P.9 A student in your class asks you for advice on learning chemistry. Which of the following might you suggest?
   a. Form a study group.
   b. Skip a lecture.
   c. Visit the professor during office hours.
   d. Wait until the night before an exam to study.
   e. Become an active learner.

P.10 A student in your class asks you for advice on learning chemistry. Which of the following might you suggest?
   a. Do the assigned problems.
   b. Don't read the book; it's never on the test.
   c. Attend review sessions.
   d. Read the assignment before lecture.
   e. Keep a problem notebook.

CONCEPT MAP

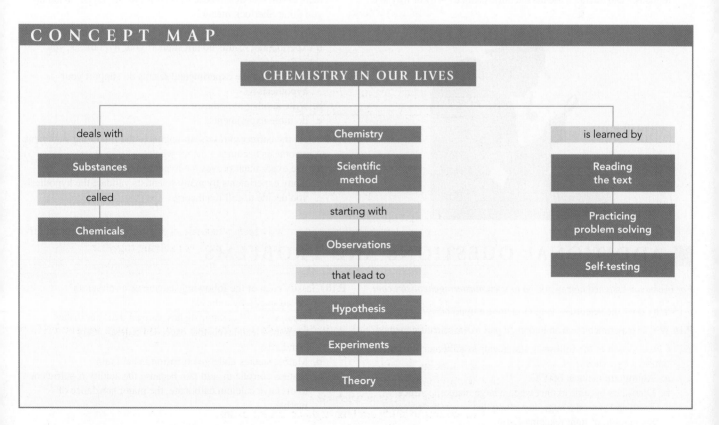

CHAPTER REVIEW

P.1 Chemistry and Chemicals
LEARNING GOAL: *Define the term* chemistry, *and identify substances as chemicals.*
Chemistry is the study of the composition of substances and the way in which they interact with other substances. A chemical is any substance used in or produced by a chemical process.

P.2 Scientific Method: Thinking like a Scientist
LEARNING GOAL: *Describe the activities that are part of the scientific method.*
The scientific method is a process of explaining natural phenomena beginning with observations, a hypothesis, and experiments, which

may lead to a theory when experimental results support the hypothesis. Technology involves the application of scientific information to industrial and commercial uses.

P.3 A Study Plan for Learning Chemistry
LEARNING GOAL: *Develop a study plan for learning chemistry.*
A study plan for learning chemistry utilizes the visual features in the text and develops an active learning approach to study. By using the *Learning Goals* and *Concept Checks* in the chapter and working the *Sample Problems* and *Study Checks* and the problems at the end of each section, the student can successfully learn the concepts of chemistry.

KEY TERMS

chemical A substance that has the same composition and properties wherever it is found.

chemistry A science that studies the composition of substances and the way they interact with other substances.

experiment A procedure that tests the validity of a hypothesis.

hypothesis An unverified explanation of a natural phenomenon.

observation Information determined by noting and recording a natural phenomenon.

scientific method The process of making observations, proposing a hypothesis, testing the hypothesis, and developing a theory that explains a natural event.

theory An explanation of an observation that has been validated by experiments that support a hypothesis.

UNDERSTANDING THE CONCEPTS

P.11 According to Sherlock Holmes, "One must follow the rules of scientific inquiry, gathering, observing, and testing data, then formulating, modifying, and rejecting hypotheses, until only one remains." Did Sherlock use the scientific method? Why or why not?

P.12 In "A Scandal in Bohemia," Sherlock Holmes receives a mysterious note. He states, "I have no data yet. It is a capital mistake to theorize before one has data. Insensibly one begins to twist facts to suit theories instead of theories to suit facts." What do you think Sherlock meant?

P.13 Select the correct phrase(s) to complete the following statement: If experimental results do not support your hypothesis, you should
   a. pretend that the experimental results do support your hypothesis.
   b. write another hypothesis.
   c. do more experiments.

P.14 Select the correct phrase(s) to complete the following statement: A hypothesis becomes a theory when
   a. one experiment proves the hypothesis.
   b. many experiments by many scientists validate the hypothesis.
   c. you decide to call it a theory.

ADDITIONAL QUESTIONS AND PROBLEMS

For instructor-assigned homework, go to ***www.masteringchemistry.com***.

P.15 Why does the scientific method include a hypothesis?

P.16 Why is experimentation an important part of the scientific method?

P.17 Classify each of the following statements as either an observation or a hypothesis:
   a. Aluminum melts at 660 °C.
   b. Dinosaurs became extinct when a large meteorite struck Earth and caused a huge dust cloud that severely decreased the amount of light reaching Earth.
   c. The 100-yard dash was run in 9.8 seconds.

P.18 Classify each of the following statements as either an observation or a hypothesis:
   a. Analysis of 10 ceramic dishes showed that four dishes contained lead levels that exceeded federal safety standards.
   b. Marble statues undergo corrosion in acid rain.
   c. Statues corrode in acid rain because the acidity is sufficient to dissolve calcium carbonate, the major substance of marble.

CHALLENGE QUESTIONS

P.19 Classify each of the following statements as an observation, hypothesis, or experiment:
  a. The bicycle tire is flat.
  b. If I add air to the bicycle tire, it will expand to the proper size.
  c. When I added air to the bicycle tire, it was still flat.
  d. The bicycle tire must have a leak in it.

P.20 Classify each of the following statements as an observation, hypothesis, or experiment:
  a. A big log in the fire does not burn well.
  b. If I chop the log into small pieces, it will burn better.
  c. The smaller pieces of wood burn brighter and make a hotter fire.
  d. The small wood pieces burn faster than burning the big log.

ANSWERS

ANSWERS TO STUDY CHECKS

P.1 **a.**, **b.**, and **d.**

P.2 **a.** E   **b.** O   **c.** H

P.3 **b.**, **c.**, and **e.**

ANSWERS TO SELECTED QUESTIONS AND PROBLEMS

P.1 Many chemicals are listed on a vitamin bottle such as vitamin A, vitamin B_3, vitamin B_{12}, folic acid, etc.

P.3 No. All of the ingredients listed are chemicals.

P.5 One advantage of a pesticide is that it gets rid of insects that bite humans or animals or damage crops. One disadvantage is that a pesticide can destroy beneficial insects or be retained in a crop that is eventually eaten by animals or humans.

P.7 **a.** O   **b.** H   **c.** E   **d.** O   **e.** O   **f.** T

P.9 **a.**, **c.**, and **e.**

P.11 Yes. Sherlock's investigation includes making observations (gathering data), formulating a hypothesis, testing the hypothesis, and modifying it until one of the hypotheses is validated.

P.13 **b.** and **c.**

P.15 A hypothesis, which is a possible explanation for an observation, can be tested with experiments.

P.17 **a.** observation   **b.** hypothesis   **c.** observation

P.19 **a.** observation   **b.** hypothesis   **c.** experiment   **d.** hypothesis

1 Measurements

"I use measurement in just about every part of my nursing practice," says registered nurse Vicki Miller. "When I receive a doctor's order for a medication, I have to verify that order. Then I draw a carefully measured volume from an IV or a vial to create that particular dose. Some dosage orders are specific to the size of the patient. I measure the patient's weight and calculate the dosage required for the weight of that patient."

Nurses use measurement each time they determine a patient's temperature, height, weight, or blood pressure. Measurement is used to obtain the correct amounts for injections and medications and to determine the volumes of fluid intake and output. For each measurement, the amounts and units are recorded in the patient's records.

Mastering**CHEMISTRY**™

Visit **www.masteringchemistry.com** for self-study materials and instructor-assigned homework.

Introduction to Organic Chemistry: Alkanes

11

"When we have a hazardous materials spill, the first thing we do is isolate it," says Don Dornell, assistant fire chief, Burlingame Fire Station. "Then our technicians and a county chemist identify the product from its flammability and solubility in water so we can use the proper materials to clean up the spill. We use different methods for alcohol, which mixes with water, than for gasoline, which floats. Because hydrocarbons are volatile, we use foam to cover them and trap the vapors. At oil refineries, we will use foams, but many times we squirt water on the tanks to cool the contents below their boiling points, too. By knowing the boiling point of the product and its density and vapor density, we know if it floats or sinks in water and where its vapors will go."

Mastering**CHEMISTRY**™

Visit **www.masteringchemistry.com** for self-study materials and instructor-assigned homework.

*O*rganic chemistry is the chemistry of compounds that contain carbon and hydrogen. The element carbon has a special role in chemistry because it bonds with other carbon atoms to give a vast array of molecules. The variety of molecules is so great that we find organic compounds in many common products we use, such as gasoline, medicine, shampoos, plastic bottles, and perfumes. The food we eat is composed of different organic compounds that supply us with fuel for energy and the carbon atoms needed to build and repair the cells of our bodies.

Although many organic compounds occur in nature, chemists have synthesized even more. The cotton, wool, or silk in your clothes contains naturally occurring organic compounds, whereas materials such as polyester, nylon, or plastic have been synthesized through organic reactions. Sometimes it is convenient to synthesize a molecule in the lab even though that molecule is also found in nature. For example, vitamin C synthesized in a laboratory has the same structure as the vitamin C in oranges or lemons. In these chapters on organic chemistry, you will learn about the structures and reactions of organic molecules, which will provide a foundation for understanding the more complex molecules of biochemistry.

11.1 Organic Compounds

LEARNING GOAL

Identify characteristic properties of organic or inorganic compounds.

At the beginning of the nineteenth century, scientists classified chemical compounds as inorganic and organic. An inorganic compound was a substance that was composed of minerals, and an organic compound was a substance that came from an organism, thus the origin of the word "organic." Early scientists thought that some type of "vital force," which could be found only in living cells, was required to synthesize an organic compound. This perception was shown to be incorrect in 1828 when the German chemist Friedrick Wöhler synthesized urea, a product of protein metabolism, by heating an inorganic compound, ammonium cyanate.

$$NH_4CNO \xrightarrow{\text{Heat}} H_2N-\overset{\overset{\displaystyle O}{\|}}{C}-NH_2$$

Ammonium cyanate (inorganic)   Urea (organic)

We now define organic chemistry as the study of carbon compounds. **Organic compounds** always contain carbon (C), usually hydrogen (H), and sometimes other nonmetallic elements such as oxygen (O), sulfur (S), nitrogen (N), phosphorus (P), or a halogen such as chlorine (Cl). In any organic compound, there are always four bonds to every carbon. Organic compounds are usually nonpolar, with weak attractions between molecules, which accounts for their low melting and boiling points. Typically, organic compounds are not soluble in water. For example, vegetable oil, which is a mixture of organic compounds, does not dissolve in water, but floats on top. Many organic compounds undergo combustion and burn vigorously in air.

In contrast, many of the inorganic compounds are ionic, which leads to high melting and boiling points. Inorganic compounds that have ionic or polar covalent bonds are usually soluble in water. Most inorganic substances do not burn in air. Table 11.1 contrasts some of the properties associated with organic compounds, such as propane (C_3H_8) and inorganic compounds, such as sodium chloride (NaCl). (See Figure 11.1.)

TABLE 11.1 Some Typical Properties of Organic and Inorganic Compounds

Property	Organic	Example: C_3H_8	Inorganic	Example: NaCl
Elements	C and H, sometimes O, S, N, P, or (F, Br, I) Cl	C and H	Most metals and nonmetals	Na and Cl
Bonding	Mostly covalent	Covalent (4 bonds to each C)	Many are ionic, some covalent	Ionic
Polarity of bonds	Nonpolar, unless a very electronegative atom is present	Nonpolar	Most are ionic or polar covalent, a few are nonpolar covalent	Ionic
Melting point	Usually low	$-188\,°C$	Usually high	$801\,°C$
Boiling point	Usually low	$-42\,°C$	Usually high	$1413\,°C$
Flammability	High	Burns in air	Low	Does not burn
Solubility in water	Not soluble, unless a polar group is present	No	Most are soluble, unless nonpolar	Yes

---

CONCEPT CHECK 11.1

■ Properties of Organic Compounds

Indicate whether the following properties are most typical of organic or inorganic compounds:

a. not soluble in water   **b.** high melting point   **c.** burns in air

ANSWER
a. Many organic compounds are not soluble in water.
b. Inorganic compounds are most likely to have high melting points.
c. Organic compounds are most likely to be flammable.

FIGURE 11.1 Propane, C_3H_8, is an organic compound, whereas sodium chloride, NaCl, is an inorganic compound.

Q Why is propane used as a fuel?

Bonding in Organic Compounds

Hydrocarbons, as the name suggests, are organic compounds that consist of only carbon and hydrogen. In the simplest hydrocarbon, methane (CH_4), the carbon atom forms an octet by sharing four valence electrons with four hydrogen atoms. In the electron-dot formula, each shared pair of electrons represents a single bond. In organic molecules, every carbon atom has four bonds. A hydrocarbon is referred to as a *saturated hydrocarbon* when all of the bonds in the molecule are single bonds. An **expanded structural formula** is written when we show the bonds between all of the atoms.

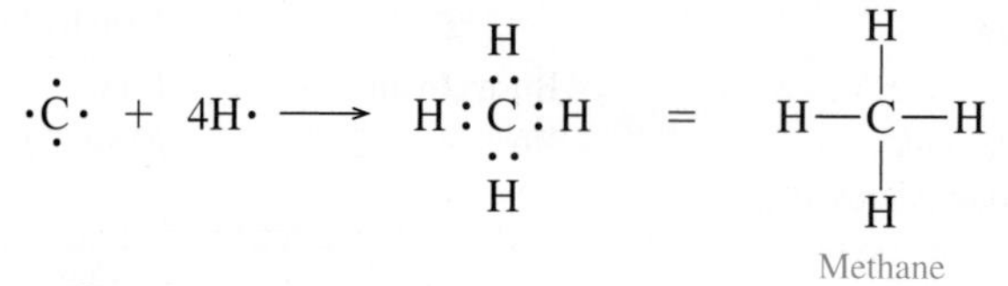

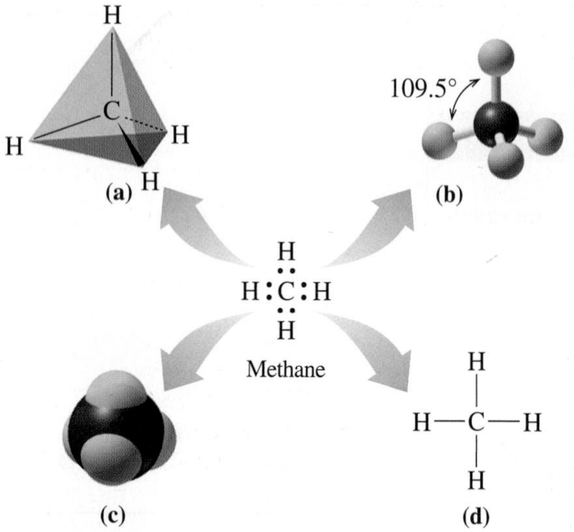

$$\cdot\overset{\cdot}{\underset{\cdot}{C}}\cdot \;+\; 4H\cdot \longrightarrow \;\; H\!:\!\overset{\overset{\displaystyle H}{\cdot\cdot}}{\underset{\underset{\displaystyle H}{\cdot\cdot}}{C}}\!:\!H \;\;=\;\; H\!-\!\underset{\underset{\displaystyle H}{|}}{\overset{\overset{\displaystyle H}{|}}{C}}\!-\!H$$

Methane

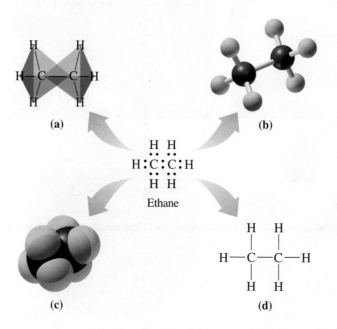

H:C:H
H

Methane

The Tetrahedral Structure of Carbon

The VSEPR theory (Chapter 5) predicts that a molecule with four atoms bonded to a central atom has a tetrahedral shape. In CH_4, the bonds from the carbon atom to the four hydrogen atoms are directed to the corners of a tetrahedron with bond angles of 109.5°. The structure of methane is illustrated as both a ball-and-stick model and a space-filling model in Figure 11.2.

In ethane, C_2H_6, each carbon atom is bonded to another carbon and three hydrogen atoms. As in methane, each carbon retains the tetrahedral shape with bond angles close to 109.5°. In the ball-and-stick model of ethane, C_2H_6, two tetrahedra are attached to each other. (See Figure 11.3.)

FIGURE 11.2 Representations of methane, CH_4: **(a)** tetrahedron, **(b)** ball-and-stick model, **(c)** space-filling model, **(d)** expanded structural formula.

Q Why does methane have a tetrahedral shape and not a flat shape?

FIGURE 11.3 Representations of ethane, C_2H_6: **(a)** tetrahedral shape of each carbon, **(b)** ball-and-stick model, **(c)** space-filling model, **(d)** expanded structural formula.

Q How is the tetrahedral shape maintained by each carbon in a molecule with two carbon atoms?

QUESTIONS AND PROBLEMS

Organic Compounds

11.1 Identify the following as formulas of organic or inorganic compounds:
  a. KCl   **b.** C_4H_{10} **c.** C_3H_6O
  d. H_2SO_4 **e.** $CaCl_2$ **f.** C_2H_5Cl

11.2 Identify the following as formulas of organic or inorganic compounds:
  a. $C_6H_{12}O_6$ **b.** Na_2SO_4 **c.** I_2
  d. C_4H_9Cl **e.** $C_{10}H_{22}$ **f.** CH_4

11.3 Identify the following properties as most typical of organic inorganic compounds:
  a. soluble in water   **b.** low boiling point
  c. burns in air   **d.** high melting point

11.4 Identify the following properties as most typical of organic inorganic compounds:
  a. contains Na   **b.** boils at $-50\ ^{\circ}C$
  c. covalent bonds   **d.** produces ions in water

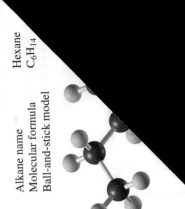

Hexane
C_6H_{14}

Alkane name
Molecular formula
Ball-and-stick model

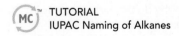

Condensed

In a conden
are writte
carbon

11.2 Alkanes

More than 90% of the compounds in the world are organic compounds. This large number of carbon compounds is possible because the covalent bond between carbon atoms (C—C) is very strong, allowing carbon atoms to form long, stable chains. To help us study this large group of compounds, we organize them into classes that have similar structures and chemical properties.

The **alkanes** are a class of hydrocarbons in which the atoms are connected by single bonds. One of the most common uses of alkanes is as fuels. Methane, used in gas heaters and gas cooktops, is an alkane with one carbon atom. The alkanes ethane, propane, and butane contain two, three, and four carbon atoms, respectively, connected in a row or a *continuous chain*. These names are part of the **IUPAC** (International Union of Pure and Applied Chemistry) **system**, which chemists use to name organic compounds. Alkanes with five or more carbon atoms in a chain are named using Greek prefixes: *pent*(5), *hex*(6), *hept*(7), *oct*(8), *non*(9), and *dec*(10). (See Table 11.2.)

LEARNING GOAL

Write the IUPAC names and condensed structural formulas for alkanes.

MC ™ TUTORIAL
IUPAC Naming of Alkanes

TABLE 11.2 IUPAC Names for the First Ten Alkanes

Number of Carbon Atoms	Prefix	Name	Molecular Formula	Condensed Structural Formula
1	Meth	Methane	CH_4	CH_4
2	Eth	Ethane	C_2H_6	CH_3-CH_3
3	Prop	Propane	C_3H_8	$CH_3-CH_2-CH_3$
4	But	Butane	C_4H_{10}	$CH_3-CH_2-CH_2-CH_3$
5	Pent	Pentane	C_5H_{12}	$CH_3-CH_2-CH_2-CH_2-CH_3$
6	Hex	Hexane	C_6H_{14}	$CH_3-CH_2-CH_2-CH_2-CH_2-CH_3$
7	Hept	Heptane	C_7H_{16}	$CH_3-CH_2-CH_2-CH_2-CH_2-CH_2-CH_3$
8	Oct	Octane	C_8H_{18}	$CH_3-CH_2-CH_2-CH_2-CH_2-CH_2-CH_2-CH_3$
9	Non	Nonane	C_9H_{20}	$CH_3-CH_2-CH_2-CH_2-CH_2-CH_2-CH_2-CH_2-CH_3$
10	Dec	Decane	$C_{10}H_{22}$	$CH_3-CH_2-CH_2-CH_2-CH_2-CH_2-CH_2-CH_2-CH_2-CH_3$

Structural Formulas

In the condensed structural formula, each carbon atom and its attached hydrogen atoms are written as a group. A subscript indicates the number of hydrogen atoms bonded to each carbon atom.

$$H-\underset{\underset{H}{|}}{\overset{\overset{H}{|}}{C}}- \; = \; CH_3- \qquad -\underset{\underset{H}{|}}{\overset{\overset{H}{|}}{C}}- \; = \; -CH_2-$$

Expanded   Condensed   Expanded   Condensed

By contrast, the molecular formula gives the total number of each kind of atom but does not indicate their arrangement in the molecule. When a molecule consists of a chain of three or more carbon atoms, the carbon atoms do not lie in a straight line. The tetrahedral shape of carbon arranges the carbon bonds in a zigzag pattern, which is seen in the ball-and-stick model of hexane. An abbreviated structure called the **line-bond formula** shows only the bonds from carbon to carbon. The ends of the lines and the corners where the lines meet are understood to be carbon atoms attached to the proper number of hydrogen atoms to give four bonds. (See Figure 11.4.)

Because an alkane has only single C—C bonds, the groups attached to each C are not in fixed positions. They can rotate freely about the bond connecting the carbon atoms. This motion is analogous to the independent rotation of the wheels of a toy car. Thus different arrangements, known as *conformations*, occur during the rotation about a single bond.

Suppose we could look at butane, C_4H_{10}, as it rotates. Sometimes the —CH_3 groups line up in front of each other, and at other times they are opposite each other. As the —CH_3 groups turn around the single bond, many arrangements are possible. Butane can be depicted by a variety of two-dimensional condensed structural formulas, as shown in Table 11.3. All of these condensed structural formulas represent the same compound with four carbon atoms.

Expanded structural formula

$$H-\underset{\underset{H}{|}}{\overset{\overset{H}{|}}{C}}-\underset{\underset{H}{|}}{\overset{\overset{H}{|}}{C}}-\underset{\underset{H}{|}}{\overset{\overset{H}{|}}{C}}-\underset{\underset{H}{|}}{\overset{\overset{H}{|}}{C}}-\underset{\underset{H}{|}}{\overset{\overset{H}{|}}{C}}-\underset{\underset{H}{|}}{\overset{\overset{H}{|}}{C}}-H$$

Condensed structural formulas

$$CH_3 \quad CH_2 \quad CH_2 \quad CH_3$$
$$\qquad CH_2 \quad CH_2 \quad CH_2$$

$$CH_3-CH_2-CH_2-CH_2-CH_2-CH_3$$

Line-bond formula

FIGURE 11.4 A ball-and-stick model and structural formulas of hexane.

Q Why do the carbon atoms in hexane appear to be arranged in a zigzag chain?

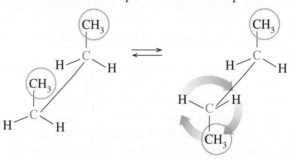

TABLE 11.3 Structural Representations for Butane, C_4H_{10}

Expanded structural formula

$$H-\underset{\underset{H}{|}}{\overset{\overset{H}{|}}{C}}-\underset{\underset{H}{|}}{\overset{\overset{H}{|}}{C}}-\underset{\underset{H}{|}}{\overset{\overset{H}{|}}{C}}-\underset{\underset{H}{|}}{\overset{\overset{H}{|}}{C}}-H$$

Condensed structural formulas

$$CH_3-CH_2-CH_2-CH_3 \qquad \underset{CH_3 \quad CH_3}{CH_2-CH_2} \qquad \underset{CH_2-CH_2}{\overset{CH_3}{|}}{\quad}\underset{CH_3}{|} \qquad \underset{\overset{|}{CH_2}}{\overset{CH_3}{|}}$$

$$\underset{CH_2-CH_3}{CH_3-CH_2} \qquad \underset{CH_2-CH_2-CH_3}{CH_3} \qquad \underset{CH_3}{\overset{|}{CH_3}}\qquad \underset{CH_3}{\overset{|}{CH_2}}$$

$$CH_3 \quad CH_2 \qquad\qquad CH_2 \quad CH_3$$

Line-bond formulas

SAMPLE PROBLEM 11.1

■ Drawing Structural Formulas for Alkanes

A molecule of butane, C_4H_{10}, has four carbon atoms in a row. What are its expanded, condensed, and line-bond structural formulas?

SOLUTION

In the expanded structural formula, the four carbon atoms are connected to each other and to hydrogen atoms with single bonds to give each carbon atom a total of four bonds. In the condensed structural formula, each carbon atom and its attached hydrogen atoms are written as CH_3— or —CH_2—. The line-bond formula shows only the carbon-to-carbon bonds.

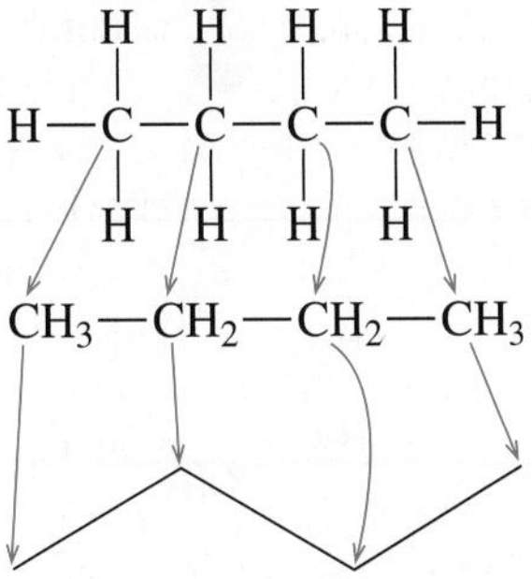

H   H   H   H
| | | |
H—C—C—C—C—H   Expanded structural formula
| | | |
H   H   H   H

CH_3—CH_2—CH_2—CH_3 Condensed structural formula

Line-bond formula

STUDY CHECK

Write the expanded, condensed, and line-bond structural formulas of pentane, C_5H_{12}.

Cycloalkanes

Hydrocarbons can also form cyclic structures called **cycloalkanes**, which have two fewer hydrogen atoms than the corresponding alkanes. Thus, the simplest cycloalkane, cyclopropane, C_3H_6, has a ring of three carbon atoms bonded to six hydrogen atoms. A simplified formula, which omits the hydrogen atoms and looks like a geometric figure, is a convenient way to show cyclic structures. Each corner of the triangle represents a carbon atom with four bonds to other carbon and hydrogen atoms.

The ball-and-stick models, their condensed structural formulas, and geometric formulas for several cycloalkanes are shown in Table 11.4. A cycloalkane is named by adding the prefix *cyclo* to the name of the alkane with the same number of carbon atoms.

SAMPLE PROBLEM 11.2

■ Naming Alkanes

Give the IUPAC name for each of the following:

a. CH_3—CH_2—CH_2—CH_2—CH_3 **b.** 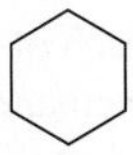 ⬡   **c.** CH_3—CH_2—CH_3

SOLUTION

a. A chain with five carbon atoms is pentane.
b. The ring of six carbon atoms is named cyclohexane.
c. This alkane is named propane because it has three carbon atoms.

STUDY CHECK

What is the IUPAC name of the following compound?

TABLE 11.4 Formulas of Some Common Cycloalkanes

Ball-and-Stick Models

Condensed Structural Formulas

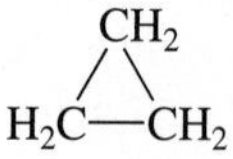

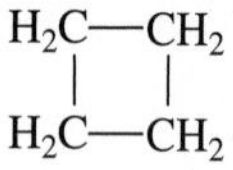

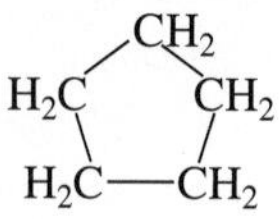

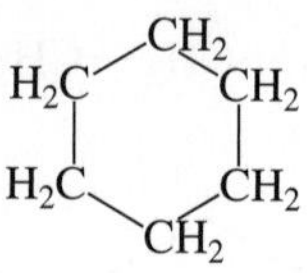

Geometric Formulas

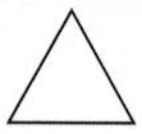

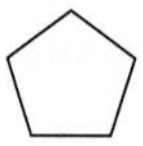

△   ▢   ⬠   ⬡

Name

Cyclopropane   Cyclobutane   Cyclopentane   Cyclohexane

QUESTIONS AND PROBLEMS

Alkanes

11.9 Write the stated type of structural formula for each of the following:
  a. an expanded structural formula for propane
  b. the condensed structural formula for hexane
  c. a line-bond formula for hexane

11.10 Write the stated type of structural formula for each of the following:
  a. an expanded structural formula for butane
  b. the condensed structural formula for octane
  c. a line-bond formula for decane

11.11 Give the IUPAC name for each of the following:

  a. 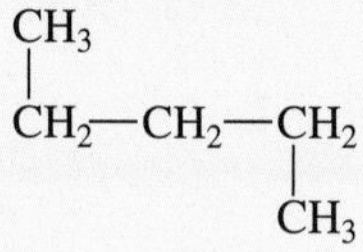 CH_3
      |
    CH_2—CH_2—CH_2
               |
               CH_3

  b.  ∧∧∧

            CH_2—CH_3
            |
            CH_2
  c. 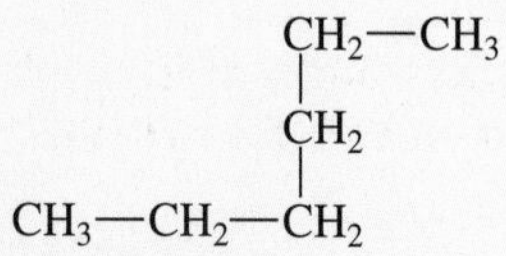 CH_3—CH_2—CH_2
                              d. ▢

11.12 Give the IUPAC name for each of the following alkanes:
  a. CH_4 **b.** 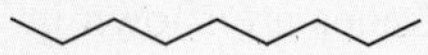 ∨∨∨∨

          CH_3
          |
          CH_2
          |
  c. 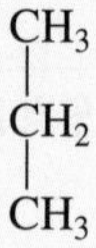 CH_3 **d.** 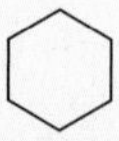 ⬡

11.13 Write the condensed structural formula or geometric formula for each of the following:
  a. methane
  b. ethane
  c. pentane
  d. cyclopropane

11.14 Write the condensed structural formula or geometric formula for each of the following:
  a. propane
  b. hexane
  c. heptane
  d. cyclopentane

11.3 Alkanes with Substituents

When an alkane has four or more carbon atoms, the atoms can be arranged so that a side group called a **branch** or **substituent** is attached to a carbon chain. For example, there are two different ball-and-stick models for the molecular formula C_4H_{10}. One model is shown as a chain of four carbon atoms. In the other model, a carbon atom is attached as a branch or substituent to a carbon in a chain of three atoms. (See Figure 11.5.) An alkane with at least one branch is called a **branched alkane**. When two compounds have the same molecular formula but different arrangements of atoms, they are called **isomers**.

In another example, we can write three different structural isomers that have the molecular formula C_5H_{12} as follows:

LEARNING GOAL

Write the IUPAC names for alkanes with substituents.

Isomers of C_5H_{12}

Alkane	Branched Alkanes
$CH_3-CH_2-CH_2-CH_2-CH_3$	$\begin{array}{c} CH_3 \\ | \\ CH_3-CH-CH_2-CH_3 \end{array}$ $\begin{array}{c} CH_3 \\ | \\ CH_3-C-CH_3 \\ | \\ CH_3 \end{array}$

The number of structural isomers for alkanes increases rapidly as the number of carbon atoms increases.

FIGURE 11.5 The isomers of C_4H_{10} have the same number and type of atoms, which are bonded in a different order.

Q What makes these molecules isomers?

SAMPLE PROBLEM 11.3

■ Isomers

Identify each pair of condensed structural formulas as isomers or the same molecule:

a. $\begin{array}{c} CH_3 \quad CH_3 \\ | \qquad | \\ CH_2-CH_2 \\ | \\ CH_3 \end{array}$ and $CH_2-CH_2-CH_3$

b. $\begin{array}{c} CH_3 \\ | \\ CH_3-CH-CH_2-CH_2-CH_3 \end{array}$ and $\begin{array}{c} CH_3 \quad CH_3 \\ | \qquad | \\ CH_3-CH-CH-CH_3 \end{array}$

SOLUTION

a. The condensed structural formulas represent the same molecule because they both have four C atoms in a chain with no substituents.
b. These are isomers because the molecular formula C_6H_{14} is identical, but the C atoms are bonded in a different order. One has a $—CH_3$ group attached to a five-carbon chain, and the other has two $—CH_3$ groups attached to a four-carbon chain.

STUDY CHECK

Is the following condensed structural formula an isomer or identical to the molecules in Sample Problem 11.3b?

$\begin{array}{c} CH_3 \\ | \\ CH_3-CH_2-CH-CH_2-CH_3 \end{array}$

Possible Isomers for Alkanes with 1–10 Carbon Atoms

Number of Carbon Atoms	Numbers of Isomers
1	1
2	1
3	1
4	2
5	3
6	5
7	9
8	18
9	35
10	75

Substituents in Alkanes

In the IUPAC names for alkanes, a carbon branch is named as an **alkyl group**, which is an alkane that is missing one hydrogen atom. The alkyl group is named by replacing the *ane* ending of the corresponding alkane name with *yl*. Alkyl groups cannot exist on their own;

 SELF STUDY ACTIVITY
Isomers: Diversity in Molecules

TABLE 11.5 Names and Formulas of Some Common Substituents

Substituent	Name
CH_3—	Methyl
CH_3—CH_2—	Ethyl
CH_3—CH_2—CH_2—	Propyl
CH_3—$\overset{\mid}{CH}$—CH_3	Isopropyl
F—, Cl—, Br—, I—	Fluoro, chloro, bromo, iodo

TUTORIAL
Naming Alkanes with Substituents

they must be attached to a carbon chain. When a halogen atom is attached to a carbon chain, it is named as a *halo* group: fluoro (F), chloro (Cl), bromo (Br), or iodo (I). Some of the common groups attached to carbon chains are illustrated in Table 11.5.

Rules for Naming Alkanes with Substituents

In the IUPAC system, a carbon chain with a substituent is numbered to give the location of that substituent. Let's take a look at how we use the IUPAC system to name the following alkane:

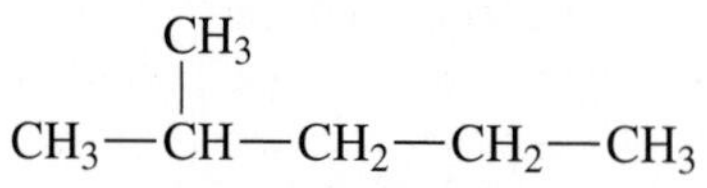

$$\overset{\displaystyle CH_3}{\underset{}{\overset{\mid}{CH_3—CH—CH_2—CH_2—CH_3}}}$$

STEP 1 **Write the alkane name of the longest chain of carbon atoms.**   In this alkane, the longest chain has five carbon atoms, which is *pentane*:

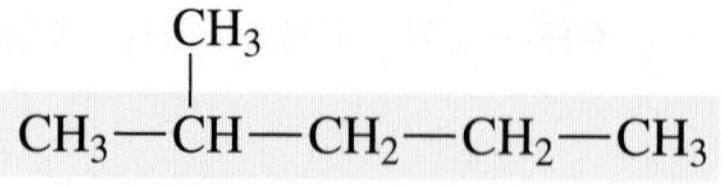

$$\overset{\displaystyle CH_3}{\overset{\mid}{CH_3—CH—CH_2—CH_2—CH_3}} \quad \text{pentane}$$

STEP 2 **Number the carbon atoms starting from the end nearest a substituent.** Once you start numbering, continue in that same direction:

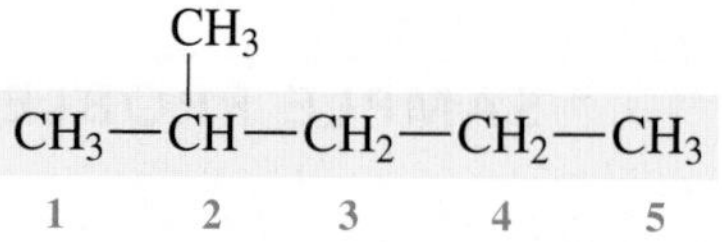

$$\overset{\displaystyle CH_3}{\overset{\mid}{CH_3—CH—CH_2—CH_2—CH_3}} \quad \text{pentane}$$
$$\;\;1\quad\;2\quad\;\;3\quad\;\;4\quad\;\;5$$

STEP 3 **Give the location and name of each substituent as a prefix to the alkane name.**   Place a hyphen between the number and the substituent name:

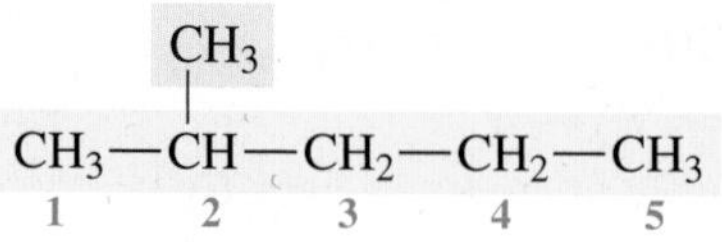

$$\overset{\displaystyle CH_3}{\overset{\mid}{CH_3—CH—CH_2—CH_2—CH_3}} \quad \text{2-methylpentane}$$
$$\;\;1\quad\;2\quad\;\;3\quad\;\;4\quad\;\;5$$

Below are more examples giving the locations of the substituents. Place the names of different substituents in alphabetical order.

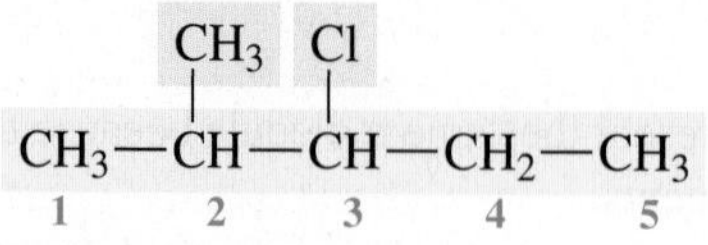

$$\overset{\displaystyle CH_3\;\; Cl}{\overset{\mid\qquad\mid}{CH_3—CH—CH—CH_2—CH_3}} \quad \text{3-chloro-2-methylpentane}$$
$$\;\;1\quad\;2\quad\;\;3\quad\;\;4\quad\;\;5$$

Use a prefix (*di, tri, tetra*) to indicate a group that appears more than once. Use commas to separate two or more numbers. However, prefixes are not used to determine the alphabetical order:

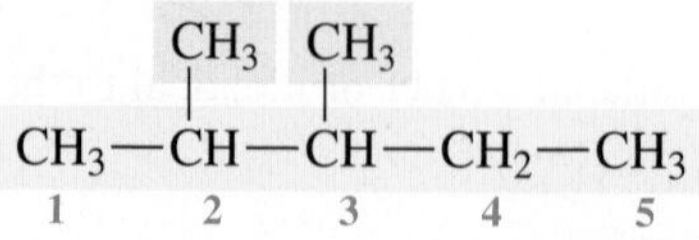

$$\overset{\displaystyle CH_3\;\; CH_3}{\overset{\mid\qquad\mid}{CH_3—CH—CH—CH_2—CH_3}} \quad \text{2,3-dimethylpentane}$$
$$\;\;1\quad\;2\quad\;\;3\quad\;\;4\quad\;\;5$$

When there are two or more substituents, the main chain is numbered in the direction that gives the lowest set of numbers:

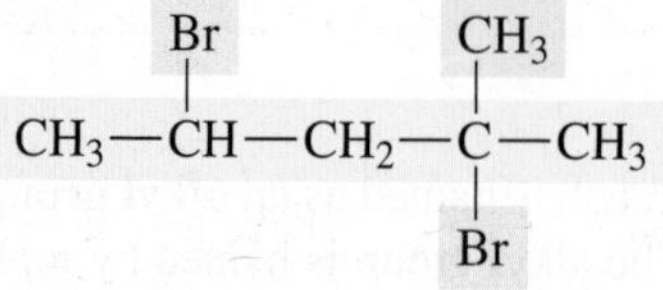

$$\overset{\displaystyle Br\qquad\qquad CH_3}{\overset{\mid\qquad\qquad\quad\mid}{CH_3—CH—CH_2—C—CH_3}} \quad \text{2,4-dibromo-2-methylpentane}$$
$$\underset{\displaystyle Br}{\overset{\mid}{}}$$
$$\;\;5\qquad\;4\qquad\;3\qquad 2\quad\;\;1$$

No number is necessary for a compound with one or two carbon atoms and one substituent:

CH_3—Br   bromomethane

CH_3—CH_2—Cl   chloroethane

Naming Cycloalkanes

When one substituent is attached to a carbon atom in a ring, the name of the substituent is placed in front of the cycloalkane name. No number is needed for a single alkyl group or halogen atom because the carbon atoms in the cycloalkane are equivalent. However, if two or more groups are attached, the ring is numbered to show the location of each group. The numbering starts by assigning carbon 1 to the substituent that gives the lowest numbers to the other substituents. When there are two substituents, the one that comes first alphabetically is attached to carbon 1. We may count clockwise or counterclockwise around a cycloalkane to give the lowest combination of numbers to the substituents.

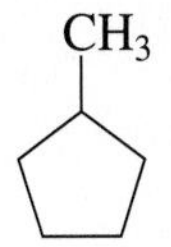

TUTORIAL
Naming Cycloalkanes

Methylcyclopentane

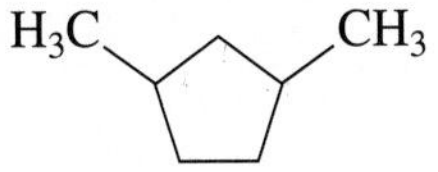

1,3-Dimethylcyclopentane

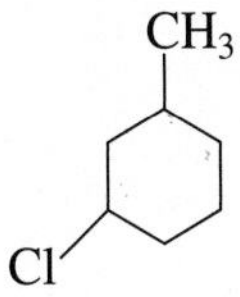

1-Chloro-3-methylcyclohexane

CONCEPT CHECK 11.2

■ Naming Compounds with Substituents

A six-carbon chain has a CH_3— group attached to carbon 2 and a Cl— atom attached to carbon 3. What is the name of this compound?

ANSWER

The CH_3— group is named as a methyl and the Cl— atom is named as a chloro. In alphabetical order, these substituents are named 3-chloro-2-methyl. The six-carbon chain is named hexane, and the compound is named 3-chloro-2-methylhexane.

SAMPLE PROBLEM 11.4

■ Writing IUPAC Names

Give the IUPAC name for the following alkane:

$$CH_3—\underset{\underset{}{\overset{|}{CH}}}{\overset{\overset{CH_3}{|}}{}}—CH_2—\underset{\underset{CH_3}{|}}{\overset{\overset{Br}{|}}{C}}—CH_2—CH_3$$

SOLUTION

STEP 1   Write the alkane name of the longest chain of carbon atoms.   In this alkane, the longest chain has six carbon atoms, which is *hexane*:

$$CH_3—\underset{\underset{}{\overset{|}{CH}}}{\overset{\overset{CH_3}{|}}{}}—CH_2—\underset{\underset{CH_3}{|}}{\overset{\overset{Br}{|}}{C}}—CH_2—CH_3$$ hexane

Guide to Naming Alkanes

STEP 1
Write the alkane name of the longest chain of carbon atoms.

STEP 2
Number the carbon atoms starting from the end nearest a substituent.

STEP 3
Give the location and name of each substituent (alphabetical order) as a prefix to the name of the main chain.

STEP 2   **Number the carbon atoms starting from the end nearest a substituent:**

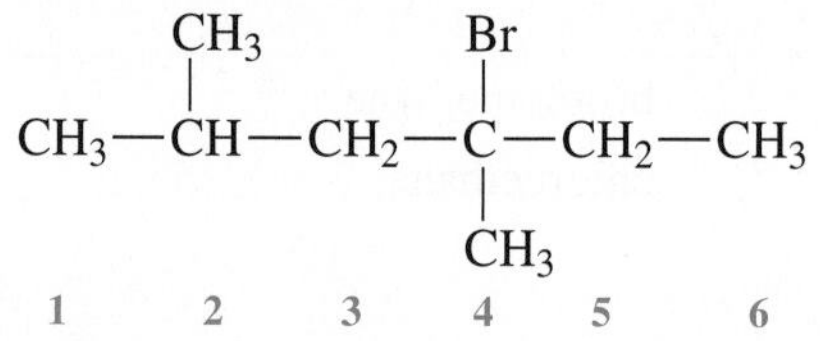

$$CH_3-\overset{\overset{\displaystyle CH_3}{|}}{CH}-CH_2-\overset{\overset{\displaystyle Br}{|}}{\underset{\underset{\displaystyle CH_3}{|}}{C}}-CH_2-CH_3 \qquad \text{hexane}$$

1   2   3   4   5   6

STEP 3   **Give the location and name of each substituent in front of the name of the longest chain. List the names of different substituents in alphabetical order.**   Place hyphens between the numbers and the substituent names and add commas to separate two or more numbers. A prefix (*di, tri, tetra*) indicates a group that appears more than once.

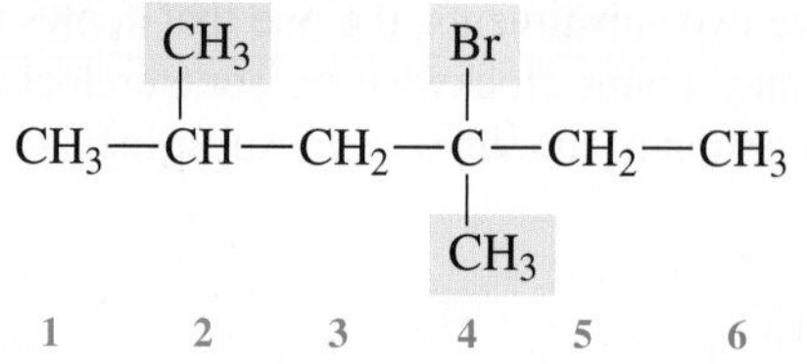

$$CH_3-\overset{\overset{\displaystyle CH_3}{|}}{CH}-CH_2-\overset{\overset{\displaystyle Br}{|}}{\underset{\underset{\displaystyle CH_3}{|}}{C}}-CH_2-CH_3 \qquad \text{4-bromo-2,4-dimethylhexane}$$

1   2   3   4   5   6

STUDY CHECK

Give the IUPAC name for the following compound:

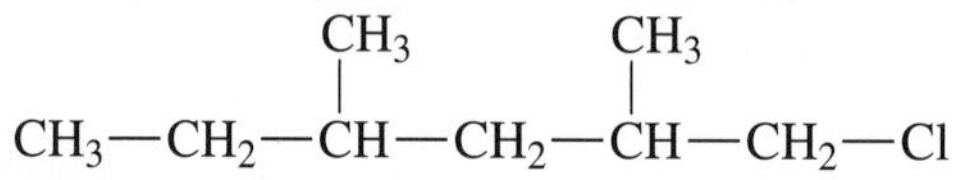

$$CH_3-CH_2-\overset{\overset{\displaystyle CH_3}{|}}{CH}-CH_2-\overset{\overset{\displaystyle CH_3}{|}}{CH}-CH_2-Cl$$

Drawing Structural Formulas for Alkanes

The IUPAC name gives all the information needed to draw the condensed structural formula of an alkane. Suppose you are asked to draw the condensed structural formula of 2,3-dimethylbutane. The alkane name gives the number of carbon atoms in the longest chain. The names in the beginning indicate the substituents and where they are attached. We can break down the name in the following way.

2,3-Dimethylbutane

2,3-	di	methyl	but	ane
Substituents on carbons 2 and 3	Two identical groups	CH_3— alkyl groups	4 carbon atoms in the main chain	Single C—C bonds

SAMPLE PROBLEM   11.5

■ **Drawing Condensed Structural Formulas from IUPAC Names**

Write the condensed structural formula for 2,3-dimethylbutane.

SOLUTION

We can use the following guide to draw the condensed structural formula:

Guide to Drawing Alkane Formulas

STEP 1
Draw the main chain of carbon atoms.

STEP 2
Number the chain and place the substituents on the carbons indicated by the numbers.

STEP 3
Add the correct number of hydrogen atoms to give four bonds to each C atom.

STEP 1   **Draw the main chain of carbon atoms.**   For butane, we draw a chain of four carbon atoms:

C—C—C—C

STEP 2   **Number the chain and place the substituents on the carbons indicated by the numbers.**   The first part of the name indicates two methyl groups (CH_3—), one on carbon 2 and one on carbon 3:

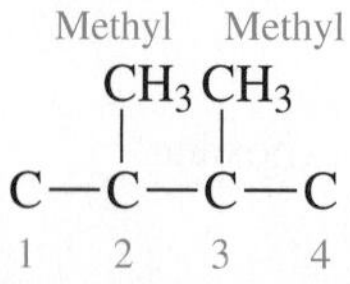

Methyl Methyl
$$\overset{\displaystyle CH_3}{|} \quad \overset{\displaystyle CH_3}{|}$$
$$C-C-C-C$$
1   2   3   4

STEP 3   Add the correct number of hydrogen atoms to give four bonds to each C atom:

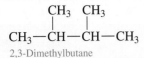

CH₃—CH—CH—CH₃
with CH₃ groups above the two middle carbons

2,3-Dimethylbutane

STUDY CHECK

Draw the condensed structural formula for 2,4-dimethylpentane.

Haloalkanes

In a **haloalkane**, halogen atoms replace hydrogen atoms in an alkane. The halogen substituents are numbered and arranged alphabetically, just as we did with the alkyl groups. Many times chemists use the common, traditional name for these compounds rather than the systematic IUPAC name. Simple haloalkanes are commonly named as alkyl halides; the carbon group is named as an alkyl group followed by the halide name:

$CH_3—Cl$ $CH_3—CH_2—Br$ $CH_3—\underset{\underset{F}{|}}{CH}—CH_3$

IUPAC:	Chloromethane	Bromoethane	2-Fluoropropane
Common:	Methyl chloride	Ethyl bromide	Isopropyl fluoride

SAMPLE PROBLEM 11.6

■ Naming Haloalkanes

Freon 11 and Freon 12 are compounds, known as *chlorofluorocarbons* (CFCs), that were used as refrigerants and aerosol propellants. What are their IUPAC names?

Cl—C—F with Cl above and Cl below (Freon 11)

F—C—F with Cl above and Cl below (Freon 12)

Freon 11   Freon 12

SOLUTION

Freon 11, trichlorofluoromethane; Freon 12, dichlorodifluoromethane.

STUDY CHECK

Ethylene dibromide is the common name of a haloalkane used as a fumigant. What is its IUPAC name?

H—C—C—H with Br, Br above and H, H below

Ethylene dibromide

CAREER FOCUS

Geologist

"Chemistry underpins geology," says Vic Abadie, consulting geologist. "I am a self-employed geologist consulting in exploration for petroleum and natural gas. Predicting the occurrence of an oil reservoir depends in part on understanding chemical reactions of minerals. This is because over geologic time such reactions create or destroy pore spaces that host crude oil or gas in a reservoir rock formation. Chemical analysis can match oil in known reservoir formations with distant formations that generated oil and from which oil migrated into the reservoirs in the geologic past. This can help identify target areas to explore for new reservoirs."

"I evaluate proposals to drill for undiscovered oil and gas. I recommend that my clients invest in proposed wells that my analysis suggests have strong geologic and economic merit. This is a commercial application of the scientific method: the proposal to drill is the hypothesis, and the drill bit tests it. A successful well validates the hypothesis and generates oil or gas production and revenue for my clients and me. I do this and other consulting for private and corporate clients. The risk is high, the work is exciting, and my time is flexible."

TUTORIAL
Drawing Haloalkanes
and Branched Alkanes

HEALTH NOTE

Common Uses of Haloalkanes

Some common uses of haloalkanes include solvents and anesthetics. For many years, carbon tetrachloride was widely used in dry cleaners and in home spot removers to take oils and grease out of clothes. However, this use was discontinued when carbon tetrachloride was found to be toxic to the liver, where it can cause cancer. Today, dry cleaners use other halogenated compounds such as dichloromethane; 1,1,1-trichloroethane; and 1,1,2-trichloro-1,2,2-trifluoroethane.

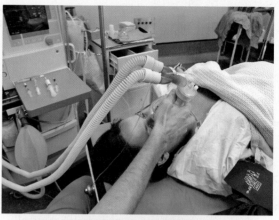

CH_2Cl_2 $Cl_3C—CH_3$ $FCl_2C—CClF_2$
Dichloromethane   1,1,1-Trichloroethane   1,1,2-Trichloro-
                                               1,2,2-trifluoroethane

General anesthetics are compounds that are inhaled or injected to cause a loss of sensation so that surgery or other procedures can be done without causing pain to the patient. As nonpolar compounds, anesthetics are soluble in the nonpolar nerve membranes, where they decrease the ability of the nerve cells to conduct the sensation of pain. Trichloromethane, commonly called chloroform, $CHCl_3$, was once used as an anesthetic, but it is toxic and may be carcinogenic. One of the most widely used general anesthetics is halothane (2-bromo-2-chloro-1,1,1-trifluoroethane), also called Fluothane. It has a pleasant odor, is nonexplosive, has few side effects, undergoes few reactions, and is eliminated quickly from the body.

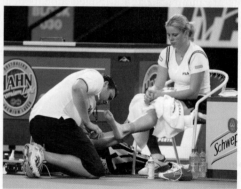

Halothane (Fluothane)

For minor surgeries, a local anesthetic such as chloroethane (ethyl chloride), $CH_3—CH_2—Cl$, is applied to an area of the skin. Chloroethane evaporates quickly, which cools the skin and causes a loss of sensation.

QUESTIONS AND PROBLEMS

Alkanes with Substituents

11.15 Indicate whether each of the following pairs of condensed structural formulas represent isomers or the same molecule:

a.
$$CH_3—CH—CH_3$$
with CH_3 above the central carbon

and

$$CH—CH_3$$
with CH_3 above and CH_3 below

b.
$$CH_3—CH—CH_2—CH_3$$
with CH_3 above the second carbon

and

$$CH_2—CH_2—CH_2$$
with CH_3 above the middle carbon

c.
$$CH_2—CH—CH_2—CH_3$$
with CH_3 above the first two carbons

and

$$CH_3—CH—CH—CH_3$$
with CH_3 above the middle two carbons

11.16 Indicate whether each of the following pairs of condensed structural formulas represent isomers or the same molecule:

a.
$$CH_3—C—CH_3$$
with CH_3 above and CH_3 below the central carbon

and

$$CH—CH_2—CH_3$$
with CH_3 above and CH_3 below the first carbon

b.
$$CH_3—CH—CH—CH_2$$
with CH_3, CH_3, CH_3 above

and

$$CH_3—CH—CH_2—CH—CH_3$$
with CH_3 above the second and fourth carbons

c.
$$CH_3—CH—CH_2—CH_3$$
with CH_3 above the second carbon

and

$$CH_3—CH_2—CH—CH_3$$
with CH_3 above the third carbon

11.17 Give the IUPAC name for each of the following alkanes:

a. CH₃—CH—CH₂—CH₃ with CH₃ above the CH

b. CH₃—C—CH₃ with CH₃ above and CH₃ below the C

c. CH₃—CH₂—CH—CH—CH₃ with CH₃ and CH₃ above the two middle carbons

d. CH₃—C—CH₂—CH—CH₂—CH₃ with CH₃ above and CH₃ below the C, and CH₂—CH₃ above the CH

11.18 Give the IUPAC name for each of the following alkanes:

a. CH₃—CH—CH₂—CH₂—CH₃ with CH₃ above the CH

b. CH₃—CH—CH—CH₃ with CH₃ and CH₃ above the two middle carbons

c. CH₃—CH₂—CH—CH₂—CH—CH₃ with CH₃ and CH₃ above

d. CH₃—CH₂—CH—CH—CH₂—CH₃ with CH₂—CH₃ above and CH₂—CH₃ below

11.19 Give the IUPAC name for each of the following:

a. (cyclopentane with Cl)

b. (cyclohexane with CH₃)

c. CH₃ (cyclobutane with CH₃ and Br)

d. (cyclopentane with Cl and Br)

11.20 Give the IUPAC name for each of the following:

a. Cl (cyclobutane with Cl)

b. CH₃ (cyclopentane with CH₃ and Br)

c. CH₃—C—CH₂—CH₃ (cyclohexane ring)

d. (cyclohexane with Cl and Cl)

11.21 Draw a condensed structural formula for each of the following alkanes:
a. 2-methylbutane
b. 3,3-dimethylpentane
c. 2,3,5-trimethylhexane
d. 3-ethyl-2,5-dimethyloctane

11.22 Draw a condensed structural formula for each of the following alkanes:
a. 3-ethylpentane
b. 3-ethyl-2-methylpentane
c. 2,2,3,5-tetramethylhexane
d. 4-ethyl-2,2-dimethyloctane

11.23 Draw the structural formula for each of the following cycloalkanes using their geometric formulas:
a. methylcyclopentane
b. chlorocyclohexane
c. 1,3-dimethylcyclobutane
d. 1-bromo-2,3-dimethylcyclopentane

11.24 Draw the structural formula for each of the following cycloalkanes using their geometric formulas:
a. bromocyclopropane
b. ethylcyclohexane
c. 1,2-dichlorocyclobutane
d. 1,3-dibromocyclopentane

11.25 Give the IUPAC name for each of the following compounds:
a. CH₃—CH₂—Br
b. CH₃—CH₂—CH₂—F
c. CH₃—CH—Cl with CH₃ above the CH
d. CHCl₃

11.26 Give the IUPAC name for each of the following compounds:
a. CH₃—CH₂—CH—CH₃ with Cl above the CH
b. CCl₄
c. CH₃—C—I with CH₃ above and CH₃ below the C
d. CH₃F

11.27 Write the condensed structural formula for each of the following compounds:
a. 2-chloropropane
b. 2-bromo-3-chlorobutane
c. methyl bromide
d. tetrabromomethane

11.28 Write the condensed structural formula for each of the following compounds:
a. 1,1,2,2-tetrabromopropane
b. 2-bromopropane
c. 2,3-dichloro-2-methylbutane
d. dibromodichloromethane

11.4 Properties of Alkanes

Many types of alkanes are the components of fuels that power our cars and oil that heats our homes. You may have used a mixture of hydrocarbons such as mineral oil as a laxative or petrolatum (Vaseline) to soften your skin. The differences in uses of many of the alkanes result from their physical properties, including solubility, density, and boiling point.

LEARNING GOAL

Identify the properties of alkanes, and write chemical equations for combustion.

Solubility and Density

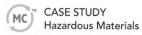
Alkanes are nonpolar, which makes them insoluble in water. However, they are soluble in nonpolar solvents such as other alkanes. Alkanes have densities from 0.6 g/mL to about 0.8 g/mL, which is less dense than water (1.0 g/mL). If there is an oil spill in the ocean, the alkanes in the crude oil remain on the surface and spread over a large area. In the *Exxon Valdez* oil spill in 1989, 40 million liters of oil covered over 25 000 square kilometers of water in Prince William Sound, Alaska. (See Figure 11.6.) If the crude oil reaches the beaches and inlets, there can be considerable damage to beaches, shellfish, fish, birds, and wildlife habitats. Cleanup includes both mechanical and chemical methods. In one method, a nonpolar compound that is "oil-attracting" is used to pick up oil, which is then scraped off into recovery tanks. Most of the cleanup started in 1989 and ended by 1991. Surveys in 2002 indicated that some oil still remains on the shoreline and that of the 30 species injured, most are recovering. However, the recovery of about 10 species, including some seals, birds, and fish, is not known.

Some Uses of Alkanes

The first four alkanes—methane, ethane, propane, and butane—are gases at room temperature and are widely used as heating fuels.

Alkanes having 5–8 carbon atoms (pentane, hexane, heptane, and octane) are liquids at room temperature. They are highly volatile, which makes them useful in fuels such as gasoline. Liquid alkanes with 9–17 carbon atoms have higher boiling points and are found in kerosene, diesel, and jet fuels. Motor oil is a mixture of high-molecular-weight liquid hydrocarbons and is used to lubricate the internal components of engines. Mineral oil is a mixture of liquid hydrocarbons and is used as a laxative and a lubricant. Alkanes with 18 or more carbon atoms are waxy solids at room temperature. The high-molecular-weight alkanes, known as paraffins, are used in waxy coatings on fruits and vegetables to retain moisture, inhibit mold growth, and enhance appearance. (See Figure 11.7.) Petrolatum, or Vaseline, is a mixture of low-boiling liquid hydrocarbons that are encapsulated in solid hydrocarbons. It is used in ointments and cosmetics and as a lubricant.

FIGURE 11.6 In oil spills, large quantities of oil spread over the water.

Q What physical properties cause oil to remain on the surface of water?

Melting and Boiling Points

Alkanes have the lowest melting and boiling points of all the organic compounds. The only attractions between nonpolar alkanes in the solid and liquid states result from dispersion forces. In longer carbon chains, the greater number of electrons produces more attractions between molecules, which results in higher melting and boiling points:

CH_4 CH_3—CH_3 CH_3—CH_2—CH_3

Methane, bp $-164\ °C$ Ethane, bp $-89\ °C$ Propane, bp $-42\ °C$

The boiling points of branched alkanes are generally lower than straight-chain alkanes with the same number of carbon atoms. The branched chain alkanes tend to be more compact, which reduces the amount of contact between the molecules. Cycloalkanes have higher boiling points than the straight-chain alkanes. Because rotation of carbon bonds is restricted, cycloalkanes maintain a rigid structure. Those rigid structures are like a set of dishes that can be stacked closely together with many points of contact and therefore many attractions to each other. We can compare the boiling points of alkanes and cycloalkanes with five carbon atoms as shown in Table 11.6.

FIGURE 11.7 The solid alkanes that make up waxy coatings on fruits and vegetables help retain moisture, inhibit mold, and enhance appearance.

Q Why does the waxy coating help the fruits and vegetables retain moisture?

Combustion of Alkanes

An alkane undergoes **combustion** when it reacts completely with oxygen to produce carbon dioxide, water, and energy. Carbon–carbon single bonds are difficult to break, which makes alkanes the least reactive family of organic compounds. However, alkanes burn readily in oxygen:

$$Alkane + O_2 \longrightarrow CO_2 + H_2O + energy$$

Methane is the gas we use to cook our foods and heat our homes. Propane is the gas used in portable heaters and gas barbecues. (See Figure 11.8.)

TABLE 11.6 Comparison of Boiling Points of Alkanes and Cycloalkanes with Five Carbons

Formula	Name	Boiling Point (°C)
Cycloalkanes		
(cyclopentane structure)	Cyclopentane	49
(methylcyclobutane structure) CH$_3$	Methylcyclobutane	36.3
Alkane		
CH$_3$—CH$_2$—CH$_2$—CH$_2$—CH$_3$	Pentane	36
Branched alkanes		
CH$_3$—CH—CH$_2$—CH$_3$ with CH$_3$	2-Methylbutane	28
CH$_3$—C—CH$_3$ with CH$_3$ above and CH$_3$ below	Dimethylpropane	10

Gasoline, a mixture of liquid hydrocarbons, is the fuel that powers our cars, lawn mowers, and snow blowers. As alkanes, they all undergo combustion. The equations for the combustion of methane (CH_4) and propane (C_3H_8) follow:

$$CH_4 + 2O_2 \longrightarrow CO_2 + 2H_2O + \text{energy}$$
Methane

$$C_3H_8 + 5O_2 \longrightarrow 3CO_2 + 4H_2O + \text{energy}$$
Propane

In the cells of our bodies, energy is produced by the combustion of glucose. Although a series of reactions is involved, we can write the overall combustion of glucose in our cells as follows:

$$C_6H_{12}O_6 + 6O_2 \xrightarrow{\text{Enzymes}} 6CO_2 + 6H_2O + \text{energy}$$

FIGURE 11.8 The propane fuel in the tank undergoes combustion, which provides energy.

Q What is the balanced equation for the combustion of propane?

EXPLORE YOUR WORLD

Combustion

In this exploration, we will look at the behavior of the products of combustion. You will need one or two candles, a Pyrex glass such as a measuring cup, and some matches or wooden splints.

Hold a Pyrex cup upside down, and place a burning match inside it. The match will continue to burn as long as oxygen is available. Light a candle and hold the inverted Pyrex cup above it for 15–20 seconds. Remove the cup from the candle and immediately place a burning match into it. The CO_2 accumulated from the combustion of the candle should extinguish the match.

Add some water and a lot of ice to the same Pyrex cup. It should become cold to the touch. Wipe the bottom of the cup and carefully hold the bottom of the Pyrex cup over a burning candle. Look for condensation as water is formed from the combustion reaction.

QUESTIONS

1. What are the products of combustion?
2. What was the evidence for the production of CO_2?
3. What observations gave evidence for the production of H_2O during combustion?

TUTORIAL
Writing Balanced Equations for
Combustion of Alkanes

CASE STUDY
Poison in the Home:
Carbon Monoxide

SAMPLE PROBLEM 11.7

■ **Combustion**

Write a balanced equation for the complete combustion of butane.

SOLUTION

The balanced equation for the complete combustion of butane can be written

$$2C_4H_{10} + 13O_2 \longrightarrow 8CO_2 + 10H_2O$$

STUDY CHECK

Write a balanced equation for the complete combustion of the following:

$$\begin{array}{c} CH_3 \\ | \\ CH_3-CH-CH_2-CH_3 \end{array}$$

HEALTH NOTE

Toxicity of Carbon Monoxide

When a propane heater, fireplace, or wood stove is used in a closed room, there must be adequate ventilation. If the supply of oxygen is limited, *incomplete combustion* from burning gas, oil, or wood produces carbon monoxide. The incomplete combustion of methane in natural gas is written as follows:

$$2CH_4(g) + 3O_2(g) \longrightarrow 2CO(g) + 4H_2O(g) + heat$$

Limited oxygen supply — Carbon monoxide

Carbon monoxide (CO) is a colorless, odorless, poisonous gas. When inhaled, CO passes into the bloodstream, where it attaches to hemoglobin. When CO binds to the hemoglobin, it reduces the amount of oxygen (O_2) reaching the organs and cells. As a result, a healthy person can experience a reduction in exercise capability, visual perception, and manual dexterity.

When the amount of hemoglobin bound to CO (COHb) is about 10%, a person may experience shortness of breath, mild headache, and drowsiness. Heavy smokers can have levels of COHb in their blood as high as 9%. When as much as 30% of the hemoglobin is bound to CO, a person may experience more severe symptoms, including dizziness, mental confusion, severe headache, and nausea. If 50% or more of the hemoglobin is bound to CO, a person could become unconscious and die if not treated immediately with oxygen.

QUESTIONS AND PROBLEMS

Properties of Alkanes

11.29 Heptane has a density of 0.68 g/mL and boils at 98 °C.
a. Draw the condensed structural formula of heptane.
b. Is it a solid, liquid, or gas at room temperature?
c. Is it soluble in water?
d. Will it float or sink in water?

11.30 Nonane has a density of 0.72 g/mL and boils at 151 °C.
a. Draw the condensed structural formula of nonane.
b. Is it a solid, liquid, or gas at room temperature?
c. Is it soluble in water?
d. Will it float or sink in water?

11.31 In each of the following pairs of hydrocarbons, which one would you expect to have the higher boiling point?
a. pentane or heptane
b. propane or cyclopropane
c. hexane or 2-methylpentane

11.32 In each of the following pairs of hydrocarbons, which one would you expect to have the higher boiling point?
a. propane or butane
b. hexane or cyclohexane
c. 2,2-dimethylpentane or heptane

11.33 Write a balanced equation for the complete combustion of each of the following compounds:
a. ethane
b. cyclopropane, C_3H_6
c. octane
d. cyclohexane, C_6H_{12}

11.34 Write a balanced equation for the complete combustion of each of the following compounds:
a. hexane
b. cyclopentane, C_5H_{10}
c. nonane
d. 2-methylbutane

GREEN CHEMISTRY NOTE

Crude Oil

Crude oil, or petroleum, contains a wide variety of hydrocarbons. At an oil refinery, the components in crude oil are separated by fractional distillation, a process that removes groups or fractions of hydrocarbons by continually heating the mixture to higher temperatures. (See Table 11.7.) Fractions containing alkanes with longer carbon chains require higher temperatures before they reach their boiling temperature and form gases. The gases are removed and passed through a distillation column where they cool and condense back to liquids. The major use of crude oil is to obtain gasoline. To increase the production of gasoline, heating oils are broken down using specialized catalysts to give the lower-weight alkanes.

TABLE 11.7 Typical Alkane Mixtures Obtained by Distillation of Crude Oil

Distillation Temperatures (°C)	Number of Carbon Atoms	Product
Below 30	1–4	Natural gas
30–200	5–12	Gasoline
200–250	12–16	Kerosene, jet fuel
250–350	16–18	Diesel fuel, heating oil
350–450	18–25	Lubricating oil
Nonvolatile residue	Over 25	Asphalt, tar

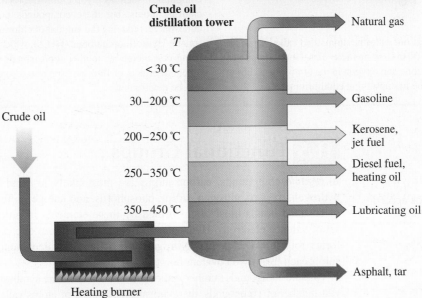

Crude oil distillation tower

T

< 30 °C → Natural gas

30–200 °C → Gasoline

200–250 °C → Kerosene, jet fuel

250–350 °C → Diesel fuel, heating oil

350–450 °C → Lubricating oil

→ Asphalt, tar

Crude oil

Heating burner

Nonvolatile residue

ENVIRONMENTAL NOTE

CFCs and Ozone Depletion

The compounds called *chlorofluorocarbons* (CFCs) were used as propellants for hair sprays and paints, and as refrigerants in home and car air conditioners. Two widely used CFCs, Freon 11 (CCl_3F) and Freon 12 (CCl_2F_2), were developed during the 1920s as nontoxic refrigerants, which were safer than the sulfur dioxide and ammonia used at the time:

$$
\begin{array}{cc}
\begin{array}{c}
\quad Cl \\
\quad | \\
Cl - C - F \\
\quad | \\
\quad Cl
\end{array}
&
\begin{array}{c}
\quad Cl \\
\quad | \\
F - C - F \\
\quad | \\
\quad Cl
\end{array} \\
\text{Freon 11} & \text{Freon 12}
\end{array}
$$

In the stratosphere, a layer of ozone (O_3) absorbs the ultraviolet (UV) radiation of the Sun and acts as a protective shield for plants and animals on Earth. Ozone is produced in the stratosphere when oxygen reacts with ultraviolet light and breaks into oxygen atoms that quickly combine with oxygen molecules to form ozone. In the color image, the pink areas have the lowest levels of ozone.

$$O_2 \xrightarrow{\text{UV light}} O + O$$
$$O_2 + O \longrightarrow O_3$$

During the 1970s, scientists became concerned that CFCs entering the atmosphere were accelerating the depletion of ozone and threatening the stability of the ozone layer. CFCs decompose in the upper atmosphere in the presence of UV light to produce highly reactive chlorine atoms:

$$CCl_3F \xrightarrow{\text{UV light}} CCl_2F + Cl$$

The reactive chlorine atoms catalyze the breakdown of ozone molecules:

$$Cl + O_3 \longrightarrow ClO + O_2$$
$$ClO + O_3 \longrightarrow Cl + 2O_2$$

It has been estimated that one chlorine atom, also called a *radical*, can destroy as many as 100 000 ozone molecules. Normally, there is a balance between the ozone and oxygen in the atmosphere, but the rapid destruction of ozone has upset that equilibrium.

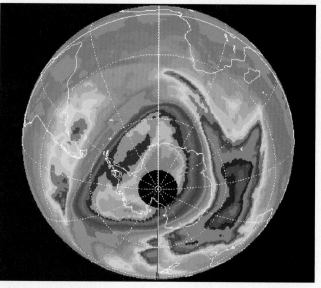

In the color image, the pink areas have the lowest levels of ozone.

Reports of polar ozone depletion over Antarctica in March 1985 prompted scientists to call for a freeze on the production of CFCs. In some areas, as much as 50% of the ozone had been depleted, causing an ozone hole to appear at certain times of the year.

There is evidence of thinning in the ozone layer over the Arctic as well, but to a somewhat lesser degree due to warmer temperatures. It is interesting that in the lower atmosphere ozone is an automobile and industrial pollutant, but in the stratosphere ozone is a life-protecting compound.

Today, the use of CFCs is being phased out. However, it is expected that ozone levels will remain low for several decades due to the stability of CFCs. Chemical companies are developing substitutes for CFCs that are not as damaging to the ozone. Replacement compounds such as hydrochlorofluorocarbons (HCFCs) contain chlorine atoms, but these compounds break down in the lower atmosphere, reducing the amount of chlorine that reaches the stratosphere. Hydrofluorocarbons (HFCs), which contain no chlorine, are being considered as another replacement for CFCs. However, the potential effects of fluorine compounds on ozone destruction must still be determined.

11.5 Functional Groups

LEARNING GOAL

Classify organic molecules according to their functional groups.

 SELF STUDY ACTIVITY
Functional Groups

 TUTORIAL
Identifying Functional Groups

In organic compounds, carbon atoms are most likely to bond with nonmetals such as hydrogen, oxygen, nitrogen, sulfur, phosphorus, and halogens. Table 11.8 lists the number of covalent bonds most often formed by these elements in order to achieve a complete set of valence electrons. Hydrogen and the halogens form one covalent bond, and carbon forms four covalent bonds. Nitrogen forms three covalent bonds, whereas oxygen and sulfur each form two covalent bonds.

Organic compounds number in the millions, and more are synthesized every day. Within this vast number of compounds, there are specific groups of atoms called **functional groups** that give compounds similar properties. The identification of functional groups allows us to classify organic compounds according to their structure, to name compounds within each family, and to predict their chemical reactions. We will focus on recognizing the patterns of atoms that make up each of the functional groups, which we will discuss in more detail in the following chapters.

TABLE 11.8 Covalent Bonds for Elements in Organic Compounds

Element	Group	Covalent Bonds	Structure of Atoms
H	1A (1)	1	H—
C	4A (4)	4	$-\overset{\displaystyle |}{\underset{\displaystyle |}{C}}-$
N, P	5A (15)	3	$-\overset{\displaystyle |}{\underset{\displaystyle ..}{N}}-$ $-\overset{\displaystyle |}{\underset{\displaystyle ..}{P}}-$
O, S	6A (16)	2	$-\overset{\displaystyle ..}{\underset{\displaystyle ..}{O}}-$ $-\overset{\displaystyle ..}{\underset{\displaystyle ..}{S}}-$
F, Cl, Br, I	7A (17)	1	$-\overset{\displaystyle ..}{\underset{\displaystyle ..}{X}}:$ (X = F, Cl, Br, I)

Alkene

Alkyne

Alkenes, Alkynes, and Aromatic Compounds

In the hydrocarbon family, there are also alkenes, alkynes, and aromatics. An **alkene** contains one or more double bonds between carbon atoms; an **alkyne** contains a triple bond. An **aromatic** compound contains benzene, a molecule that has a ring of six carbon atoms with one hydrogen atom attached to each carbon. The benzene structure is represented as a hexagon with a circle in the center:

Aromatic

Alkene	Alkyne	Aromatic
Functional group		
Condensed structural formula $H_2C=CH_2$	$HC\equiv CH$	

Alcohol

Alcohols, Thiols, and Ethers

The characteristic functional group in an **alcohol** is the *hydroxyl* (—OH) *group* bonded to a carbon atom. In an **ether**, the characteristic structural feature is an oxygen atom bonded to two carbon atoms. The oxygen atom also has two unshared pairs of electrons, but they are not shown in the condensed structural formulas. In a **thiol**, the functional group —SH is bonded to a carbon atom.

$$CH_3-CH_2-OH \qquad CH_3-CH_2-SH \qquad CH_3-O-CH_3$$

Alcohol	Thiol	Ether
Functional group **—O—H**	**—S—H**	**—O—**

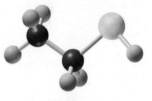

Thiol

Ether

Aldehydes and Ketones

The aldehydes and ketones contain a **carbonyl group** (C=O), which is a carbon with a double bond to oxygen. In an **aldehyde**, the first carbon of a carbon chain is a carbonyl group that is bonded to a hydrogen atom. Only the simplest aldehyde, CH_2O, has a carbonyl group attached to two hydrogen atoms. In a **ketone**, the carbonyl group is bonded to two other carbon atoms.

$$CH_3-\overset{\displaystyle O}{\overset{\displaystyle \|}{C}}-H \qquad CH_3-\overset{\displaystyle O}{\overset{\displaystyle \|}{C}}-CH_3$$

Aldehyde   Ketone

Aldehyde

Functional group $-\overset{\displaystyle O}{\overset{\displaystyle \|}{C}}-H$ $-\overset{\displaystyle O}{\overset{\displaystyle \|}{C}}-$

Ketone

CONCEPT CHECK 11.3

■ **Identifying Functional Groups**

Describe the differences among the functional groups found in alcohols, ethers, and thiols.

ANSWER

In alcohols, the functional group is a hydroxyl group (—OH) attached to a carbon atom. The functional group in ethers is an oxygen atom bonded to two carbon atoms (—O—). In thiols, the functional group —SH is attached to a carbon atom.

SAMPLE PROBLEM 11.8

■ **Classifying Organic Compounds**

Classify the following organic compounds according to their functional groups:

a. CH_3—CH_2—CH_2—OH   **b.** CH_3—CH=CH—CH_3

$$\text{c.} \quad CH_3-CH_2-\overset{\displaystyle O}{\overset{\displaystyle \|}{C}}-CH_2-CH_3 \qquad \text{d.} \quad CH_3-\overset{\displaystyle SH}{\overset{\displaystyle |}{C}H}-CH_3$$

SOLUTION

a. When the functional group —OH is bonded to a carbon atom, the compound is an alcohol.
b. An alkene contains one or more double bonds between carbon atoms.
c. A ketone contains a carbonyl group bonded to two other carbon atoms.
d. When the functional group —SH is bonded to a carbon atom, the compound is a thiol.

STUDY CHECK

Why is CH_3—CH_2—O—CH_3 an ether?

Carboxylic Acids and Esters

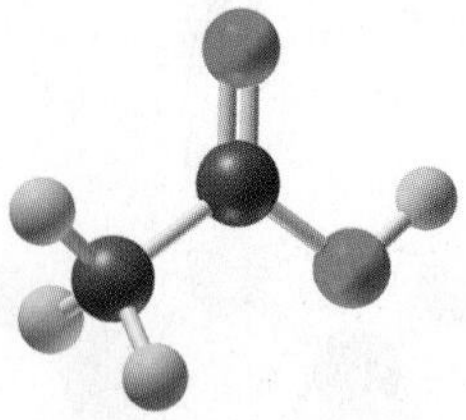

In a **carboxylic acid**, the functional group is the *carboxyl group*, which is a combination of the *carbo*nyl and hydro*xyl* groups. In a carboxylic acid, the first carbon atom is part of a carboxyl group:

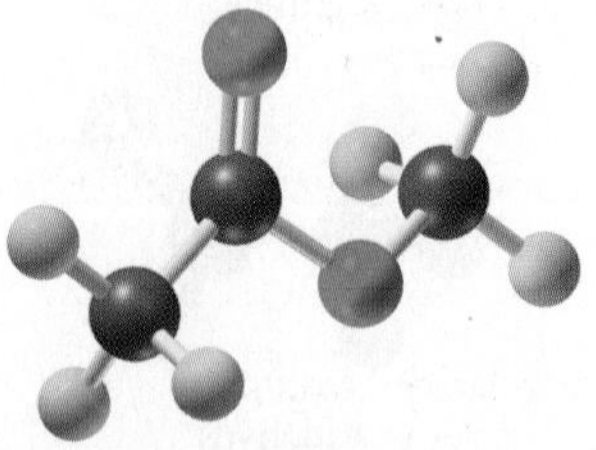

$$CH_3-\overset{\displaystyle O}{\overset{\displaystyle \|}{C}}-O-H \qquad \text{or} \qquad \textbf{CH}_3\textbf{COOH}$$

Carboxylic acid

Carboxylic acid

$$\text{Functional group} \qquad -\overset{\displaystyle O}{\overset{\displaystyle \|}{C}}-O-H \qquad \text{or} \qquad \textbf{—COOH}$$

An **ester** is similar to a carboxylic acid, except that the oxygen of the carboxyl group is attached to a carbon and not to hydrogen:

Ester

$$CH_3-\overset{\displaystyle O}{\overset{\displaystyle \|}{C}}-O-CH_3 \qquad \text{or} \qquad \textbf{CH}_3\textbf{COOCH}_3$$

Ester

$$\text{Functional group} \qquad -\overset{\displaystyle O}{\overset{\displaystyle \|}{C}}-O- \qquad \text{or} \qquad \textbf{—COO—}$$

Amines and Amides

In an **amine**, the central atom is a nitrogen atom. Amines are derivatives of ammonia, NH_3, in which carbon atoms replace one, two, or three of the hydrogen atoms:

NH_3 $CH_3—NH_2$ $CH_3—NH$ $CH_3—N—CH_3$
                                                                    | |
                                                                  CH_3 CH_3

Ammonia   Examples of amines

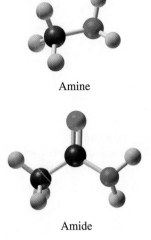

Amine

In an **amide**, the hydroxyl group of a carboxylic acid is replaced by a nitrogen group:

$$CH_3—\overset{\overset{\displaystyle O}{\|}}{C}—NH_2$$

Amide

Amide

> **CONCEPT CHECK 11.4**
>
> ■ **The Amine Functional Group**
> Describe the functional group found in amines.
>
> ANSWER
> The amine functional group has a central nitrogen atom bonded to one, two, or three carbon atoms.

A list of the common functional groups in organic compounds is shown in Table 11.9.

TABLE 11.9 Classification of Organic Compounds

Class	Example	Functional Group	Characteristic
Alkene	$H_2C{=}CH_2$	$\diagdown C{=}C\diagup$	Carbon–carbon double bond
Alkyne	$HC{\equiv}CH$	$—C{\equiv}C—$	Carbon–carbon triple bond
Aromatic	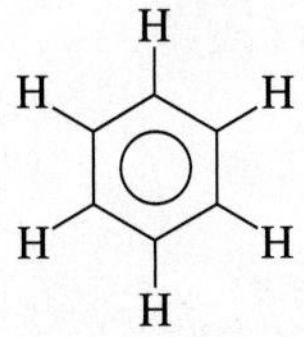 (benzene ring with H atoms)	 (benzene ring)	Benzene ring (six carbon atoms and six hydrogen atoms)
Haloalkane	$CH_3—Cl$	$—F, —Cl, —Br, —I$	One or more halogen atoms
Alcohol	$CH_3—CH_2—OH$	$—OH$	Hydroxyl group ($—OH$)
Ether	$CH_3—O—CH_3$	$—O—$	Oxygen atom bonded to two carbons
Thiol	$CH_3—SH$	$—SH$	Thiol group ($—SH$)
Aldehyde	$CH_3—\overset{\overset{O}{\|}}{C}—H$	$—\overset{\overset{O}{\|}}{C}—H$	Carbonyl group (carbon–oxygen double bond) with $—H$
Ketone	$CH_3—\overset{\overset{O}{\|}}{C}—CH_3$	$—\overset{\overset{O}{\|}}{C}—$	Carbonyl group (carbon–oxygen double bond) between carbon atoms
Carboxylic acid	$CH_3—\overset{\overset{O}{\|}}{C}—O—H$	$—\overset{\overset{O}{\|}}{C}—O—H$	Carboxyl group (carbon–oxygen double bond and $—OH$)
Ester	$CH_3—\overset{\overset{O}{\|}}{C}—O—CH_3$	$—\overset{\overset{O}{\|}}{C}—O—$	Carboxyl group with $—H$ replaced by a carbon
Amine	$CH_3—NH_2$	$—\overset{}{\underset{}{N}}—$	Nitrogen atom with one or more carbon groups
Amide	$CH_3—\overset{\overset{O}{\|}}{C}—NH_2$	$—\overset{\overset{O}{\|}}{C}—N—$	Carbonyl group bonded to nitrogen

■ Identifying Functional Groups

Classify the following organic compounds according to their functional groups:

a. $CH_3—CH_2—NH—CH_3$

b. $CH_3—\overset{\overset{O}{\|}}{C}—O—CH_2—CH_3$ c. $CH_3—CH_2—\overset{\overset{O}{\|}}{C}—OH$

SOLUTION

a. amine   **b.** ester   **c.** carboxylic acid

STUDY CHECK

How does a carboxylic acid differ from an ester?

TUTORIAL
Drawing Organic Compounds
with Functional Groups

ENVIRONMENTAL NOTE

Functional Groups in Familiar Compounds

The flavors and odors of foods and many household products can be attributed to the functional groups of organic compounds. As we discuss these familiar products, look for the functional groups we have described.

$CH_3—CH_2—OH$ $CH_3—\overset{\overset{OH}{|}}{CH}—CH_3$
Ethyl alcohol   Isopropyl alcohol

Ethyl alcohol is the alcohol found in alcoholic beverages. Isopropyl alcohol is another alcohol commonly used to disinfect skin before giving injections and to treat cuts.

Ketones and aldehydes are in many items we use or eat each day. Acetone, or dimethyl ketone, is produced in great amounts commercially. Acetone is used as an organic solvent because it dissolves a wide variety of organic substances. You may be familiar with acetone as fingernail polish remover. Ketones and aldehydes used in the food industry are found in flavorings such as vanilla, cinnamon, and spearmint. When we buy a small bottle of liquid flavoring, the aldehyde or ketone is dissolved in alcohol because the compounds are not very soluble in water. The aldehyde butyraldehyde adds a "buttery" taste to foods and margarine.

$CH_3—CH_2—CH_2—\overset{\overset{O}{\|}}{C}—H$
Butyraldehyde "butter" flavoring

The sour tastes of vinegar and fruit juices and the pain from ant stings are all due to carboxylic acids. Acetic acid is the carboxylic acid that makes up vinegar. Aspirin also contains a carboxylic acid group. Esters found in fruits produce the pleasant aromas and tastes of bananas, oranges, pears, and pineapples. Esters are also used as solvents in many household cleaners, polishes, and glues.

One of the characteristics of fish is their odor, which is due to the amines produced when proteins decay; they have a particularly pungent and offensive odor.

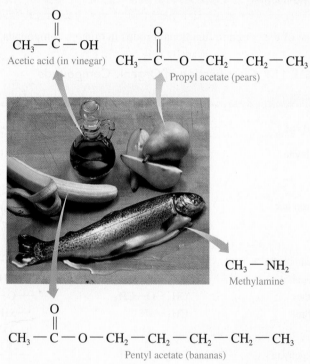

$CH_3—\overset{\overset{O}{\|}}{C}—OH$
Acetic acid (in vinegar)

$CH_3—\overset{\overset{O}{\|}}{C}—O—CH_2—CH_2—CH_3$
Propyl acetate (pears)

$CH_3—NH_2$
Methylamine

$CH_3—\overset{\overset{O}{\|}}{C}—O—CH_2—CH_2—CH_2—CH_2—CH_3$
Pentyl acetate (bananas)

$H_2N—CH_2—CH_2—CH_2—CH_2—NH_2$
Putrescine

$H_2N—CH_2—CH_2—CH_2—CH_2—CH_2—NH_2$
Cadaverine

Alkaloids are biologically active amines synthesized by plants to ward off insects and animals. Some typical alkaloids include caffeine, nicotine, histamine, and the decongestant epinephrine. Many are painkillers and hallucinogens, such as morphine, LSD, marijuana, and cocaine. Certain parts of our neurons have receptor sites that respond to the various alkaloids. By modifying the structures of certain alkaloids to eliminate side effects, chemists have synthesized painkillers such as Novocain and codeine, and other drugs, such as Valium.

QUESTIONS AND PROBLEMS

Functional Groups

11.35 Identify the class of compounds that contains each of the following functional groups:
  a. hydroxyl group attached to a carbon chain
  b. carbon–carbon double bond
  c. carbonyl group attached to a hydrogen atom
  d. carboxyl group attached to two carbon atoms

11.36 Identify the class of compounds that contains each of the following functional groups:
  a. a nitrogen atom attached to one or more carbon atoms
  b. carboxyl group
  c. oxygen atom bonded to two carbon atoms
  d. a carbonyl group between two carbon atoms

11.37 Classify the following molecules according to their functional groups. The possibilities are alcohol, ether, ketone, carboxylic acid, or amine.
  a. $CH_3-CH_2-O-CH_2-CH_3$
  b. $CH_3-\overset{\displaystyle OH}{\underset{|}{CH}}-CH_3$
  c. $CH_3-\overset{\displaystyle O}{\overset{\|}{C}}-CH_2-CH_3$

  d. $CH_3-CH_2-CH_2-COOH$
  e. $CH_3-CH_2-NH_2$

11.38 Classify the following molecules according to their functional groups. The possibilities are alkene, aldehyde, carboxylic acid, ester, or amide.
  a. $CH_3-CH_2-\overset{\displaystyle O}{\overset{\|}{C}}-O-CH_2-CH_3$
  b. $CH_3-\overset{\displaystyle O}{\overset{\|}{C}}-NH_2$
  c. $CH_3-CH_2-CH_2-\overset{\displaystyle O}{\overset{\|}{C}}-H$
  d. $CH_3-CH_2-CH_2-COOH$
  e. $CH_3-CH=CH-CH_3$

CONCEPT MAP

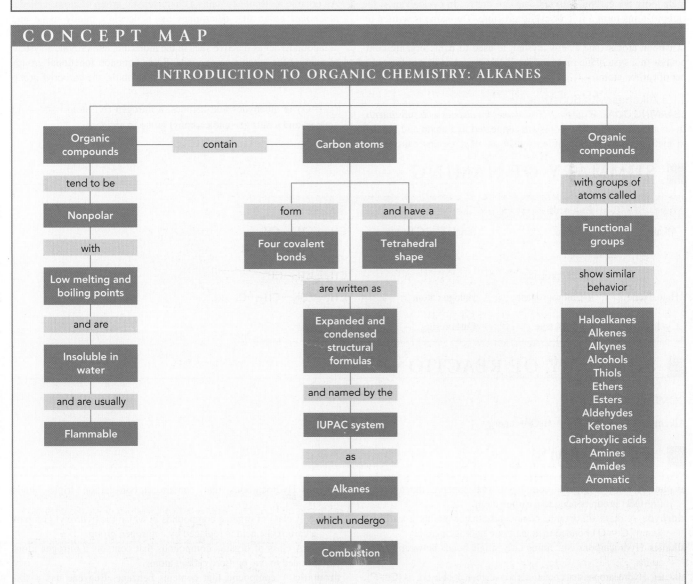

INTRODUCTION TO ORGANIC CHEMISTRY: ALKANES

Organic compounds — contain — Carbon atoms — Organic compounds

Organic compounds tend to be Nonpolar with Low melting and boiling points and are Insoluble in water and are usually Flammable

Carbon atoms form Four covalent bonds and have a Tetrahedral shape are written as Expanded and condensed structural formulas and named by the IUPAC system as Alkanes which undergo Combustion

Organic compounds with groups of atoms called Functional groups show similar behavior

Haloalkanes
Alkenes
Alkynes
Alcohols
Thiols
Ethers
Esters
Aldehydes
Ketones
Carboxylic acids
Amines
Amides
Aromatic

CHAPTER REVIEW

11.1 Organic Compounds

LEARNING GOAL: *Identify characteristic properties of organic or inorganic compounds.*

Organic compounds have covalent bonds, and most form nonpolar molecules. Often, they have low melting points and low boiling points, are not very soluble in water, produce molecules in solutions, and burn vigorously in air. In contrast, many inorganic compounds are ionic or contain polar covalent bonds and form polar molecules. Many have high melting and boiling points, are usually soluble in water, produce ions in water, and do not burn in air. Carbon atoms share four valence electrons to form four covalent bonds. In the simplest organic molecule, methane, CH_4, the four bonds that bond hydrogen to the carbon atom are directed to the corners of a tetrahedron with bond angles of 109.5°.

11.2 Alkanes

LEARNING GOAL: *Write the IUPAC names and condensed structural formulas for alkanes.*

Alkanes are hydrocarbons that have only C—C single bonds. In the expanded structural formula, a separate line is drawn for every bonded atom. A condensed structural formula depicts groups composed of each carbon atom and its attached hydrogen atoms. In a line-bond formula, only the carbon–carbon bonds are drawn. In cycloalkanes, the carbon atoms form a ring or cyclic structure. The name is written by placing the prefix *cyclo* before the alkane name with the same number of carbon atoms. The IUPAC system is used to name organic compounds in a systematic manner. The IUPAC name indicates the number of carbon atoms.

11.3 Alkanes with Substituents

LEARNING GOAL: *Write the IUPAC names for alkanes with substituents.*

In an alkane, the carbon atoms are connected in a chain and bonded to hydrogen atoms. Substituents such as alkyl groups can replace hydrogen atoms on an alkane. A haloalkane contains one or more F, Cl, Br, or I atoms. In the IUPAC system, halogen atoms are named as *fluoro*, *chloro*, *bromo*, or *iodo* substituents attached to the main chain. In the common name, the name of the alkyl group precedes the halide, for example methyl chloride.

11.4 Properties of Alkanes

LEARNING GOAL: *Identify the properties of alkanes, and write chemical equations for combustion.*

As nonpolar molecules, alkanes are not soluble in water. They are less dense than water. With only weak attractions, they have low melting and boiling points. For alkanes of similar mass, cycloalkanes have higher boiling points and branched alkanes have lower boiling points than the nonbranched chain alkanes. Although the C—C bonds in alkanes resist most reactions, alkanes undergo combustion. In combustion, or burning, alkanes react with oxygen to produce carbon dioxide and water.

11.5 Functional Groups

LEARNING GOAL: *Classify organic molecules according to their functional groups.*

An organic molecule contains a characteristic group of atoms called a *functional group* that determines the molecule's family name and chemical reactivity. Functional groups are used to classify organic compounds, act as reactive sites in the molecule, and provide a system of naming for organic compounds. Some common functional groups include the hydroxyl group (—OH) in alcohols, the carbonyl group (C=O) in aldehydes and ketones, a nitrogen (N) atom —N— in amines, and a nitrogen and carbonyl group in amides.

SUMMARY OF NAMING

Type	Example	Characteristic	Structure
Alkane	Propane	Single C—C bonds	CH_3—CH_2—CH_3
	Methylpropane		CH_3—$\overset{\overset{CH_3}{\vert}}{CH}$—$CH_3$
Haloalkane	1-Chloropropane	Halogen atom	CH_3—CH_2—CH_2—Cl
Cycloalkane	Cyclobutane	Carbon ring	

SUMMARY OF REACTIONS

COMBUSTION

Alkane + O_2 $\longrightarrow$ CO_2 + H_2O + energy

KEY TERMS

alcohol A class of organic compounds that contains the hydroxyl (—OH) group bonded to a carbon atom.

aldehyde A class of organic compounds that contains a carbonyl group (C=O) bonded to at least one hydrogen atom.

alkanes Hydrocarbons containing only single bonds between carbon atoms.

alkenes Hydrocarbons that contain carbon–carbon double bonds (C=C).

alkyl group An alkane minus one hydrogen atom. Alkyl groups are named like the alkanes except a *yl* ending replaces *ane*.

alkynes Hydrocarbons that contain carbon–carbon triple bonds (C≡C).

amide A class of organic compounds in which the hydroxyl group of a carboxylic acid is replaced by a nitrogen group.

amine A class of organic compounds that contains a nitrogen atom bonded to one or more carbon atoms.

aromatic A compound that contains benzene. Benzene has a six-carbon ring with only one hydrogen atom attached to each carbon.

branch A carbon group bonded to the main carbon chain.

branched alkane A single-bonded hydrocarbon containing a substituent bonded to the main chain.

carbonyl group A functional group that contains a double bond between a carbon atom and an oxygen atom ($C=O$).

carboxylic acid A class of organic compounds that contains the carboxyl functional group.

combustion A chemical reaction in which an alkane reacts with oxygen to produce CO_2, H_2O, and energy.

condensed structural formula A structural formula that shows the arrangement of the carbon atoms in a molecule but groups each carbon atom with its bonded hydrogen atoms.

cycloalkane An alkane that is a ring or cyclic structure.

ester A class of organic compounds that contains a —COO— group with an oxygen atom bonded to carbon.

ether A class of organic compounds that contains an oxygen atom bonded to two carbon atoms (—O—).

expanded structural formula A type of structural formula that shows the arrangement of the atoms by showing each bond in the hydrocarbon as C—H, C—C, C=C, or C≡C.

functional group A group of atoms that determines the physical and chemical properties and naming of a class of organic compounds.

haloalkane A type of alkane that contains one or more halogen atoms.

hydrocarbons Organic compounds consisting of only carbon and hydrogen.

isomers Organic compounds in which identical molecular formulas have different arrangements of atoms.

IUPAC system The system for naming organic compounds devised by the International Union of Pure and Applied Chemistry.

ketone A class of organic compounds in which a carbonyl group is bonded to two carbon atoms.

line-bond formula A type of structural formula that shows only the bonds from carbon to carbon.

organic compounds Compounds made of carbon that typically have covalent bonds, are nonpolar molecules, have low melting and boiling points, are insoluble in water, and are flammable.

substituent Groups of atoms such as an alkyl group or a halogen bonded to the main chain or ring of carbon atoms.

thiol A class of organic molecules that contains the —SH functional group bonded to a carbon atom.

UNDERSTANDING THE CONCEPTS

11.39 Sunscreens contain compounds that absorb UV light such as oxybenzone and 2-ethylhexyl-*p*-methoxycinnamate:

Identify the functional groups in each of the following UV-absorbing compounds used in suncreens:
a. oxybenzone

b. 2-ethylhexyl-*p*-methoxycinnamate

11.40 Oxymetazoline is a vasoconstrictor used in nasal decongestant sprays such as Afrin:

What functional groups are in oxymetazoline?

11.41 Decimemide is used as an anticonvulsant:

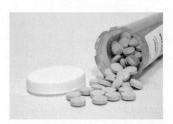

What functional groups are in decimemide?

11.42 The odor and taste of pineapples is from ethyl butyrate:

What functional group is in ethyl butyrate?

$$CH_3-CH_2-CH_2-\overset{\overset{\displaystyle O}{\|}}{C}-O-CH_2-CH_3$$

ADDITIONAL QUESTIONS AND PROBLEMS

For instructor-assigned homework, go to www.masteringchemistry.com.

11.43 Compare organic and inorganic compounds in terms of each of the following:
  a. types of bonds
  b. solubility in water
  c. melting points
  d. flammability

11.44 Identify each of the following compounds as organic or inorganic:
  a. Na_2SO_4
  b. $CH_2=CH_2$
  c. Cr_2O_3
  d. $C_{12}H_{22}O_{11}$

11.45 Match the following physical and chemical properties with the compound butane, C_4H_{10}, or potassium chloride, KCl:

  a. melts at $-138\ ^\circ C$
  b. burns vigorously in air
  c. melts at $770\ ^\circ C$
  d. produces ions in water
  e. is a gas at room temperature

11.46 Match the following physical and chemical properties with the compound cyclohexane, C_6H_{12}, or calcium nitrate, $Ca(NO_3)_2$:
  a. contains only covalent bonds
  b. melts above $500\ ^\circ C$
  c. is insoluble in water
  d. is a liquid at room temperature
  e. produces ions in water

11.47 Identify the functional group in each of the following:
  a. CH_3-NH_2
  b. $CH_3-\overset{\overset{\displaystyle O}{\|}}{C}-CH_3$
  c. $CH_3-\overset{\overset{\displaystyle O}{\|}}{C}-O-CH_2-CH_3$
  d. $CH_3-CH_2-CH_2-OH$

11.48 Identify the functional group in each of the following:
  a. $CH_3-C\equiv CH$
  b. $CH_3-CH_2-CH_2-SH$
  c. $CH_3-O-CH_2-CH_3$
  d.

11.49 Write the name of each of the following substituents:
  a. CH_3- **b.** $CH_3-CH_2-CH_2-$ **c.** $Cl-$

11.50 Write the name of each of the following substituents:
  a. $Br-$
  b. $CH_3-\overset{\overset{\displaystyle CH_3}{|}}{CH}-$
  c. CH_3-CH_2-

11.51 Give the IUPAC name for each of the following:

  a.
$$\overset{\displaystyle CH_3}{\underset{\bigcirc}{|}}$$

  b. $Cl-CH_2-\overset{\overset{\displaystyle Br}{|}}{CH}-CH_2-Br$

  c. $CH_3-\overset{\overset{\displaystyle CH_3}{|}}{CH}-\overset{\overset{\displaystyle }{|}}{\underset{\underset{\underset{\underset{}{CH_3}}{|}}{\underset{CH_2}{|}}}{CH}-CH_3$

  d. $CH_3-CH_2-\overset{\overset{\displaystyle Cl}{|}}{\underset{\underset{\underset{}{CH_3}}{|}}{\underset{CH_2}{\underset{|}{C}}}-CH_2-CH_3$

11.52 Give the IUPAC name for each of the following:

  a. $CH_3-CH_2-\overset{\overset{\displaystyle CH_3}{|}}{\underset{\underset{}{CH_3}}{\underset{|}{C}}}-CH_3$

  b. CH_3-CH_2-Cl

  c. $CH_3-CH_2-\overset{\overset{\displaystyle CH_3-CH_2}{|}}{CH}-CH_2-\overset{\overset{\displaystyle Br}{|}}{CH}-CH_3$

  d. $\bigcirc$

11.53 Draw the condensed structural formula for each of the following molecules:
    a. 3-ethylhexane   **b.** 1,3-dimethylcyclopentane
    c. 1,3-dichloro-3-methylheptane   **d.** bromocyclobutane

11.54 Draw the condensed structural formula for each of the following molecules:
    a. ethylcyclopropane   **b.** 2-methylhexane
    c. isopropylcyclopentane   **d.** 1,1-dichloropentane

11.55 Draw the line-bond formula for each of the following molecules:
    a. pentane   **b.** 2,3-dimethylhexane
    c. 2-bromo-4-methylheptane

11.56 Draw the line-bond formula for each of the following molecules:
    a. butane   **b.** 2,3,3-trimethylpentane
    c. 3,4,5-trimethyloctane

11.57 Identify the compound in each of the following pairs that has the higher boiling point:
    a. pentane or heptane   **b.** pentane or cyclopentane
    c. hexane or 2-methylpentane

11.58 Identify the compound in each of the following pairs that has the higher boiling point:
    a. butane or octane   **b.** cyclohexane or hexane
    c. propane or pentane

11.59 Write a balanced equation for the complete combustion of each of the following:
    a. propane   **b.** C_5H_{12} **c.** cyclobutane   **d.** octane

11.60 Write a balanced equation for the complete combustion of each of the following:
    a. hexane   **b.** methylcyclohexane
    c. cyclopentane   **d.** 2-methylpropane

11.61 Match each of the descriptions (**a–f**) with a corresponding term in the following list: alkane, alkene, alkyne, alcohol, ether, aldehyde, ketone, carboxylic acid, ester, amine, functional group, isomers.
    a. an organic compound that contains a hydroxyl group bonded to a carbon
    b. a hydrocarbon that contains one or more carbon–carbon double bonds
    c. an organic compound in which the carbon of a carbonyl group is bonded to a hydrogen
    d. a hydrocarbon that contains only carbon–carbon single bonds
    e. an organic compound in which the carbon of a carbonyl group is bonded to a hydroxyl group
    f. an organic compound that contains a nitrogen atom bonded to one or more carbon atoms

11.62 Match each of the descriptions (**a–f**) with a corresponding term in the following list: alkane, alkene, alkyne, alcohol, ether, aldehyde, ketone, carboxylic acid, ester, amine, functional group, isomers.
    a. organic compounds with identical molecular formulas that differ only in the arrangement of atoms
    b. an organic compound in which the hydrogen atom of a carboxyl group is replaced by a carbon atom
    c. an organic compound that contains an oxygen atom bonded to two carbon atoms
    d. a hydrocarbon that contains a carbon–carbon triple bond
    e. a characteristic group of atoms that make compounds behave and react in a particular way
    f. an organic compound in which the carbonyl group is bonded to two carbon atoms

CHALLENGE QUESTIONS

11.63 In an automobile engine, "knocking" occurs when the combustion of gasoline occurs too rapidly. The octane number of gasoline represents the ability of a gasoline mixture to reduce knocking. A sample of gasoline is compared with heptane, rated 0, because it reacts with severe knocking, and 2,2,4-trimethylpentane, which has a rating of 100 because of its low knocking. Draw the condensed structural formula, give the molecular formula, and write the balanced equation for the complete combustion of 2,2,4-trimethylpentane.

11.64 Draw the structures of the following halogenated compounds, which are used as refrigerants:
    a. Freon 14, tetrafluoromethane
    b. Freon 114, 1,2-dichloro-1,1,2,2-tetrafluoroethane
    c. Freon C318, octafluorocyclobutane

11.65 The density of pentane, a component of gasoline, is 0.63 g/mL. The heat of combustion for pentane is 845 kcal per mole.
    a. Write the balanced equation for the complete combustion of pentane.
    b. What is the molar mass?
    c. How much heat is produced when 1 gallon of pentane is burned (1 gallon = 3.78 liters)?
    d. How many liters of CO_2 at STP are produced from the complete combustion of 1 gallon of pentane?

11.66 Draw the condensed structural formulas of two esters and a carboxylic acid that each have the molecular formula $C_3H_6O_2$.

11.67 Draw all the possible structures of an organic compound with 6 carbon atoms that has a 4-carbon chain.

11.68 Draw all the possible structures of an organic compound with 4 carbon atoms that has a 3-carbon ring and a hydroxyl group.

11.69 Consider the compound propane.
    a. Draw the condensed structural formula.
    b. Write the balanced equation for the complete combustion of propane.
    c. How many grams of O_2 are needed to react with 12.0 L of propane gas at STP?
    d. How many grams of CO_2 would be produced from the reaction in part **c**?

11.70 Consider the compound ethylcyclopentane.
    a. Draw the geometric formula.
    b. Write the balanced equation for the complete combustion of ethylcyclopentane.
    c. Calculate the grams of O_2 required for the reaction of 25.0 g of ethylcyclopentane.
    d. How many liters of CO_2 would be produced at STP from the reaction in part **c**?

11.71 A tank on an outdoor heater contains 5.0 lb of propane.
    a. Write the balanced equation for the complete combustion of propane.
    b. How many kilograms of CO_2 are produced by the complete combustion of all 5.0 lb of propane?

11.72 A butane fireplace lighter contains 56.0 g of butane.
    a. Write the balanced equation for the complete combustion of butane.
    b. How many grams of oxygen are needed for the complete combustion of the butane in the lighter?

ANSWERS

ANSWERS TO STUDY CHECKS

11.1

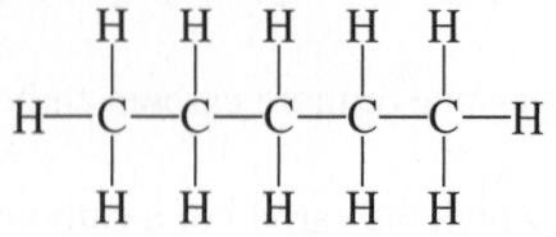

$CH_3-CH_2-CH_2-CH_2-CH_3$

11.2 cyclobutane

11.3 This is another isomer of C_6H_{14}. There is a five-carbon chain with a carbon group bonded to the middle (third) carbon.

11.4 1-chloro-2,4-dimethylhexane

11.5

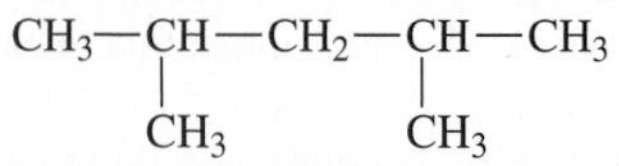

11.6 1,2-dibromoethane

11.7 $= C_5H_{12}$

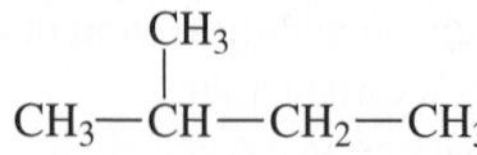

$C_5H_{12} + 8O_2 \longrightarrow 5CO_2 + 6H_2O$

11.8 $CH_3-CH_2-O-CH_3$ contains the functional group C—O—C; it is an ether.

11.9 A carboxylic acid has a carboxyl group —COOH. In an ester, the oxygen atom of the carboxyl group is attached to another carbon atom, instead of hydrogen.

ANSWERS TO SELECTED QUESTIONS AND PROBLEMS

11.1
a. inorganic
b. organic
c. organic
d. inorganic
e. inorganic
f. organic

11.3
a. inorganic
b. organic
c. organic
d. inorganic

11.5
a. ethane
b. ethane
c. NaBr
d. NaBr

11.7 VSEPR theory predicts that the four bonds in CH_4 will be as far apart as possible, which means that the hydrogen atoms are at the corners of a tetrahedron.

11.9 a.

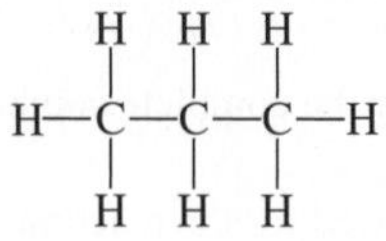

b. $CH_3-CH_2-CH_2-CH_2-CH_2-CH_3$

c.

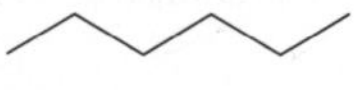

11.11
a. pentane
b. heptane
c. hexane
d. cyclobutane

11.13
a. CH_4
b. CH_3-CH_3
c. $CH_3-CH_2-CH_2-CH_2-CH_3$

d.

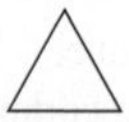

11.15
a. same molecule
b. isomers of C_5H_{12}
c. isomers of C_6H_{14}

11.17
a. 2-methylbutane
b. 2,2-dimethylpropane
c. 2,3-dimethylpentane
d. 4-ethyl-2,2-dimethylhexane

11.19
a. chlorocyclopentane
b. methylcyclohexane
c. 1-bromo-3-methylcyclobutane
d. 1-bromo-2-chlorocyclopentane

11.21 a.

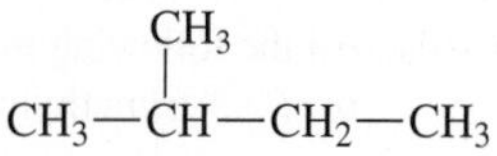

b.

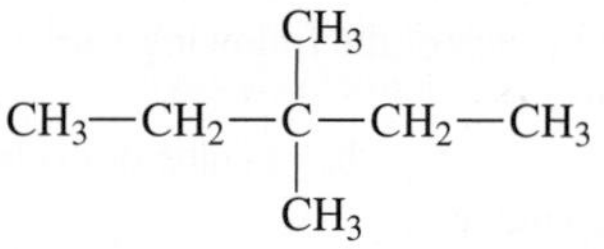

c.

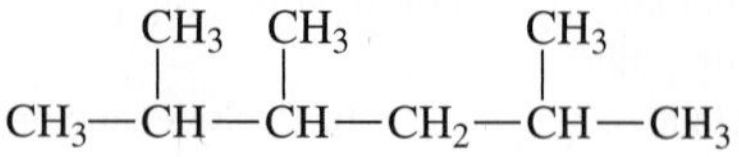

d.

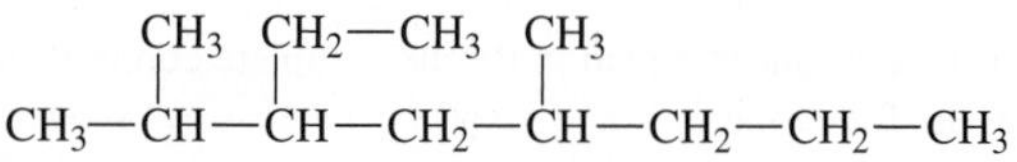

11.23 a. 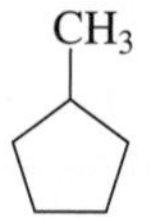
b.

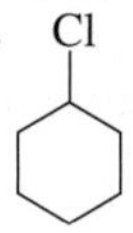

c. 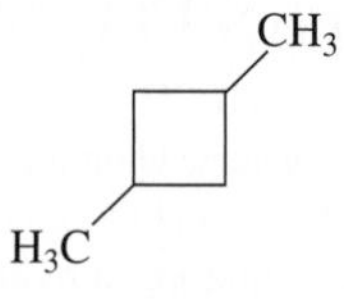
d.

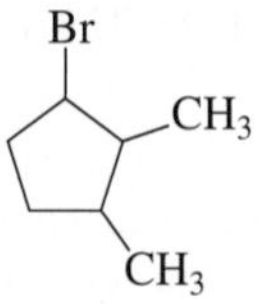

11.25
a. bromoethane
b. 1-fluoropropane
c. 2-chloropropane
d. trichloromethane

11.27 a. 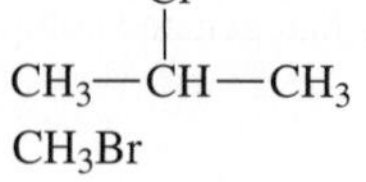
b. 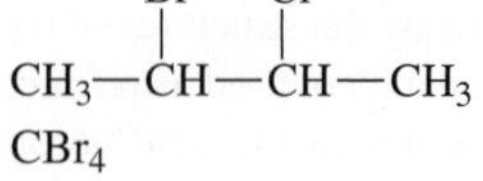
c. CH_3Br
d. CBr_4

11.29
a. $CH_3-CH_2-CH_2-CH_2-CH_2-CH_2-CH_3$
b. liquid
c. insoluble in water
d. float

11.31
a. heptane
b. cyclopropane
c. hexane

11.33
a. $2C_2H_6 + 7O_2 \longrightarrow 4CO_2 + 6H_2O$
b. $2C_3H_6 + 9O_2 \longrightarrow 6CO_2 + 6H_2O$
c. $2C_8H_{18} + 25O_2 \longrightarrow 16CO_2 + 18H_2O$
d. $C_6H_{12} + 9O_2 \longrightarrow 6CO_2 + 6H_2O$

11.35 a. alcohol   **b.** alkene
 c. aldehyde   **d.** ester

11.37 a. ether   **b.** alcohol   **c.** ketone
 d. carboxylic acid   **e.** amine

11.39 a. aromatic, ether, alcohol, ketone
 b. aromatic, ether, alkene, ester

11.41 aromatic, ether, amide

11.43 a. Organic compounds have covalent bonds; inorganic compounds have ionic as well as polar covalent bonds and a few have nonpolar covalent bonds.
 b. Most organic compounds are insoluble in water; many inorganic compounds are soluble in water.
 c. Most organic compounds have low melting points; inorganic compounds have high melting points.
 d. Most organic compounds are flammable; inorganic compounds are not usually flammable.

11.45 a. butane
 b. butane
 c. potassium chloride
 d. potassium chloride
 e. butane

11.47 a. amine   **b.** ketone
 c. ester   **d.** alcohol

11.49 a. methyl   **b.** propyl   **c.** chloro

11.51 a. methylcyclopentane
 b. 1,2-dibromo-3-chloropropane
 c. 2,3-dimethylhexane
 d. 3-chloro-3-ethylpentane

11.53 a. 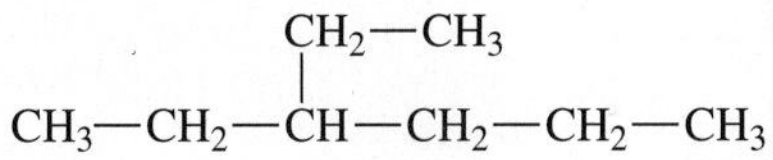
$$CH_3-CH_2-\underset{\overset{|}{CH_2-CH_3}}{CH}-CH_2-CH_2-CH_3$$

b.

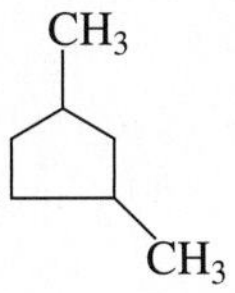

c. 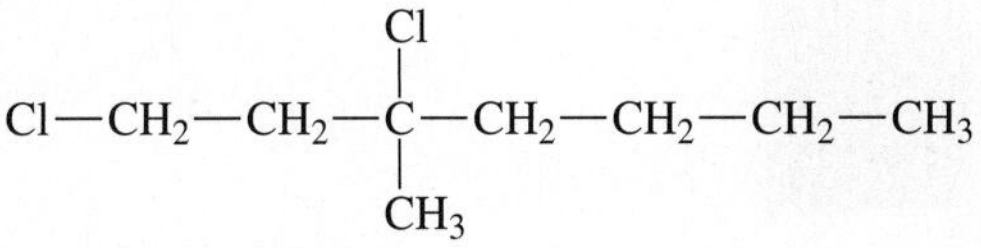
$$Cl-CH_2-CH_2-\underset{\overset{|}{CH_3}}{\overset{\overset{Cl}{|}}{C}}-CH_2-CH_2-CH_2-CH_3$$

d.

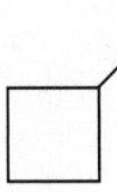

11.55 a.

b.

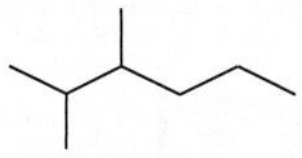

c.

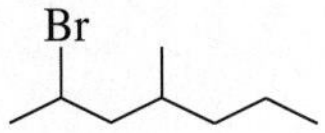

11.57 a. heptane
 b. cyclopentane
 c. hexane

11.59 a. $C_3H_8 + 5O_2 \longrightarrow 3CO_2 + 4H_2O$
 b. $C_5H_{12} + 8O_2 \longrightarrow 5CO_2 + 6H_2O$
 c. $C_4H_8 + 6O_2 \longrightarrow 4CO_2 + 4H_2O$
 d. $2C_8H_{18} + 25O_2 \longrightarrow 16CO_2 + 18H_2O$

11.61 a. alcohol   **b.** alkene
 c. aldehyde   **d.** alkane
 e. carboxylic acid   **f.** amine

11.63 Condensed structural formula:
$$CH_3-\underset{\overset{|}{CH_3}}{\overset{\overset{CH_3}{|}}{C}}-CH_2-\underset{\overset{|}{CH_3}}{CH}-CH_3$$

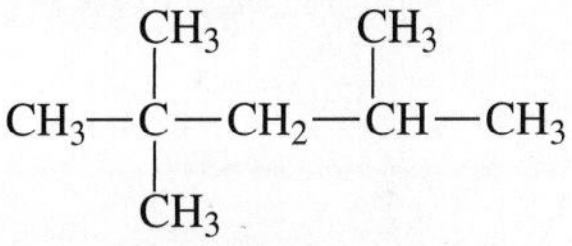

Molecular formula: C_8H_{18}
Combustion reaction:
$2C_8H_{18} + 25O_2 \longrightarrow 16CO_2 + 18H_2O$

11.65 a. $C_5H_{12} + 8O_2 \longrightarrow 5CO_2 + 6H_2O$
 b. 72.0 g/mole
 c. 2.8×10^4 kcal
 d. 3700 L of CO_2

11.67 $CH_3-\underset{\overset{|}{CH_3}}{CH}-\underset{\overset{|}{CH_3}}{CH}-CH_3$ $CH_3-\underset{\overset{|}{CH_3}}{\overset{\overset{CH_3}{|}}{C}}-CH_2-CH_3$

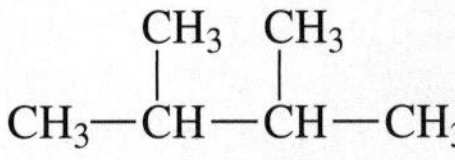

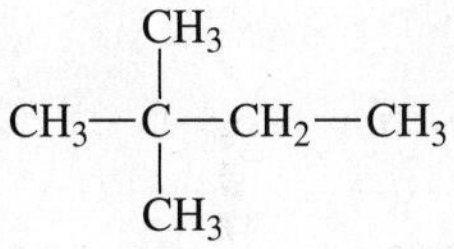

11.69 a. $CH_3-CH_2-CH_3$
 b. $C_3H_8 + 5O_2 \longrightarrow 3CO_2 + 4H_2O$
 c. 85.7 g of O_2
 d. 70.7 g of CO_2

11.71 a. $C_3H_8 + 5O_2 \longrightarrow 3CO_2 + 4H_2O$
 b. 6.8 kg of CO_2

12 Alkenes, Alkynes, and Aromatic Compounds

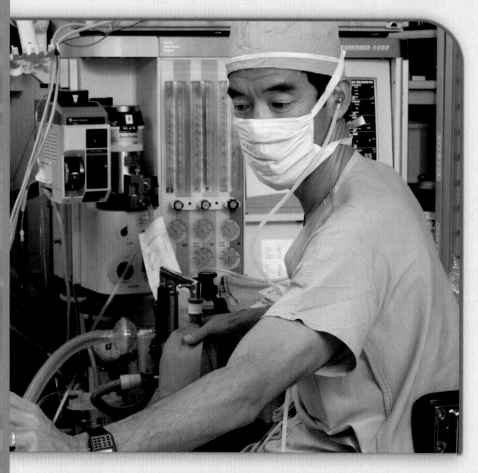

"During surgery, I work with the surgeon to provide a safe level of anesthetics that renders the patient free from pain," says Mark Noguchi, nurse anesthetist (CRNA), Kaiser Hospital. "We do spinal and epidural blocks as well as general anesthetics, which means the patient is totally asleep. We use a variety of pharmaceutical agents, including halothane ($C_2HBrClF_3$) and bupivacain ($C_{18}H_{28}N_2O$), as well as muscle relaxants such as midazolam ($C_{18}H_{13}ClFN_3$), to achieve the results we want for the surgical situation. We also assess the patient's overall hemodynamic status. If blood is lost, we replace components such as plasma, platelets, and coagulation factors. We also monitor the heart rate and run EKGs to determine cardiac function."

Mastering**CHEMISTRY**™

I n Chapter 11, we looked primarily at alkanes that contain only single bonds. Now we will investigate hydrocarbons that contain one or more double bonds or triple bonds between carbon atoms. When we cook with vegetable oils such as corn oil, safflower oil, or olive oil, we are using organic compounds called *lipids* that have one or more double bonds in their long carbon chains. Animal fats also contain long chains of carbon atoms but with fewer double bonds. If we compare the two types of fats, we find considerable differences in their physical and chemical properties. Vegetable oils are liquid at room temperature, whereas animal fats are solid. Because double bonds are more reactive than single bonds, oils are oxidized by oxygen in the air, especially at warm temperatures, forming products that have rancid, unpleasant odors.

12.1 Alkenes and Alkynes

Alkenes and alkynes are families of hydrocarbons that contain double and triple bonds, respectively. They are called *unsaturated hydrocarbons* because they do not contain the maximum number of hydrogen atoms that could be attached to each carbon atom, as do alkanes. These unsaturated hydrocarbons react with hydrogen gas to increase the number of hydrogen atoms to become alkanes, which are *saturated hydrocarbons* because they do have the maximum number of hydrogen atoms possible.

Identifying Alkenes and Alkynes

An **alkene** contains one or more carbon-carbon double bond that forms when adjacent carbon atoms share two pairs of valence electrons. Recall that a carbon atom always forms four covalent bonds. In the simplest alkene, ethene, C_2H_4, two carbon atoms are connected by a double bond, and each is also attached to two H atoms. (See Figure 12.1.)

Ethene, commonly called ethylene, is an important plant hormone involved in promoting the ripening of fruit. Commercially grown fruit, such as avocados, bananas, and tomatoes, are often picked before they are ripe. Before the fruit is brought to market, it is exposed to ethylene to accelerate the ripening process. Ethylene also accelerates the breakdown of cellulose in plants, which causes flowers to wilt and leaves to fall from trees.

In an **alkyne**, a triple bond forms when two carbon atoms share three pairs of valence electrons. In a triple bond, each carbon atom is attached to two other atoms. The simplest alkyne, ethyne (C_2H_2)—commonly called acetylene—is used in welding, where it reacts with oxygen to produce flames with temperatures above 3300 °C.

Structures of Alkenes and Alkynes

In ethene, two CH_2 groups are connected by a double bond, which represents two pairs of electrons. We already know that carbon has four electrons and needs four bonds to achieve a stable octet. In a double bond, each carbon atom is attached to three other atoms (one carbon and two hydrogens). According to VSEPR theory (Chapter 5), the three groups bonded to each carbon in the double bond are planar and arranged at angles of 120°.

LEARNING GOAL

Write the IUPAC names for alkenes and alkynes; give common names for simple structures.

 TUTORIAL
Drawing Alkenes and Alkynes

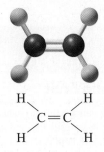

Ethene

Ethyne

$H—C\equiv C—H$

FIGURE 12.1 Ball-and-stick models of ethene and ethyne show the functional groups of double or triple bonds.

Q Why are these compounds called unsaturated hydrocarbons?

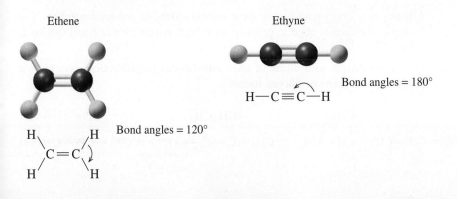

Ethene   Ethyne

Bond angles = 180°

$H—C\equiv C—H$

Bond angles = 120°

In the simplest alkyne, ethyne, two CH groups are connected by a triple bond. According to VSEPR theory, the two groups bonded to each carbon in the triple bond are linear and arranged at angles of 180°.

CONCEPT CHECK 12.1

■ **Identifying Alkanes, Alkenes, and Alkynes**

Classify each of the following condensed structural formulas as an alkane, alkene, or alkyne:

a. $CH_3—C≡C—CH_3$
b. $CH_3—CH_2—CH_3$
c. $CH_3—CH_2—CH_2—CH=CH_2$

ANSWER
a. A condensed structural formula with a triple bond is an alkyne.
b. A condensed structural formula with only single bonds between carbon atoms is an alkane.
c. A condensed structural formula with a double bond is an alkene.

Naming Alkenes and Alkynes

The IUPAC names for alkenes and alkynes are similar to those of alkanes. For alkenes or alkynes, the name is based on the longest carbon chain that contains the double or triple bond.

See Table 12.1 for a comparison of the naming for alkanes, alkenes, and alkynes.

(MC)™ TUTORIAL
Naming Alkenes and Alkynes

TABLE 12.1 Comparison of Names for Alkanes, Alkenes, and Alkynes

Alkane	Alkene	Alkyne
$H_3C—CH_3$	$H_2C=CH_2$	$HC≡CH$
Ethane	Ethene (ethylene)	Ethyne (acetylene)
$CH_3—CH_2—CH_3$	$CH_3—CH=CH_2$	$CH_3—CH≡CH$
Propane	Propene	Propyne

STEP 1   Name the longest carbon chain that contains the double or triple bond. Replace the corresponding alkane ending with *ene* for an alkene and *yne* for an alkyne. Cyclic alkenes are named as *cycloalkenes*.

STEP 2   Number the longest chain from the end nearer the double or triple bond. Indicate the position of the double or triple bond using the lowest number:

$$CH_3—CH_2—CH=CH_2 \qquad CH_3—CH=CH—CH_3 \qquad CH_3—C≡C—CH_3$$
$$\;\;4\quad\;\;3\quad\;\;2\quad\;1 \qquad\qquad 1\quad\;\;2\quad\;\;3\quad\;\;4 \qquad\qquad 1\quad\;2\quad\;3\quad\;4$$
$$\text{1-Butene} \qquad\qquad\qquad \text{2-Butene} \qquad\qquad\qquad \text{2-Butyne}$$

Alkenes or alkynes with two or three carbon atoms do not need numbers. For example, the double bond in propene must be between carbon 1 and carbon 2, which can be written $CH_2=CH—CH_3$ or $CH_3—CH=CH_2$.

STEP 3   Give the location and name of each substituent (alphabetical order) as a prefix to the alkene or alkyne name:

$$\underset{1}{CH_2}=\underset{2}{CH}—\underset{3}{CH_2}—\underset{4}{\underset{|}{CH}}—\underset{5}{CH_3} \qquad \underset{1}{CH_3}—\underset{2}{\underset{|}{C}}=\underset{3}{\underset{|}{C}}—\underset{4}{CH_3} \qquad \underset{4}{CH_3}—\underset{3}{\underset{|}{CH}}—\underset{2}{C}≡\underset{1}{CH}$$

with CH_3 on carbon 4; $CH_3\ CH_3$ on carbons 2,3; Cl on carbon 3

4-Methyl-1-pentene   2,3-Dimethyl-2-butene   3-Chloro-1-butyne

---

EXPLORE YOUR WORLD

Ripening Fruit

Obtain two unripe (green) bananas. Place one in a plastic bag and seal the bag. Leave both bananas on the counter. Check the bananas twice a day for 2 or 3 days and observe any difference in the ripening process.

QUESTIONS

1. What compound helps ripen the bananas?
2. What are some possible reasons for any difference in the ripening rate?
3. If you wish to ripen an avocado, what procedure might you use?

In a **cycloalkene** with a substituent, the double bond is understood to be between carbons 1 and 2, and the ring is numbered to give the lowest number to the substituent:

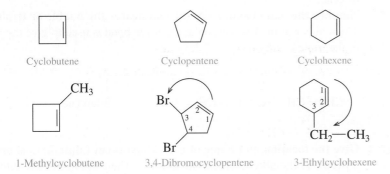

| Cyclobutene | Cyclopentene | Cyclohexene |

| 1-Methylcyclobutene | 3,4-Dibromocyclopentene | 3-Ethylcyclohexene |

■ **Comparing Alkenes and Alkynes**

Compare the condensed structural formulas of propane, propene, and propyne.

ANSWER

Propane, propene, and propyne each contain three carbon atoms. Propane contains only single bonds, propene contains a double bond, and propyne contains a triple bond. Propane has eight hydrogen atoms, propene has six hydrogen atoms, and propyne has four hydrogen atoms.

■ **Naming Alkenes and Alkynes**

Write the IUPAC name for each of the following:

$$\text{a. } CH_3-\underset{\underset{CH_3}{|}}{CH}-CH=CH-CH_3$$

$$\text{b. } CH_3-CH_2-C\equiv C-CH_2-CH_3$$

SOLUTION

a. STEP 1 Name the longest carbon chain that contains the double or triple bond. There are five carbon atoms in the longest carbon chain containing the double bond. Replacing the corresponding alkane ending with *ene* gives pentene.

STEP 2 Number the longest chain from the end nearer the double or triple bond. The number of the first carbon in the double bond is used to give the location of the double bond:

$$CH_3-\underset{\underset{CH_3}{|}}{\underset{4}{CH}}-\underset{3}{CH}=\underset{2}{CH}-\underset{1}{CH_3} \qquad \text{2-pentene}$$
$$5$$

STEP 3 Give the location and name of each substituent (alphabetical order) as a prefix to the alkene or alkyne name. The methyl group is located on carbon 4:

$$CH_3-\underset{\underset{CH_3}{|}}{\underset{4}{CH}}-\underset{3}{CH}=\underset{2}{CH}-\underset{1}{CH_3} \qquad \text{4-methyl-2-pentene}$$
$$5$$

Guide to Naming Alkenes and Alkynes

STEP 1
Name the longest carbon chain with a double or triple bond.

STEP 2
Number the carbon chain starting from the end nearer a double or triple bond.

STEP 3
Give the location and name of each substituent (alphabetical order) as a prefix to the name, if needed.

b. STEP 1 **Name the longest carbon chain that contains the double or triple bond.** There are six carbon atoms in the longest chain containing the triple bond. Replacing the corresponding alkane ending with *yne* gives hexyne.

STEP 2 **Number the main chain from the end nearer the double or triple bond.** The number of the first carbon in the triple bond is used to give the location of the triple bond:

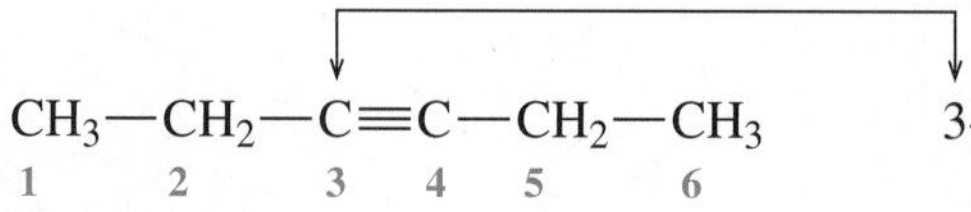

$$CH_3-CH_2-C\equiv C-CH_2-CH_3 \qquad \text{3-hexyne}$$
$$123456$$

STEP 3 **Give the location and name of each substituent (alphabetical order) as a prefix to the alkene or alkyne name.** There are no substituents in this formula.

STUDY CHECK

Draw the condensed structural formula for each of the following:

a. 2-pentyne

b. 3-methylcyclopentene

ENVIRONMENTAL NOTE

Fragrant Alkenes

The odors you associate with lemons, oranges, roses, and lavender are due to volatile compounds that are synthesized by the plants. The pleasant flavors and fragrances of many fruits and flowers are often due to unsaturated compounds. They were some of the first kinds of compounds to be extracted from natural plant material. In ancient times, they were highly valued in their pure forms. Limonene and myrcene give the characteristic odors and flavors to lemons and bay leaves, respectively. Geraniol and citronellal give roses and lemon grass their distinct aromas. In the food and perfume industries, these compounds are extracted or synthesized and used as perfumes and flavorings.

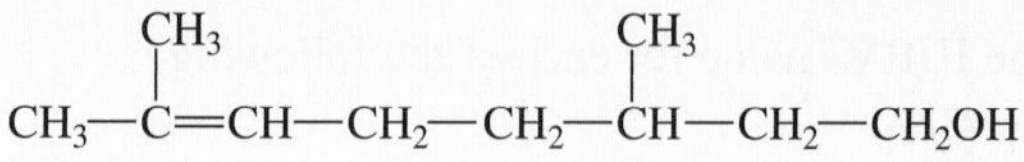

$$CH_3-\overset{\overset{\displaystyle CH_3}{|}}{C}=CH-CH_2-CH_2-\overset{\overset{\displaystyle CH_3}{|}}{CH}-CH_2-CH_2OH$$
Geraniol, roses

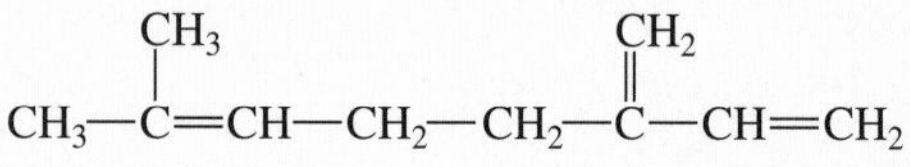

$$CH_3-\overset{\overset{\displaystyle CH_3}{|}}{C}=CH-CH_2-CH_2-\overset{\overset{\displaystyle CH_2}{||}}{C}-CH=CH_2$$
Myrcene, bay leaves

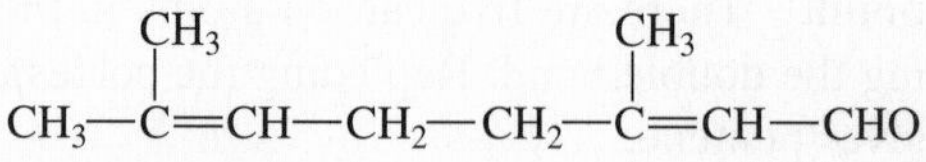

$$CH_3-\overset{\overset{\displaystyle CH_3}{|}}{C}=CH-CH_2-CH_2-\overset{\overset{\displaystyle CH_3}{|}}{C}=CH-CHO$$
Citronellal, lemongrass

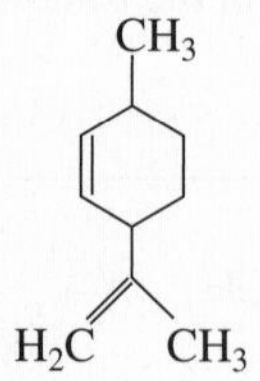

Limonene, lemons and oranges

QUESTIONS AND PROBLEMS

Alkenes and Alkynes

12.1 Identify the following as alkenes, cycloalkenes, or alkynes:

a.
$$\underset{H}{\overset{H}{\underset{|}{\overset{|}{C}}}} H\!-\!\underset{\underset{H}{|}}{\overset{\overset{H}{|}}{C}}\!-\!C\!=\!C\!-\!H$$

b. $CH_3\!-\!CH_2\!-\!C\!\equiv\!C\!-\!H$

c. [structure]

d. [structure with CH₃]

12.2 Identify the following as alkenes, cycloalkenes, or alkynes:

a. [structure with CH₃]

b. [structure]

c. $CH_3\!-\!\underset{\underset{CH_3}{|}}{\overset{\overset{CH_3}{|}}{C}}\!=\!C\!-\!CH_3$

d. [structure] $-C\!\equiv\!CH$

12.3 Give the IUPAC name for each of the following:

a. $CH_2\!=\!CH_2$
b. $CH_3\!-\!\underset{\overset{|}{}}{\overset{\overset{CH_3}{|}}{C}}\!=\!CH_2$
c. $CH_3\!-\!\underset{\overset{|}{}}{\overset{\overset{Br}{|}}{CH}}\!-\!C\!\equiv\!C\!-\!CH_3$

d. [square structure]

e. [structure with $CH_2\!-\!CH_3$]

f. [structure]

12.4 Give the IUPAC name for each of the following:

a. $CH_2\!=\!CH\!-\!CH_2\!-\!CH_2\!-\!CH_2\!-\!CH_3$

b. $CH_3\!-\!C\!\equiv\!C\!-\!CH_2\!-\!CH_2\!-\!\underset{\overset{|}{}}{\overset{\overset{CH_3}{|}}{CH}}\!-\!CH_3$

c. [structure with CH₃ and CH₃ on ring]

d. [square ring structure with two CH₃ groups]

e. $CH_3\!-\!\underset{\overset{|}{}}{\overset{\overset{Cl}{|}}{CH}}\!-\!CH_2\!-\!\underset{\overset{|}{}}{\overset{\overset{Cl}{|}}{CH}}\!-\!CH_2\!-\!CH\!=\!CH_2$

f. [structure with Cl groups]

12.5 Draw the condensed structural formula for each of the following compounds:
a. propene
b. 1-pentene
c. 2-methyl-1-butene
d. 3-methylcyclohexene
e. 2-chloro-3-hexyne
f. 1-butyne
g. 5-bromo-1-pentene

12.6 Draw the condensed structural formula for each of the following compounds:
a. 1-methylcyclopentene
b. 3-methyl-1-butyne
c. 3,4-dimethyl-1-pentene
d. 4-ethyl-1-methylcyclohexene
e. 1,2-dichlorocyclopentene
f. propyne
g. 2-methyl-2-hexene

12.2 Cis–Trans Isomers

In alkenes, the double bond is rigid, which means that the groups attached to the double bond do not rotate. (See *Explore Your World* "Modeling Cis–Trans Isomers.") Therefore, alkenes may have two different structures or isomers indicated by the prefix *cis* or *trans*. In a **cis isomer**, two large groups, usually alkyl groups or halogen atoms, are on the same side of the double bond. In the **trans isomer**, the large groups are on opposite sides of the double bond. For example, cis–trans isomers can be written for 2-butene. (See Figure 12.2.) In general, trans isomers are more stable than their cis counterparts because the large groups attached to the double bond are farther apart. As with any pair of isomers, the cis–trans isomers of 2-butene are different compounds with different

LEARNING GOAL

Write the condensed structural formulas and names for the cis–trans isomers of alkenes.

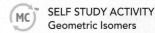
SELF STUDY ACTIVITY
Geometric Isomers

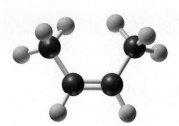

cis-2-Butene

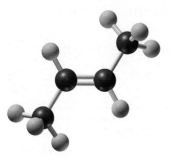

trans-2-Butene

FIGURE 12.2 Ball-and-stick models of the cis and trans isomers of 2-butene.

Q What feature in 2-butene accounts for the cis and trans isomers?

physical properties, such as melting and boiling points, as well as different chemical properties:

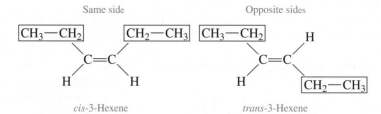

cis-2-Butene
(mp –139 °C; bp 3.7 °C)

trans-2-Butene
(mp –106 °C; bp 0.3 °C)

As long as the two groups attached to each carbon in the double bond are different, an alkene will show cis–trans isomers. Another example of cis–trans isomers is the following:

Same side

CH$_3$—CH$_2$ CH$_2$—CH$_3$
          \\   /
           C==C
          /   \\
        H   H

Opposite sides

CH$_3$—CH$_2$ H
          \\   /
           C==C
          /   \\
        H   CH$_2$—CH$_3$

cis-3-Hexene   *trans*-3-Hexene

An alkene does not have cis–trans isomers if identical groups are attached to one of the carbon atoms in the double bond. For example, in 1-butene there are two hydrogen atoms on carbon 1. In 2-methylpropene there are two methyl groups on carbon 2:

Identical atoms   H   CH$_2$—CH$_3$
                          \\   /
                           C==C
                          /   \\
                         H   H

1-Butene

                          H   CH$_3$
                          \\   /
                           C==C   Identical groups
                          /   \\
                         H   CH$_3$

2-Methylpropene

Alkynes do not have cis–trans isomers, because the carbons in the triple bond are each attached to only one group:

H—C≡C—CH$_3$ CH$_3$—C≡C—CH$_2$—CH$_3$

TUTORIAL
Cis–Trans Isomers

CONCEPT CHECK 12.3

■ **Cis-Trans Isomers**

Consider the compound 2-hexene.

a. What alkyl groups are attached to the carbon atoms in the double bond?
b. In *cis*-2-hexene, are the alkyl groups attached on the same side or opposite sides of the double bond?
c. In *trans*-2-hexene, are the hydrogen atoms attached on the same side or opposite sides of the double bond?
d. Why does 1-hexene not have cis-trans isomers?

ANSWER

a. In 2-hexene, carbon 2 is attached to a methyl (CH$_3$—) group and carbon 3 is attached to a propyl (CH$_3$—CH$_2$—CH$_2$—) group.
b. In *cis*-2-hexene, the methyl and propyl groups are attached on the same side of the double bond.
c. In *trans*-2-hexene, the hydrogen atoms are attached on opposite sides of the double bond.
d. In the condensed structural formula of 1-hexene, carbon 1 is attached to two hydrogen atoms. Because the two H atoms are identical, 1-hexene cannot have cis–trans isomers.

EXPLORE YOUR WORLD

Modeling Cis–Trans Isomers

Because cis–trans isomerism is not easy to visualize, here are some things you can do to understand the difference in rotation around a single bond compared to a double bond and how it affects groups that are attached to the carbon atoms in the double bond.

Put the fingertips of your index fingers together. This is a model of a single bond. Consider the index fingers as a pair of carbon atoms, and think of your thumbs and other fingers as other parts of a carbon chain. While your index fingers are touching, twist your hands and change the position of the thumbs relative to each other. Notice how the relationship of your other fingers changes.

Cis-hands (cis-thumbs/fingers)

Trans-hands (trans-thumbs/fingers)

Now place the tips of your index fingers and middle fingers together in a model of a double bond. As you did before, twist your hands to try to move the thumbs apart. What happens? Can you change the location of your thumbs relative to each other without breaking the double bond? The difficulty of moving your hands with two fingers touching

represents the lack of rotation about a double bond. You have made a model of a cis isomer when both thumbs are on the same side. If you turn one hand over so one thumb points down and the other thumb points up, you have made a model of a trans isomer.

Using Gumdrops and Toothpicks to Model Cis–Trans Isomers

Obtain some toothpicks and yellow, green, and black gumdrops. The black gumdrops represent C atoms, the yellow gumdrops represent H atoms, and the green gumdrops represent Cl atoms. Place a toothpick between two black gumdrops. Use three more toothpicks to attach two yellow gumdrops, and one green gumdrop to each black gumdrop (carbon atom). Rotate one of the gumdrop carbon atoms to show the conformations of the attached H and Cl atoms.

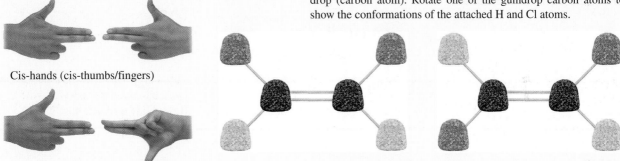

Remove a toothpick and yellow gumdrop from each black gumdrop. Place a second toothpick between the black gumdrops which makes a double bond. Try to twist the double bond of toothpicks. Can you do it? When you observe the location of the green gumdrops, does the model you made represent a cis or trans isomer? Why? If your model is a cis isomer, how would you change it to a trans isomer? If your model is a trans isomer, how would you change it to a cis isomer?

ENVIRONMENTAL NOTE

Pheromones in Insect Communication

Many insects emit minute quantities of chemicals called *pheromones* to send messages to other individuals of the same species. Some pheromones warn of danger, while others call for defense, mark a trail, or attract the opposite sex. During the past 40 years, the structures of many pheromones have been chemically determined. One of the most studied is bombykol, the sex pheromone produced by the female silkworm moth. Even a few nanograms of bombykol will attract male silkworm moths from distances of over 1 kilometer. The bombykol molecule is a 16-carbon chain with one cis double bond, one trans double bond, and an alcohol group. The effectiveness of many of these pheromones depends on the cis or trans configuration of the double bonds in the molecules. A certain species will respond to one isomer but not the other.

Scientists are interested in synthesizing pheromones to use as nontoxic alternatives to pesticides. When placed in a trap, bombykol can be used to isolate male silkworm moths. When a synthetic pheromone is released in a field, the males cannot locate the females, which disrupts the reproductive cycle. This technique has been successful in controlling the oriental fruit moth, the grapevine moth, and the pink bollworm.

Bombykol, sex attractant for the silkworm moth

HEALTH NOTE

Cis–Trans Isomers for Night Vision

The retinas of the eyes consist of two types of cells: rods and cones. The rods on the edge of the retina allow us to see in dim light, and the cones, in the center, produce our vision in bright light. The rods contain a substance called *rhodopsin* that absorbs light. Rhodopsin is composed of *cis*-11-retinal, an unsaturated compound, attached to a protein. When rhodopsin absorbs light, the *cis*-11-retinal isomer is converted to its trans isomer, which changes its shape. The trans form no longer fits, and it separates from the protein. The change from the cis to trans isomer and the separation from the protein generate an electrical signal that the brain converts into an image.

An enzyme (isomerase) converts the trans isomer back to the *cis*-11-retinal isomer and the rhodopsin re-forms. If there is a deficiency of rhodopsin in the rods of the retina, night blindness may occur. One common cause of night blindness is a lack of vitamin A in the diet. We obtain vitamin A from β-carotene, which is found in foods such as carrots, squash, and spinach. In the small intestine, β-carotene is converted to vitamin A, which can be converted to *cis*-11-retinal or stored in the liver for future use. Without a sufficient quantity of retinal, not enough rhodopsin is produced to enable us to see adequately in dim light.

Cis–Trans Isomers of Retinal

Cis double bond   Trans double bond

cis-11-Retinal   Light →   *trans*-11-Retinal

■ Identifying Cis and Trans Isomers

Identify each of the following statements as describing a cis or trans isomer. Give the name of each.

a. In an isomer of 3-hexene, the ethyl groups are attached on opposite sides of the double bond.

b. In an isomer of 2,3-dibromo-2-butene, the bromine atoms are attached on the same side of the double bond.

ANSWER

a. When the alkyl groups are attached on the opposite sides of the carbon atoms of the double bond, the isomer is a trans isomer; *trans*-3-hexene.

b. When the bromine atoms are attached on the same side of the double bond, the isomer is a cis isomer; *cis*-2,3-dibromo-2-butene.

SAMPLE PROBLEM 12.2

■ Naming Cis–Trans Isomers

Name each of the following as a cis or trans isomer:

a.

$$\underset{H}{\overset{Br}{}}C=C\underset{H}{\overset{Cl}{}}$$

b.

$$\underset{H}{\overset{CH_3}{}}C=C\underset{CH_2-CH_3}{\overset{Br}{}}$$

SOLUTION

a. This isomer is a cis isomer because the Br and Cl atoms are on the same side of the double bond; *cis*-1-bromo-2-chloroethene.

b. This isomer is a trans isomer because the CH_3— group and —CH_2—CH_3 group are on opposite sides of the double bond; *trans*-3-bromo-2-pentene.

STUDY CHECK

Is the following compound *cis-* or *trans-*3-heptene?

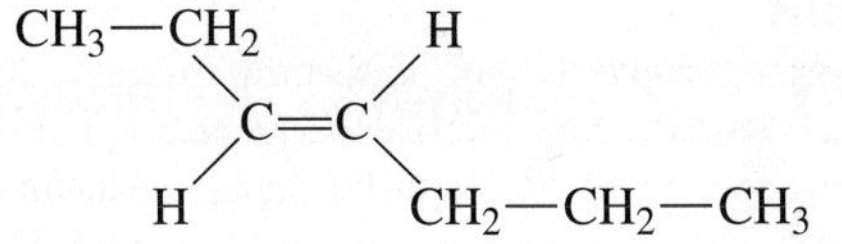

CH₃—CH₂   H
      \\   /
       C＝C
      /   \\
     H   CH₂—CH₂—CH₃

QUESTIONS AND PROBLEMS

Cis–Trans Isomers

12.7 Which of the following can be written as cis–trans isomers?
   a. CH₂＝CH—CH₃
   b. CH₃—CH₂—CH＝CH—CH₃

   c. 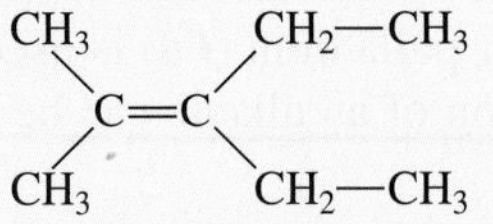 CH₃   CH₂—CH₃
          \\   /
           C＝C
          /   \\
        CH₃   CH₂—CH₃

12.8 Which of the following do not have cis–trans isomers?

   a. 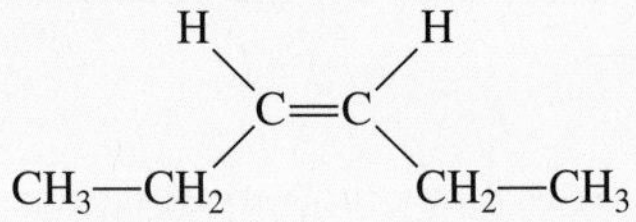   H   H
               \\   /
                C＝C
               /   \\
        CH₃—CH₂   CH₂—CH₃

   b. CH₃—CH₂—CH₂—CH＝CH₂

                      CH₃
                       |
   c. CH₂＝CH—CH₂—CH—CH₃

12.9 Write the IUPAC name of each of the following using *cis* or *trans* prefixes:

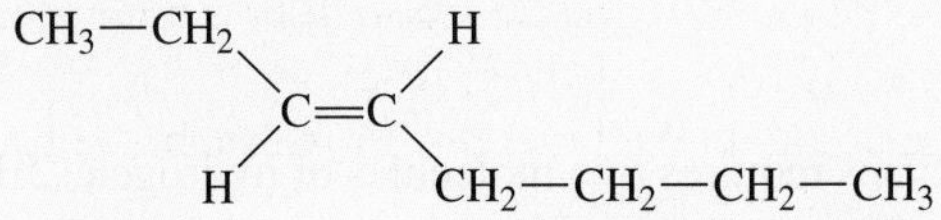

   a. 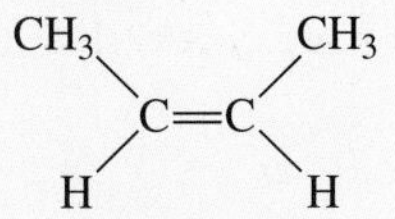 CH₃   CH₃
           \\   /
            C＝C
           /   \\
          H   H

   b. CH₃—CH₂   H
               \\   /
                C＝C
               /   \\
              H   CH₂—CH₂—CH₂—CH₃

   c. CH₃—CH₂—CH₂   CH₂—CH₃
                     \\   /
                      C＝C
                     /   \\
                    H   H

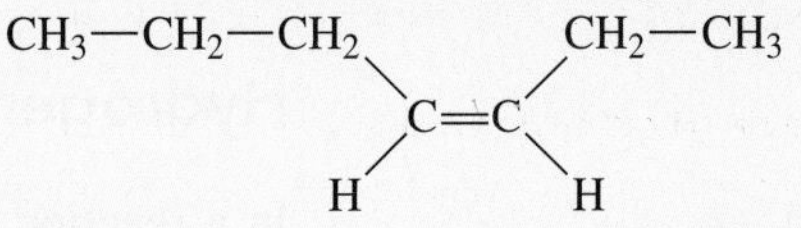

12.10 Write the IUPAC name of each of the following using *cis* or *trans* prefixes:

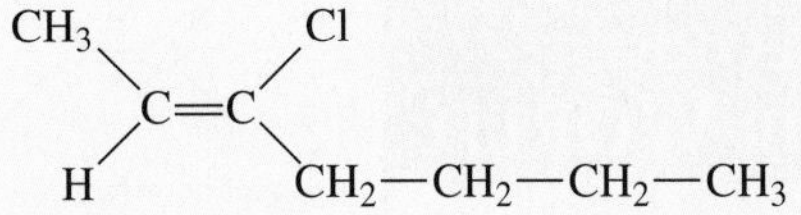

   a. 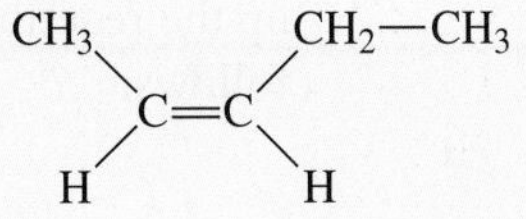 CH₃   CH₂—CH₃
           \\   /
            C＝C
           /   \\
          H   H

   b. CH₃   Cl
           \\   /
            C＝C
           /   \\
          H   CH₂—CH₂—CH₂—CH₃

   c. CH₃—CH₂—CH₂   H
                     \\   /
                      C＝C
                     /   \\
                    H   CH₃

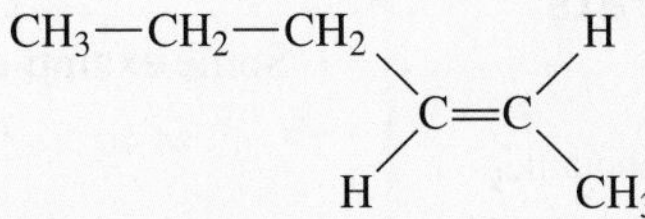

12.11 Draw the condensed structural formula for each of the following:
   a. *trans*-1-chloro-2-butene
   b. *cis*-2-pentene
   c. *trans*-3-heptene

12.12 Draw the condensed structural formula for each of the following:
   a. *cis*-3-hexene
   b. *trans*-2-pentene
   c. *cis*-4-octene

12.3 | Addition Reactions

The most characteristic reaction of alkenes and alkynes is the **addition** of atoms or groups of atoms to the carbons of the double or triple bond. Addition occurs because double and triple bonds are easily broken, which provides electrons to form new single bonds. The general equation for the addition of a reactant A—B to an alkene can be written as follows:

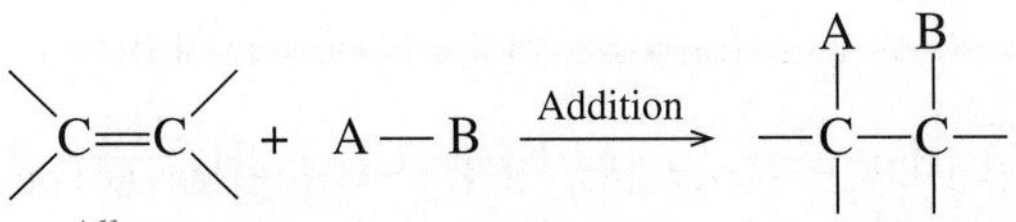

LEARNING GOAL

Write the condensed structural formulas and names for the organic products of addition reactions of alkenes and alkynes.

                                    A   B
                                    | |
   C＝C   +   A—B   ──Addition──→   —C—C—
                                    | |
   Alkene

The addition reactions have different names that depend on the type of reactant we add to the alkene, as shown in Table 12.2.

TABLE 12.2 Summary of Addition Reactions

Name of Addition Reaction	Reactants	Catalysts	Products
Hydrogenation	Alkene + H_2	Pt, Ni, or Pd	Alkane
	Alkyne + $2H_2$	Pt, Ni, or Pd	Alkane
Halogenation	Alkene + Cl_2 (Br_2)		Haloalkane
	Alkyne + $2Cl_2$ ($2Br_2$)		Haloalkane
Hydrohalogenation	Alkene + HCl (HBr)		Haloalkane
Hydration	Alkene + H_2O	H^+ (strong acid)	Alcohol

Hydrogenation

MC TUTORIAL
Addition Reactions

In a reaction called **hydrogenation**, H atoms add to a double bond or triple bond to form alkanes. During hydrogenation, double or triple bonds are converted to single bonds. A catalyst such as platinum (Pt), nickel (Ni), or palladium (Pd) is used to speed up the reaction. The general equation for hydrogenation of an alkene can be written as follows:

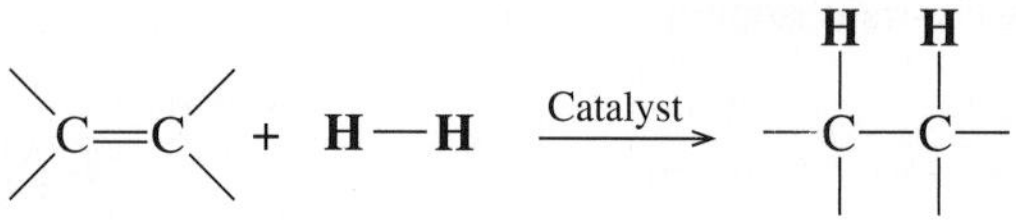

Some examples of the hydrogenation of alkenes follow:

$$CH_3-CH=CH-CH_3 + H-H \xrightarrow{Pt} CH_3-\overset{\overset{\displaystyle H}{|}}{C}H-\overset{\overset{\displaystyle H}{|}}{C}H-CH_3$$

2-Butene   Butane

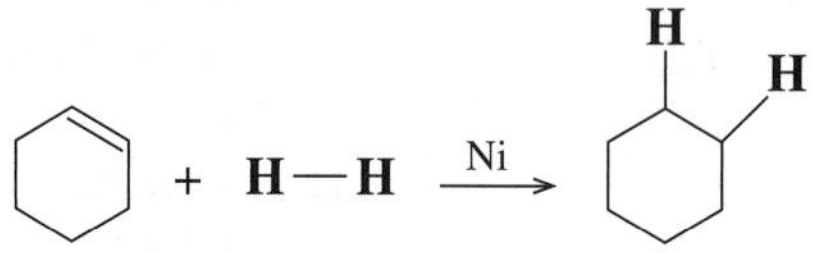

The complete hydrogenation of alkynes requires two molecules of hydrogen ($2H_2$) to form the alkane product:

$$CH_3-C\equiv C-CH_3 + 2\ H-H \xrightarrow{Pt} CH_3-\overset{\overset{\displaystyle H}{|}}{\underset{\underset{\displaystyle H}{|}}{C}}-\overset{\overset{\displaystyle H}{|}}{\underset{\underset{\displaystyle H}{|}}{C}}-CH_3$$

2-Butyne   Butane

EXPLORE YOUR WORLD

Unsaturation in Fats and Oils

Read the labels on some containers of vegetable oils, margarine, peanut butter, and shortenings.

QUESTIONS

1. What terms on the label tell you that the compounds contain double bonds?
2. A label on a bottle of canola oil lists saturated, polyunsaturated, and monounsaturated fats. What do these terms tell you about the type of bonding in the fats?
3. A peanut butter label states that it contains partially hydrogenated vegetable oils or completely hydrogenated vegetable oils. What does this tell you about the type of reaction that took place in preparing the peanut butter?

SAMPLE PROBLEM 12.3

■ **Writing Equations for Hydrogenation**

Write the condensed structural formula for the product of the following hydrogenation reactions:

a. $CH_3-CH=CH_2 + H_2 \xrightarrow{Pt} ?$ b. 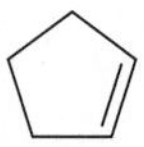 ⬠ + $H_2 \xrightarrow{Pt} ?$ c. $HC\equiv CH + 2H_2 \xrightarrow{Ni} ?$

SOLUTION

In an addition reaction, hydrogen adds to the double or triple bond to give an alkane.

a. $CH_3-CH_2-CH_3$ **b.** ⬠   **c.** CH_3-CH_3

STUDY CHECK

Draw the condensed structural formula of the product of the hydrogenation of 2-methyl-1-butene using a platinum catalyst.

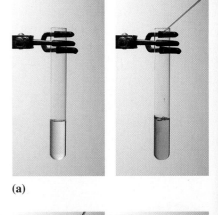

(a)

Halogenation

In the **halogenation** reactions of alkenes or alkynes, halogen atoms such as chlorine or bromine are added to the double or triple bonds. The reaction occurs readily, without the use of any catalyst, and adds halogen atoms to yield a di- or tetrahaloalkane product. In the general equation for halogenation, the symbol X—X or X_2 is used for Cl_2 or Br_2:

$$\underset{}{\overset{}{C}}=\underset{}{\overset{}{C} + X-X \longrightarrow -\overset{\overset{X}{|}}{C}-\overset{\overset{X}{|}}{C}-}$$

Here are some examples of adding Cl_2 or Br_2 to alkenes:

$$CH_2=CH_2 + Cl-Cl \longrightarrow \overset{\overset{Cl}{|}}{CH_2}-\overset{\overset{Cl}{|}}{CH_2}$$
Ethene   1,2-Dichloroethane

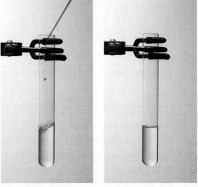

Cyclohexene   1,2-Dibromocyclohexane

$$CH_3-C\equiv C-H + 2Cl-Cl \longrightarrow CH_3-\overset{\overset{Cl}{|}}{\underset{\underset{Cl}{|}}{C}}-\overset{\overset{Cl}{|}}{\underset{\underset{Cl}{|}}{C}}-H$$
Propyne   1,1,2,2-Tetrachloropropane

The addition reaction of bromine is sometimes used to test for the presence of double and triple bonds, as shown in Figure 12.3.

(b)

FIGURE 12.3 (a) When bromine is added to an alkane in the first test tube, the red color of bromine remains because the alkane does not react or reacts slowly. **(b)** When bromine is added to an alkene in the second test tube, the red color immediately disappears as bromine atoms add to the double bond.

Q Will the red color disappear when bromine is added to cyclohexane or cyclohexene?

SAMPLE PROBLEM 12.4

■ Writing Products of Halogenation

Write the condensed structural formula of the product of the following reaction:

$$CH_3-\overset{\overset{CH_3}{|}}{C}=CH_2 + Br_2 \longrightarrow$$

SOLUTION

The addition of bromine to an alkene places a bromine atom on each of the carbon atoms of the double bond.

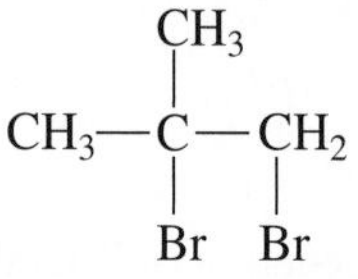

$$CH_3-\underset{\underset{Br}{|}}{\overset{\overset{CH_3}{|}}{C}}-\underset{\underset{Br}{|}}{CH_2}$$

STUDY CHECK

What is the name of the product formed when chlorine is added to 1-butene?

HEALTH NOTE

Hydrogenation of Unsaturated Fats

Vegetable oils such as corn oil or safflower oil are unsaturated fats composed of fatty acids that contain double bonds. The process of hydrogenation is used commercially to convert the double bonds in the unsaturated fats in vegetable oils to saturated fats such as margarine, which are more solid. Adjusting the amount of added hydrogen produces partially hydrogenated fats such as soft margarine, solid margarine in sticks, and shortenings, which are used in cooking. For example, oleic acid is a typical unsaturated fatty acid in olive oil and has a cis double bond at carbon 9. When oleic acid is hydrogenated, it is converted to stearic acid, a saturated fatty acid:

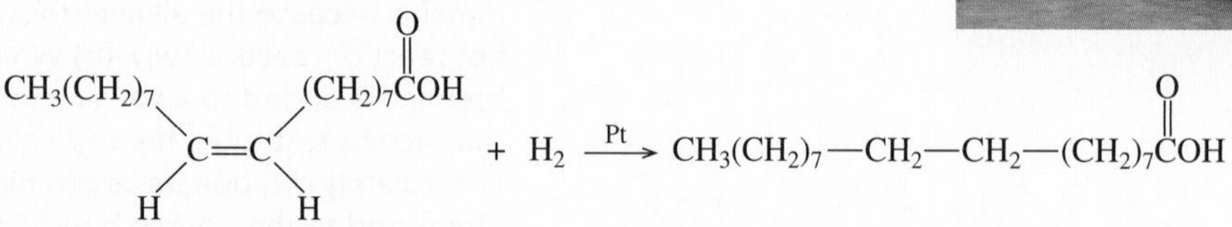

$$CH_3(CH_2)_7 \overset{(CH_2)_7COH}{\underset{H}{\overset{O}{\underset{}{C}}}}=\underset{H}{C} \quad + \quad H_2 \xrightarrow{Pt} CH_3(CH_2)_7-CH_2-CH_2-(CH_2)_7\overset{O}{\overset{\|}{C}}OH$$

Oleic acid (the cis isomer
is found in olive oil and other
unsaturated fats)

Stearic acid (found in
saturated fats)

Hydrohalogenation

In the reaction called **hydrohalogenation**, a hydrogen halide (HCl, HBr, or HI) adds to an alkene to yield a haloalkane. The hydrogen atom bonds to one carbon of the double bond, and the halogen atom adds to the other carbon. The general reaction, in which HX represents HCl, HBr, or HI, can be written as follows:

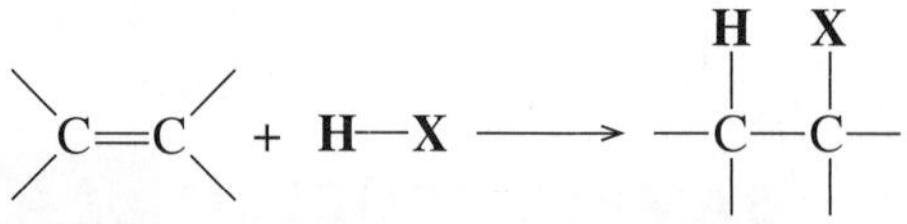

$$\overset{}{\underset{}{C}}=\overset{}{\underset{}{C} \quad + \quad H-X \quad \longrightarrow \quad -\overset{\overset{H}{|}}{C}-\overset{\overset{X}{|}}{C}-}$$

Alkene   Haloalkane (alkyl halide)

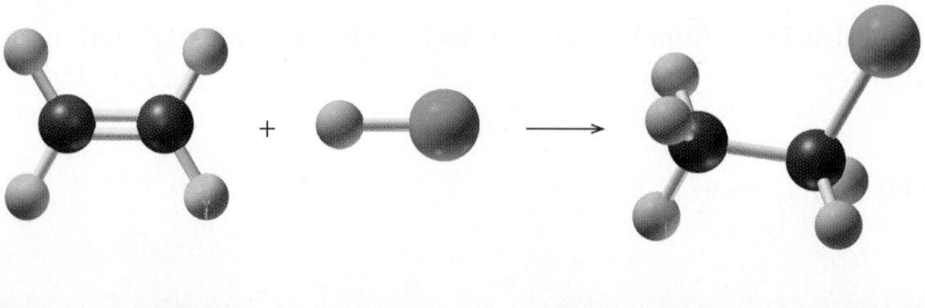

Two examples of hydrohalogenation follow:

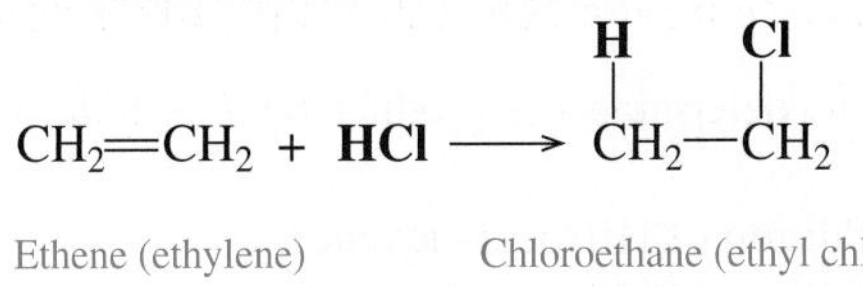

$$CH_2\!=\!CH_2 + HCl \longrightarrow \overset{\overset{\textstyle H}{|}}{C}H_2\!-\!\overset{\overset{\textstyle Cl}{|}}{C}H_2$$

Ethene (ethylene)   Chloroethane (ethyl chloride)

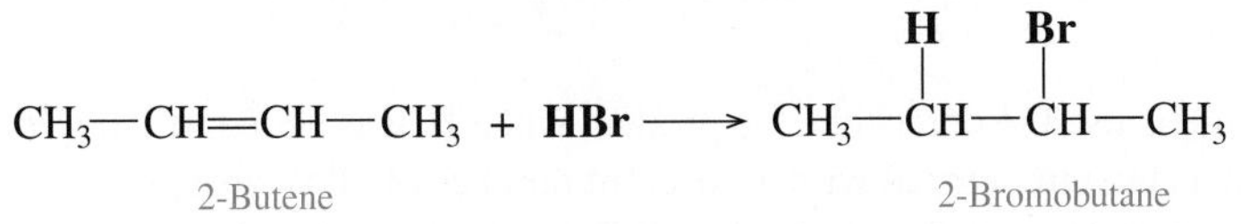

$$CH_3\!-\!CH\!=\!CH\!-\!CH_3 + HBr \longrightarrow CH_3\!-\!\overset{\overset{\textstyle H}{|}}{C}H\!-\!\overset{\overset{\textstyle Br}{|}}{C}H\!-\!CH_3$$

2-Butene   2-Bromobutane

Steps in Addition Reactions of H—X to Alkenes

We have seen that in the addition reaction of an alkene, two groups add to the carbons in the double bond to give a saturated compound. To understand how the addition of H—X or H—OH takes place, we can consider the two steps involved when HBr adds to ethene. First, a pair of electrons in the double bond reacts with a proton (H^+) from the HBr, which is shown by a curved arrow. This reaction produces a **carbocation** (a carbon cation) with a positive charge. In the second step, a pair of electrons from the bromide ion Br^- reacts rapidly with the carbocation.

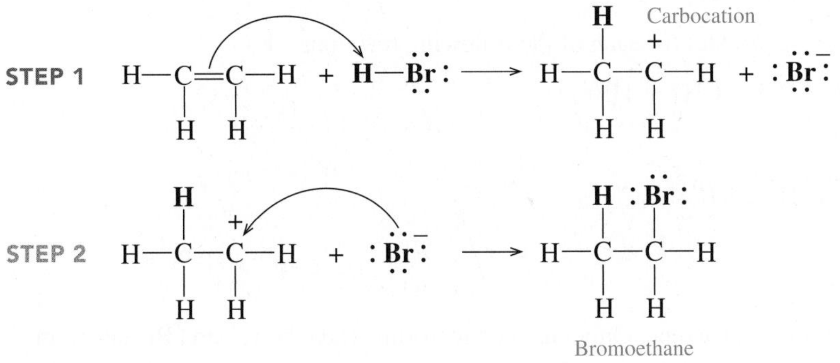

STEP 1

STEP 2

Bromoethane

Markovnikov's Rule

When HBr adds to a symmetrical alkene, a single product is formed. However, when HBr adds to a double bond in an unsymmetrical alkene, two products are possible. In 1870, Vladimir Markovnikov, a Russian chemist, observed that when HX adds to a double bond, the H attaches to the carbon that has more hydrogen atoms, and the X attaches to the carbon that has fewer hydrogen atoms. This observation is now called **Markovnikov's rule**.

When an unsymmetrical alkene forms a carbocation, the more stable form is the one where the C^+ is attached to the most alkyl groups. Therefore, in the initial step, the H^+ adds to the carbon that has fewer alkyl groups, which is the carbon in the double bond that has the greater number of hydrogen atoms.

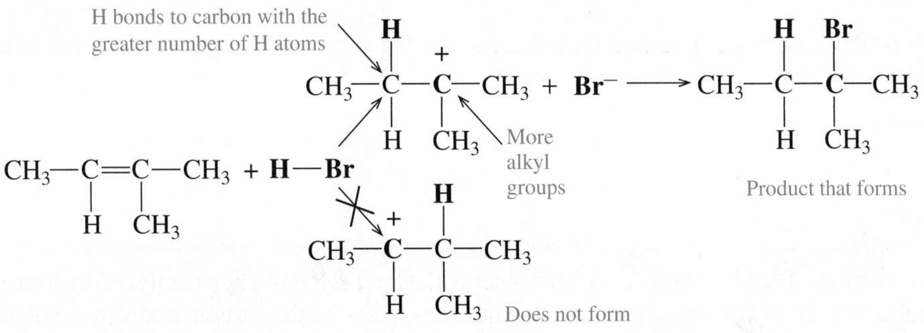

■ Markovnikov's Rule

a. Why would you use Markovnikov's rule to determine the product for the addition of HBr to 1-hexene but not to 3-hexene?

b. What is the name of the product for the addition of HBr to 1-hexene?

c. What is the name of the product for the addition of HBr to 3-hexene?

ANSWER

a. Markovnikov's rule is used to determine the product when HBr is added to 1-hexene because 1-hexene is unsymmetrical with a different number of alkyl groups attached to the carbon atoms in the double bond. Thus, the product is formed from the carbocation that has more alkyl groups attached. Markovnikov's rule is not needed when HBr is added to 3-hexene, because 3-hexene is symmetrical.

b. The H of HBr adds to carbon 1, which has more hydrogen atoms, and the Br adds to carbon 2 to form 2-bromohexane.

c. Since 3-hexene is symmetrical, addition of HBr gives 3-bromohexane.

CAREER FOCUS

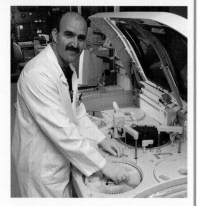

Laboratory Technologist

"We use serum or plasma specimens, which are collected in tubes, spun down, and separated," says Fariborz Azarchehr, laboratory technologist. "I place the specimens in an analyzer, which adds reagents that react chemically with various components in the blood. Their products are then measured using spectrophotometry. We use the test results to determine normal, elevated, or decreased values of compounds that circulate in the blood including electrolytes such as sodium, or potassium. I also test for high cholesterol and triglycerides. Doctors want to know about any abnormal results."

Laboratory technologists analyze the components of body fluids for abnormal levels using automated machines that perform several tests simultaneously. The results are analyzed and passed on to doctors.

■ Addition to Alkenes

Predict the organic product for each of the following reactions:

a. $CH_3-CH=CH-CH_3$ + HBr ⟶

b.

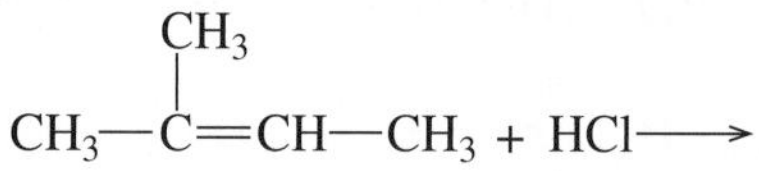

$$CH_3-\overset{\overset{\displaystyle CH_3}{|}}{C}=CH-CH_3 + HCl⟶$$

SOLUTION

a. This is a symmetrical alkene. Only one product forms when the H^+ and Br^- add to the carbons of the double bond:

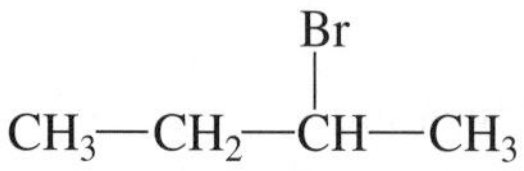

$$CH_3-CH_2-\overset{\overset{\displaystyle Br}{|}}{CH}-CH_3$$

b. In the double bond of this unsymmetrical alkene, carbon 3 has the greater number of hydrogen atoms. Using Markovnikov's rule, the H from HCl adds to carbon 3 and the Cl adds to carbon 2. The product is the most substituted alkyl halide.

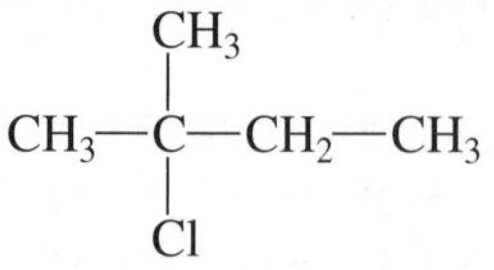

$$CH_3-\overset{\overset{\displaystyle CH_3}{|}}{\underset{\underset{\displaystyle Cl}{|}}{C}}-CH_2-CH_3$$

STUDY CHECK

Draw the condensed structural formula and give the name of the organic product obtained when HBr adds to 1-methylcyclopentene.

Hydration

In a reaction called **hydration**, alkenes react with water (HOH) when catalyzed by a strong acid such as H_2SO_4. In this reaction, H— attaches to one of the carbon atoms in the double bond, and —OH attaches to the other carbon. Hydration is used to prepare alcohols, which have the functional group —OH. In the general equation, water is written H—OH, and the acid is represented by H^+:

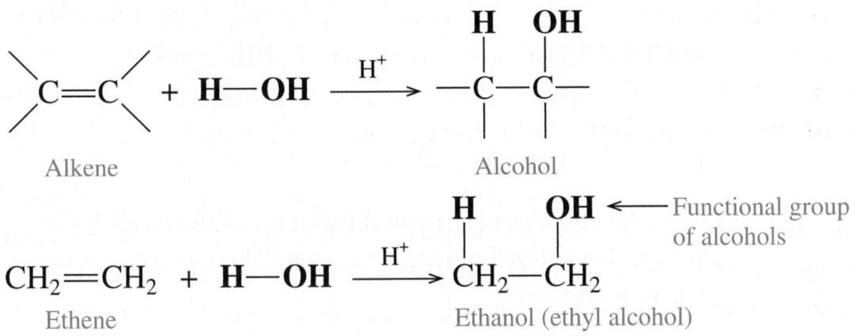

Alkene   Alcohol

$$CH_2=CH_2 + H-OH \xrightarrow{H^+} CH_2-CH_2$$

Ethene   Ethanol (ethyl alcohol)

The addition of water to a double bond in an unsymmetrical alkene follows Markovnikov's rule: the H— from HOH attaches to the carbon that already has more H atoms:

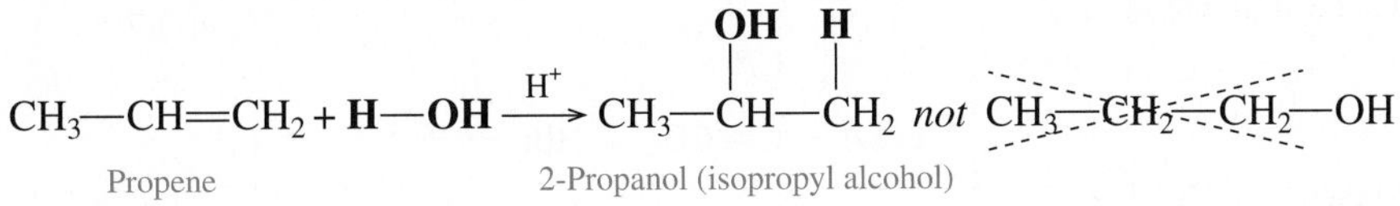

$$CH_3-CH=CH_2 + H-OH \xrightarrow{H^+} CH_3-CH-CH_2 \; not \; CH_3-CH_2-CH_2-OH$$

Propene   2-Propanol (isopropyl alcohol)

SAMPLE PROBLEM 12.6

■ Writing Products of Hydration

Write the condensed structural formulas for the products that form in the following hydration reactions:

a. $CH_3-CH_2-CH_2-CH=CH_2 + HOH \xrightarrow{H^+}$

b.  ☐ + $HOH \xrightarrow{H^+}$

SOLUTION

a. The H— and —OH from water (HOH) add to the carbon atoms in the double bond. Using Markovnikov's rule, the H— adds to the CH_2, which has more H atoms, and the —OH groups attaches to the CH:

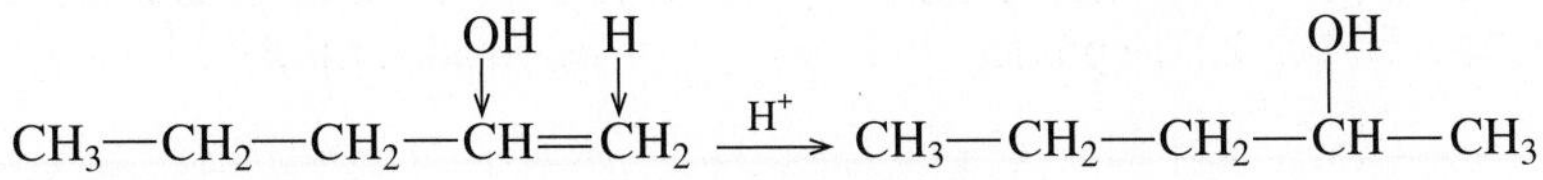

$$CH_3-CH_2-CH_2-CH=CH_2 \xrightarrow{H^+} CH_3-CH_2-CH_2-CH-CH_3$$

b. In cyclobutene, each carbon atom in the double bond has one H. The H— from water adds to one carbon in the double bond, and the —OH group adds to the other carbon. It is not necessary to use Markovnikov's rule, because cyclobutene is symmetrical:

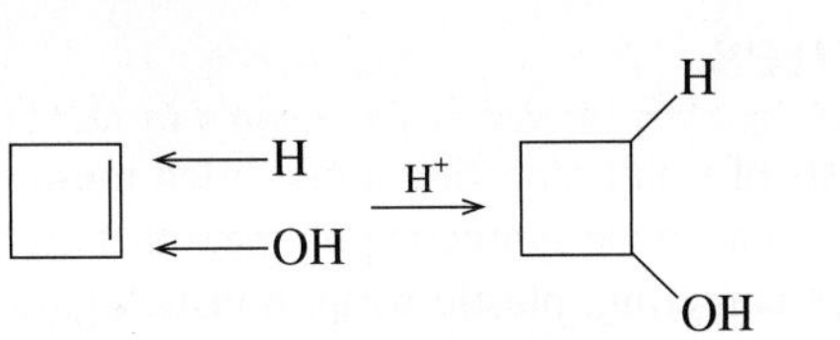

STUDY CHECK

Draw the condensed structural formula for the alcohol obtained by the hydration of 2-methyl-2-butene.

QUESTIONS AND PROBLEMS

Addition Reactions

12.13 Give the condensed structural formula and name of the products in each of the following reactions:

a. $CH_3-CH_2-CH_2-CH=CH_2 + H_2 \xrightarrow{Pt}$

b.
$$
\begin{array}{c}
CH_3 \\
|
\end{array}
$$
$CH_2=C-CH_2-CH_3 + Cl_2 \longrightarrow$

c. 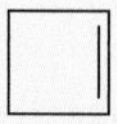 ☐ + Br₂ ⟶   **d.** cyclopentene + H₂ $\xrightarrow{Pt}$

e. 2-methyl-2-butene + Cl₂ ⟶

f. 2-pentyne + 2H₂ $\xrightarrow{Pd}$

12.14 Give the condensed structural formula and name of the products in each of the following reactions:

a. $CH_3-CH_2-CH=CH_2 + Br_2 \longrightarrow$

b. cyclohexene + H₂ $\xrightarrow{Pt}$ **c.** *cis*-2-butene + H₂ $\xrightarrow{Pt}$

d.
$$
\begin{array}{c}
CH_3 \\
|
\end{array}
$$
$CH_3-C=CH-CH_2-CH_3 + Cl_2 \longrightarrow$

e. 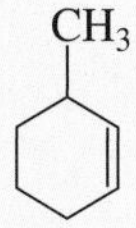 [cyclohexene with CH₃ group] + Br₂ ⟶

f.
$$
\begin{array}{c}
CH_3 \\
|
\end{array}
$$
$CH_3-CH-C\equiv CH + 2Cl_2 \longrightarrow$

12.15 Give the condensed structural formulas of the products in each of the following reactions, using Markovnikov's rule when necessary:

a. $CH_3-CH=CH-CH_3 + HBr \longrightarrow$

b. cyclopentene + HOH $\xrightarrow{H^+}$

c. $CH_2=CH-CH_2-CH_3 + HCl \longrightarrow$

d.
$$
\begin{array}{c}
CH_3 \\
|
\end{array}
$$
$CH_3-C=C-CH_3 + HI \longrightarrow$
$$
\begin{array}{c}
| \\
CH_3
\end{array}
$$

e.
$$
\begin{array}{c}
CH_3 \\
|
\end{array}
$$
$CH_3-CH_2-C=CH-CH_3 + HBr \longrightarrow$

f. 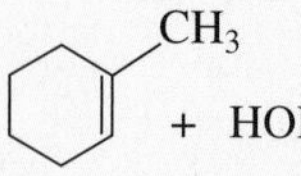 [cyclohexene with CH₃ group] + HOH $\xrightarrow{H^+}$

12.16 Give the condensed structural formulas of the products in each of the following reactions, using Markovnikov's rule when necessary:

a.
$$
\begin{array}{c}
CH_3 \\
|
\end{array}
$$
$CH_3-C=CH-CH_3 + HCl \longrightarrow$

b. $CH_3-CH_2-CH=CH-CH_2-CH_3 + HOH \xrightarrow{H^+}$

c.
$$
\begin{array}{c}
CH_3 \\
|
\end{array}
$$
$CH_3-C=CH_2 + HBr \longrightarrow$

d. 4-methylcyclopentene + HOH $\xrightarrow{H^+}$

e. 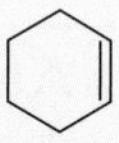 [cyclohexene] + HBr ⟶

f. $CH_3-C\equiv C-CH_3 + 2HCl \longrightarrow$

12.17 Write an equation, including any catalysts, for each of the following reactions:
  a. hydrogenation of methylpropene
  b. addition of hydrogen chloride to cyclopentene
  c. addition of bromine to 2-pentene
  d. hydration of propene
  e. addition of chlorine to 2-butyne

12.18 Write an equation, including any catalysts, for each of the following reactions:
  a. hydration of 1-methylcyclobutene
  b. hydrogenation of 3-hexene
  c. addition of hydrogen bromide to 2-methyl-2-butene
  d. addition of chlorine to 2,3-dimethyl-2-pentene
  e. addition of HCl to 1-methylcyclopentene

12.4 Polymers of Alkenes

LEARNING GOAL

Draw condensed structural formulas of monomers that form a polymer or a three-monomer section of a polymer.

A **polymer** is a large molecule that consists of small repeating units called **monomers**. In the past hundred years, the plastics industry has made synthetic polymers that are in many of the materials we use every day, such as carpeting, plastic wrap, nonstick pans, plastic cups, and rain gear. In medicine, synthetic polymers are used to replace diseased or damaged body parts such as hip joints, teeth, heart valves, and blood vessels. (See Figure 12.4.) There are about 100 billion kg of plastics now produced every year, which is over 15 kg for every person on Earth.

Many of the synthetic polymers are made by addition reactions of monomers that are small alkenes. Many polymerization reactions require high temperature and high pressure.

SELF STUDY ACTIVITY
Polymers

In polymerization, addition reactions join one monomer to the next to form a long carbon chain that contains as many as 1000 monomers. Polyethylene, a polymer made from ethylene monomers, is used in plastic bottles, film, and plastic dinnerware. More polyethylene is produced worldwide than any other polymer.

FIGURE 12.4 Synthetic polymers are used to replace diseased veins and arteries.

Q Why are the substances in these plastic devices called polymers?

Ethene (ethylene) monomers → Polyethylene section

Monomer unit repeats

Table 12.3 lists several alkene monomers that are used to produce common synthetic polymers, and Figure 12.5 shows examples of each. The alkane-like nature of these plastic synthetic polymers makes them unreactive. Thus, they do not decompose easily (they are nonbiodegradable). As a result, they have become significant contributors to pollution. Efforts are being made to make them more degradable.

TABLE 12.3 Some Alkenes and Their Polymers

Monomer	Polymer Section	Common Uses
$CH_2{=}CH_2$ Ethene (ethylene)	Polyethylene	Plastic bottles, film, insulation materials
$CH_2{=}CH$ — Cl Chloroethene (vinyl chloride)	Polyvinyl chloride (PVC)	Plastic pipes and tubing, garden hoses, garbage bags
$CH_2{=}CH$ — CH_3 Propene (propylene)	Polypropylene	Ski and hiking clothing, carpets, artificial joints
F—C=C—F Tetrafluoroethene	Polytetrafluoroethylene (Teflon®)	Nonstick coatings
$CH_2{=}C$—Cl 1,1-Dichloroethene	Polydichloroethylene (Saran™)	Plastic film and wrap
$H_2C{=}CH$ Phenylethene (styrene)	Polystyrene	Plastic coffee cups and cartons, insulation

TUTORIAL
Polymers

EXPLORE YOUR WORLD

Polymers and Recycling Plastics

1. Make a list of the items you use or have in your room or home that are made of polymers.
2. Recycling information on the bottom or side of a plastic bottle includes a triangle with a code number that identifies the type of polymer used to make the plastic. Make a collection of several different kinds of plastic bottles. Try to find plastic items with each type of polymer.

QUESTIONS

1. What are the most common types of plastics among the plastic containers in your collection?
2. What are the monomer units of some of the plastics you looked at?

Polyethylene

Polyvinyl chloride

Polypropylene

Polytetrafluoroethylene (Teflon®)

Polydichloroethylene (Saran™)

Polystyrene

FIGURE 12.5 Synthetic polymers provide a wide variety of items that we use every day.
Q What are some alkenes used to make the polymers in these plastic items?

You can identify the type of polymer used to manufacture a plastic item by looking for the recycle symbol (arrows in a triangle) found on the label or on the bottom of the plastic container. The number 5 or the letters PP inside the triangle is the code for a polypropylene plastic. It is important to recycle plastic material rather than add to our growing landfills.

1	2	3	4	5	6	7
PETE	HDPE	PVC	LDPE	PP	PS	O
Polyethylene terephthalate	High-density polyethylene	Polyvinyl chloride	Low-density polyethylene	Polypropylene	Polystyrene	Other

Today, many products such as lumber, tables and benches, trash receptacles, and pipes used for irrigation systems are made from recycled plastics.

SAMPLE PROBLEM 12.7

■ **Polymers**

What are the names and condensed structural formulas of the starting monomers for the following polymers?

a. polypropylene

b.

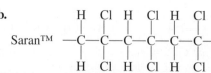

Saran™

SOLUTION

a. propene (propylene), $CH_2{=}\overset{\displaystyle CH_3}{\underset{\displaystyle |}{CH}}$ **b.** 1,1-dichloroethene, $CH_2{=}\overset{\displaystyle Cl}{\underset{\displaystyle |}{C}}{-}Cl$

STUDY CHECK

What is the name and condensed structural formula of the monomer for PVC?

QUESTIONS AND PROBLEMS

Polymers of Alkenes

12.19 What is a polymer?

12.20 What is a monomer?

12.21 Write an equation that represents the formation of a part of the Teflon polymer from three of the monomer units.

12.22 Write an equation that represents the formation of a part of the polystyrene polymer from three of the monomer units.

12.23 The plastic polyvinylidene difluoride, PVDF, is made from monomers of 1,1-difluoroethene. Write the structure of the polymer formed from the addition of three monomers of 1,1-difluoroethene.

12.24 An alkene called acrylonitrile is the monomer used to form the polymer used in the fabric material called Orlon. Write an equation that represents the formation of a part of the polyacrylonitrile polymer from three of the monomer units.

Acrylonitrile $CH_2{=}\overset{\displaystyle CN}{\underset{\displaystyle |}{CH}}$

12.5 Aromatic Compounds

In 1825, Michael Faraday isolated a hydrocarbon called *benzene*, which had the molecular formula C_6H_6. Because many compounds containing benzene had fragrant odors, the family of benzene compounds became known as **aromatic compounds**. A **benzene** molecule consists of a ring of six carbon atoms with one hydrogen atom attached to each carbon. Each carbon atom uses three valence electrons to bond to the hydrogen atom and two adjacent carbons. That leaves one valence electron to share in a double bond with an adjacent carbon. When first discovered, scientists expected benzene to be very reactive, like alkenes, but it was found to be much less reactive. It behaved more like an alkane. In 1865, August Kekulé proposed that the carbon atoms in benzene were arranged in a flat ring with alternating single and double bonds between the carbon atoms. This idea led to two ways of writing the benzene structure:

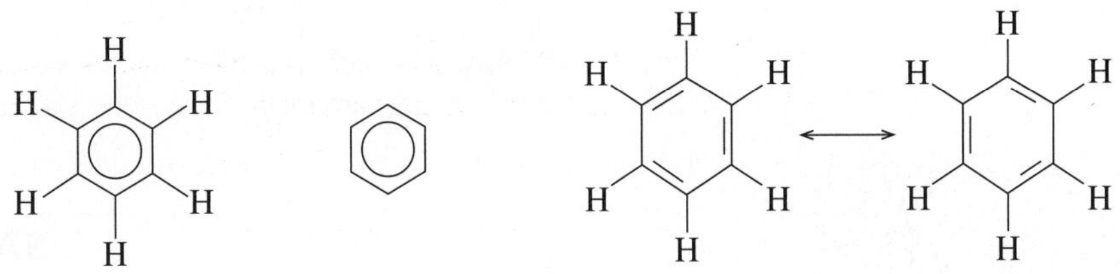

LEARNING GOAL

Describe the bonding in benzene. Name aromatic compounds and draw their structural formulas and the products formed by substitution reactions.

Structures for benzene

However, there is only one structure of benzene. Today we know that all the bonds in benzene are identical and that the electrons are shared equally. This unique feature makes aromatic compounds especially stable. Today, the benzene structure is represented as a hexagon with a circle in the center.

Naming Aromatic Compounds

Aromatic compounds that contain a benzene ring with a single substituent are usually named as benzene derivatives. However, many of these compounds have been important for many years and still use their common names. Names such as toluene, ethylbenzene, aniline, and phenol are allowed by IUPAC rules:

Toluene (methylbenzene)   Ethylbenzene   Aniline (benzenamine)   Phenol (hydroxybenzene)

When a benzene ring is a substituent, C_6H_5—, it is named as a phenyl group:

$$H_3C—CH—CH=CH_2$$

Phenyl group   3-Phenyl-1-butene

When there are two substituents, the benzene ring is numbered to give the lowest numbers to the substituents. When a common name, such as toluene, phenol, or aniline, can be used, the carbon atom attached to the methyl, hydroxyl, or amine group is numbered as carbon 1. The position of two substituents is often shown by prefixes. The prefix **ortho** (*o*) indicates a 1,2 arrangement, **meta** (*m*) is a 1,3 arrangement, and **para** (*p*) is used for 1,4 arrangements.

1,2-Dichlorobenzene   1,3-Dichlorobenzene   1,4-Dichlorobenzene
o-dichlorobenzene   *m*-dichlorobenzene   *p*-dichlorobenzene

The common name xylene is used for the isomers of dimethylbenzene:

1,2-Dimethylbenzene   1,3-Dimethylbenzene   1,4-Dimethylbenzene
o-xylene   *m*-xylene   *p*-xylene

When there are three or more substituents on the benzene ring, numbers are used to show their arrangement. The substituents are numbered to give the lowest numbers and named alphabetically:

1,3,5-Trichlorobenzene   4-Bromo-2-chlorotoluene   2,6-Dibromo-4-chlorotoluene

SAMPLE PROBLEM 12.8

MC™ TUTORIAL
Naming Aromatic Compounds

■ Naming Aromatic Compounds

Give IUPAC and any common name for each of the following aromatic compounds:

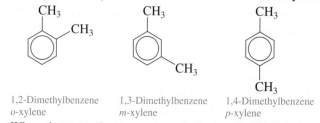

a. Cl   b. CH₃ Cl Br   c. CH₃ CH₃

SOLUTION

a. chlorobenzene
b. 4-bromo-3-chlorotoluene
c. 1,2-dimethylbenzene; *o*-xylene

STUDY CHECK

Name the following compound:

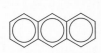

HEALTH NOTE

Polycyclic Aromatic Hydrocarbons (PAHs)

Large aromatic compounds known as polycyclic aromatic hydrocarbons are formed by fusing together two or more benzene rings edge to edge. In a fused-ring compound, neighboring benzene rings share two or more carbon atoms. Naphthalene, with two benzene rings, is known for its use in mothballs. Anthracene, with three rings, is used in the manufacture of dyes.

Benz[a]pyrene

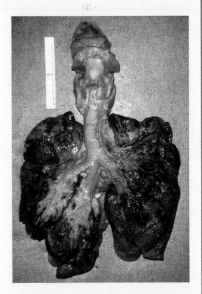

Naphthalene   Anthracene   Phenanthrene

When a polycyclic compound contains the three fused rings of phenanthrene, it may act as a carcinogen, a substance known to cause cancer. For example, some aromatic compounds in cigarette smoke cause cancer, as shown in the lung tissue of a heavy smoker. Benz[a]pyrene, a product of combustion, has been identified in coal tar, tobacco smoke, barbecued meats, and automobile exhaust.

Compounds containing five or more fused benzene rings such as benz[a]pyrene are potent carcinogens. The molecules interact with the DNA in the cells, causing abnormal cell growth and cancer. Increased exposure to carcinogens increases the chance of DNA alterations in the cells.

Properties of Aromatic Compounds

The symmetrical structure of benzene allows the cyclic structures to stack close together, which contributes to the higher melting points and boiling points of benzene and its derivatives. For example, hexane melts at −95 °C, while benzene melts at 6 °C. Among the disubstituted benzene compounds, the para isomers are more symmetric and have higher melting points than the ortho and meta isomers: *o*-xylene melts at −26 °C and *m*-xylene melts at −48 °C, while *p*-xylene melts at 13 °C.

Aromatic compounds are less dense than water, although they are somewhat denser than other hydrocarbons. Halogenated benzene compounds are denser than water. Aromatic hydrocarbons are insoluble in water and are used as solvents for other organic compounds. Only those containing strongly polar functional groups such as —OH or —COOH will be more soluble. Benzene and other aromatic compounds are resistant to reactions that break up the aromatic system, although they are flammable, as are other hydrocarbon compounds.

TUTORIAL
Substitution Reactions of
Aromatic Compounds

Chemical Properties

The most important type of reaction for benzene and aromatic compounds is **substitution**, in which an atom or group of atoms replaces a hydrogen atom on a benzene ring. A substitution reaction, rather than addition, retains the stability of the aromatic bonding system. Substitution reactions of benzene include halogenation, nitration, and sulfonation.

Halogenation

In the chlorination or bromination of benzene, a chlorine or bromine atom replaces a hydrogen atom on the benzene ring. A catalyst such as $FeCl_3$ is required for chlorination; $FeBr_3$ is a catalyst in bromination:

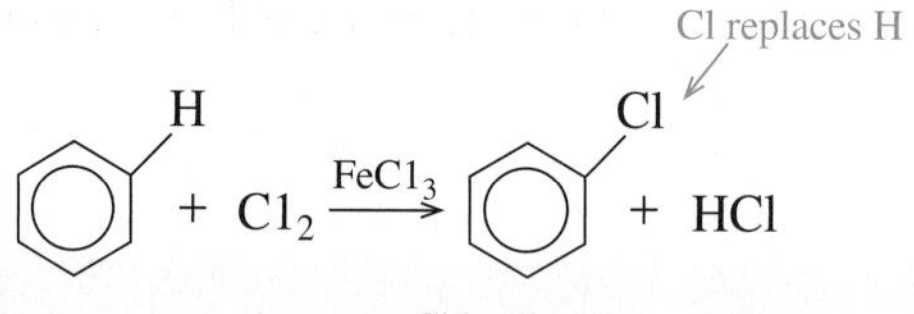

Chlorobenzene

When toluene (methylbenzene) undergoes halogenation, a mixture of isomers is obtained as products. However, the presence of a methyl group in toluene has the effect of producing mostly ortho and para isomers. In most substitution reactions of toluene, the meta isomer is produced in very small amounts:

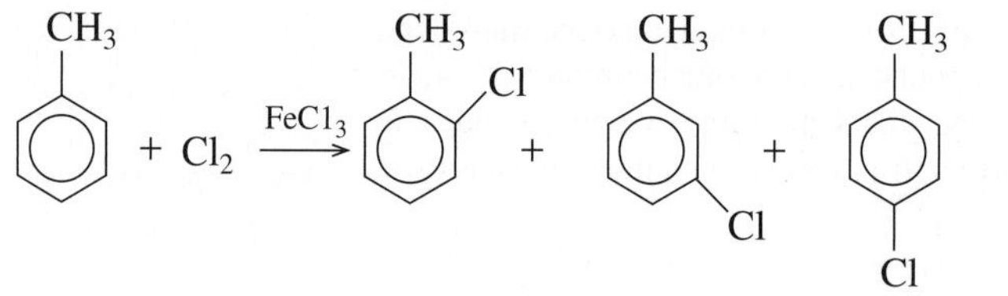

Toluene   o-Chlorotoluene   m-Chlorotoluene p-Chlorotoluene
                                    (very little)

Nitration

When benzene is heated with nitric acid, nitrobenzene is produced. Sulfuric acid (H_2SO_4) is required as a catalyst for the nitration:

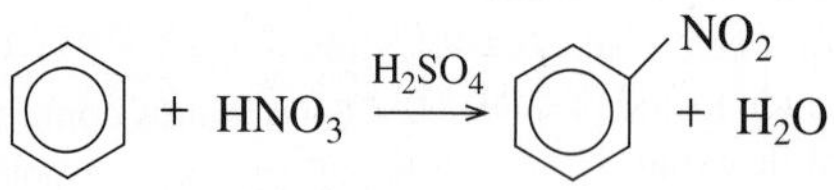

Nitrobenzene

Sulfonation

When benzene reacts with a mixture of $SO_3 + H_2SO_4$, known as "fuming sulfuric acid," the product is benzenesulfonic acid:

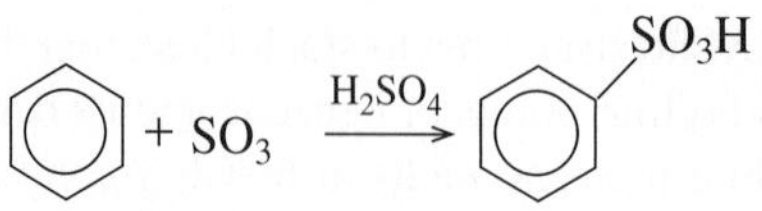

Benzenesulfonic acid

The sulfonation of aromatic compounds is one way to produce sulfa drugs:

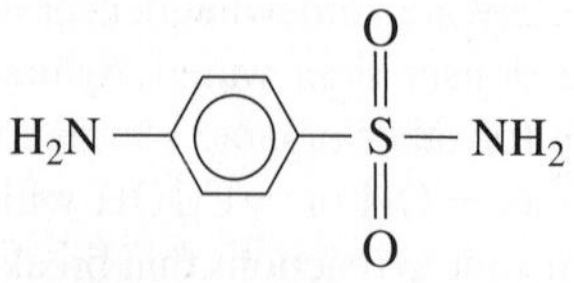

Sulfanilamide, a sulfa drug

CONCEPT CHECK 12.6

■ **Reactions of Aromatic Compounds**

Consider the reactions of cyclohexene and benzene with chlorine (Cl_2).

a. What is required (if anything) by each compound to react with Cl_2?
b. Identify the reaction for each compound as addition or substitution.
c. What is the name of the product of each reaction?

ANSWER

a. Cyclohexene reacts readily with Cl_2; no catalyst is needed. The reaction of benzene and Cl_2 requires a catalyst such as $FeCl_3$.
b. The reaction of Cl_2 with cyclohexene is an addition reaction, whereas the reaction of Cl_2 with benzene is a substitution.
c. The reaction of Cl_2 with cyclohexene forms 1,2-dichlorocyclohexane. The reaction of Cl_2 with benzene produces chlorobenzene.

SAMPLE PROBLEM 12.9

■ **Reactions of Benzene**

Write the structure of the organic product when benzene reacts with the following:

a. Br_2 and $FeBr_3$ **b.** HNO_3 and H_2SO_4

SOLUTION

a. 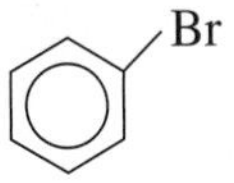   **b.**

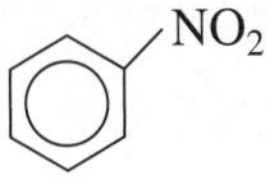

STUDY CHECK

A chemist needs to synthesize chlorobenzene. If benzene is available in the lab, how could she prepare this compound?

QUESTIONS AND PROBLEMS

Aromatic Compounds

12.25 Cyclohexane and benzene each have six carbon atoms. How are they different?

12.26 In the Health Note "Some Common Aromatic Compounds," what part of each molecule is the aromatic portion?

12.27 Give the IUPAC and any common name for each of the following:

a. 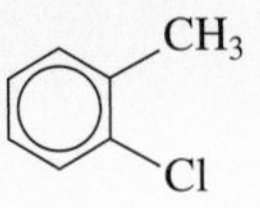   **b.** 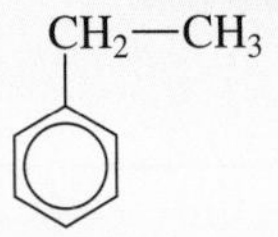 CH_2—CH_3 **c.**

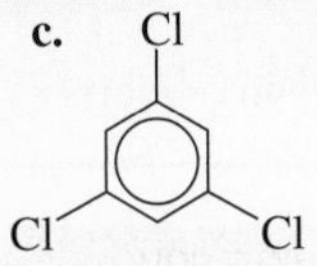

d. 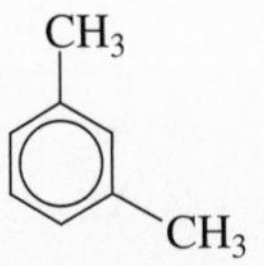 CH_3 **e.** 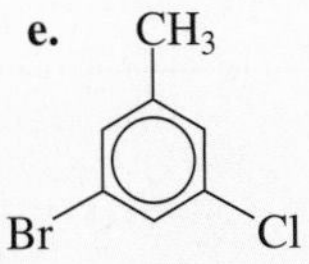 CH_3 **f.** 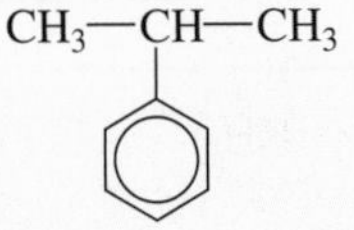 CH_3—CH—CH_3

12.28 Give the IUPAC and any common name for each of the following:

a.   **b.** CH_3 **c.** Cl

d. 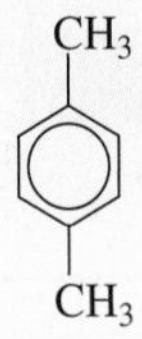 CH_3 **e.** 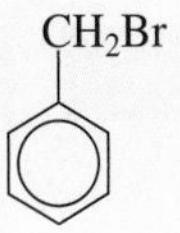 CH_2Br **f.** 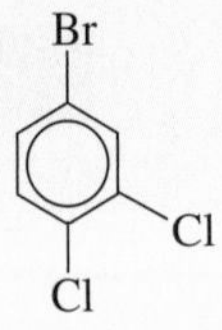 Br

12.29 Draw the condensed structural formula for each of the following compounds:
a. methylbenzene
b. 1-bromo-3-chlorobenzene
c. 1-ethyl-4-methylbenzene
d. *p*-chlorotoluene

12.30 Draw the condensed structural formula for each of the following compounds:
   a. benzene
   b. *o*-chloromethylbenzene
   c. propylbenzene
   d. 1,2,4-trichlorobenzene

12.31 Alkenes undergo addition reactions, but benzene does not. How does benzene react and why?

12.32 What is the product of the reaction of styrene with HCl? Explain.

$$CH{=}CH_2$$

Styrene

12.33 Draw the structures of the organic product(s), if any, for the following reactants:

   a. benzene + Cl_2 $\xrightarrow{FeCl_3}$

   b. benzene + HNO_3 $\xrightarrow{H_2SO_4}$

12.34 Draw the structures of the organic product(s), if any, for the following reactants:

   a. toluene + Br_2 $\xrightarrow{FeBr_3}$

   b. benzene + SO_3 $\xrightarrow{H_2SO_4}$

CONCEPT MAP

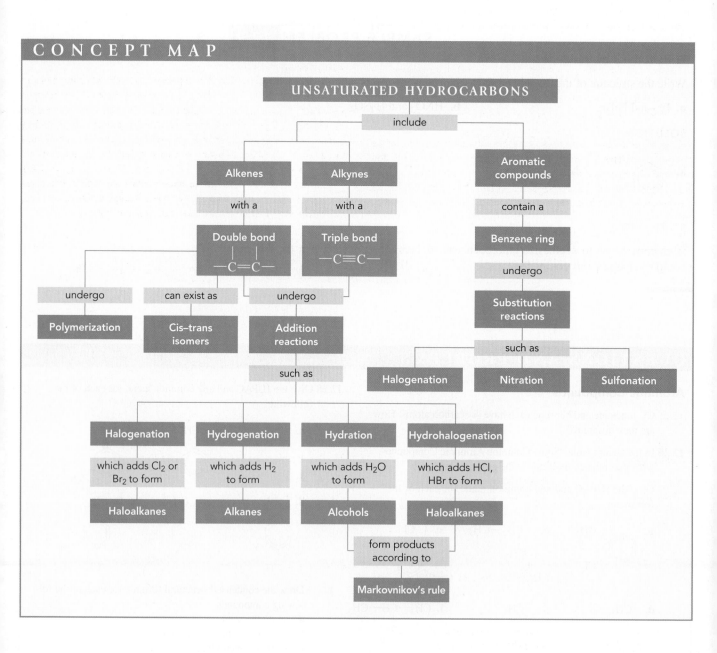

CHAPTER REVIEW

12.1 Alkenes and Alkynes

LEARNING GOAL: *Write the IUPAC names for alkenes and alkynes; give common names for simple structures.*

Alkenes are unsaturated hydrocarbons that contain carbon–carbon double bonds (C=C). Alkynes contain a triple bond (C≡C). The IUPAC names of alkenes end with *ene*, while alkyne names end with *yne*. The main chain is numbered from the end nearer the double or triple bond. In a cycloalkene, the double bond is carbon 1 and 2, and the ring is numbered to give the lower numbers to any substituents, which are named alphabetically.

12.2 Cis–Trans Isomers

LEARNING GOAL: *Write the condensed structural formulas and names for the cis-trans isomers of alkenes.*

Isomers of alkenes occur when the carbon atoms in the double bond are connected to different atoms or groups. In the cis isomer, alkyl groups or halogen atoms are on the same side of the double bond, whereas in the trans isomer, they are connected on opposite sides of the double bond.

12.3 Addition Reactions

LEARNING GOAL: *Write the condensed structural formulas and names for the organic products of addition reactions of alkenes and alkynes.*

The addition of small molecules to the double bond is a characteristic reaction of alkenes. Hydrogenation adds hydrogen atoms to the double bond of an alkene to yield an alkane. Halogenation adds bromine or chlorine atoms to produce dihaloalkanes. Hydrogen halides and water can also add to a double bond. When there are a different number of hydrogen atoms attached to the carbons in the double bond, Markovnikov's rule states that the H from the reactant (H—X or H—OH) adds to the carbon with the greater number of hydrogen atoms.

12.4 Polymers of Alkenes

LEARNING GOAL: *Draw condensed structural formulas of monomers that form a polymer or a three-monomer section of a polymer.*

Polymers are long-chain molecules that consist of many repeating units of smaller carbon molecules called monomers. In nature, cellulose and starch are polymers of glucose, and proteins are polymers of amino acids. Many materials that we use every day are synthetic polymers, including carpeting, plastic wrap, nonstick pans, and nylon. These synthetic materials are often made by addition reactions in which a catalyst links the carbon atoms from various kinds of alkene molecules.

12.5 Aromatic Compounds

LEARNING GOAL: *Describe the bonding in benzene. Name aromatic compounds and draw their structural formulas and the products formed by substitution reactions.*

Most aromatic compounds contain benzene, a cyclic structure containing six CH units. The structure of benzene is represented as a hexagon with a circle in the center. Aromatic compounds containing benzene are named using the parent name benzene, although common names such as toluene are retained. The benzene ring is numbered, and the substituents are listed in alphabetical order. For two substituents, the positions are often shown by the prefixes *ortho* (1,2-), *meta* (1,3-), and *para* (1,4-). Aromatic compounds undergo substitution reactions such as halogenation, nitration, and sulfonation. They do not undergo addition reactions, which would disrupt their stable aromatic bonding system.

SUMMARY OF NAMING

Type	Example	Characteristic	Structure
Alkene	Propene (propylene)	Double bond	$CH_3—CH=CH_2$
	cis-1,2-dibromoethene	Large groups on same side	
	trans-1,2-dibromoethene	Large groups on opposite sides	
Cycloalkene	Cyclopropene	Double bond in a carbon ring	
Alkyne	Propyne	Triple bond	$CH_3—C≡CH$
Aromatic	Benzene	Aromatic ring of six carbons	
	Methylbenzene or toluene		
	1,4-dichlorobenzene or *para*-dichlorobenzene		

SUMMARY OF REACTIONS

HYDROGENATION

$$CH_2=CH-CH_3 + H_2 \xrightarrow{Pt} CH_3-CH_2-CH_3$$

Propene   Propane

$$CH_3-C\equiv CH + 2H_2 \xrightarrow{Pt} CH_3-CH_2-CH_3$$

Propyne   Propane

HALOGENATION

$$CH_2=CH-CH_3 + Cl_2 \longrightarrow \underset{\underset{\text{1,2-Dichloropropane}}{}}{CH_2-CH-CH_3}$$

Propene

(Cl and Cl substituents on carbons)

SUBSTITUTION REACTIONS OF BENZENE

Halogenation (Cl_2 / $FeCl_3$ → Cl)

Nitration (HNO_3 / H_2SO_4 → NO_2)

Sulfonation (SO_3 / H_2SO_4 → SO_3H)

HYDROHALOGENATION

Markovnikov's rule

$$CH_2=CH-CH_3 + HCl \longrightarrow \underset{\underset{\text{2-Chloropropane}}{}}{CH_3-CH-CH_3}$$

Propene

(Cl substituent)

HYDRATION OF ALKENES

Markovnikov's rule

$$CH_2=CH-CH_3 + H-OH \xrightarrow{H^+} \underset{\underset{\text{2-Propanol}}{}}{CH_3-CH-CH_3}$$

Propene

(OH substituent)

KEY TERMS

addition A reaction in which atoms or groups of atoms bond to a double bond. Addition reactions include the addition of hydrogen (hydrogenation), halogens (halogenation), hydrogen halides (hydrohalogenation), and water (hydration).

alkene A hydrocarbon containing a carbon–carbon double bond.

alkyne A hydrocarbon containing a carbon–carbon triple bond.

aromatic compounds Compounds that usually have fragrant odors and often contain the ring structure of benzene.

benzene A ring of six carbon atoms each of which is attached to a hydrogen atom, C_6H_6.

carbocation A carbon cation that has only three bonds and a positive charge and is formed during the addition reactions of hydration and hydrohalogenation.

cis isomer An isomer of an alkene in which large groups are attached to the same side of the double bond.

cycloalkene A cyclic hydrocarbon that contains a double bond in the ring.

halogenation The addition of Cl_2 or Br_2 to an alkene or benzene to form halogen-containing compounds.

hydration An addition reaction in which the components of water, H— and —OH, bond to the carbon–carbon double bond to form an alcohol.

hydrogenation The addition of hydrogen (H_2) to the double bond of alkenes to yield alkanes.

hydrohalogenation The addition of a hydrogen halide such as HCl or HBr to a double bond.

Markovnikov's rule When adding HX or HOH to alkenes with different numbers of groups attached to the double bonds, the H— adds to the carbon that has the greater number of hydrogen atoms.

meta A method of naming that indicates substituents at carbons 1 and 3 of a benzene ring.

monomer The small organic molecule that is repeated many times in a polymer.

ortho A method of naming that indicates substituents at carbons 1 and 2 of a benzene ring.

para A method of naming that indicates substituents at carbons 1 and 4 of a benzene ring.

polymer A very large molecule that is composed of many small, repeating structural units that are identical.

substitution The reactions of benzene and other aromatic compounds in which an atom or group of atoms replaces a hydrogen on a benzene ring.

trans isomer An isomer of an alkene in which large groups are attached on opposite sides of the double bond.

UNDERSTANDING THE CONCEPTS

12.35 Draw a part of the polymer of Teflon using four monomers of 1,1,2,2-tetrafluoroethene.

12.36 A garden hose is made of polyvinylchloride (PVC) from chloroethene (vinyl chloride). Draw a part of the polymer (use four monomers) for PVC.

12.37 Explosives used in mining contain TNT or 2,4,6-trinitrotoluene.

a. If the functional group *nitro* is —NO₂, what is the structural formula of TNT?

b. TNT is actually a mixture of isomers of trinitrotoluene. Draw two possible isomers.

12.38 Margarine is produced from the hydrogenation of vegetable oils, which contain unsaturated fatty acids. How many grams of hydrogen are required to completely saturate 75.0 g oleic acid, $C_{18}H_{34}O_2$, which has one double bond?

ADDITIONAL QUESTIONS AND PROBLEMS

For instructor-assigned homework, go to www.masteringchemistry.com.

12.39 Compare the formulas and bonding in propane, cyclopropane, propene, and propyne.

12.40 Compare the formulas and bonding in butane, cyclobutane, cyclobutene, and 2-butyne.

12.41 Give the IUPAC name for each of the following compounds:

a.

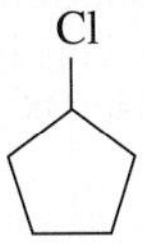

Cl

b.

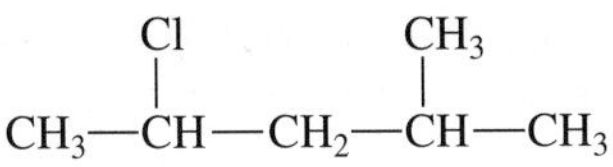

CH_3—CH—CH_2—CH—CH_3 with Cl on second carbon and CH₃ on fourth carbon

c.

CH_2=C—CH_2—CH_2—CH_3 with CH₃ branch

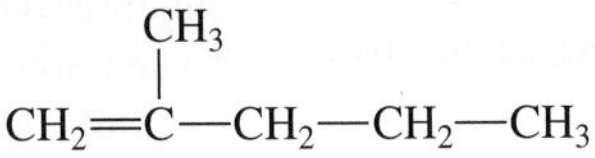

d. CH_3—CH_2—$C\equiv C$—CH_3

12.42 Give the IUPAC name for each of the following compounds:

a.

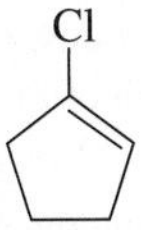

Cl

b.

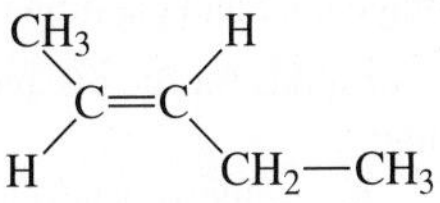

CH_3 and H on left carbon, H and CH_2—CH_3 arranged around C=C

c.

Cl and Cl on ring

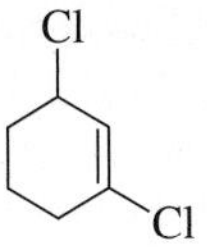

d. 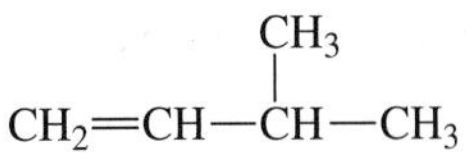 CH_2=CH—CH—CH_3 with CH_3 branch

12.43 Write the condensed structural formula of each of the following compounds:
a. 1,2-dibromocyclopentene
b. 2-pentyne $CH_3-C\equiv C-CH_2CH_3$
c. *cis*-2-heptene
d. 3-chloro-2-methyl-1-pentene

12.44 Write the condensed structural formula of each of the following compounds:
a. *trans*-3-hexene
b. 2-bromo-3-chlorocyclohexene
c. 2,3-dichloro-1-butene
d. 3-iodo-1-propyne

12.45 Indicate if the following pairs represent structural isomers, cis–trans isomers, or identical compounds:

a.

b.

12.46 Indicate if the following pairs represent structural isomers, cis–trans isomers, or identical compounds:

a. $CH_2{=}CH$ and $CH_3{-}CH_2{-}CH_2{-}CH{=}CH_2$
 with $CH_2{-}CH_2$ and CH_3 substituent

b.

12.47 Methylcyclopentane is formed by four different cycloalkenes that react with hydrogen (H_2) in the presence of a Ni catalyst. Draw the condensed structural formulas of each of these alkenes.

12.48 Draw the condensed structural formulas and give the names for all the isomers of C_4H_8 including cyclic and cis–trans isomers.

12.49 Write the condensed structural formulas for the cis and trans isomers for each of the following:
a. 2-pentene   b. 2-chloro-3-hexene

12.50 Write the condensed structural formulas for the cis and trans isomers for each of the following:
a. 2-butene   b. 2-hexene

12.51 Give the name of the product from complete hydrogenation of each of the following:
a. 3-methyl-2-pentene
b. cyclohexene
c. 2-pentyne

12.52 Give the name of the product from complete hydrogenation of each of the following:
a. 3-hexene
b. 2-methyl-2-butene
c. propyne

12.53 Write the condensed structural formulas of the products, if any, for the following:

a. $CH_3{-}CH{=}CH{-}CH_3 + HBr \longrightarrow$

b. $+ HBr \longrightarrow$

c. $CH_3{-}CH{=}CH{-}CH_3 + Cl_2 \longrightarrow$

12.54 Write the condensed structural formulas of the products, if any, for the following:

a. $CH_3{-}CH{=}CH{-}CH_3 + HOH \xrightarrow{H^+}$

b. $+ HOH \xrightarrow{H^+}$

c. $CH_3{-}\underset{\underset{CH_3}{|}}{\overset{\overset{CH_3}{|}}{C}}{=}C{-}CH_3 + HCl \longrightarrow$

12.55 What is the condensed structural formula of the organic compound needed to prepare each of the following products?

a. ? $+ H_2 \xrightarrow{Ni}$

b. ? $+ Br_2 \longrightarrow CH_3{-}\underset{\underset{Br}{|}}{CH}{-}\underset{\underset{Br}{|}}{CH}{-}CH_2{-}CH_3$

12.56 What is the condensed structural formula of the organic compound needed to prepare each of the following products?

a. ? $+ HCl \longrightarrow CH_3{-}\underset{\underset{Cl}{|}}{CH}{-}CH_3$

b. ? $+ HOH \xrightarrow{H^+}$

12.57 Copolymers contain more than one type of monomer. One copolymer used in medicine is made of alternating units of styrene and acrylonitrile. Write a section of the copolymer that would have three each of these alternating units. (For structure of styrene, see Table 12.3.)

$$H_2C{=}\underset{\underset{CH}{|}}{\overset{\overset{CN}{|}}{}}$$
Acrylonitrile

12.58 Lucite, or Plexiglas, is a polymer of methylmethacrylate. Write the part of the polymer that is made from the addition of three of these monomers.

$$CH_2{=}\underset{\underset{CH_3}{|}}{C}{-}\overset{\overset{O}{\|}}{C}{-}O{-}CH_3$$
Methylmethacrylate

12.59 Name the organic product(s) produced, if any, in each of the following reactions:

a. benzene and Cl_2 $\xrightarrow{FeCl_3}$

b. toluene and Br_2 $\xrightarrow{FeBr_3}$

c. benzene and SO_3 $\xrightarrow{H_2SO_4}$

d. benzene and Br_2 $\xrightarrow{light}$

12.60 Write the condensed structural formula for each of the following:
a. ethylbenzene
b. *m*-dichlorobenzene
c. 1,2,4-trimethylbenzene
d. 1,4-dimethylbenzene

12.61 Name each of the following aromatic compounds:

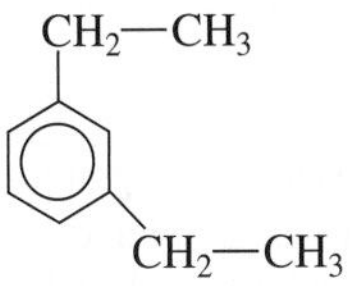

12.62 What reactants and catalysts are needed to synthesize the following products?
a. nitrobenzene   **b.** benzenesulfonic acid
c. bromobenzene

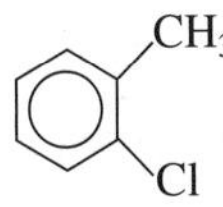

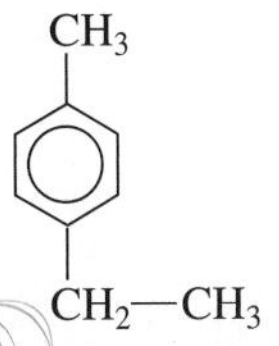

CHALLENGE QUESTIONS

12.63 If a female silkworm moth secretes 50 ng of bombykol, a sex attractant, how many molecules did she secrete? (See Environmental Note "Pheromones in Insect Communication.")

12.64 How many grams of hydrogen are needed to hydrogenate 30.0 g of 2-butene?

12.65 Using each of the following carbon chains for C_5H_{10}, write and name all the possible alkenes, including those with cis and trans isomers:

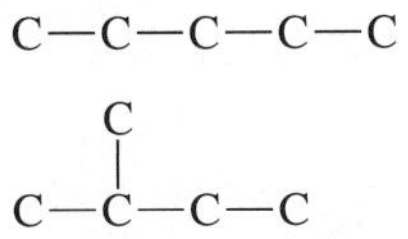

C—C—C—C—C

C—C—C—C with C on second carbon

12.66 Acetylene gas reacts with oxygen and burns at high temperature in an acetylene torch:
a. Write the balanced equation for the complete combustion of acetylene.
b. How many grams of oxygen are needed to react with 8.5 L of acetylene at STP?
c. How many liters of CO_2 (at STP) are produced when 30.0 g of acetylene undergoes combustion?

ANSWERS

ANSWERS TO STUDY CHECKS

12.1 **a.** $CH_3-C\equiv C-CH_2-CH_3$ **b.** 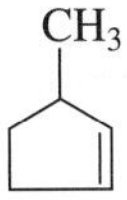 CH₃ methylcyclopentene structure

12.2 *trans*-3-heptene

12.3 $CH_3-\overset{\overset{\displaystyle CH_3}{|}}{CH}-CH_2-CH_3$

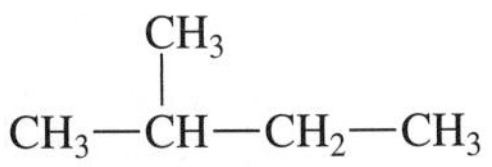

12.4 1,2-dichlorobutane

12.5 CH₃ Br 1-bromo-1-methylcyclopentane

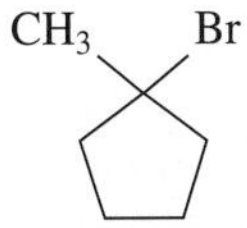

12.6 $CH_3-\overset{\overset{\displaystyle CH_3}{|}}{\underset{\underset{\displaystyle OH}{|}}{C}}-CH_2-CH_3$

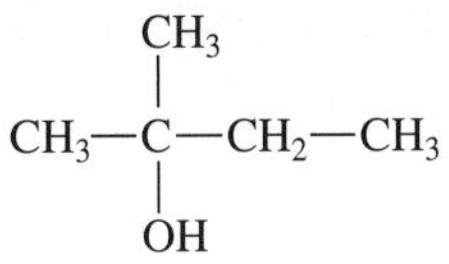

12.7 The monomer of PVC, polyvinyl chloride, is chloroethene:

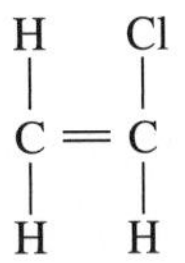

$$\underset{\displaystyle H}{\overset{\displaystyle H}{|}}C=\underset{\displaystyle H}{\overset{\displaystyle Cl}{|}}C$$

12.8 1,3-diethylbenzene; *m*-diethylbenzene

12.9   Chlorobenzene can be prepared from benzene and chlorine, using $FeCl_3$ as a catalyst.

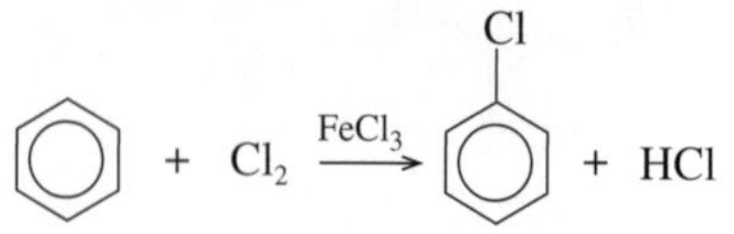

ANSWERS TO SELECTED QUESTIONS AND PROBLEMS

12.1   a. An alkene has a double bond.
   b. An alkyne has a triple bond.
   c. An alkene has a double bond.
   d. A cycloalkene has a double bond in a ring.

12.3   a. ethene
   b. 2-methylpropene
   c. 4-bromo-2-pentyne
   d. cyclobutene
   e. 4-ethylcyclopentene
   f. 4-ethyl-2-hexene

12.5   a. $CH_3-CH=CH_2$
   b. $CH_2=CH-CH_2-CH_2-CH_3$

   c. 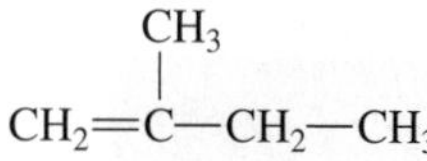 $CH_2=\overset{\overset{\displaystyle CH_3}{|}}{C}-CH_2-CH_3$ **d.**

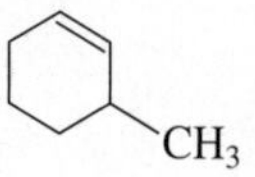

   e. 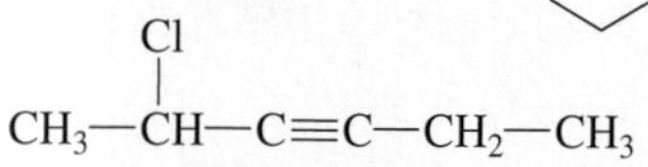 $CH_3-\overset{\overset{\displaystyle Cl}{|}}{CH}-C\equiv C-CH_2-CH_3$
   f. $H-C\equiv C-CH_2-CH_3$
   g. $Br-CH_2-CH_2-CH_2-CH=CH_2$

12.7   a. There are no cis–trans isomers.
   b. This alkene has cis–trans isomers.
   c. There are no cis–trans isomers.

12.9   a. *cis*-2-butene   **b.** *trans*-3-octene   **c.** *cis*-3-heptene

12.11 a.

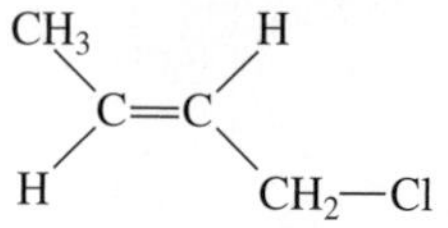

   b.

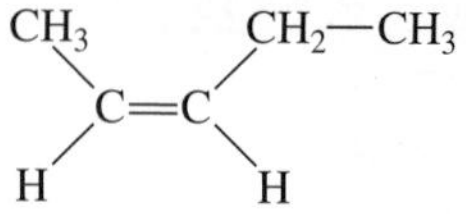

   c.

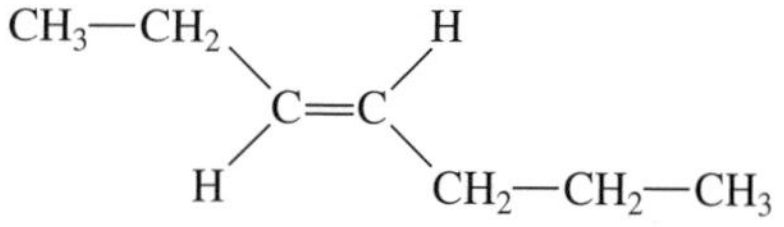

12.13 a. $CH_3-CH_2-CH_2-CH_2-CH_3$ Pentane

   b. 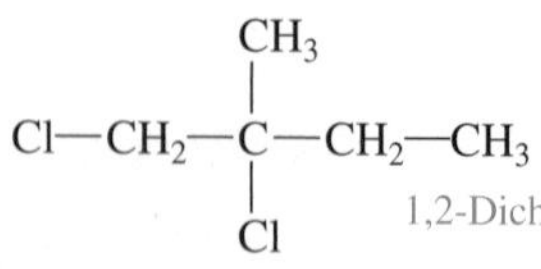 $Cl-CH_2-\overset{\overset{\displaystyle CH_3}{|}}{\underset{\underset{\displaystyle Cl}{|}}{C}}-CH_2-CH_3$ 1,2-Dichloro-2-methylbutane

   c. 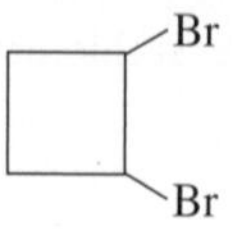 1,2-Dibromocyclobutane

   d. 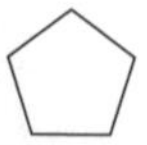 Cyclopentane

e. 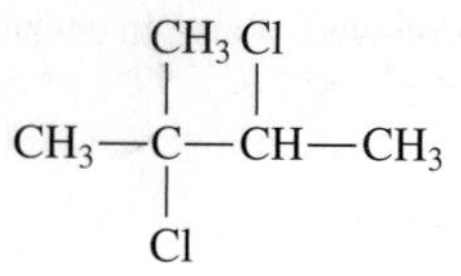 $CH_3-\overset{\overset{\displaystyle CH_3}{|}}{\underset{\underset{\displaystyle Cl}{|}}{C}}-\overset{\overset{\displaystyle Cl}{|}}{CH}-CH_3$ 2,3-Dichloro-2-methylbutane

f. $CH_3-CH_2-CH_2-CH_2-CH_3$ Pentane

12.15 a. 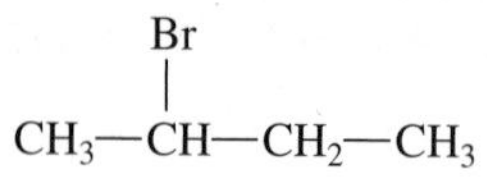 $CH_3-\overset{\overset{\displaystyle Br}{|}}{CH}-CH_2-CH_3$ **b.**

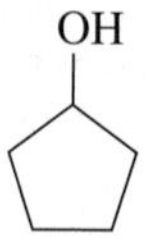

   c. 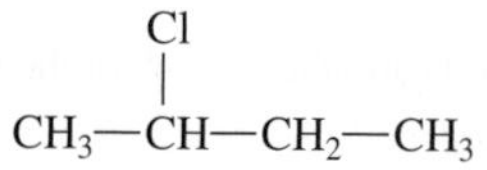 $CH_3-\overset{\overset{\displaystyle Cl}{|}}{CH}-CH_2-CH_3$ **d.** 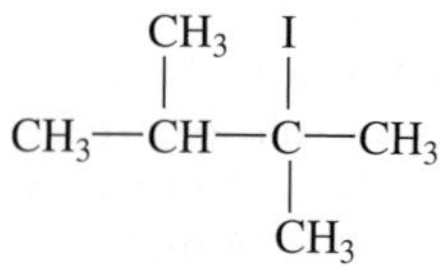 $CH_3-\overset{\overset{\displaystyle CH_3}{|}}{CH}-\overset{\overset{\displaystyle I}{|}}{\underset{\underset{\displaystyle CH_3}{|}}{C}}-CH_3$

   e. 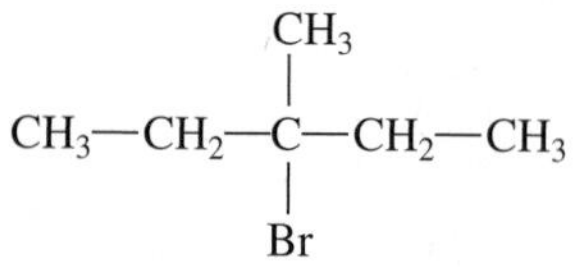 $CH_3-CH_2-\overset{\overset{\displaystyle CH_3}{|}}{\underset{\underset{\displaystyle Br}{|}}{C}}-CH_2-CH_3$

   f.

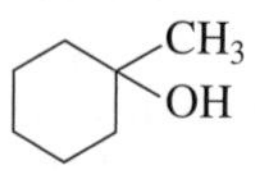

12.17
   a. 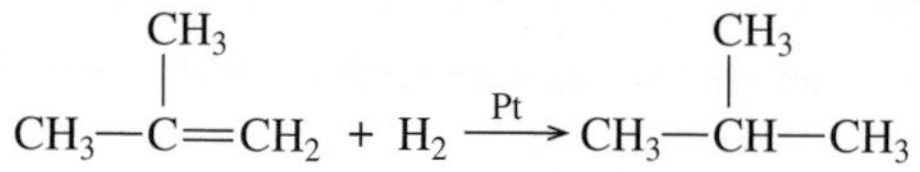 $CH_3-\overset{\overset{\displaystyle CH_3}{|}}{C}=CH_2 + H_2 \xrightarrow{Pt} CH_3-\overset{\overset{\displaystyle CH_3}{|}}{CH}-CH_3$

   b. + HCl ⟶

   c. $CH_3-CH=CH-CH_2-CH_3 + Br_2 \longrightarrow$
   $CH_3-\overset{\overset{\displaystyle Br}{|}}{CH}-\overset{\overset{\displaystyle Br}{|}}{CH}-CH_2-CH_3$

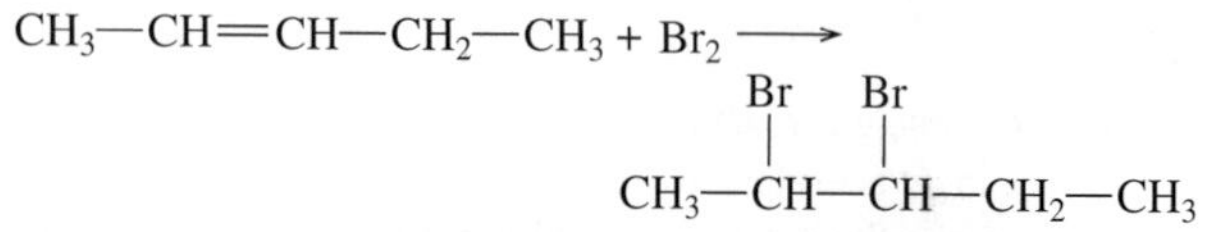

   d. 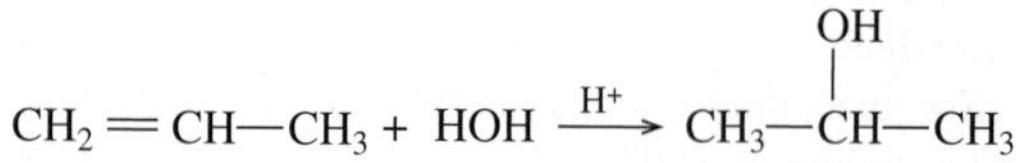 $CH_2=CH-CH_3 + HOH \xrightarrow{H^+} CH_3-\overset{\overset{\displaystyle OH}{|}}{CH}-CH_3$

   e. 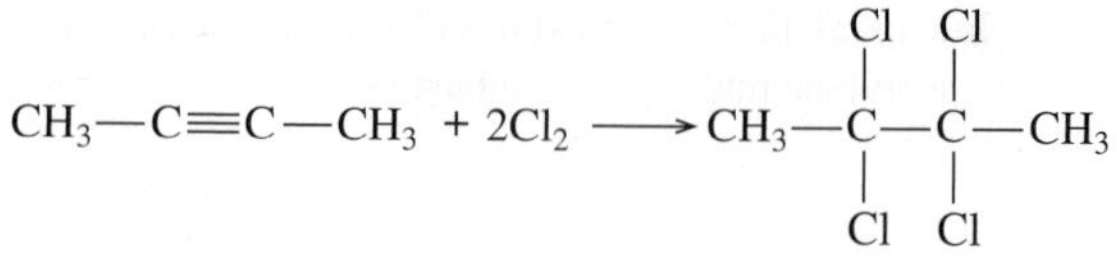 $CH_3-C\equiv C-CH_3 + 2Cl_2 \longrightarrow CH_3-\overset{\overset{\displaystyle Cl}{|}}{\underset{\underset{\displaystyle Cl}{|}}{C}}-\overset{\overset{\displaystyle Cl}{|}}{\underset{\underset{\displaystyle Cl}{|}}{C}}-CH_3$

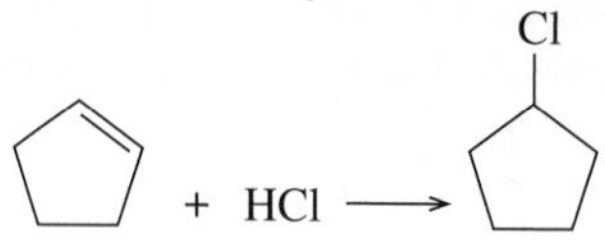

12.19 A polymer is a very large molecule composed of small units that are repeated many times.

12.21 $3F-C=C-F \longrightarrow$

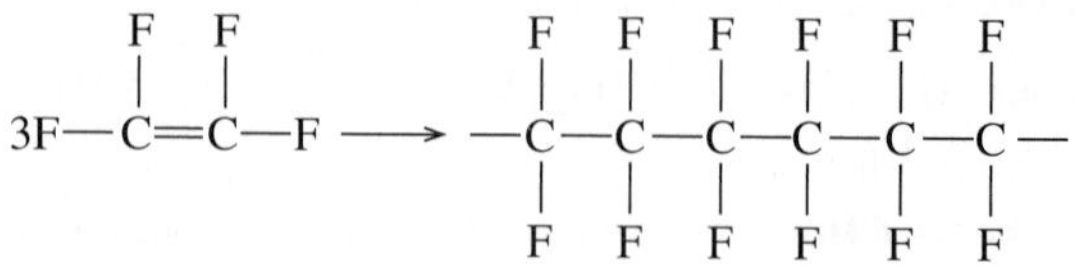

12.23

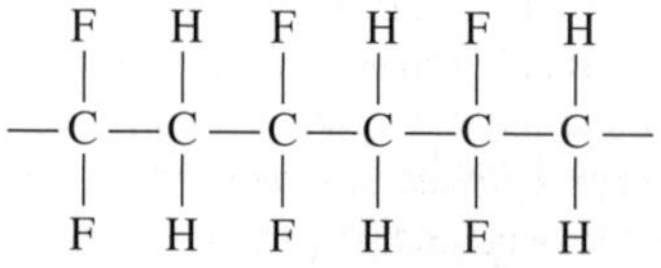

12.25 Cyclohexane, C_6H_{12}, is a cycloalkane in which six carbon atoms in a ring are linked by single bonds. In benzene, C_6H_6, electrons are shared equally by the six carbon atoms.

12.27 a. 1-chloro-2-methylbenzene, 2-chlorotoluene, o-chlorotoluene
  b. ethylbenzene
  c. 1,3,5-trichlorobenzene
  d. 3-methyltoluene, m-xylene, 1,3-dimethylbenzene, m-dimethylbenzene, m-methyltoluene
  e. 3-bromo-5-chlorotoluene, 1-bromo-3-chloro-5-methylbenzene
  f. isopropylbenzene

12.29 a. CH_3 **b.** Br ... Cl
  c. CH_2—CH_3 ... CH_3 **d.** CH_3 ... Cl

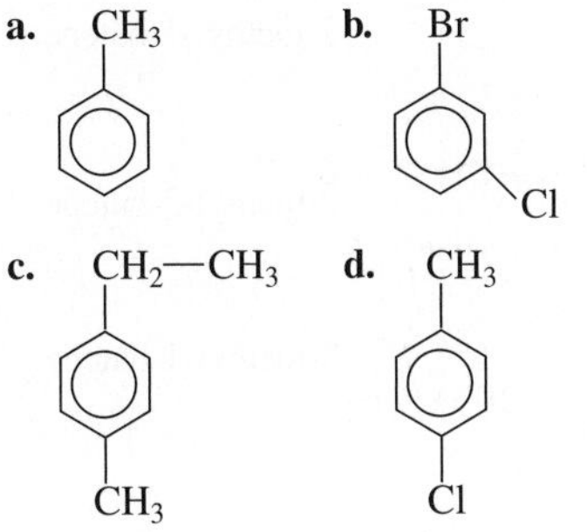

12.31 Benzene undergoes substitution reactions because a substitution reaction allows benzene to retain the stability of the aromatic system.

12.33 a. Cl   **b.** NO_2

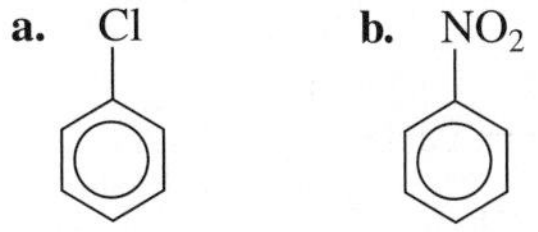

12.35 F F F F F F F F / —C—C—C—C—C—C—C—C— / F F F F F F F F

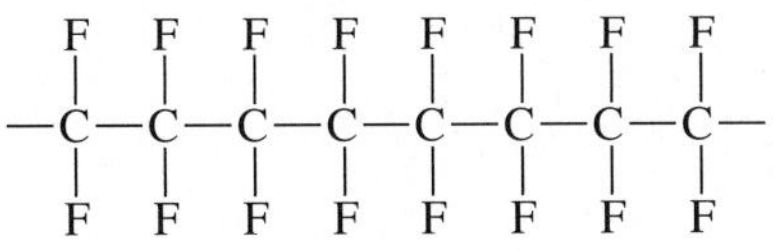

12.37 a. CH_3 / NO_2 ... NO_2 / NO_2

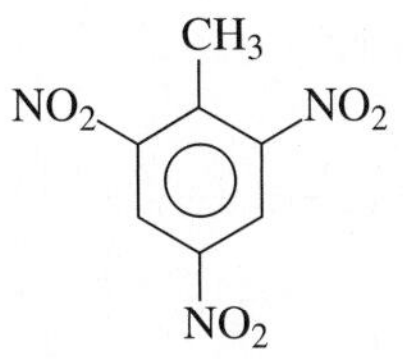

  b.
  CH_3 / O_2N ... NO_2 / NO_2
  CH_3 / O_2N ... NO_2 / NO_2
  CH_3 / ... NO_2 / O_2N ... NO_2
  CH_3 / ... NO_2 / NO_2
  CH_3 / ... NO_2 / O_2N ... NO_2
  NO_2

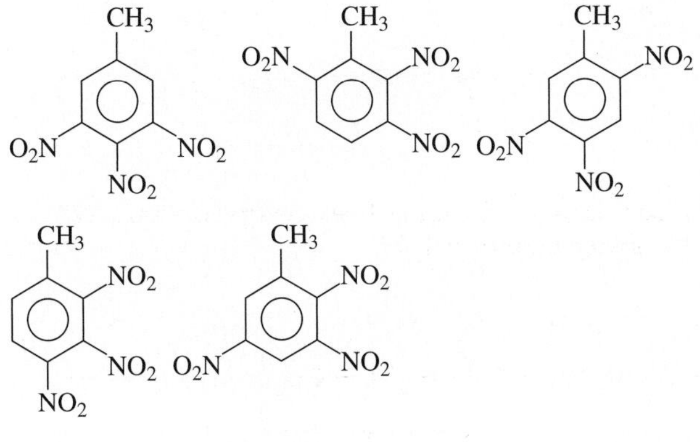

12.39 All the compounds have three carbon atoms. The formula of propane is C_3H_8; the formulas of propene and cyclopropane are both C_3H_6 and the formula of propyne is C_3H_4. Propane is a saturated alkane, and cyclopropane is a saturated cyclic hydrocarbon. Both propene and propyne are unsaturated hydrocarbons, but propene has a double bond and propyne has a triple bond.

12.41 a. chlorocyclopentane
  b. 2-chloro-4-methylpentane
  c. 2-methyl-1-pentene
  d. 2-pentyne

12.43 a. Br ... Br (cyclopentene)

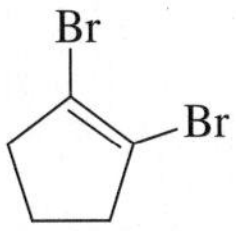

  b. CH_3—$C{\equiv}C$—CH_2—CH_3

  c. CH_3 ... CH_2—CH_2—CH_2—CH_3 / C=C / H ... H

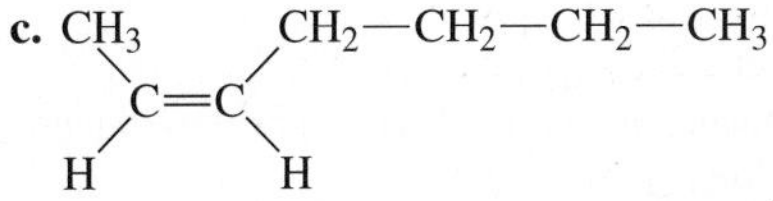

  d. CH_3 / CH_2=C—CH—CH_2—CH_3 / Cl

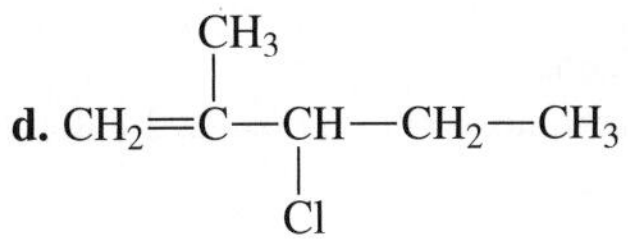

12.45 a. structural isomers
  b. cis–trans isomers

12.47 CH_3 CH_3 CH_3 CH_2

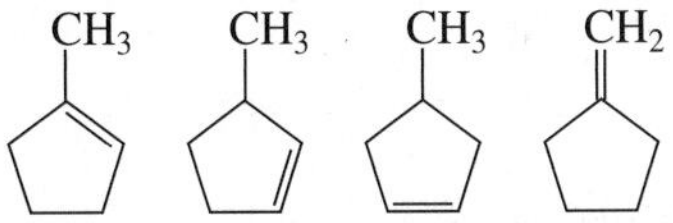

12.49 a. CH_3 ... H / C=C / H ... CH_2—CH_3 *trans*-2-Pentene
  CH_3 ... CH_2—CH_3 / C=C / H ... H   *cis*-2-Pentene

  b. CH_3—CH_2 ... H / C=C / H ... CH_2—CH_3 *trans*-3-Hexene
  CH_3—CH_2 ... CH_2—CH_3 / C=C / H ... H   *cis*-3-Hexene

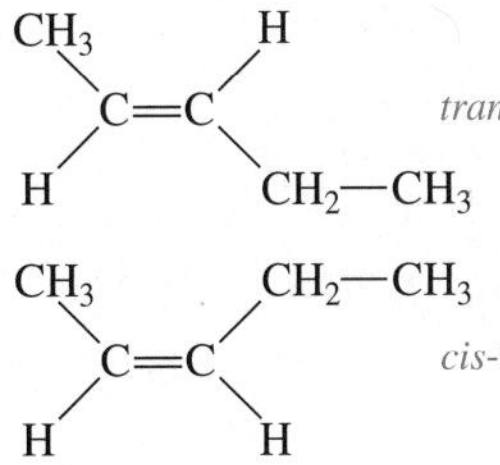

12.51 a. 3-methylpentane
  b. cyclohexane
  c. pentane

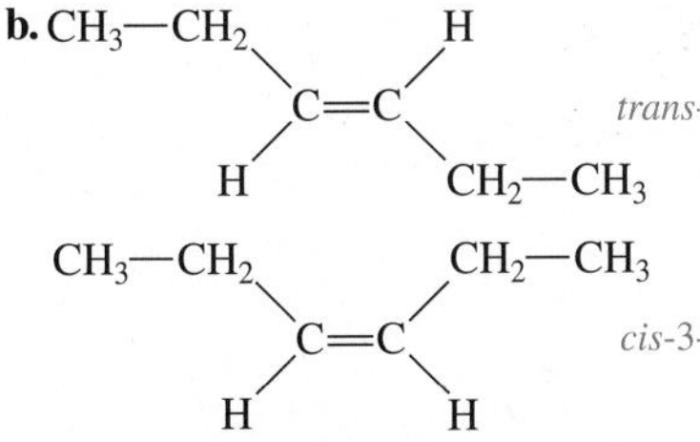

12.53 a. Br / CH_3—CH_2—CH—CH_3

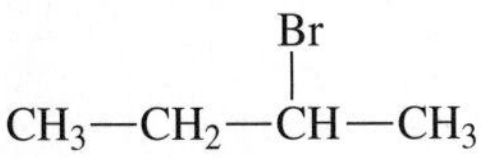

  b. Br (bromocyclopentane)

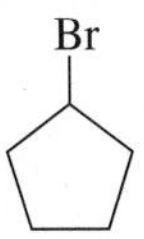

  c. Cl Cl / CH_3—CH—CH—CH_3

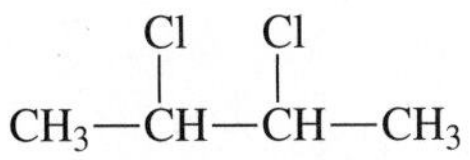

12.55

a.

b. $CH_3—CH\!=\!CH—CH_2—CH_3$

12.57

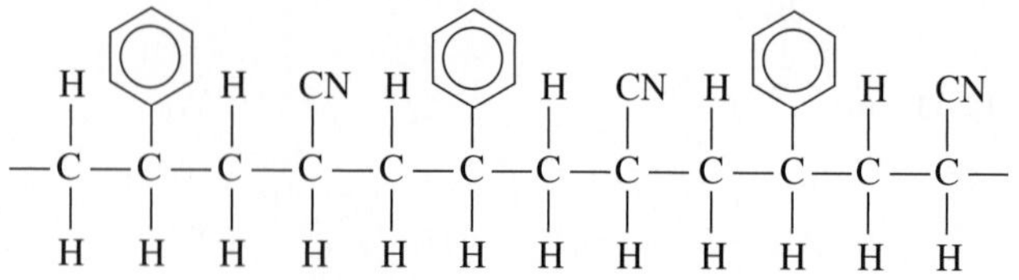

12.59 a. chlorobenzene

b. *o*-bromotoluene, *m*-bromotoluene, *p*-bromotoluene

c. benzenesulfonic acid

d. no products

12.61 a. methylbenzene, toluene

b. 1-chloro-2-methylbenzene, *o*-chlorotoluene, 2-chlorotoluene

c. 1-ethyl-4-methylbenzene, *p*-ethylmethylbenzene, *p*-ethyltoluene

d. 1,3-diethylbenzene, *m*-diethylbenzene

12.63 1×10^{14} molecules of bombykol

12.65

$CH_3—CH\!=\!CH—CH_2—CH_3$	*cis*-2-pentene or *trans*-2-pentene
$H_2C\!=\!CH—CH_2—CH_2—CH_3$	1-pentene
$CH_2\!=\!\overset{\displaystyle CH_3}{\overset{\displaystyle \vert}{C}}—CH_2—CH_3$	2-methyl-1-butene
$CH_3—\overset{\displaystyle CH_3}{\overset{\displaystyle \vert}{C}}\!=\!CH—CH_3$	2-methyl-2-butene
$CH_3—\overset{\displaystyle CH_3}{\overset{\displaystyle \vert}{C}H}—CH\!=\!CH_2$	3-methyl-1-butene

Alcohols, Phenols, Thiols, and Ethers

13

"We use mass spectrometry to analyze and confirm the presence of drugs," says Valli Vairavan, clinical lab technologist—mass spectrometry, Santa Clara Valley Medical Center. "A mass spectrometer separates and identifies compounds including drugs by mass. When we screen a urine sample, we look for metabolites, which are the products of drugs that have metabolized in the body. If the presence of one or more drugs such as heroin and cocaine is indicated, we confirm it by using mass spectrometry."

    Drugs or their metabolites are detected in urine 24–48 hours after use. Cocaine metabolizes to benzoylecgonine and hydroxycocaine, morphine to morphine-3-glucuronide, and heroin to acetylmorphine. Amphetamines and methamphetamines are detected unchanged.

Visit **www.masteringchemistry.com** for self-study materials and instructor-assigned homework.

I n this chapter, we will look at organic compounds that contain single bonds to Group 6A (16) atoms of oxygen and sulfur. Alcohols, which contain the hydroxyl group (—OH), are commonly found in nature and used in industry and at home. For centuries, grains, vegetables, and fruits have been fermented to produce the ethanol present in alcoholic beverages. The hydroxyl group is important in biomolecules, such as sugars and starches, as well as in steroids, such as cholesterol and estradiol. Menthol is a cyclic alcohol with a minty odor and flavor that is used in cough drops, shaving creams, and ointments. Ethers are compounds that contain an oxygen atom connected to two carbon atoms (—O—). They are important solvents in chemistry and medical laboratories. Beginning in 1842, diethyl ether was used for about 100 years as a general anesthetic. Today less flammable and more easily tolerated anesthetics are used. Thiols, which contain the —SH group, give the strong odors we associate with garlic and onions.

13.1 Alcohols, Phenols, and Thiols

LEARNING GOAL

Give IUPAC and common names for alcohols, phenols, and thiols; draw their condensed structural formulas. Classify alcohols as primary, secondary, or tertiary.

As we learned in Chapter 11, alcohols are a class of organic compounds that contain an oxygen (O) atom, shown in red in the ball-and-stick models. Thiols contain a sulfur (S) atom, shown in yellow. In an **alcohol**, a **hydroxyl group** (—OH) replaces a hydrogen atom in a hydrocarbon. In a **phenol**, the hydroxyl group is attached to an aromatic ring. Molecules of alcohols and phenols have a bent shape around the oxygen atom, similar to that of water. An alkyl or aromatic group replaces one hydrogen atom.

Thiols are a family of sulfur-containing organic compounds that have a *thiol* (—SH) *group*. They have structures similar to alcohols except that —SH takes the place of —OH.

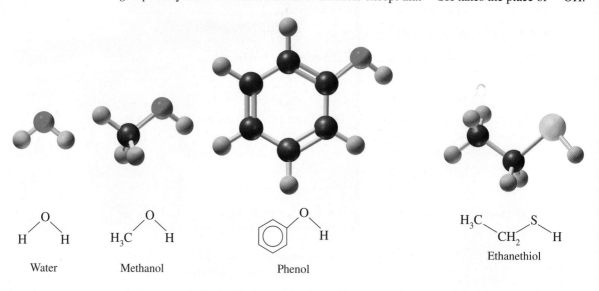

Water   Methanol   Phenol   Ethanethiol

Classification of Alcohols

Alcohols are classified by the number of carbon groups attached to the carbon atom bonded to the hydroxyl (—OH) group. **A primary (1°) alcohol** has one alkyl group attached to the carbon atom bonded to the —OH. The simplest alcohol, methanol, which has a carbon attached to three H atoms but no alkyl group, is considered a primary alcohol. A **secondary (2°) alcohol** has two alkyl groups, and a **tertiary (3°) alcohol** has three alkyl groups.

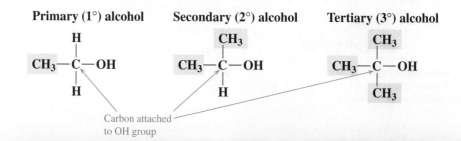

Primary (1°) alcohol   Secondary (2°) alcohol   Tertiary (3°) alcohol

Carbon attached to OH group

CONCEPT CHECK 13.1

■ Classifying Alcohols

Classify each of the following alcohols as primary (1°), secondary (2°), or tertiary (3°):

a. $CH_3—CH_2—CH_2—OH$

b. 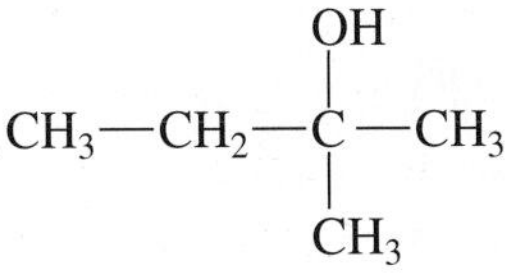
$$CH_3—CH_2—\overset{\overset{\displaystyle OH}{|}}{\underset{\underset{\displaystyle CH_3}{|}}{C}}—CH_3$$

c. (cyclopentane ring with OH)

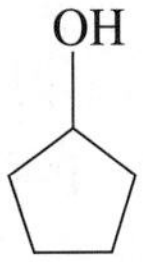

ANSWER

a. One alkyl group attached to the carbon atom bonded to the —OH makes this a primary (1°) alcohol.

b. Three alkyl groups attached to the carbon atom bonded to the —OH makes this a tertiary (3°) alcohol.

c. In a cyclic alcohol, there are two carbon atoms attached to the carbon atom bonded to the —OH, which makes this a secondary (2°) alcohol.

Naming Alcohols, Phenols, and Thiols

The IUPAC rules for the naming of alcohols, phenols, and thiols are similar to those we used to name other families of organic compounds. The alcohol family is indicated by an *ol* ending, which is numbered to show the location of the hydroxyl group on the main chain.

Naming Alcohols

In the IUPAC system, the alcohol family is indicated by the *ol* ending.

STEP 1 **Name the longest carbon chain containing the —OH group.** Replace the *e* in the alkane name with *ol*:

$CH_3—CH_2—CH_2—OH$ propanol

STEP 2 **Number the longest chain starting at the end closer to the —OH group.** For simple alcohols, the common name (shown in parentheses) gives the name of the carbon chain as an alkyl group followed by *alcohol*.

$CH_3—CH_2—CH_2—OH$ 1-propanol
  3   2   1   (propyl alcohol)

Alcohols with one or two carbon atoms do not require a number for the hydroxyl group.

$CH_3—OH$ $CH_3—CH_2—OH$ $Cl—CH_2—CH_2—OH$
Methanol   Ethanol   2-Chloroethanol
(methyl alcohol)   (ethyl alcohol)

STEP 3 **Name and number other substituents relative to the —OH group:**

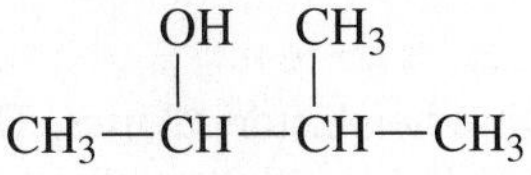

$$CH_3—\overset{\overset{\displaystyle OH}{|}}{CH}—\overset{\overset{\displaystyle CH_3}{|}}{CH}—CH_3$$
  1   2   3   4
3-Methyl-2-butanol

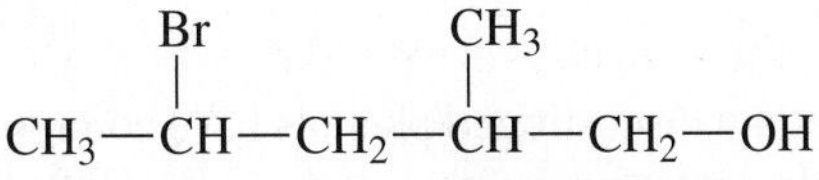

$$CH_3—\overset{\overset{\displaystyle Br}{|}}{CH}—CH_2—\overset{\overset{\displaystyle CH_3}{|}}{CH}—CH_2—OH$$
  5   4   3   2   1
4-Bromo-2-methyl-1-pentanol

STEP 4 **Name a cyclic alcohol as a *cycloalkanol*.** For other substituents, the ring is numbered with the —OH group on carbon 1. Compounds with no other substituents on the ring do not require a number for the hydroxyl group:

(cyclohexane ring with OH)   (cyclopentane ring with OH and CH₃)

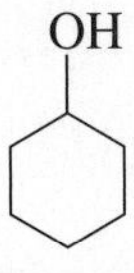

Cyclohexanol 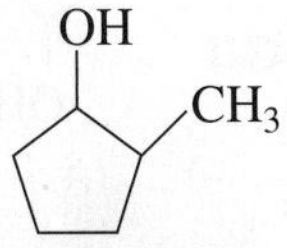   2-Methylcyclopentanol

MC TUTORIAL
Naming Alcohols, Phenols,
and Thiols

MC TUTORIAL
Drawing Alcohols, Phenols,
and Thiols

Guide to Naming Alcohols

STEP 1
Name the longest carbon chain
with the —OH group.

STEP 2
Number the longest chain starting
at the end closer to the —OH.

STEP 3
Name substituents counting
from the —OH.

STEP 4
Name a cyclic alcohol as
a *cycloalkanol.*

SAMPLE PROBLEM 13.1

■ **Naming Alcohols**

Give the IUPAC name for the following:

$$CH_3 \quad\quad OH$$
a. $CH_3—CH—CH_2—CH—CH_3$

SOLUTION

STEP 1   **Name the longest carbon chain containing the —OH group.**   The parent chain is pentane; the alcohol is named pentanol.

STEP 2   **Number the longest chain starting at the end closer to the —OH group.** The carbon chain is numbered to give the position of the —OH group as carbon 2 to give 2-pentanol.

STEP 3   **Name and number other substituents relative to the —OH group.** With a methyl group on carbon 4, the compound is named 4-methyl-2-pentanol.

STUDY CHECK

Give the IUPAC name for the following:

$$Cl$$
$$CH_3—CH—CH_2—CH_2—OH$$

EXPLORE YOUR WORLD

Alcohols in Household Products

Read the labels on household products such as mouthwashes, cold remedies, rubbing alcohol, and flavoring extracts. Look for names of alcohols, such as ethyl alcohol, isopropyl alcohol, thymol, and menthol.

QUESTIONS

1. What part of the name tells you that it is an alcohol?
2. What alcohol is usually meant by the term "alcohol"?
3. What is the percentage of alcohol in the products?
4. Write out the structures of the alcohols you find listed on the labels. You may need to use the Internet or a reference book for some structures.

Naming Phenols

The term *phenol* is the IUPAC name for a benzene ring bonded to a hydroxyl group (—OH) and is used in the name of the family of organic compounds derived from phenol. When there is a second substituent, the benzene ring is numbered starting from the carbon 1, which is bonded to the —OH group. The terms *ortho*, *meta*, and *para* are used for the common names of simple phenols:

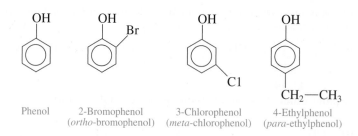

Phenol   2-Bromophenol   3-Chlorophenol   4-Ethylphenol
(*ortho*-bromophenol) (*meta*-chlorophenol) (*para*-ethylphenol)

Certain disubstituted phenols have common names based on historical uses. The methylphenols are commonly named as *cresols*, while benzenediols, which are benzene rings with two —OH groups, have a variety of common names:

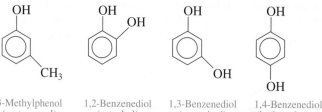

3-Methylphenol   1,2-Benzenediol   1,3-Benzenediol   1,4-Benzenediol
(*meta*-cresol)   (catechol)   (resorcinol)   (hydroquinone)

HEALTH NOTE

Some Important Alcohols and Phenols

Methanol (*methyl alcohol*), the simplest alcohol, is found in many solvents and paint removers. If ingested, methanol is oxidized to formaldehyde, which can cause headaches, blindness, and death. Methanol is used to make plastics, medicines, and fuels. In car racing, it is used as a fuel because it is less flammable and has a higher octane rating than does gasoline.

Ethanol (*ethyl alcohol*) has been known since prehistoric times as an intoxicating product formed by the fermentation of grains, sugars, and starches:

$$C_6H_{12}O_6 \xrightarrow{\text{Fermentation}} 2CH_3-CH_2-OH + 2CO_2$$

Ethanol for commercial uses is produced by allowing ethene and water to react at high temperatures and pressures. Ethanol is used as a solvent for perfumes, varnishes, and some medicines, such as tincture of iodine. Recent interest in alternative fuels has led to increased production of ethanol by the fermentation of sugars from grains such as corn, wheat, and rice. "Gasohol" is a mixture of ethanol and gasoline used as a fuel:

$$H_2C{=}CH_2 + H_2O \xrightarrow{\text{300 °C, 200 atm, catalyst}} CH_3-CH_2-OH$$

1,2,3-Propanetriol (*glycerol or glycerin*), a trihydroxy alcohol, is a viscous liquid obtained from oils and fats during the production of soaps. The presence of several polar —OH groups makes it strongly attracted to water, a feature that makes glycerin useful as a skin softener in products such as skin lotions, cosmetics, shaving creams, and liquid soaps:

$$\text{HO}-CH_2-\overset{\displaystyle \overset{\text{OH}}{|}}{CH}-CH_2-\text{OH}$$

1,2,3-Propanetriol (glycerol)

1,2-Ethanediol (*ethylene glycol*) is used as antifreeze in heating and cooling systems. It is also a solvent for paints, inks, and plastics, and it is used in the production of synthetic fibers such as Dacron. If ingested, it is extremely toxic. In the body, it is oxidized to oxalic acid, which forms insoluble salts in the kidneys that cause renal damage, convulsions, and death. Because its sweet taste is attractive to pets and children, ethylene glycol solutions must be carefully stored:

$$\text{HO}-CH_2-CH_2-OH \xrightarrow{[O]} \text{HO}-\overset{\displaystyle \overset{O}{\|}}{C}-\overset{\displaystyle \overset{O}{\|}}{C}-OH$$

1,2-Ethanediol (ethylene glycol)   Oxalic acid

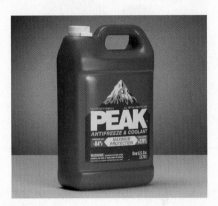

Phenols are found in several of the essential oils of plants, which produce the odor or flavor of the plant. Eugenol is found in cloves, vanillin in vanilla bean, isoeugenol in nutmeg, and thymol in thyme and mint. Thymol has a pleasant, minty taste and is used in mouthwashes and by dentists to disinfect a cavity before adding a filling compound.

Bisphenol A (BPA) is used to make polycarbonate, a clear plastic that is used to manufacture beverage bottles, including baby bottles. Washing polycarbonate bottles with certain detergents or at high temperatures disrupts the polymer, causing small amounts of BPA to leach from the bottles. Because BPA is an estrogen mimic, there are concerns about the harmful effects from low levels of BPA. In April 2008, Canada banned the use of polycarbonate baby bottles. Plastic bottles and containers made of polycarbonate have the recycling symbol "7".

Bisphenol A (BPA)

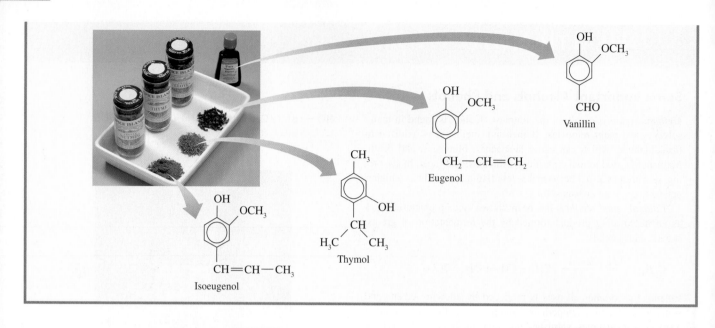

■ **Naming Phenols**

Give the IUPAC and common name for the following:

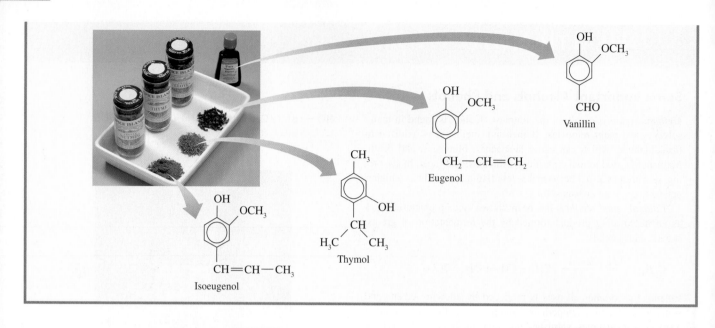

ANSWER

The compound is a *phenol* because the —OH group is attached to a benzene ring. The ring is numbered starting with carbon attached to the —OH group in the direction that gives the bromine the lower number. The IUPAC name for the compound is 2-bromophenol; its common name is *ortho*-bromophenol or *o*-bromophenol.

Naming Thiols

In the IUPAC system, thiols are named by adding *thiol* to the alkane name of the longest carbon chain bonded to the —SH group. The location of the —SH group is indicated by numbering the carbon chain from the end nearer the —SH group:

$$CH_3—OH \qquad CH_3—SH \qquad CH_3—\overset{\displaystyle SH}{\underset{\displaystyle |}{CH}}—CH_2—CH_3$$

Methanol   Methanethiol   2-Butanethiol

An important property of thiols is a strong, sometimes disagreeable, odor. Methanethiol is the characteristic odor of oysters and cheddar cheese. (See Figure 13.1.) To help us detect natural gas (methane) leaks, a small amount of ethanethiol is added to the gas supply. There are thiols in the spray emitted when a skunk senses danger. The odor of onions is due to 1-propanethiol, which is also a lachrymator, a substance that makes eyes tear. Garlic contains thiols such as 2-propene-1-thiol. We can break this name down as follows:

2-	Prop	ene	-1-	thiol
Carbon 2 has C=C	3 carbons in chain	alkene	on carbon 1	—SH group

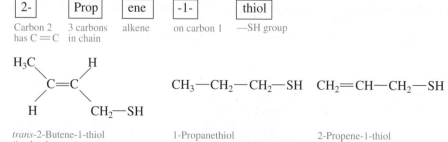

trans-2-Butene-1-thiol   1-Propanethiol   2-Propene-1-thiol
(in skunk spray)   (in onions)   (in garlic)

CH_3—SH
Methanethiol
Oysters and cheese

CH_3—CH_2—CH_2—SH
1-Propanethiol
Onions

CH_2=CH—CH_2—SH
2-Propene-1-thiol
Garlic

FIGURE 13.1 Thiols are sulfur-containing compounds with a —SH group.
Q Why do thiols have structures similar to alcohols?

SAMPLE PROBLEM 13.2

■ Thiols

Draw the condensed structural formula of the following:

a. 1-butanethiol   **b.** cyclohexanethiol

SOLUTION

a. This compound has a —SH group on the first carbon of a butane chain:

CH_3—CH_2—CH_2—CH_2—SH

b. This compound has a —SH group on cyclohexane:

SH

STUDY CHECK

What is the condensed structural formula of ethanethiol?

QUESTIONS AND PROBLEMS

Alcohols, Phenols, and Thiols

13.1 Classify each of the following as a primary (1°), secondary (2°), or tertiary (3°) alcohol:

CH_3
|
a. CH_3—CH—CH_2—CH_2—OH

b. CH_3—CH_2—CH_2—CH_2—OH

OH
|
c. CH_3—C—CH_2—CH_3
|
CH_3

d.   OH

13.2 Classify each of the following as a primary (1°), secondary (2°), or tertiary (3°) alcohol:

a.

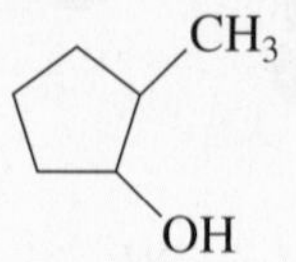

b. $CH_3-CH-CH_2-OH$ (with CH_3 above)

c. 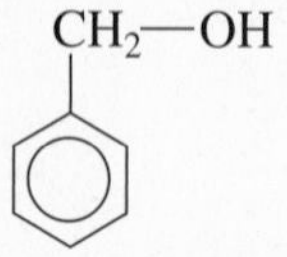 CH_2-OH (attached to benzene ring)

d. $CH_3-CH_2-CH_2-C-OH$ (with CH_3 above and CH_3 below)

13.3 Give the IUPAC name for each of the following alcohols:

a. CH_3-CH_2-OH

b. $CH_3-CH_2-CH-CH_3$ (with OH above)

c. $CH_3-CH-CH_2-CH_2-CH_3$ (with OH above)

d. 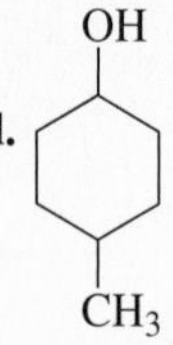 (cyclohexane ring with OH at top and CH_3 at bottom)

13.4 Give the IUPAC name for each of the following alcohols:

a. 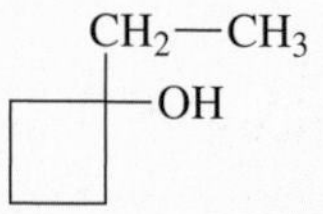 (cyclobutane ring with CH_2-CH_3 and $-OH$)

b. $CH_3-CH_2-CH-CH_2-OH$ (with CH_3 above)

c. $CH_3-CH_2-CH-CH-CH_2-OH$ (with CH_3 and CH_3 above)

d. $CH_3-CH_2-CH-CH_2-CH_3$ (with OH above)

13.5 Draw the condensed structural formula of each of the following alcohols:
   a. 1-propanol   b. methyl alcohol
   c. 3-pentanol   d. 2-methyl-2-butanol
   e. cyclohexanol

13.6 Draw the condensed structural formula of each of the following alcohols:
   a. ethyl alcohol
   b. 3-methyl-1-butanol
   c. 2,4-dichlorocyclohexanol
   d. propyl alcohol
   e. 1,3-cyclopentanediol

13.7 Name each of the following phenols:

a.  OH (on benzene ring)

b. 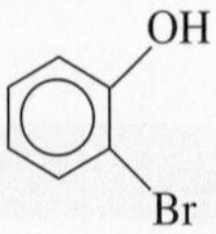 OH (on benzene ring with Br)

c. 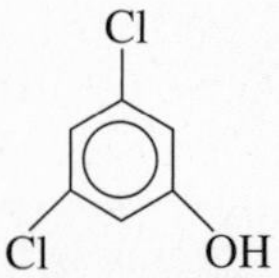 (benzene ring with Cl, Cl, OH)

d. 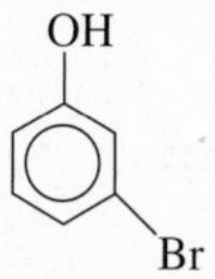 (benzene ring with OH, Br)

13.8 Name each of the following phenols:

a. 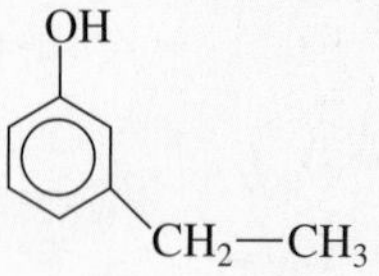 OH (benzene ring with CH_2-CH_3)

b. 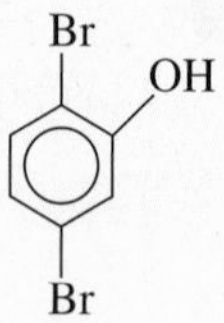 Br, OH, Br (on benzene ring)

c. 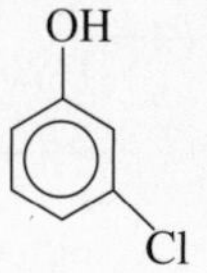 OH (benzene ring with Cl)

d. 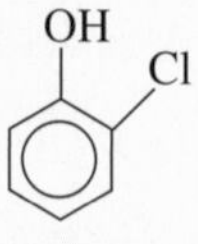 OH, Cl (on benzene ring)

13.9 Draw the condensed structural formula of each of the following phenols:
   a. *m*-bromophenol   b. *p*-chlorophenol
   c. 2,5-dichlorophenol   d. *o*-phenylphenol

13.10 Draw the condensed structural formula of each of the following phenols:
   a. *o*-ethylphenol
   b. 2,4-dichlorophenol
   c. 2,4-dimethylphenol
   d. 2-ethyl-5-methylphenol

13.11 Give the IUPAC name for each of the following thiols:

a. CH_3-SH

b. $CH_3-CH-CH_3$ (with SH above)

c. $CH_3-CH-CH-CH_2-SH$ (with CH_3 and CH_3 above)

d. 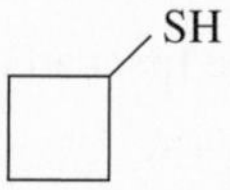 (cyclobutane ring with SH)

13.12 Give the IUPAC name for each of the following thiols:
   a. $CH_3-CH_2-CH_2-SH$

b. $CH_3-CH_2-CH_2-CH-CH_3$ (with SH above)

c. CH_3-C-CH_2-SH (with CH_3 above and CH_3 below)

d. 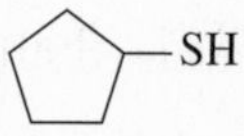 (cyclopentane ring with $-SH$)

13.2 Ethers

LEARNING GOAL

Give the IUPAC and common names of ethers; draw the condensed structural formula.

An **ether** contains an oxygen atom that is attached by single bonds to two carbon groups that are alkyls or aromatic rings. Ethers have a bent structure like that of water and alcohols, except both hydrogen atoms are replaced by alkyl groups.

Naming Ethers

TUTORIAL
Naming Ethers

TUTORIAL
Drawing Ethers

Simple ethers use their common names. Write the name of each alkyl or aromatic group attached to the oxygen atom in alphabetical order followed by the word *ether*.

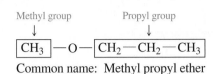

CH₃—O—CH₂—CH₂—CH₃

Common name: Methyl propyl ether

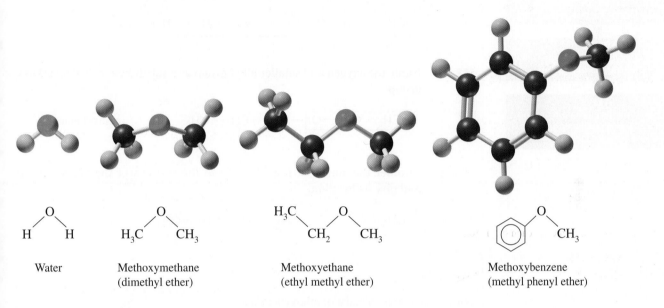

| Water | Methoxymethane (dimethyl ether) | Methoxyethane (ethyl methyl ether) | Methoxybenzene (methyl phenyl ether) |

This ether can also be named using the IUPAC system using the following steps:

STEP 1 **Write the alkane name of the longer carbon chain:**

CH₃—O—CH₂—CH₂—CH₃   propane

Longer carbon chain

STEP 2 **Name the oxygen and smaller alkyl group as a substituent called an *alkoxy group*:**

CH₃—O —CH₂—CH₂—CH₃   methoxypropane

↑
Methoxy group

STEP 3 **Number the longer carbon chain from the end nearer the alkoxy group to give the location of the alkoxy group:**

CH₃—O—CH₂—CH₂—CH₃   1-methoxypropane
            1   2   3

More examples of naming ethers with both IUPAC and common names follow:

CH₃—O—CH₃   CH₃—CH₂—O—CH₂—CH₃
Methoxymethane   Ethoxyethane
(dimethyl ether)   (diethyl ether)

$$O-CH_3$$
CH₃—CH—CH₂—CH₃
2-Methoxybutane

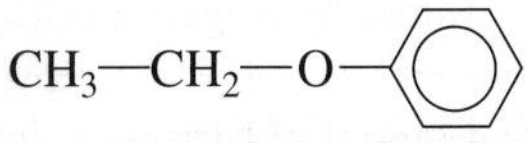

CH₃—CH₂—O—⬡
Ethoxybenzene
(ethyl phenyl ether)

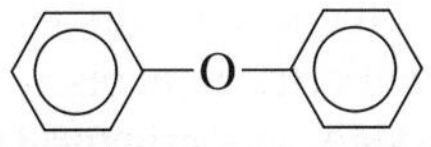

⬡—O—⬡
Phenoxybenzene
(diphenyl ether)

Guide to Naming Ethers

STEP 1
Write the alkane name of the longer carbon chain.

STEP 2
Name the oxygen and smaller alkyl group as an *alkoxy group*.

STEP 3
Number the longer chain from the end nearer the alkoxy group and give its location.

SAMPLE PROBLEM 13.3

■ Ethers

Give the IUPAC name for the following:

$$CH_3—CH_2—O—CH_2—CH_2—CH_2—CH_3$$

SOLUTION

STEP 1   **Write the alkane name of the longer carbon chain:**

$$CH_3—CH_2—O—\underbrace{CH_2—CH_2—CH_2—CH_3}_{\text{Longer carbon chain}}\quad \text{butane}$$

STEP 2   **Name the oxygen and smaller alkyl group as a substituent called an alkoxy group:**

$$\boxed{CH_3—CH_2—O}—CH_2—CH_2—CH_2—CH_3\quad \text{ethoxybutane}$$
$$\underset{\text{Ethoxy group}}{}$$

STEP 3   **Number the longer carbon chain from the end nearer the alkoxy group and give its location.**

$$CH_3—CH_2—O—\underset{1}{CH_2}—\underset{2}{CH_2}—\underset{3}{CH_2}—\underset{4}{CH_3}\quad \text{1-ethoxybutane}$$

STUDY CHECK

What is the common name of ethoxybenzene?

Isomers of Alcohols and Ethers

Alcohols and ethers can have the same molecular formula. For example, we can write condensed structural formulas for the isomers with the molecular formula C_2H_6O as follows:

$$CH_3—CH_2—OH \qquad\qquad CH_3—O—CH_3$$
Ethanol   Methoxymethane
(ethyl alcohol)   (dimethyl ether)

CONCEPT CHECK 13.3

■ Isomers of Alcohols and Ethers

Determine the molecular formulas of the following alcohols and ethers. Identify the compounds that are structural isomers. Explain.

1-butanol, 2-butanol, methyl ethyl ether, diethyl ether, 3-pentanol, methyl propyl ether

ANSWER

The molecular formulas are as follows:

1-Butanol	$C_4H_{10}O$	2-Butanol	$C_4H_{10}O$
Methyl ethyl ether	C_3H_8O	Diethyl ether	$C_4H_{10}O$
3-Pentanol	$C_5H_{12}O$	Methyl propyl ether	$C_4H_{10}O$

Structural isomers have the same number of carbon atoms, hydrogen atoms, and oxygen atoms but in different arrangements.

Four of these compounds are structural isomers: 1-butanol, 2-butanol, diethyl ether, and methyl propyl ether.

HEALTH NOTE

Ethers as Anesthetics

Anesthesia is the loss of all sensation and consciousness. A general anesthetic is a substance that blocks signals to the awareness centers in the brain, so the person has a loss of memory, a loss of feeling pain, and an artificial sleep. The term *ether* has been associated with anesthesia because diethyl ether was the most widely used anesthetic for more than a hundred years. Although it is easy to administer, ether is very volatile and highly flammable. A small spark in the operating room could cause an explosion. Since the 1950s, anesthetics such as Forane (isoflurane), Ethrane (enflurane), and Penthrane (methoxyflurane) have been developed that are not as

flammable and do not cause nausea. Most of these anesthetics retain the ether group, but the addition of many halogen atoms reduces the volatility and flammability of the ethers. More recently, they have been replaced by halothane (2-bromo-2-chloro-1,1,1-trifluoroethane), discussed in Chapter 11, because of the side effects of the ether-type inhalation anesthetics.

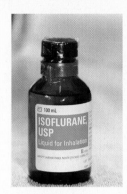

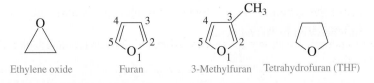

Forane® (isoflurane)   Ethrane® (enflurane)   Penthrane® (methoxyflurane)

SAMPLE PROBLEM 13.4

■ Isomers

Draw the condensed structural formulas and give the IUPAC and common names of two alcohols and one ether with a molecular formula of C_3H_8O.

SOLUTION

To draw the condensed structural formulas for alcohols, the hydroxyl group is bonded to two different atoms in a chain of three carbon atoms. For the ether, two alkyl groups are bonded to an oxygen atom:

$$CH_3-CH_2-CH_2-OH \qquad CH_3-\overset{\overset{\displaystyle OH}{|}}{CH}-CH_3 \qquad CH_3-CH_2-O-CH_3$$

1-Propanol (propyl alcohol)   2-Propanol (isopropyl alcohol)   Methoxyethane (ethyl methyl ether)

STUDY CHECK

Write the IUPAC names of the unbranched isomers of $C_4H_{10}O$.

Cyclic Ethers

A **cyclic ether** contains an oxygen atom in a carbon ring. They are *heterocyclic compounds* because there is a ring with one or more atoms that are not carbon. The cyclic ethers are usually given common names. The five-atom rings with an oxygen atom use common names derived from the aromatic ring *furan*. The four-atom cyclic ethers are not common. The rings are numbered from the oxygen atom as 1:

Ethylene oxide   Furan   3-Methylfuran   Tetrahydrofuran (THF)

An unsaturated ether ring of six atoms is named *pyran*:

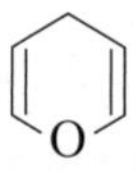

Pyran 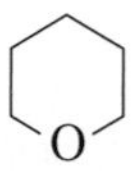   Tetrahydropyran (THP) 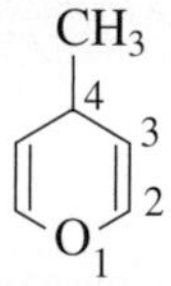   4-Methylpyran

Cyclic ethers containing two oxygen atoms in a ring of six atoms are called *dioxanes*. The oxygen atoms are numbered because they can take different positions in the ring:

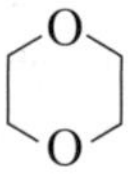

1,4-Dioxane 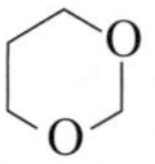   1,3-Dioxane

ENVIRONMENTAL NOTE

Toxic Ethers

Dioxin is a term used for a group of highly toxic compounds composed of dioxanes bonded to aromatic rings. One of the most toxic is 2,3,7,8-tetrachlorodibenzo-*p*-dioxin (TCDD), now considered carcinogenic (cancer causing) because its structure interferes with DNA. Dioxin is formed during forest fires and as a by-product of many industrial processes involving chlorine, such as chemical and pesticide manufacturing and pulp and paper bleaching. The herbicide Agent Orange used in Vietnam was contaminated by highly toxic dioxin, which formed during the synthesis of Agent Orange.

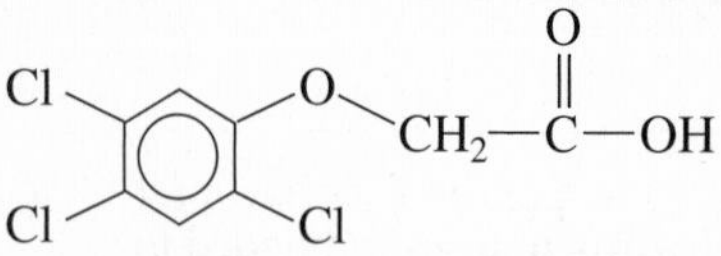

2,4,5-Trichlorophenoxyacetic acid
(2,4,5-T; Agent Orange)

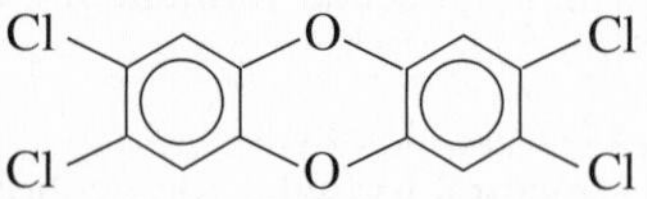

2,3,7,8-Tetrachlorodibenzo-*p*-dioxin
(TCDD, "dioxin")

SAMPLE PROBLEM 13.5

■ Cyclic Ethers

Identify the following as a cyclic alcohol, ether, or cyclic ether:

a. 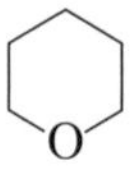   b. 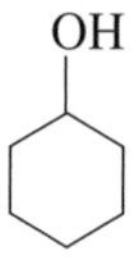   OH   c. 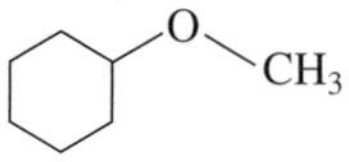   O—CH$_3$

SOLUTION

a. A cyclic ether has an oxygen atom in the ring.
b. A cyclic alcohol has a hydroxyl group bonded to a cycloalkane.
c. An ether has an oxygen atom with single bonds to two carbon groups.

STUDY CHECK

What is the difference between furan and pyran?

QUESTIONS AND PROBLEMS

Ethers

13.13 Give the IUPAC name and a common name for each of the following ethers:

a. $CH_3-O-CH_2-CH_3$ **b.** 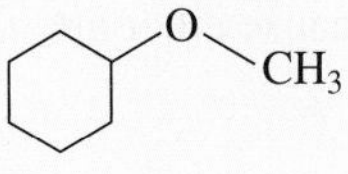 [cyclohexane ring with O—CH$_3$ substituent]

c. 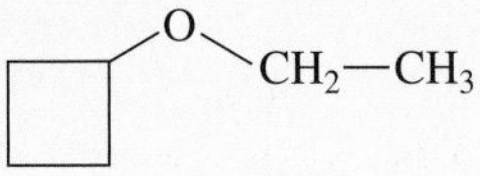 [cyclobutane ring with O—CH$_2$—CH$_3$ substituent]

d. $CH_3-O-CH_2-CH_2-CH_3$

13.14 Give the IUPAC name and a common name for each of the following ethers:

a. $CH_3-CH_2-O-CH_2-CH_2-CH_3$

b. 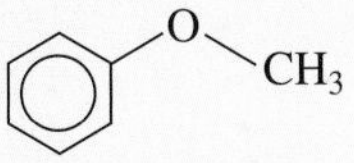 [benzene ring with O—CH$_3$ substituent]   **c.** 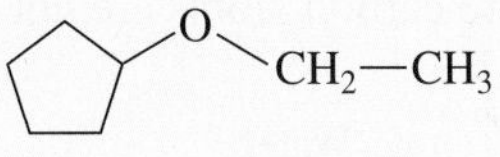 [cyclopentane ring with O—CH$_2$—CH$_3$ substituent]

d. CH_3-O-CH_3

13.15 Draw the condensed structural formula for each of the following ethers:

a. ethyl propyl ether   **b.** cyclopropyl ethyl ether
c. methoxycyclopentane   **d.** 1-ethoxy-2-methylbutane
e. 2,3-dimethoxypentane

13.16 Draw the condensed structural formula for each of the following ethers:

a. diethyl ether   **b.** diphenyl ether

c. ethoxycyclohexane
d. 2-methoxy-2,3-dimethylbutane
e. 1,2-dimethoxybenzene

13.17 Indicate whether each of the following pairs represent isomers, the same compound, or different compounds:

a. 2-pentanol and 2-methoxybutane
b. 2-butanol and cyclobutanol
c. ethyl propyl ether and 2-methyl-1-butanol

13.18 Indicate whether each of the following pairs represent isomers, the same compound, or different compounds:

a. 2-methoxybutane and 3-methyl-2-butanol
b. 1-hexanol and dipropyl ether
c. 2-methyl-2-propanol and diethyl ether

13.19 Give the name for each of the following cyclic ethers:

a. 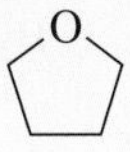 [five-membered ring with O]   **b.** 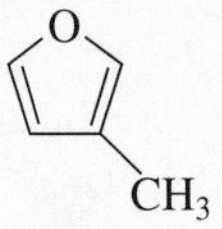 [five-membered ring with O and CH$_3$]   **c.** [six-membered ring with two O and H$_3$C]

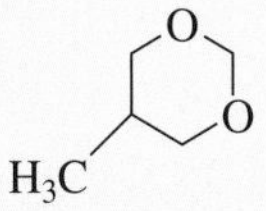

13.20 Give the name for each of the following cyclic ethers:

a.  [five-membered ring with O]   **b.** 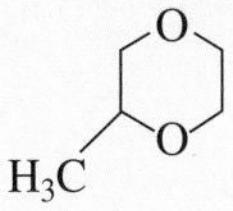 [six-membered ring with two O and H$_3$C]   **c.** [six-membered ring with O and CH$_3$]

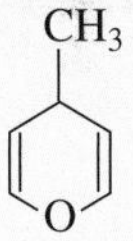

13.3 Physical Properties of Alcohols, Phenols, and Ethers

LEARNING GOAL

Describe some physical properties of alcohols, phenols, and ethers.

In Chapters 11 and 12, we learned that hydrocarbons, which are composed of only carbon and hydrogen, are nonpolar. In this chapter, we have looked at compounds containing the element oxygen. The high electronegativity of oxygen determines the boiling points and solubility in water of alcohols and ethers.

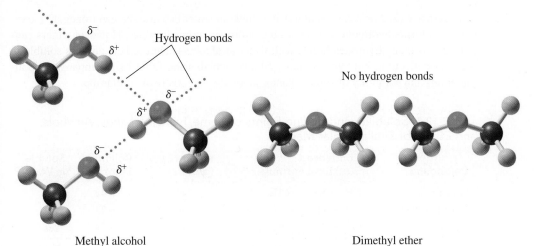

Methyl alcohol   Dimethyl ether

Boiling Points

In an alcohol, the electronegativity of the oxygen makes the O—H bond very polar, which gives the hydrogen in O—H a partially positive charge. Hydrogen bonds form between the oxygen of one alcohol and hydrogen in the O—H of another alcohol.

TUTORIAL
Physical Properties of
Alcohols and Ethers

Ethers do not form hydrogen bonds with other ether molecules, because they do not have a polar O—H bond.

Because of hydrogen bonding, alcohols have much higher boiling points than ethers of similar mass. In alcohols, higher temperatures are required to provide the energy needed to break the many hydrogen bonds between alcohol molecules. The boiling points of ethers are similar to those of alkanes because ether and alkanes do not form hydrogen bonds.

Solubility in Water

The electronegativity of the oxygen atom influences the solubility of both alcohol and ethers in water. In alcohols, the atoms in the O—H group form hydrogen bonds with the H and O atoms of water. As the number of carbon atoms increases, the solubility effect of the —OH group is diminished. Only an alcohol with one to four carbon atoms is soluble in water. Alcohols with five or more carbon atoms are not soluble.

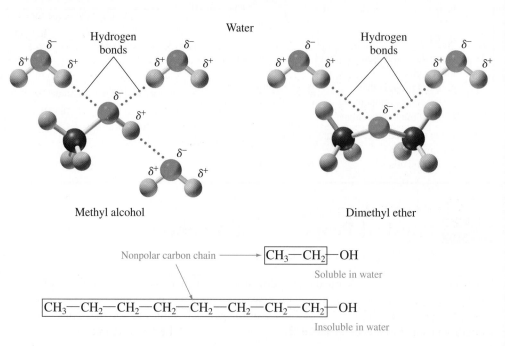

An ether with 2 or 3 carbon atoms is soluble in water because the electronegative oxygen atom forms hydrogen bonds with the hydrogen atoms in water. However, ethers cannot form as many hydrogen bonds with water as alcohols. Thus, ethers are less soluble in water than alcohols, but they are more soluble than alkanes. Table 13.1 compares the boiling points and solubility of some alkanes, alcohols, and ethers of similar mass.

TABLE 13.1 Solubility and Boiling Points of Some Typical Alkanes, Alcohols, and Ethers of Similar Molar Mass

Compound	Condensed Structural Formula	Molar Mass (g/mole)	Boiling Point (°C)	Soluble in Water?
Propane	$CH_3—CH_2—CH_3$	44	−42	No
Dimethyl ether	$CH_3—O—CH_3$	46	−23	Yes
Ethanol	$CH_3—CH_2—OH$	46	78	Yes
Butane	$CH_3—CH_2—CH_2—CH_3$	58	0	No
Ethyl methyl ether	$CH_3—O—CH_2—CH_3$	60	8	Yes
1-Propanol	$CH_3—CH_2—CH_2—OH$	60	97	Yes

Ethers such as diethyl ether are very useful as solvents for hydrocarbons. However, ether vapors are highly flammable and react with oxygen to form explosive compounds. The utmost care must be taken when working with ethers.

CONCEPT CHECK 13.4

■ **Properties of Alcohols and Ethers**

Consider 1-butanol and diethyl ether, which are isomers of $C_4H_{10}O$.

a. Which has a higher boiling point? Explain.
b. Which is more soluble in water? Explain

ANSWER

a. The —OH group in 1-butanol forms hydrogen bonds, requiring more energy and a higher temperature to boil. Diethyl ether does not form hydrogen bonds with other molecules of diethyl ether.
b. The —OH in 1-butanol can form more hydrogen bonds with water than diethyl ether. Thus, 1-butanol is more soluble in water than diethyl ether.

Phenols

Phenol has a high boiling point (182 °C) because the O—H group allows phenol molecules to hydrogen bond with other phenol molecules. Phenol is slightly soluble in water because phenol molecules can form hydrogen bonds with water molecules. In water, the O—H group of phenol ionizes slightly, which makes it a weak acid ($K_a = 1 \times 10^{-10}$). In fact, an early name for phenol was *carbolic acid*. Phenol is very corrosive and highly irritating to the skin; it can cause severe burns and ingestion can be fatal. Dilute solutions of phenol were previously used in hospitals as antiseptics, but they have generally been replaced.

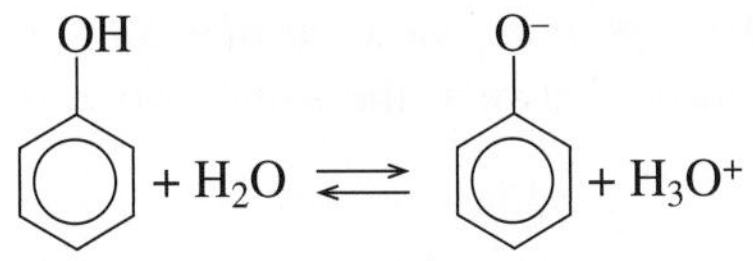

Phenol   Phenoxide ion

SAMPLE PROBLEM 13.6

■ **Physical Properties of Alcohols, Ethers, and Phenols**

Predict which compound in each of the following pairs will be more soluble in water:

a. butane or 1-propanol   **b.** 1-propanol or 1-heptanol

SOLUTION

a. 1-Propanol is more soluble because it can form hydrogen bonds with water.
b. The 1-propanol is more soluble because it has a shorter carbon chain.

STUDY CHECK

Dimethyl ether and ethanol both have molar masses of 46 g/mole. However, ethanol has a much higher boiling point than dimethyl ether. How would you explain this difference in boiling points?

QUESTIONS AND PROBLEMS

Physical Properties of Alcohols, Phenols, and Ethers

13.21 Predict the compound with the higher boiling point in the following pairs:
    a. ethane or methanol   **b.** diethyl ether or 1-butanol
    c. 1-butanol or pentane

13.22 Glycerol (1,2,3-propanetriol) has a boiling point of 290 °C. 1-Pentanol, which has about the same molar mass as glycerol, boils at 138 °C. Why is the boiling point of glycerol so much higher?

13.23 Are each of the following soluble in water? Explain.
a. $CH_3—CH_2—OH$ b. $CH_3—O—CH_3$
c. $CH_3—CH_2—CH_2—CH_2—CH_2—CH_2—OH$
d. OH

13.24 Give an explanation for the following observations:
a. Ethanol is soluble in water, but propane is not.
b. Dimethyl ether is soluble in water, but pentane is not.
c. 1-Propanol is soluble in water, but 1-hexanol is not.

13.4 | Reactions of Alcohols and Thiols

LEARNING GOAL

Write equations for the combustion, dehydration, and oxidation of alcohols and thiols.

In Chapter 11, we learned that hydrocarbons undergo combustion in the presence of oxygen. Alcohols burn with oxygen, too. For example, in a restaurant, a dessert may be prepared by pouring a liquor on fruit or ice cream and lighting it. (See Figure 13.2.) The combustion of the ethanol in the liquor proceeds as follows:

$$CH_3—CH_2—OH + 3O_2 \longrightarrow 2CO_2 + 3H_2O + energy$$

Dehydration of Alcohols to Form Alkenes

FIGURE 13.2 A flaming dessert is prepared using a liquor that undergoes combustion.

Q What is the equation for the combustion of the ethanol in the liquor?

Earlier we saw that water can be added to alkenes to yield alcohols. In the reverse reaction, alcohols lose a water molecule when they are heated (180 °C) with an acid catalyst such as H_2SO_4. During the **dehydration** of an alcohol, H— and —OH are removed from *adjacent carbon atoms of the same alcohol* to produce a water molecule. A double bond forms between the same two carbon atoms to produce an alkene product:

H OH
—C—C— $\xrightarrow[Heat]{H^+}$ C=C + H_2O
Alcohol   Alkene   Water

Examples

H OH
H—C—C—H $\xrightarrow[Heat]{H^+}$ C=C + H_2O
H H
Ethanol   Ethene

OH
H
$\xrightarrow[Heat]{H^+}$ + H_2O
Cyclopentanol   Cyclopentene

 TUTORIAL
MC Dehydration and
Oxidation of Alcohols

The dehydration of a secondary alcohol can result in the formation of two products. **Saytzeff's rule** states that the major product is the one that forms by removing the hydrogen from the carbon atom that has the smaller number of hydrogen atoms. A hydrogen atom is easier to remove from the carbon atom adjacent to the carbon atom attached to the —OH group that has the fewer hydrogen atoms and thus the most alkyl groups:

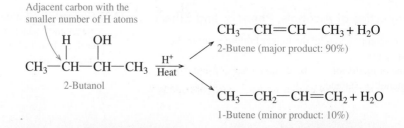

Adjacent carbon with the smaller number of H atoms

H OH
$CH_3—CH—CH—CH_3$ $\xrightarrow[Heat]{H^+}$
2-Butanol

$CH_3—CH=CH—CH_3 + H_2O$
2-Butene (major product: 90%)

$CH_3—CH_2—CH=CH_2 + H_2O$
1-Butene (minor product: 10%)

■ Dehydration of Alcohols

Consider the dehydration of 1-pentanol and 2-pentanol.

a. Is Saytzeff's rule needed to determine the dehydration product from each alcohol?
b. What is the name of the major dehydration product from each alcohol?

ANSWER

a. Saytzeff's rule is used to determine the major product from the dehydration of 2-pentanol but not from the dehydration of 1-pentanol. Carbon 2 in 2-pentanol is attached to adjacent carbon atoms with different numbers of hydrogen atoms.
b. The 1-pentanol loses the —OH from carbon 1 and a —H from carbon 2 to form 1-pentene. This is the only possible product. Using Saytzeff's rule, dehydration of 2-pentanol removes the —OH from carbon 2 and a —H from carbon 3, which has the smaller number of H atoms. The major product is 2-pentene.

■ Dehydration of Alcohols

Draw the condensed structural formula for the alkenes produced by the dehydration of the following alcohols:

$$\text{a. } CH_3-CH_2-\underset{\underset{OH}{|}}{CH}-CH_2-CH_3 \xrightarrow[\text{Heat}]{H^+}$$

b. 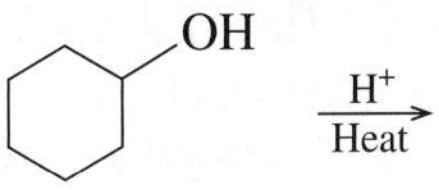 (cyclohexanol with OH) $\xrightarrow[\text{Heat}]{H^+}$

SOLUTION

a. Because the molecule is a symmetrical alcohol, the —H may be removed from the either carbon adjacent to the carbon attached to the —OH group, which forms the following product:

$$CH_3-CH_2-CH=CH-CH_3$$

b. The —OH of this alcohol is removed along with a —H from an adjacent carbon. Remember that the hydrogen atoms are not drawn in this type of geometric formula:

(cyclohexene structure)

STUDY CHECK

What is the name of the alkene produced by the dehydration of cyclopentanol?

■ Predicting Reactants

Draw the condensed structural formula of the alcohol that is needed to produce each of the following products:

a. 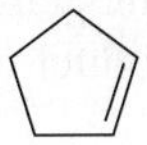 (cyclopentane)

$$\text{b. } CH_3-\underset{\underset{CH_3}{|}}{C}=CH-CH_3$$

SOLUTION

a. 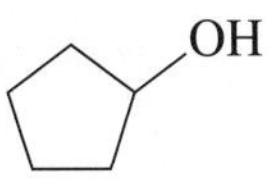 (cyclopentane with OH)

$$\text{b. } CH_3-\underset{\underset{CH_3}{|}}{\overset{\overset{OH}{|}}{C}}-CH_2-CH_3 \quad \text{or} \quad CH_3-\underset{\underset{CH_3}{|}}{CH}-\overset{\overset{OH}{|}}{CH}-CH_3$$

STUDY CHECK

What is the name of an alcohol that forms 2-methylpropene?

Formation of Ethers

Ethers form when the dehydration of alcohols occurs at lower temperatures (130° C) in the presence of an acid catalyst. Then the components of water are removed from two molecules: an H— from one alcohol, and the —OH from another. When the remaining portions of the two alcohols join, an ether is produced:

$$CH_3—OH + HO—CH_3 \xrightarrow[\text{Heat}]{H^+} CH_3—O—CH_3 + H_2O$$

Methanol   Methanol   Dimethyl ether

Oxidation of Alcohols

As we know from Chapter 6, **oxidation** is a loss of hydrogen atoms or the addition of oxygen. In organic chemistry, we find that an oxidation reaction also occurs when there is an increase in the number of carbon–oxygen bonds. In a reduction reaction, the product has fewer bonds between carbon and oxygen:

HEALTH NOTE

Methanol Poisoning

Methanol, or "wood alcohol," is a highly toxic alcohol present in products such as windshield-washer fluid, Sterno, and paint strippers. Methanol is rapidly absorbed in the gastrointestinal tract. In the liver, it is metabolized to formaldehyde and then formic acid, a substance that causes nausea, severe abdominal pain, and blurred vision. Blindness can occur because the intermediate products destroy the retina of the eye. As little as 4 mL of methanol can produce blindness. The formic acid, which is not readily eliminated from the body, lowers blood pH so severely that just 30 mL of methanol can lead to coma and death.

The treatment for methanol poisoning involves giving sodium bicarbonate to neutralize the formic acid in the blood. In some cases, ethanol is given intravenously to the patient. The enzymes in the liver pick up ethanol molecules to oxidize instead of methanol molecules. This process gives time for the methanol to be eliminated via the lungs without the formation of its dangerous oxidation products.

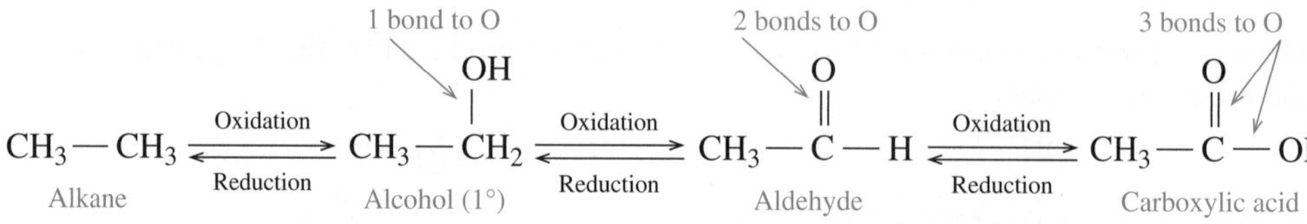

Oxidation of Primary and Secondary Alcohols

The oxidation of a primary alcohol produces an aldehyde, which contains a double bond between carbon and oxygen. The oxidation occurs by removing two hydrogen atoms, one from the —OH group and another from the carbon that is bonded to the —OH. To indicate the presence of an oxidizing agent, such as $KMnO_4$ or $K_2Cr_2O_7$, reactions are often written with the symbol [O]:

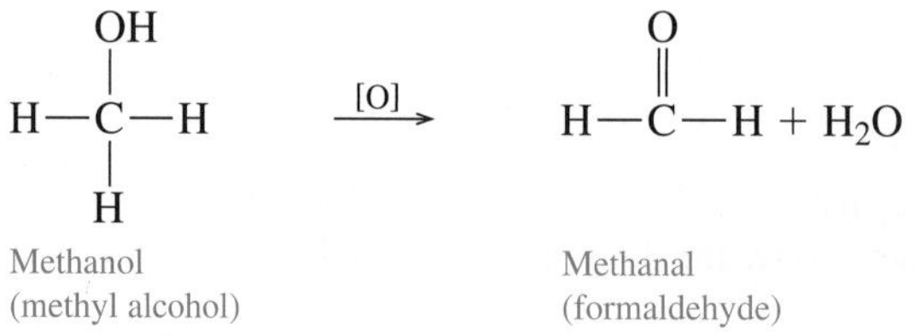

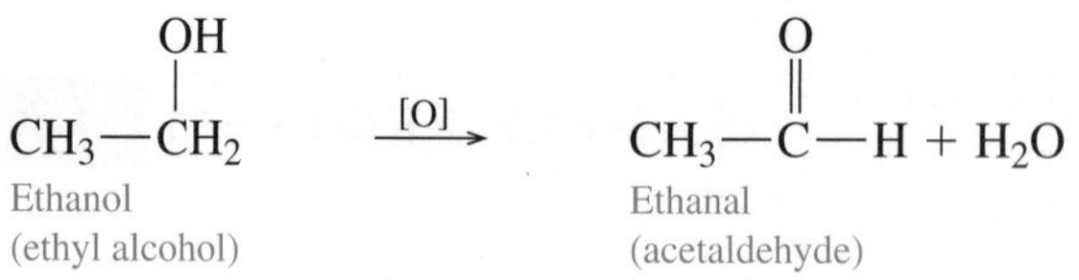

Aldehydes oxidize further by the addition of oxygen to form a carboxylic acid. This step occurs so readily that it is often difficult to isolate the aldehyde product during oxidation:

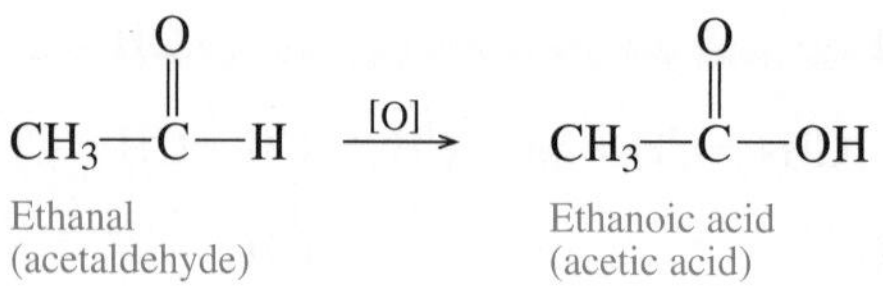

We will learn more about carboxylic acids in Chapter 16.

In the oxidation of secondary alcohols, the products are ketones. One hydrogen is removed from the —OH and another from the carbon bonded to the —OH group. The result is a ketone that has the carbon-oxygen double bond attached to alkyl groups on both sides. There is no further oxidation of a ketone because there are no hydrogen atoms attached to the carbon of the ketone group:

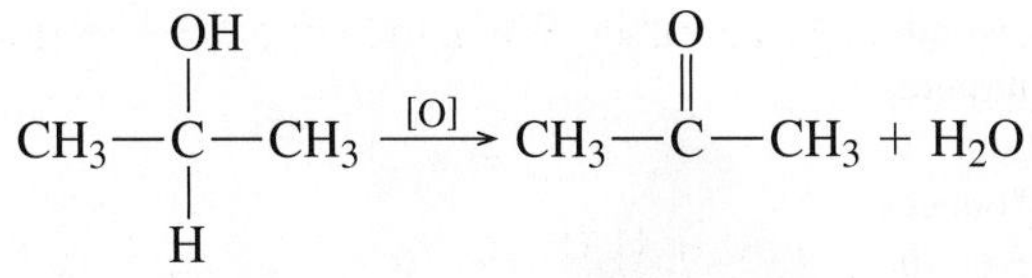

$$\underset{\substack{\text{OH} \\ | \\ \text{CH}_3-\text{C}-\text{CH}_3 \\ | \\ \text{H}}}{} \xrightarrow{[\text{O}]} \text{CH}_3-\overset{\text{O}}{\overset{||}{\text{C}}}-\text{CH}_3 + \text{H}_2\text{O}$$

2-Propanol
(isopropyl alcohol)

Propanone
(dimethyl ketone; acetone)

Tertiary alcohols do not oxidize readily, because there are no hydrogen atoms on the carbon bonded to the —OH group. Because C—C bonds are usually too strong to oxidize, tertiary alcohols resist oxidation:

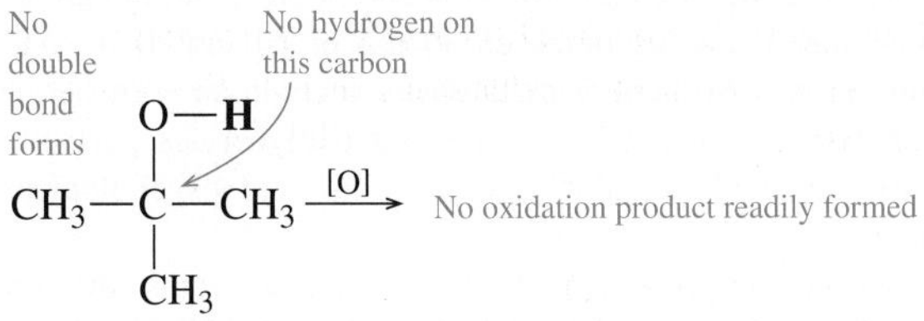

No double bond forms

No hydrogen on this carbon

$$\text{CH}_3-\underset{\substack{| \\ \text{CH}_3}}{\overset{\text{O}-\text{H}}{\text{C}}}-\text{CH}_3 \xrightarrow{[\text{O}]} \text{No oxidation product readily formed}$$

3° Alcohol

SAMPLE PROBLEM 13.9

■ Oxidation of Alcohols

Draw the condensed structural formula of the aldehyde or ketone formed by the oxidation of each of the following:

a. 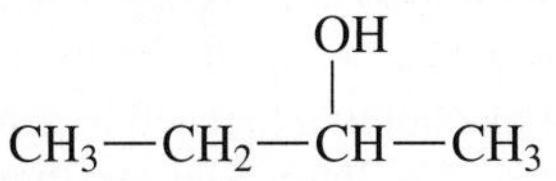 $\text{CH}_3-\text{CH}_2-\underset{\substack{| \\ }}{\overset{\text{OH}}{\text{CH}}}-\text{CH}_3$

b. $\text{CH}_3-\text{CH}_2-\text{CH}_2-\text{OH}$

SOLUTION

a. A secondary (2°) alcohol oxidizes to a ketone:

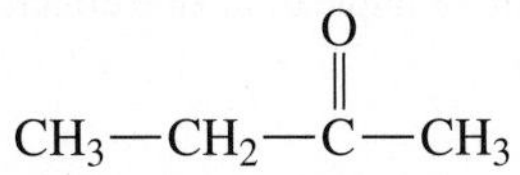

$$\text{CH}_3-\text{CH}_2-\overset{\text{O}}{\overset{||}{\text{C}}}-\text{CH}_3$$

b. A primary (1°) alcohol oxidizes to an aldehyde:

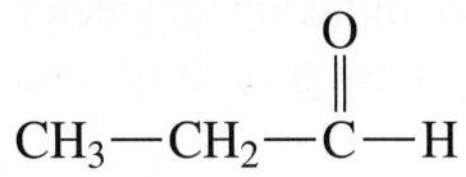

$$\text{CH}_3-\text{CH}_2-\overset{\text{O}}{\overset{||}{\text{C}}}-\text{H}$$

MC CASE STUDY
Alcohol Toxicity

STUDY CHECK

Draw the condensed structural formula of the product formed by the oxidation of 2-propanol.

During vigorous exercise, lactic acid accumulates in the muscles and causes fatigue. When the activity level is decreased, oxygen enters the muscles. The secondary —OH group in lactic acid is oxidized to a ketone group in pyruvic acid, which eventually is oxidized to

HEALTH NOTE

Oxidation of Alcohol in the Body

Ethanol is the most commonly abused drug in the United States. When ingested in small amounts, ethanol may produce a feeling of euphoria despite the fact that it is a depressant. In the liver, enzymes such as alcohol dehydrogenase oxidize ethanol to acetaldehyde, a substance that impairs mental and physical coordination. If the blood alcohol concentration exceeds 0.4%, coma or death may occur. Table 13.2 gives some of the typical behaviors exhibited at various levels of blood alcohol.

$$CH_3-CH_2-OH \xrightarrow{[O]} CH_3-\overset{\overset{O}{\|}}{C}-H \xrightarrow{[O]} 2CO_2 + H_2O$$

Ethanol (ethyl alcohol)   Ethanal (acetaldehyde)

The acetaldehyde produced from ethanol in the liver is further oxidized to acetic acid, which is eventually converted to carbon dioxide and water. However, the intermediate products of acetaldehyde and acetic acid can cause considerable damage while they are present within the cells of the liver.

TABLE 13.2 Typical Behaviors Exhibited by a 150-lb Person Consuming Alcohol

Number of Beers (12 oz) or Glasses of Wine (5 oz) in 1 hour	Blood Alcohol Level (% m/v)	Typical Behavior
1	0.025	Slightly dizzy, talkative
2	0.05	Euphoria, loud talking and laughing
4	0.10	Loss of inhibition, loss of coordination, drowsiness, legally drunk in most states
8	0.20	Intoxicated, quick to anger, exaggerated emotions
12	0.30	Unconscious
16–20	0.40–0.50	Coma and death

A person weighing 150 lb requires about one hour to metabolize 10 ounces of beer. However, the rate of metabolism of ethanol varies between nondrinkers and drinkers. Typically, nondrinkers and social drinkers can metabolize 12–15 mg of ethanol/dL of blood in one hour, but an alcoholic can metabolize as much as 30 mg of ethanol/dL in one hour. Some effects of alcohol metabolism include an increase in liver lipids (fatty liver), an increase in serum triglycerides, gastritis, pancreatitis, ketoacidosis, alcoholic hepatitis, and psychological disturbances.

When alcohol is present in the blood, it evaporates through the lungs. Thus, the percentage of alcohol in the lungs can be used to calculate the blood alcohol concentration (BAC). Several devices are used to measure the BAC. When a Breathalyzer is used, a suspected drunk driver exhales through a mouthpiece into a solution containing the orange Cr^{6+} ion. Any alcohol present in the exhaled air is oxidized, which reduces the orange Cr^{6+} to a green Cr^{3+}:

$$CH_3-CH_2-OH + Cr^{6+} \xrightarrow{[O]} CH_3-\overset{\overset{O}{\|}}{C}-OH + Cr^{3+}$$

Ethanol   Orange   Acetic acid   Green

The Alcosensor uses an oxidation of alcohol in a fuel cell to generate an electric current that is measured. The Intoxilyzer measures the amount of light absorbed by the alcohol molecules.

Sometimes alcoholics are treated with a drug called Antabuse (disulfiram), which prevents the oxidation of acetaldehyde to acetic acid. As a result, acetaldehyde accumulates in the blood, which causes nausea, profuse sweating, headache, dizziness, vomiting, and respiratory difficulties. Because of these unpleasant side effects, the patient is less likely to use alcohol.

CO_2 and H_2O. The muscles in highly trained athletes are capable of taking up greater quantities of oxygen so that vigorous exercise can be maintained for longer periods of time.

$$CH_3-\overset{OH}{\underset{|}{CH}}-\overset{\overset{O}{\|}}{C}-OH \xrightarrow[dehydrogenase]{Lactic acid} CH_3-\overset{\overset{O}{\|}}{C}-\overset{\overset{O}{\|}}{C}-OH$$

Secondary alcohol — Lactic acid   Keto group — Pyruvic acid

Oxidation of Thiols

Thiols also undergo oxidation by a loss of hydrogen atoms from the —SH groups. The oxidized product is called a **disulfide**:

$$CH_3-S-H + H-S-CH_3 \xrightarrow{[O]} CH_3-S-S-CH_3 + H_2O$$

Methanethiol   Dimethyl disulfide

Much of the protein in the hair is cross-linked by disulfide bonds, which occur mostly between the thiol groups of the amino acid cysteine:

Protein Chain—CH_2—SH + HS—CH_2—Protein Chain $\xrightarrow{[O]}$

Cysteine side groups

Protein Chain—CH_2—S—S—CH_2—Protein Chain + H_2O

Disulfide bond

When a person is given a "perm," a reducing substance is used to break the disulfide bonds. While the hair is still wrapped around the curlers, an oxidizing substance is then applied that causes new disulfide bonds to form between different parts of the protein hair strands, which gives the hair a new shape.

MC TUTORIAL
Oxidation of Thiols

QUESTIONS AND PROBLEMS

Reactions of Alcohols and Thiols

13.25 Draw the condensed structural formula of the alkene that is the major product from each of the following dehydration reactions:

a. CH_3—CH_2—CH_2—CH_2—OH $\xrightarrow[\text{Heat}]{H^+}$

b. 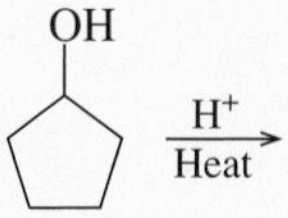
(cyclopentane with OH) $\xrightarrow[\text{Heat}]{H^+}$

c. 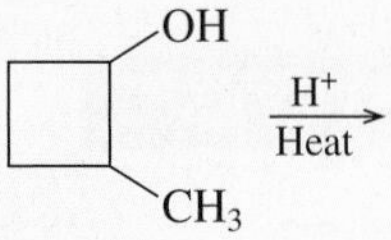
(cyclobutane with OH and CH_3) $\xrightarrow[\text{Heat}]{H^+}$

d. CH_3—CH_2—CH_2—$\overset{\overset{\text{OH}}{|}}{C}H$—$CH_3$ $\xrightarrow[\text{Heat}]{H^+}$

13.26 Draw the condensed structural formula of the alkene that is the major product from each of the following dehydration reactions:

a. CH_3—$\overset{\overset{\text{CH}_3}{|}}{C}H$—$CH_2$—OH $\xrightarrow[\text{Heat}]{H^+}$

b. CH_3—$\overset{\overset{\text{OH}}{|}}{C}H$—$\overset{\overset{\text{CH}_3}{|}}{C}H$—$CH_2$—$CH_3$ $\xrightarrow[\text{Heat}]{H^+}$

c. 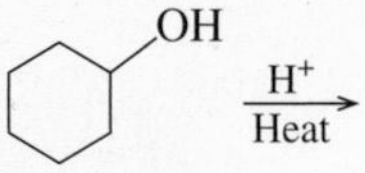
(cyclohexane with OH) $\xrightarrow[\text{Heat}]{H^+}$

d. 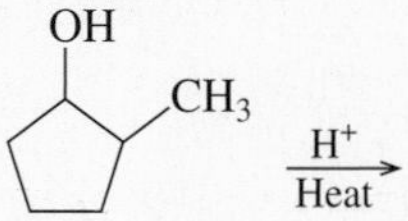
(cyclopentane with OH and CH_3) $\xrightarrow[\text{Heat}]{H^+}$

13.27 Draw the condensed structural formula of the ether produced by each of the following reactions:

a. $2CH_3$—OH $\xrightarrow[\text{Heat}]{H^+}$

b. $2CH_3$—CH_2—CH_2—OH $\xrightarrow[\text{Heat}]{H^+}$

13.28 Draw the condensed structural formula of the ether produced by each of the following reactions:

a. $2CH_3$—CH_2—OH $\xrightarrow[\text{Heat}]{H^+}$

b. $2CH_3$—$\overset{\overset{\text{CH}_3}{|}}{C}H$—$CH_2$—OH $\xrightarrow[\text{Heat}]{H^+}$

13.29 What alcohol(s) could be used to produce each of the following compounds?

a. CH_2=CH_2

b. CH_3—O—CH_2—CH_3

c. 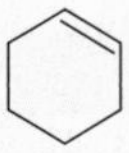
(cyclohexene)

13.30 What alcohol(s) could be used to produce each of the following compounds?

a. CH_3—CH_2—O—CH_2—CH_3

b. CH_3—$\overset{\overset{\text{CH}_3}{|}}{C}$=$CH$—$CH_3$

c. 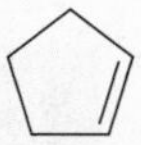
(cyclopentene)

13.31 Draw the condensed structural formula of the aldehyde or ketone produced when each of the following alcohols is oxidized [O] (if no reaction, write *none*):

a. CH_3—CH_2—CH_2—CH_2—CH_2—OH

b. CH_3—CH_2—$\overset{\overset{\text{OH}}{|}}{C}H$—$CH_3$

c. 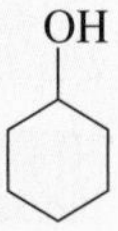
(cyclohexane with OH)

d. CH_3—$\overset{\overset{\text{OH}}{|}}{C}H$—$CH_2$—$\overset{\overset{\text{CH}_3}{|}}{C}H$—$CH_3$

e. CH_3—$\overset{\overset{\text{CH}_3}{|}}{C}H$—$CH_2$—$CH_2$—OH

13.32 Draw the condensed structural formula of the aldehyde or ketone produced when each of the following alcohols is oxidized [O] (if no reaction, write *none*):

a. 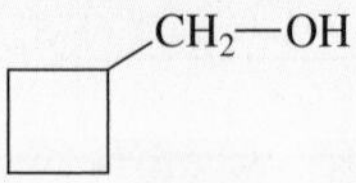
(cyclobutane with CH_2—OH)

b. CH_3—$\overset{\overset{\text{CH}_3}{|}}{C}H$—$CH_2$—$\overset{\underset{\underset{\text{CH}_3}{|}}{}}{C}H$—OH

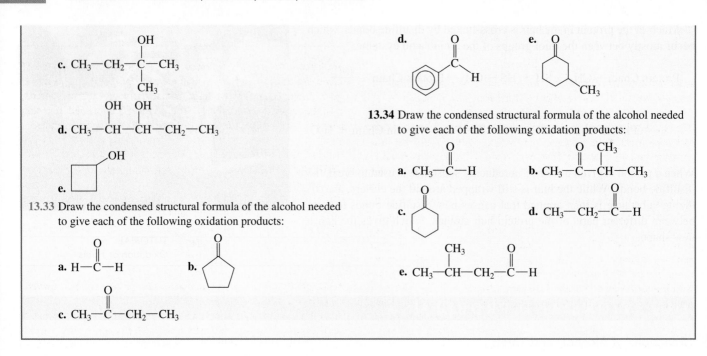

c. CH₃—CH₂—$\overset{\overset{\displaystyle OH}{|}}{\underset{\underset{\displaystyle CH_3}{|}}{C}}$—CH₃

d. CH₃—$\overset{\overset{\displaystyle OH}{|}}{CH}$—$\overset{\overset{\displaystyle OH}{|}}{CH}$—CH₂—CH₃

e.

13.33 Draw the condensed structural formula of the alcohol needed to give each of the following oxidation products:

a. H—$\overset{\overset{\displaystyle O}{\|}}{C}$—H

b.

c. CH₃—$\overset{\overset{\displaystyle O}{\|}}{C}$—CH₂—CH₃

d.

e.

13.34 Draw the condensed structural formula of the alcohol needed to give each of the following oxidation products:

a. CH₃—$\overset{\overset{\displaystyle O}{\|}}{C}$—H

b. CH₃—$\overset{\overset{\displaystyle O}{\|}}{C}$—$\overset{\overset{\displaystyle CH_3}{|}}{CH}$—CH₃

c.

d. CH₃—CH₂—$\overset{\overset{\displaystyle O}{\|}}{C}$—H

e. CH₃—$\overset{\overset{\displaystyle CH_3}{|}}{CH}$—CH₂—$\overset{\overset{\displaystyle O}{\|}}{C}$—H

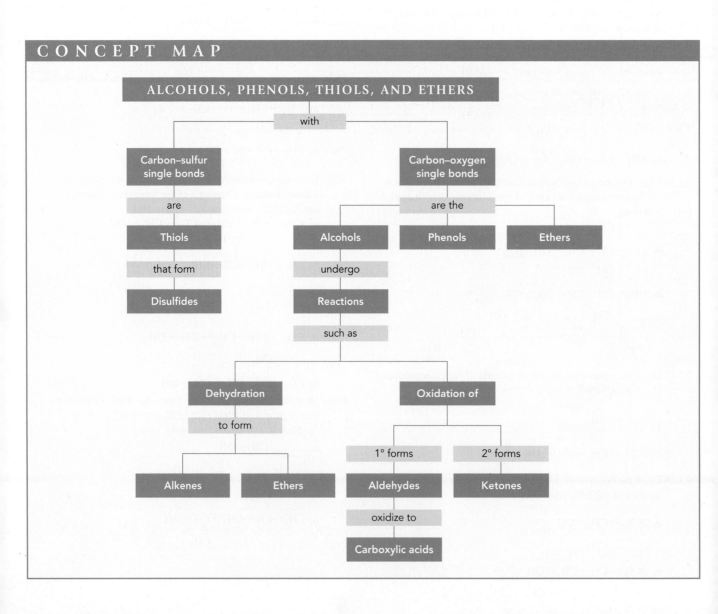

CONCEPT MAP

ALCOHOLS, PHENOLS, THIOLS, AND ETHERS

with

Carbon–sulfur single bonds   Carbon–oxygen single bonds

are   are the

Thiols   Alcohols   Phenols   Ethers

that form   undergo

Disulfides   Reactions

                 such as

Dehydration   Oxidation of

to form

Alkenes   Ethers   1° forms   2° forms

                        Aldehydes   Ketones

                        oxidize to

                        Carboxylic acids

CHAPTER REVIEW

13.1 Alcohols, Phenols, and Thiols
LEARNING GOAL: *Give IUPAC and common names for alcohols, phenols, and thiols; draw their condensed structural formulas. Classify alcohols as primary, secondary, or tertiary.*

The functional group of an alcohol is the hydroxyl group —OH bonded to a carbon chain. In a phenol, the hydroxyl group is bonded to an aromatic ring. In thiols, the functional group is —SH, which is analogous to the —OH group of alcohols. Alcohols are classified according to the number of alkyl or aromatic groups bonded to the carbon that holds the —OH. In a primary (1°) alcohol, one group is attached to the hydroxyl carbon. In a secondary (2°) alcohol, two groups are attached. In a tertiary (3°) alcohol, there are three groups bonded to the hydroxyl carbon. In the IUPAC system, the names of alcohols have *ol* endings, and the location of the —OH group is given by numbering the carbon chain. Simple alcohols are generally named by their common names with the alkyl name preceding the term *alcohol*. A cyclic alcohol is named as a cycloalkanol. An aromatic alcohol is named as a phenol.

13.2 Ethers
LEARNING GOAL: *Give the IUPAC and common names of ethers; draw the condensed structural formula.*

In an ether, an oxygen atom is connected by single bonds to two alkyl or aromatic groups. In the common names of ethers, the alkyl groups are listed alphabetically followed by the name *ether*. In the IUPAC name, the smaller alkyl group with the oxygen is named as an alkoxy group and is attached to the longer alkane chain, which is numbered to give the location of the alkoxy group. Some alcohols and ethers are isomers, which means that they have the same molecular formulas.

13.3 Physical Properties of Alcohols, Phenols, and Ethers
LEARNING GOAL: *Describe some physical properties of alcohols, phenols, and ethers.*

The —OH group allows alcohols to hydrogen bond, which causes alcohols to have higher boiling points than alkanes and ethers of similar mass. Short-chain alcohols and ethers can hydrogen bond with water, which makes them soluble.

13.4 Reactions of Alcohols and Thiols
LEARNING GOAL: *Write equations for the combustion, dehydration, and oxidation of alcohols and thiols.*

At high temperatures, alcohols dehydrate in the presence of an acid to yield alkenes. At lower temperatures, two molecules of alcohol lose —H and —OH to produce an ether. Primary alcohols are oxidized to aldehydes, which can oxidize further to carboxylic acids. Secondary alcohols are oxidized to ketones. Tertiary alcohols do not oxidize. Thiols undergo oxidation to form disulfides.

SUMMARY OF NAMING

Structure	Family	IUPAC Name	Common Name
CH_3—OH	Alcohol	Methanol	Methyl alcohol
⬡—OH	Phenol	Phenol	Phenol
CH_3—SH	Thiol	Methanethiol	
CH_3—O—CH_3	Ether	Methoxymethane	Dimethyl ether
(furan ring)	Cyclic ether	Furan	
CH_3—S—S—CH_3	Disulfide	Dimethyldisulfide	

SUMMARY OF REACTIONS

COMBUSTION OF ALCOHOLS

$$CH_3-CH_2-OH + 3O_2 \longrightarrow 2CO_2 + 3H_2O$$
Ethanol · Oxygen · Carbon dioxide · Water

DEHYDRATION OF ALCOHOLS TO FORM ALKENES

$$CH_3-CH_2-CH_2-OH \xrightarrow[\text{Heat}]{H^+}$$
1-Propanol
$$CH_3-CH{=}CH_2 + H_2O$$
Propene

FORMATION OF ETHERS

$$CH_3-OH + HO-CH_3 \xrightarrow[\text{Heat}]{H^+}$$
Methanol
$$CH_3-O-CH_3 + H_2O$$
Dimethyl ether

OXIDATION OF PRIMARY ALCOHOLS TO FORM ALDEHYDES

$$CH_3-CH_2(OH) \xrightarrow{[O]} CH_3-C(=O)-H + H_2O$$
Ethanol · Acetaldehyde

OXIDATION OF SECONDARY ALCOHOLS TO FORM KETONES

$$CH_3-CH(OH)-CH_3 \xrightarrow{[O]} CH_3-C(=O)-CH_3 + H_2O$$
2-Propanol · Propanone

OXIDATION OF THIOLS TO FORM DISULFIDES

$$CH_3—S—H + H—S—CH_3 \xrightarrow{[O]} CH_3—S—S—CH_3 + H_2O$$

Methanethiol   Dimethyl disulfide

OXIDATION OF ALDEHYDES TO CARBOXYLIC ACIDS

$$CH_3—\overset{\overset{\displaystyle O}{\|}}{C}—H \xrightarrow{[O]} CH_3—\overset{\overset{\displaystyle O}{\|}}{C}—OH$$

Acetaldehyde   Acetic acid

■ KEY TERMS

alcohol An organic compound that contains the hydroxyl (—OH) functional group attached to a carbon chain.

cyclic ether A compound that contains an oxygen atom in a carbon ring.

dehydration A reaction that removes water from an alcohol in the presence of an acid to form alkenes at high temperature, or ethers at lower temperatures.

disulfide A compound formed from thiols; disulfides contain the —S—S— functional group.

ether An organic compound in which an oxygen atom is bonded to two alkyl or two aromatic groups, or a mix of the two.

hydroxyl group The —OH functional group.

oxidation The loss of two hydrogen atoms from a reactant to give a more oxidized compound, e.g., primary alcohols oxidize to aldehydes, secondary alcohols oxidize to ketones. An oxidation

can also be the addition of an oxygen atom as in the oxidation of aldehydes to carboxylic acids.

phenol An organic compound that has an —OH group attached to a benzene ring.

primary (1°) alcohol An alcohol that has one alkyl group bonded to the alcohol carbon atom.

Saytzeff's rule In the dehydration of an alcohol, hydrogen is removed from the carbon that already has the smaller number of hydrogen atoms to form an alkene.

secondary (2°) alcohol An alcohol that has two alkyl groups bonded to the carbon atom with the —OH group.

tertiary (3°) alcohol An alcohol that has three alkyl groups bonded to the carbon atom with the —OH.

thiol An organic compound that contains a thiol group (—SH).

■ UNDERSTANDING THE CONCEPTS

13.35 Urushiol is a substance in poison ivy and poison oak that causes itching and blistering of the skin. Identify the functional groups in urushiol:

13.36 BHA is an antioxidant used as a preservative in foods, such as baked goods, butter, meats, and snack foods. Identify the functional groups in BHA:

13.37 Menthol gives a peppermint taste and odor used in candy and throat lozenges. Identify the functional groups in menthol:

13.38 Vanillin is a flavoring obtained from the seeds of the vanilla bean. Identify the functional groups in vanillin:

ADDITIONAL QUESTIONS AND PROBLEMS

For instructor-assigned homework, go to www.masteringchemistry.com.

13.39 Classify each of the following as a primary (1°), secondary (2°), or tertiary alcohol (3°):

a. (cyclohexane with OH)

b. (cyclohexane with CH_2—OH)

c. CH_3—$\overset{CH_3}{\underset{|}{CH}}$—$CH_2$—OH

d. CH_3—$\overset{CH_3}{\underset{\underset{CH_3}{|}}{\overset{|}{C}}}$—$CH_2$—$\overset{OH}{\underset{|}{CH}}$—$CH_3$

e. HO—CH_2—CH_2—CH_3

f. (cyclopentane—$\overset{OH}{\underset{\underset{CH_3}{|}}{\overset{|}{C}}}$—$CH_3$)

13.40 Classify each of the following as a primary (1°), secondary (2°), or tertiary alcohol (3°):

a. (cyclohexane with OH and CH_3)

b. (cyclohexane with OH and CH_2—CH_3)

c. CH_3—$\overset{CH_2—OH}{\underset{|}{CH}}$—$CH_2$—$CH_3$

d. CH_3—$\overset{OH}{\underset{\underset{CH_3}{|}}{\overset{|}{C}}}$—$CH_2$—$\overset{CH_3}{\underset{|}{CH}}$—$CH_3$

e. CH_3—CH_2—CH_2—CH_2—OH

f. (cyclopentane—$\overset{CH_3}{\underset{|}{CH}}$—OH)

13.41 Identify each of the following as an alcohol, a phenol, an ether, a cyclic ether, or a thiol:

a. (cyclohexane with OH, CH_3, Cl)

b. (benzene—O—CH_3)

c. CH_3—$\overset{SH}{\underset{|}{CH}}$—$CH_3$

d. CH_3—$\overset{OH}{\underset{\underset{CH_3}{|}}{\overset{|}{C}}}$—$CH_2$—$\overset{CH_3}{\underset{|}{CH}}$—$CH_3$

e. CH_3—CH_2—CH_2—O—CH_3

f. (furan ring with CH_3)

g. CH_3—$\overset{Br}{\underset{|}{CH}}$—$CH_2$—$\overset{OH}{\underset{|}{CH}}$—$CH_3$

h. (phenol ring with OH and CH_3)

13.42 Identify each of the following as an alcohol, a phenol, an ether, a cyclic ether, or a thiol:

a. (benzene with OH and Cl)

b. CH_3—CH_2—CH_2—SH

c. (cyclopentane—O—CH_2—CH_3)

d. CH_3—$\overset{SH}{\underset{\underset{CH_3}{|}}{\overset{|}{C}}}$—$CH_2$—$\overset{CH_3}{\underset{|}{CH}}$—$CH_3$

e. CH_3—CH_2—$\overset{O—CH_3}{\underset{|}{CH}}$—$CH_2$—$CH_3$

f. (dioxane ring)

g. (cyclohexane with OH and Cl and Cl)

h. (benzene with OH, CH_3, CH_3)

13.43 Give the IUPAC and common names (if any) for each of the compounds in problem 13.41.

13.44 Give the IUPAC and common names (if any) for each of the compounds in problem 13.42.

13.45 Draw the condensed structural formula of each of the following compounds:
a. 3-methylcyclopentanol   b. *p*-chlorophenol
c. 2-methyl-3-pentanol   d. phenyl ethyl ether
e. 3-pentanethiol   f. *ortho*-cresol
g. 2,4-dibromophenol

13.46 Draw the condensed structural formula of each of the following compounds:
a. 3-methoxypentane   b. *meta*-chlorophenol
c. 2,3-pentanediol   d. methyl propyl ether
e. methanethiol   f. 3-methyl-2-butanol
g. 3,4-dichlorocyclohexanol

13.47 Draw the condensed structural formulas of all the alcohols with a molecular formula $C_4H_{10}O$.

13.48 Draw the condensed structural formulas of all the ethers with a molecular formula $C_5H_{12}O$.

13.49 Which compound in each of the following pairs would you expect to have the higher boiling point? Explain.
a. butane or 1-propanol
b. 1-propanol or ethyl methyl ether
c. ethanol or 1-butanol

13.50 Which compound in each of the following pairs would you expect to have the higher boiling point? Explain.
a. propane or ethyl alcohol
b. 2-propanol or 2-pentanol
c. diethyl ether or 1-butanol

13.51 Explain why each of the following compounds would be soluble or insoluble in water:
a. 2-propanol   b. dimethyl ether   c. 1-hexanol

13.52 Explain why each of the following compounds would be soluble or insoluble in water:
a. glycerol   b. butane   c. 1,3-hexanediol

13.53 Draw the condensed structural formula for the alkene (major product), aldehyde, ether, ketone, or *none* produced in each of the following:

a. CH_3—CH_2—CH_2—OH $\xrightarrow[\text{Heat}]{H^+}$

b. CH_3—CH_2—CH_2—OH $\xrightarrow{[O]}$

c. $CH_3-CH_2-\overset{\overset{\displaystyle OH}{|}}{CH}-CH_3$ $\xrightarrow[\text{Heat}]{H^+}$

d. $CH_3-CH_2-\overset{\overset{\displaystyle OH}{|}}{CH}-CH_3$ $\xrightarrow{[O]}$

e. $2CH_3-CH_2-CH_2-OH$ $\xrightarrow{H^+}$

f. $\xrightarrow[\text{Heat}]{H^+}$

g. $\xrightarrow{[O]}$

13.54 Draw the condensed structural formula for the alkene (major product), aldehyde, ether, ketone, or *none* produced in each of the following:

a. $CH_3-\overset{\overset{\displaystyle CH_3}{|}}{CH}-CH_2-OH$ $\xrightarrow[\text{Heat}]{H^+}$

b. $CH_3-\overset{\overset{\displaystyle CH_3}{|}}{CH}-\overset{\overset{\displaystyle OH}{|}}{CH}-CH_3$ $\xrightarrow[\text{Heat}]{H^+}$

c. $CH_3-\overset{\overset{\displaystyle CH_3}{|}}{CH}-\overset{\overset{\displaystyle OH}{|}}{CH}-CH_3$ $\xrightarrow{[O]}$

d. $\xrightarrow[\text{Heat}]{H^+}$

e. $\xrightarrow{[O]}$

f. $2CH_3-CH_2-OH$ $\xrightarrow[\text{Heat}]{H^+}$

g. $CH_3-CH_2-CH_2-\overset{\overset{\displaystyle OH}{|}}{CH}-CH_3$ $\xrightarrow[\text{Heat}]{H^+}$

13.55 Sometimes several steps are needed to prepare a compound. Using a combination of the reactions we have studied, indicate how you might prepare the following from the starting substance given. For example, 2-propanol could be prepared from 1-propanol by first dehydrating the alcohol to give propene and then hydrating it again to give 2-propanol according to Markovnikov's rule, as follows:

$CH_3-CH_2-CH_2-OH \xrightarrow[\text{Heat}]{H^+} CH_3-CH=CH_2 + H_2O$

$\xrightarrow{H^+} CH_3-\overset{\overset{\displaystyle OH}{|}}{CH}-CH_3$
2-Propanol

a. Prepare 2-chloropropane from 1-propanol.
b. Prepare 2-methylpropane from 2-methyl-2-propanol.
c. Prepare $CH_3-\overset{\overset{\displaystyle O}{||}}{C}-CH_3$ from 1-propanol.

13.56 As in problem 13.55, indicate how you might prepare the following from the starting substance given:
a. Prepare 1-pentene from 1-pentanol.
b. Prepare chlorocyclohexane from cyclohexanol.
c. Prepare 1,2-dibromobutane from 1-butanol.

13.57 Identify the functional groups in the following molecule:

Testosterone

13.58 Identify the functional groups in the following molecule:

Tetrahydrocannabinol (THC)

13.59 Hexylresorcinol, an antiseptic ingredient used in mouthwashes and throat lozenges, has the IUPAC name of 4-hexyl-1,3-benzenediol. Draw its condensed structural formula.

13.60 Menthol, which has a minty flavor, is used in throat sprays and lozenges. Thymol is used as a topical antiseptic to destroy mold. For each, give their IUPAC names. What is similar and what is different about their structures?

Menthol   Thymol

CHALLENGE QUESTIONS

13.61 Draw the condensed structural formula for each of the following naturally occurring compounds:
a. 2,5-dichlorophenol, a defense pheromone of a grasshopper.
b. Skunk scent, a mixture of 3-methyl-1-butanethiol and *trans*-2-butene-1-thiol.
c. Pentachlorophenol, a wood preservative.

13.62 Dimethyl ether and ethyl alcohol both have the molecular formula C_2H_6O. One has a boiling point of -24 °C, and the other, 79 °C. Draw the condensed structural formula of each compound. Decide which boiling point goes with which compound and explain.

13.63 A compound with the formula C_4H_8O is synthesized from 2-methyl-1-propanol and oxidizes easily to give a carboxylic acid. Draw the condensed structural formula of the compound.

13.64 Methyl *tert*-butyl ether (MTBE), or 2-methoxy-2-methyl-propane, has been used as a fuel additive for gasoline to boost the octane rating and to reduce CO emissions.

a. If fuel mixtures are required to contain 2.7% oxygen by mass, how many grams of MTBE must be present in each 100. g of gasoline?
b. How many liters of MTBE would be in 1.0 L of fuel if the density of both gasoline and MTBE is 0.740 g/mL?
c. Write the equation for the complete combustion of MTBE.
d. How many liters of air containing 21% (v/v) O_2 are required at STP to completely react (combust) 1.00 L of liquid MTBE?

13.65 Draw the condensed structural formulas and give the IUPAC names of all the alcohols that have the formula $C_5H_{12}O$.

ANSWERS

ANSWERS TO STUDY CHECKS

13.1 3-chloro-1-butanol

13.2 $CH_3—CH_2—SH$

13.3 ethyl phenyl ether

13.4 1-butanol, 2-butanol, 1-methoxypropane, ethoxyethane

13.5 Both are unsaturated cyclic ethers, but furan has five atoms in the ring and pyran has six atoms.

13.6 Ethanol molecules can hydrogen bond with each other, but ether molecules cannot. Thus, a higher temperature is required to break the hydrogen bonds between ethanol molecules.

13.7 cyclopentene

13.8 2-methyl-1-propanol, 2-methyl-2-propanol

13.9

$$CH_3—\overset{\overset{\displaystyle O}{\|}}{C}—CH_3$$

ANSWERS TO SELECTED QUESTIONS AND PROBLEMS

13.1 a. 1° **b.** 1° **c.** 3° **d.** 2°

13.3 a. ethanol **b.** 2-butanol
c. 2-pentanol **d.** 4-methylcyclohexanol

13.5 a. $CH_3—CH_2—CH_2—OH$
b. $CH_3—OH$
c. $CH_3—CH_2—\overset{\overset{\displaystyle OH}{|}}{CH}—CH_2—CH_3$
d. $CH_3—\overset{\overset{\displaystyle OH}{|}}{\underset{\underset{\displaystyle CH_3}{|}}{C}}—CH_2—CH_3$
e.

13.7 a. phenol
b. 2-bromophenol, *o*-bromophenol
c. 3,5-dichlorophenol
d. 3-bromophenol, *m*-bromophenol

13.9 a. 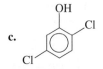 **b.**
c. **d.**

13.11 a. methanethiol **b.** 2-propanethiol
c. 2,3-dimethyl-1-butanethiol **d.** cyclobutanethiol

13.13 a. methoxyethane, ethyl methyl ether
b. methoxycyclohexane, cyclohexyl methyl ether
c. ethoxycyclobutane, cyclobutyl ethyl ether
d. 1-methoxypropane, methyl propyl ether

13.15 a. $CH_3—CH_2—O—CH_2—CH_2—CH_3$
b. $CH_3—CH_2—O—\triangleleft$ **c.**
d. $CH_3—CH_2—O—CH_2—\overset{\overset{\displaystyle CH_3}{|}}{CH}—CH_2—CH_3$
e. $CH_3—\overset{\overset{\displaystyle O—CH_3}{|}}{CH}—\underset{\underset{\displaystyle O—CH_3}{|}}{CH}—CH_2—CH_3$

13.17 a. isomers ($C_5H_{12}O$)   **b.** different compounds
     c. isomers ($C_5H_{12}O$)

13.19 a. tetrahydrofuran   **b.** 3-methylfuran
     c. 5-methyl-1,3-dioxane

13.21 a. methanol   **b.** 1-butanol   **c.** 1-butanol

13.23 a. yes, hydrogen bonding
     b. yes, hydrogen bonding
     c. no, long carbon chain diminishes effect of —OH group
     d. yes (slightly), hydrogen bonding

13.25 a. $CH_3-CH_2-CH=CH_2$ **b.**

c.

     d. $CH_3-CH_2-CH=CH-CH_3$

13.27 a. CH_3-O-CH_3
     b. $CH_3-CH_2-CH_2-O-CH_2-CH_2-CH_3$

13.29 a. CH_3-CH_2-OH **b.** $CH_3-OH + CH_3-CH_2-OH$
     c. OH

13.31 a. $CH_3-CH_2-CH_2-CH_2-\overset{\overset{O}{\|}}{C}-H$

     b. $CH_3-CH_2-\overset{\overset{O}{\|}}{C}-CH_3$ **c.**

     d. $CH_3-\overset{\overset{O}{\|}}{C}-CH_2-\overset{\overset{CH_3}{|}}{CH}-CH_3$

     e. $CH_3-\overset{\overset{CH_3}{|}}{CH}-CH_2-\overset{\overset{O}{\|}}{C}-H$

13.33 a. CH_3-OH **b.** OH

     c. $CH_3-CH_2-\overset{\overset{OH}{|}}{CH}-CH_3$ **d.** CH_2-OH

     e. OH ... CH_3

13.35 phenol, alcohol

13.37 cycloalkane, alcohol

13.39 a. 2°   **b.** 1°   **c.** 1°
     d. 2°   **e.** 1°   **f.** 3°

13.41 a. alcohol   **b.** ether   **c.** thiol
     d. alcohol   **e.** ether   **f.** cyclic ether
     g. alcohol   **h.** phenol

13.43 a. 2-chloro-4-methylcyclohexanol
     b. methoxybenzene, methyl phenyl ether
     c. 2-propanethiol

d. 2,4-dimethyl-2-pentanol
e. 1-methoxypropane, methyl propyl ether
f. 3-methylfuran
g. 4-bromo-2-pentanol
h. *meta*-cresol, 3-methylphenol

13.45 a. OH ... CH_3 **b.** OH ... Cl

     c. $CH_3-\overset{\overset{CH_3}{|}}{CH}-\overset{\overset{OH}{|}}{CH}-CH_2-CH_3$ **d.** O—CH_2-CH_3

     e. $CH_3-CH_2-\overset{\overset{SH}{|}}{CH}-CH_2-CH_3$ **f.** CH_3 ... OH

     g. OH, Br, Br

13.47 $CH_3-CH_2-CH_2-CH_2-OH$

$CH_3-\overset{\overset{CH_3}{|}}{CH}-CH_2-OH$

$CH_3-\overset{\overset{OH}{|}}{CH}-CH_2-CH_3$

$CH_3-\overset{\overset{OH}{|}}{\underset{\underset{CH_3}{|}}{C}}-CH_3$

13.49 a. 1-propanol, hydrogen bonding
     b. 1-propanol, hydrogen bonding
     c. 1-butanol, higher molar mass

13.51 a. soluble, hydrogen bonding
     b. soluble, hydrogen bonding
     c. insoluble, long carbon chain diminishes effect
       of polar —OH on hydrogen bonding

13.53 a. $CH_3-CH=CH_2$ **b.** $CH_3-CH_2-\overset{\overset{O}{\|}}{C}-H$

     c. $CH_3-CH=CH-CH_3$ **d.** $CH_3-CH_2-\overset{\overset{O}{\|}}{C}-CH_3$
     e. $CH_3-CH_2-CH_2-O-CH_2-CH_2-CH_3$

     f.   **g.**

13.55 a. $CH_3-CH_2-CH_2-OH \xrightarrow[\text{Heat}]{H^+}$

$CH_3-CH=CH_2 + HCl \longrightarrow CH_3-\overset{\overset{Cl}{|}}{CH}-CH_3$

b. 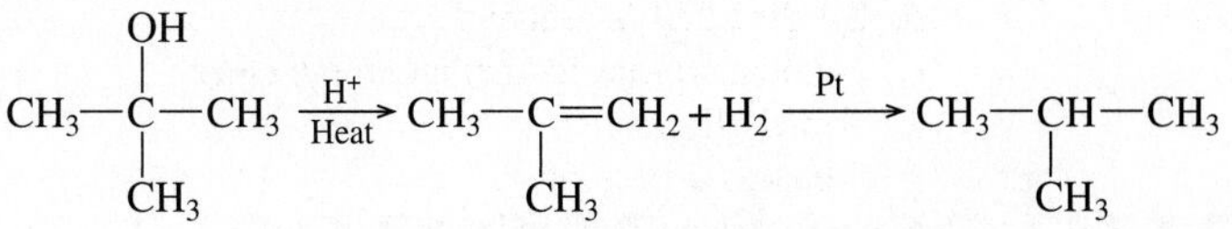 $CH_3-\overset{\overset{\displaystyle OH}{|}}{\underset{\underset{\displaystyle CH_3}{|}}{C}}-CH_3 \xrightarrow[\text{Heat}]{H^+} CH_3-\overset{}{\underset{\underset{\displaystyle CH_3}{|}}{C}}=CH_2 + H_2 \xrightarrow{\text{Pt}} CH_3-\overset{}{\underset{\underset{\displaystyle CH_3}{|}}{CH}}-CH_3$

c. $CH_3-CH_2-CH_2-OH \xrightarrow[\text{Heat}]{H^+} CH_3-CH=CH_2 + H_2O \xrightarrow[\text{Heat}]{H^+} CH_3-\overset{\overset{\displaystyle OH}{|}}{CH}-CH_3 \xrightarrow{[O]} CH_3-\overset{\overset{\displaystyle O}{\|}}{C}-CH_3$

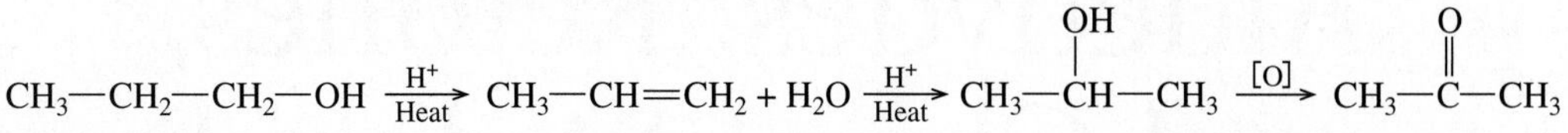

13.57 cycloalkane, cycloalkene, ketone, and alcohol functional groups

13.59

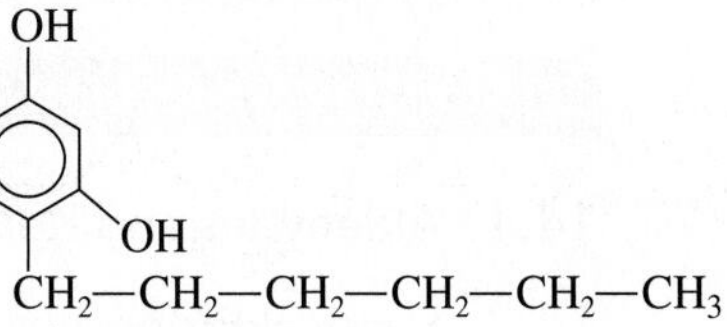

13.61 a.

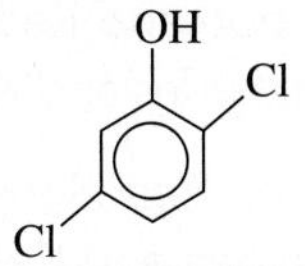

b. 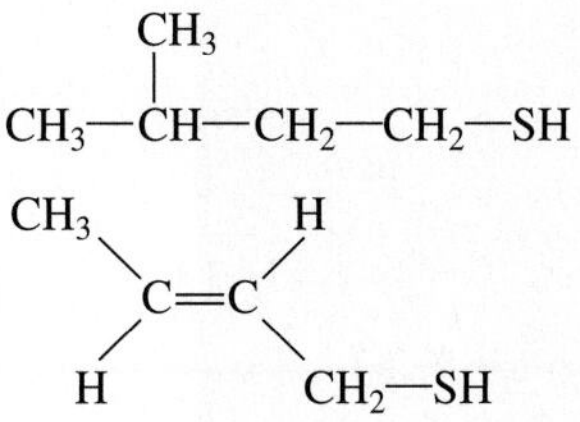 $\overset{\overset{\displaystyle CH_3}{|}}{CH_3-CH-CH_2-CH_2-SH}$

c.

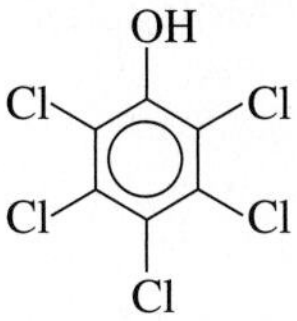

13.63 $\overset{\overset{\displaystyle CH_3}{|}}{CH_3-CH}-\overset{\overset{\displaystyle O}{\|}}{C}-H$

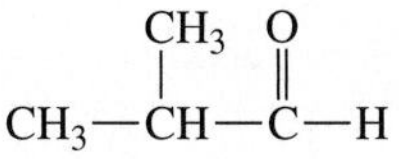

13.65 $CH_3-CH_2-CH_2-CH_2-CH_2-OH$ 1-pentanol

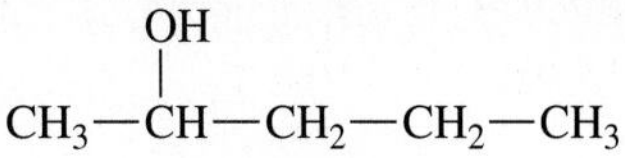

$CH_3-\overset{\overset{\displaystyle OH}{|}}{CH}-CH_2-CH_2-CH_3$ 2-pentanol

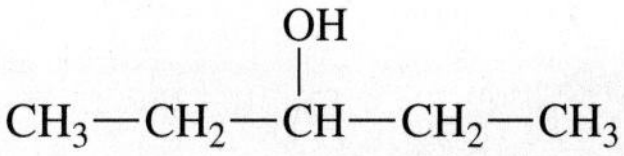

$CH_3-CH_2-\overset{\overset{\displaystyle OH}{|}}{CH}-CH_2-CH_3$ 3-pentanol

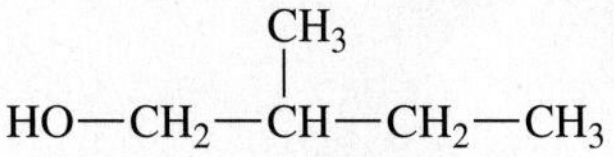

$HO-CH_2-\overset{\overset{\displaystyle CH_3}{|}}{CH}-CH_2-CH_3$ 2-methyl-1-butanol

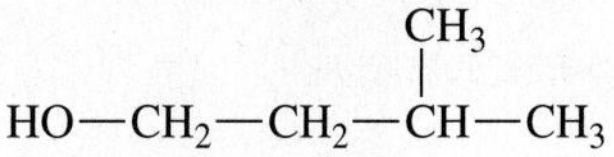

$HO-CH_2-CH_2-\overset{\overset{\displaystyle CH_3}{|}}{CH}-CH_3$ 3-methyl-1-butanol

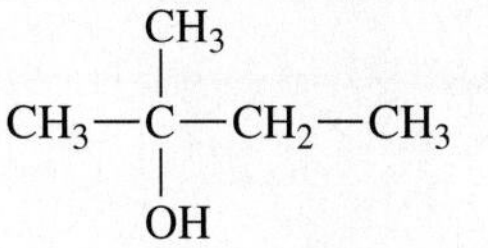

$CH_3-\overset{\overset{\displaystyle CH_3}{|}}{\underset{\underset{\displaystyle OH}{|}}{C}}-CH_2-CH_3$ 2-methyl-2-butanol

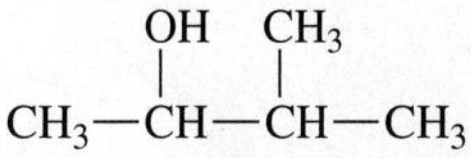

$CH_3-\overset{\overset{\displaystyle OH}{|}}{CH}-\overset{\overset{\displaystyle CH_3}{|}}{CH}-CH_3$ 3-methyl-2-butanol

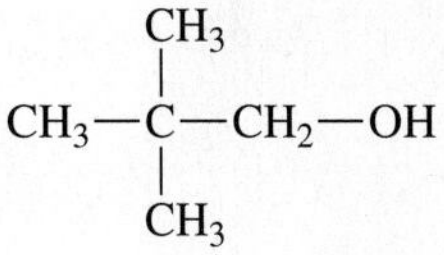

$CH_3-\overset{\overset{\displaystyle CH_3}{|}}{\underset{\underset{\displaystyle CH_3}{|}}{C}}-CH_2-OH$ 2,2-dimethyl-1-propanol

14 Aldehydes, Ketones, and Chiral Molecules

"Dentures replace natural teeth that are extracted due to cavities, bad gums, or trauma," says Dr. Irene Hilton, dentist, La Clinica De La Raza. "I make an impression of teeth using alginate, which is a polysaccharide extracted from seaweed. I mix the compound with water and place the gel-like material in the patient's mouth, where it becomes a hard, cementlike substance. I fill this mold with gypsum ($CaSO_4$) and water, which form a solid to which I add teeth made of plastic or porcelain. When I get a good match to the patient's own teeth, I prepare a preliminary wax denture. This is placed in the patient's mouth to check the bite and adjust the position of the replacement teeth. Then a permanent denture is made using a hard plastic polymer (methyl methacrylate)."

Mastering**CHEMISTRY**™

Visit **www.masteringchemistry.com** for self-study materials and instructor-assigned homework.

I n this chapter, we will study two families of organic compounds: aldehydes and ketones. Many of the odors that you associate with flavorings and perfumes are due a carbon–oxygen double bond called a *carbonyl group* (C=O). Aldehydes in foods and perfumes provide the odors and flavors of vanilla, almond, and cinnamon. In biology, you may have seen specimens preserved in a solution of formaldehyde. You probably notice the odor of a ketone if you use paint or nail polish remover.

In later chapters, we will see how the carbonyl group influences the structures of carbohydrates, proteins, and nucleic acids. Aldehydes and ketones are also important compounds in industry, providing the solvents and reactants that make up many common materials we use in our lives.

14.1 Aldehydes and Ketones

In an **aldehyde**, the carbon of the carbonyl group is bonded to at least one hydrogen atom. That carbon may also be bonded to another hydrogen atom, a carbon of an alkyl group, or an aromatic ring. (See Figure 14.1.) In a **ketone**, the carbonyl group is bonded to two alkyl groups or aromatic rings.

Structure of the Carbonyl Group

The carbonyl group consists of a carbon–oxygen double bond with bonds at angles of 120° to two other atoms. The double bond in the carbonyl group is similar to that of alkenes, except the carbonyl group has a dipole. The oxygen atom with two lone pairs of electrons is much more electronegative than the carbon atom. Therefore, the carbonyl group has a strong dipole with a partial negative charge (δ^-) on the oxygen and a partial positive charge (δ^+) on the carbon. The polarity of the carbonyl group strongly influences the physical and chemical properties of aldehydes and ketones.

There are several ways to draw the structural formulas of aldehydes and ketones. In the condensed structural formula, the aldehyde group may be drawn as separate atoms, or it may be written as —CHO at the beginning of a carbon chain. An aldehyde would not be written as —COH, which looks like a hydroxyl group. The keto group (C=O) located in the middle of the carbon chain is sometimes written as CO. For convenience, the line-bond formulas are also used, with the functional group atoms written separately. Isomers, which have the same molecular formula, can be written for aldehydes and ketones as follows:

LEARNING GOAL

Identify compounds with the carbonyl group as aldehydes and ketones. Give the IUPAC and common names for aldehydes and ketones; draw their condensed structural formulas.

 SELF STUDY ACTIVITY
Aldehydes and Ketones

 TUTORIAL
Naming Aldehydes and Ketones

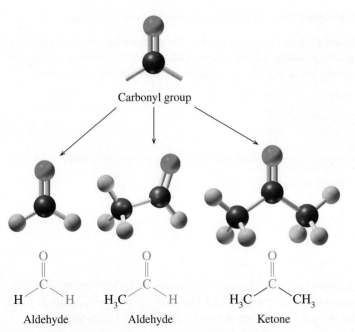

Carbonyl group

H—C(=O)—H   H₃C—C(=O)—H   H₃C—C(=O)—CH₃

Aldehyde   Aldehyde   Ketone

FIGURE 14.1 The carbonyl group in aldehydes and ketones.

Q If aldehydes and ketones both contain a carbonyl group, how can you differentiate between compounds from each family?

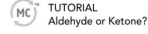 **TUTORIAL**
Aldehyde or Ketone?

Formulas for Isomers of C_3H_6O

Aldehyde

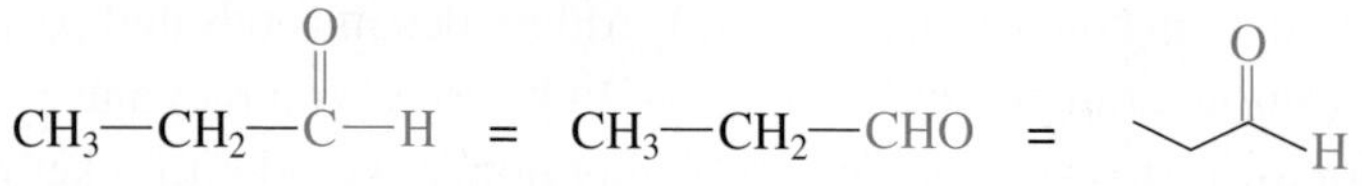

$$CH_3-CH_2-\overset{\overset{\displaystyle O}{\|}}{C}-H \quad = \quad CH_3-CH_2-CHO \quad = \quad$$

Ketone

$$CH_3-\overset{\overset{\displaystyle O}{\|}}{C}-CH_3 \quad = \quad CH_3-CO-CH_3 \quad = \quad$$

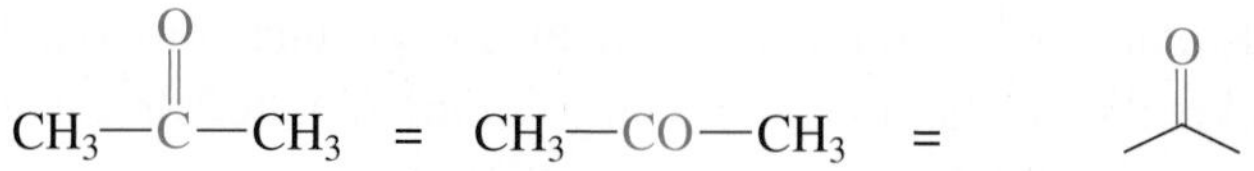

CONCEPT CHECK 14.1

■ Identifying Aldehydes and Ketones

Identify each of the following compounds as an aldehyde or ketone:

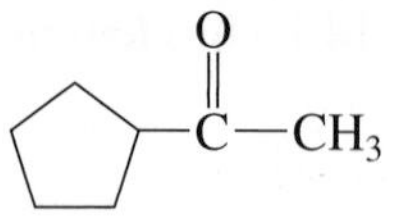

a. 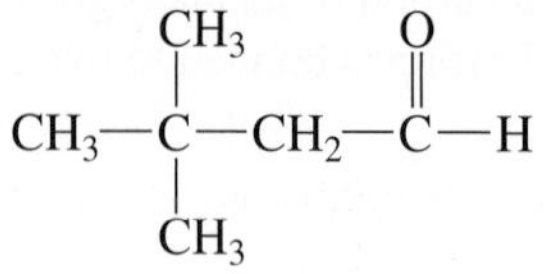 $$CH_3-\overset{\overset{\displaystyle CH_3}{|}}{\underset{\underset{\displaystyle CH_3}{|}}{C}}-CH_2-\overset{\overset{\displaystyle O}{\|}}{C}-H$$

b. (cyclopentane ring)$-\overset{\overset{\displaystyle O}{\|}}{C}-CH_3$

c. (benzene ring)$-CHO$

d. 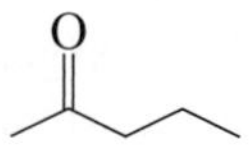 (ketone structure)

ANSWER

a. When the carbon atom of the carbonyl group (C=O) is attached to a hydrogen atom, the compound is an aldehyde.

b. When the carbon atom of the carbonyl group (C=O) is attached to two carbon atoms, the compound is a ketone.

c. When the carbon atom of the carbonyl group (C=O) is attached to a hydrogen atom, the compound is an aldehyde.

d. When the carbon atom of the carbonyl group (C=O) is attached to two carbon atoms, the compound is a ketone.

Naming Aldehydes

In the IUPAC names of aldehydes, the *e* of the alkane name is replaced with *al*.

STEP 1 **Name the longest carbon chain containing the carbonyl group by replacing the *e* in the corresponding alkane name with *al*.** No number is needed for the aldehyde group because it always appears at the beginning of the chain.

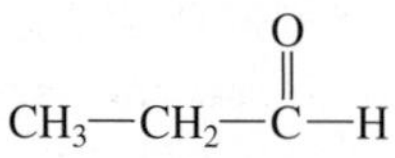

$$CH_3-CH_2-\overset{\overset{\displaystyle O}{\|}}{C}-H$$
Propanal

The IUPAC system names the aldehyde of benzene as benzaldehyde:

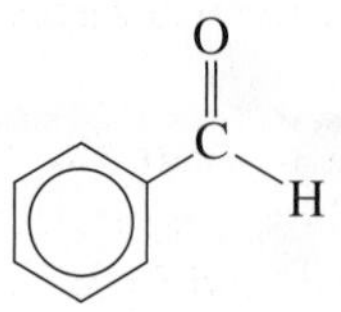

(benzaldehyde structure with benzene ring, C=O, and H)

Benzaldehyde

The first four unbranched aldehydes are often referred to by their common names, which end in *aldehyde*. (See Figure 14.2.) The roots (*form-*, *acet-*, *propion-*, and *butyr-*) of these common names are derived from Latin or Greek words.

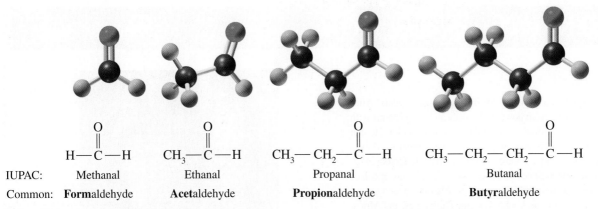

FIGURE 14.2 In the structures of aldehydes, the carbonyl group is always the end carbon.
Q Why is the carbon in the carbonyl group in aldehydes always at the end of the chain?

STEP 2 **Name and number any substituents on the carbon chain by counting the carbonyl carbon as carbon 1.** In an aldehyde, the —OH group is counted as a substituent and named *hydroxy*:

$$CH_3-CH-C-H$$
2-Methylpropanal

$$CH_3-CH-CH_2-CH_2-C-H$$
4-Methylpentanal

SAMPLE PROBLEM 14.1

■ Naming Aldehydes

Give the IUPAC names for the following aldehydes:

a. $CH_3-CH_2-CH-CH_2-C-H$ (OH on carbon 3)

b. Cl—⟨benzene ring⟩—$C-H$

SOLUTION

a. STEP 1 Name the longest carbon chain by replacing the *e* with *al*. The longest carbon chain containing the carbonyl group has five carbon atoms. It is named by replacing the *e* in the alkane name with *al* to give pentanal.

STEP 2 **Name and number substituents by counting from the carbonyl group.** The —OH group on carbon 3 is named hydroxy, which gives an IUPAC name of 3-hydroxypentanal.

b. STEP 1 Name the longest carbon chain by replacing the *e* with *al*. The longest carbon chain consists of a benzene ring attached to a carbonyl group, which is named benzaldehyde.

STEP 2 **Name and number substituents by counting from the carbonyl group.** Counting from carbon 1 attached to the carbonyl group, the chloro group is attached to carbon 4. The name is 4-chlorobenzaldehyde.

Guide to Naming Aldehydes

STEP 1
Name the longest carbon chain by replacing the *e* in the alkane name with *al*.

STEP 2
Name and number substituents by counting the carbonyl group as carbon 1.

STUDY CHECK

What are the IUPAC and common names of the aldehyde with three carbon atoms?

ENVIRONMENTAL NOTE

Vanilla

Vanilla has been used as a flavoring for over a thousand years. After drinking a beverage made from powdered vanilla and cocoa beans with Emperor Montezuma in Mexico, the Spanish conquistador Hernán Cortés took vanilla back to Europe, where it became popular for flavoring and for scenting perfumes and tobacco. Thomas Jefferson introduced vanilla to the United States during the late 1700s. Today, much of the vanilla we use in the world is grown in Mexico, Madagascar, Réunion, Seychelles, Tahiti, Sri Lanka, Java, the Philippines, and Africa.

The vanilla plant is a member of the orchid family. There are many species of *Vanilla*, but *Vanilla planifolia* (or *V. fragrans*) is considered to produce the best flavor. The vanilla plant grows like a vine and can grow to 100 feet in length. Its flowers are hand-pollinated to produce a green fruit that is picked in 8 or 9 months. The fruit is sun-dried to form a long, dark brown pod, which is called "vanilla bean" because it looks like a string bean. The flavor and fragrance of the vanilla bean comes from the tiny black seeds found inside the dried bean.

The seeds and pod are used to flavor desserts such as custards and ice cream. The extract of vanilla is made by chopping up vanilla beans and mixing them with a 35% ethanol–water mixture. The liquid, which contains the aldehyde *vanillin*, is drained from the bean residue and used for flavoring.

Vanillin

Naming Ketones

Aldehydes and ketones are some of the most important classes of organic compounds. Because they have played a major role in organic chemistry for more than a century, the common names for unbranched ketones are still in use. In the common names, the alkyl groups bonded to the carbonyl group are named as substituents and listed alphabetically followed by *ketone*. Acetone, which is another name for propanone, has been retained by the IUPAC system.

In the IUPAC system, the name of a ketone is obtained by replacing the *e* in the corresponding alkane name with *one*.

STEP 1   **Name the longest carbon chain containing the carbonyl group by replacing the *e* in the corresponding alkane name with *one*.**

STEP 2   **Number the main chain starting from the end nearer the carbonyl group.** Place the number of the carbonyl carbon in front of the ketone name. (Propanone and butanone do not require numbers.)

$$CH_3-\overset{\overset{\displaystyle O}{\|}}{C}-CH_3 \qquad CH_3-CH_2-\overset{\overset{\displaystyle O}{\|}}{C}-CH_3 \qquad CH_3-CH_2-\overset{\overset{\displaystyle O}{\|}}{C}-CH_2-CH_3$$

Propanone
(dimethyl ketone; acetone)

Butanone
(ethyl methyl ketone)

3-Pentanone
(diethyl ketone)

STEP 3   **Name and number any substituents on the carbon chain.**   In a ketone, an —OH group is a substituent and named *hydroxy*:

$$CH_3-\overset{\overset{\displaystyle O}{\|}}{C}-\overset{\overset{\displaystyle CH_3}{|}}{C}H-CH_3 \qquad CH_3-\overset{\overset{\displaystyle OH}{|}}{C}H-\overset{\overset{\displaystyle O}{\|}}{C}-CH_2-CH_3$$

3-Methylbutanone

2-Hydroxy-3-pentanone

STEP 4   **For cyclic ketones, the prefix *cyclo* is used in front of the ketone name.** Any substituents are located by numbering the ring starting with the carbonyl carbon as carbon 1. The ring is numbered so that the substituents have the lowest possible number:

Cyclopentanone   3-Methylcyclohexanone   2,3-Dichlorocyclopentanone

HEALTH NOTE

Some Important Aldehydes and Ketones

Formaldehyde, the simplest aldehyde, is a colorless gas with a pungent odor. Commercially, formaldehyde is used to make fabrics, insulation materials, carpeting, pressed wood products such as plywood, and plastics for kitchen counters. An aqueous solution called formalin, which contains 40% formaldehyde, is used as a germicide and to preserve biological specimens. Exposure to formaldehyde fumes can irritate the eyes, nose, and upper respiratory tract and cause skin rashes, headaches, dizziness, and general fatigue. Formaldehyde is classified as a carcinogen.

Acetone, or propanone (dimethyl ketone), which is the simplest ketone, is a colorless liquid with a mild odor that has wide use as a solvent in cleaning fluids, paint and nail polish removers, and rubber cement. It is extremely flammable, and care must be taken when using acetone. In the body, acetone may be produced in uncontrolled diabetes, fasting, and high-protein diets when large amounts of fats are metabolized for energy.

Several naturally occurring aromatic aldehydes are used to flavor food and as fragrances in perfumes. Benzaldehyde is found in almonds, vanillin in vanilla beans, and cinnamaldehyde in cinnamon:

Benzaldehyde   Vanillin   Cinnamaldehyde
(almond)   (vanilla)   (cinnamon)

The flavor of butter or margarine is from butanedione, muscone is used to make musk perfumes, and oil of spearmint contains carvone:

Muscone   Carvone
(musk)   (spearmint oil)

Butanedione

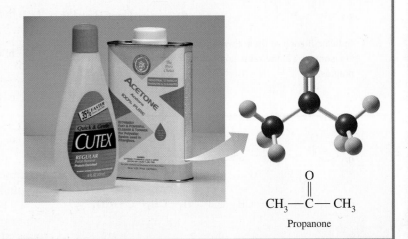

Propanone

Guide to Naming Ketones

STEP 1
Name the longest carbon chain by replacing the *e* in the alkane name by *one*.

STEP 2
Number the carbon chain starting from the end nearer the carbonyl group and indicate its location.

STEP 3
Name and number any substituents on other carbons in the chain.

STEP 4
For cyclic ketones, add the prefix *cyclo* and number substituents from the carbonyl carbon as carbon 1.

SAMPLE PROBLEM 14.2

■ Names of Ketones

Give the IUPAC name for the following ketone:

$$CH_3-\underset{\underset{CH_3}{|}}{CH}-CH_2-\underset{\underset{\|}{O}}{C}-CH_3$$

SOLUTION

STEP 1 **Name the longest carbon chain by replacing the *e* with *one*.** The longest chain containing the carbonyl has five carbon atoms, which is named by replacing the *e* of the alkane name: pentanone.

STEP 2 **Number the carbon chain from the end nearer the ketone group.** The carbonyl group on carbon 2 gives 2-pentanone.

STEP 3 **Name and number any substituents on the chain.** Counting from the end nearer the carbonyl group places the methyl group on carbon 4. The IUPAC name is 4-methyl-2-pentanone.

STUDY CHECK

What is the common name of 3-hexanone?

QUESTIONS AND PROBLEMS

Aldehydes and Ketones

14.1 Identify the following compounds as aldehydes or ketones:

a. $CH_3-CH_2-\underset{\underset{\|}{O}}{C}-CH_3$

b.

c.

d.

14.2 Identify the following compounds as aldehydes or ketones:

a.

b. $CH_3-\underset{\underset{CH_3}{|}}{CH}-\underset{\underset{\|}{O}}{C}-H$

c.

d.

14.3 Indicate if each of the following pairs of formulas represents (1) isomers, (2) the same compound, or (3) different compounds:

a. $CH_3-\underset{\underset{\|}{O}}{C}-CH_3$ and $CH_3-CH_2-\underset{\underset{\|}{O}}{C}-H$

b. and

c. $CH_3-\underset{\underset{\|}{O}}{C}-CH_2-CH_3$ and $CH_3-CH_2-\underset{\underset{\|}{O}}{C}-CH_3$

14.4 Indicate if each of the following pairs of formulas represents (1) isomers, (2) the same compound, or (3) different compounds:

a. $CH_3-CH_2-CH_2-\underset{\underset{\|}{O}}{C}-H$ and

b. and

c. and

14.5 Give the IUPAC name for each of the following compounds:

a. $CH_3-CH_2-\underset{\underset{\|}{O}}{C}-H$

b. $CH_3-CH_2-\underset{\underset{\|}{O}}{C}-\underset{\underset{CH_3}{|}}{CH}-CH_3$

c. $CH_3-\underset{\underset{Br}{|}}{CH}-CH_2-\underset{\underset{\|}{O}}{C}-H$

d.

e.

f.

14.6 Give the IUPAC name for each of the following compounds:

a. $CH_3\!-\!CH_2\!-\!CH_2\!-\!\overset{\displaystyle O}{\overset{\|}{C}}\!-\!H$

b. $CH_3\!-\!\overset{\displaystyle CH_3}{\underset{|}{CH}}\!-\!CH_2\!-\!\overset{\displaystyle O}{\overset{\|}{C}}\!-\!CH_3$

c.

d.

e.

f. $CH_3\!-\!CH_2\!-\!CH_2\!-\!\overset{\displaystyle CH_3}{\underset{|}{CH}}\!-\!\overset{\displaystyle O}{\overset{\|}{C}}\!-\!H$

14.7 Give a common name for each of the following compounds:

a. $CH_3\!-\!\overset{\displaystyle O}{\overset{\|}{C}}\!-\!H$

b. $CH_3\!-\!\overset{\displaystyle O}{\overset{\|}{C}}\!-\!CH_2\!-\!CH_2\!-\!CH_3$

c. $H\!-\!\overset{\displaystyle O}{\overset{\|}{C}}\!-\!H$

14.8 Give the common name for each of the following compounds:

a. $CH_3\!-\!\overset{\displaystyle O}{\overset{\|}{C}}\!-\!CH_2\!-\!CH_3$

b. $CH_3\!-\!CH_2\!-\!\overset{\displaystyle O}{\overset{\|}{C}}\!-\!CH_2\!-\!CH_3$

c. $CH_3\!-\!CH_2\!-\!\overset{\displaystyle O}{\overset{\|}{C}}\!-\!H$

14.9 Draw the condensed structural formula for each of the following compounds:
  a. acetaldehyde
  b. 4-methyl-2-pentanone
  c. 2,3-dibromobutanal
  d. methyl butyl ketone
  e. 3-methylpentanal

14.10 Draw the condensed structural formula for each of the following compounds:
  a. propionaldehyde
  b. butanal
  c. 3,4-dichlorohexanal
  d. 4-bromobutanone
  e. acetone

14.11 Anisaldehyde, from Korean mint or blue licorice, is one of the medicinal herbs used in Chinese medicine. If its IUPAC name is 4-methoxybenzaldehyde, what is its condensed structural formula?

14.12 The IUPAC name of vanillin, a naturally occurring compound in vanilla beans, is 4-hydroxy-3-methoxybenzaldehyde. What is the structural formula of vanillin?

14.2 Physical Properties of Aldehydes and Ketones

At room temperature, formaldehyde and acetaldehyde are gases. Aldehydes containing from 3 to 10 carbon atoms are liquids. The polar carbonyl group with a partially negative oxygen atom and a partially positive carbon atom has an influence on the boiling points and the solubility of aldehydes and ketones in water.

LEARNING GOAL

Compare the boiling points and solubility of aldehydes and ketones to those of alkanes and alcohols.

Boiling Points

The polar carbonyl group gives aldehydes and ketones higher boiling points than alkanes and ethers of similar mass. The increase in boiling points is due to dipole–dipole attractions:

TUTORIAL
Properties of Aldehydes and Ketones

Dipole–dipole attractions

$$\text{>}C^{\delta+}\!=\!O^{\delta-}\bullet\bullet\bullet\bullet\bullet\bullet\bullet\bullet\bullet\text{>}C^{\delta+}\!=\!O^{\delta-}\bullet\bullet\bullet\bullet\bullet\bullet\bullet\bullet\bullet\text{>}C^{\delta+}\!=\!O^{\delta-}$$

However, because there is no hydrogen on the oxygen atom, aldehydes and ketones cannot form hydrogen bonds with each other. Thus, they have boiling points that are lower than alcohols of similar molar mass:

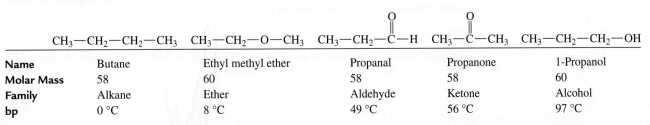

	$CH_3\!-\!CH_2\!-\!CH_2\!-\!CH_3$	$CH_3\!-\!CH_2\!-\!O\!-\!CH_3$	$CH_3\!-\!CH_2\!-\!\overset{O}{\overset{\|}{C}}\!-\!H$	$CH_3\!-\!\overset{O}{\overset{\|}{C}}\!-\!CH_3$	$CH_3\!-\!CH_2\!-\!CH_2\!-\!OH$
Name	Butane	Ethyl methyl ether	Propanal	Propanone	1-Propanol
Molar Mass	58	60	58	58	60
Family	Alkane	Ether	Aldehyde	Ketone	Alcohol
bp	0 °C	8 °C	49 °C	56 °C	97 °C

Increasing boiling point →

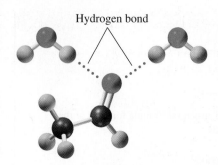

Hydrogen bond

Acetaldehyde

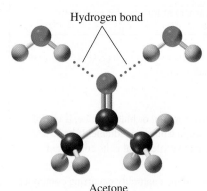

Hydrogen bond

Acetone

FIGURE 14.3 Hydrogen bonding of acetaldehyde and acetone with water.

Q Would you expect propanal to be soluble in water?

Solubility of Aldehydes and Ketones in Water

Although aldehydes and ketones do not hydrogen bond with each other, the electronegative oxygen atom does hydrogen bond with water molecules. Carbonyl compounds with one to four carbons are very soluble in water. However, those with five carbon atoms or more are not very soluble, because the alkyl portions diminish the effect of the polar carbonyl group. (See Figure 14.3.)

Table 14.1 compares the boiling points of some carbonyl compounds, as well as their solubilities in water.

TABLE 14.1 Comparison of Physical Properties of Some Selected Compounds

Compound	Boiling Point (°C)	Solubility in Water
Methanal (formaldehyde)	−21	Very soluble
Ethanal (acetaldehyde)	21	Very soluble
Propanal (propionaldehyde)	49	Soluble
Propanone (acetone)	56	Soluble
Butanal (butyraldehyde)	75	Soluble
Butanone	80	Soluble
Pentanal	103	Slightly soluble
2-Pentanone	102	Slightly soluble
3-Pentanone	102	Slightly soluble
Hexanal	129	Not soluble
2-Hexanone	127	Not soluble
3-Hexanone	124	Not soluble
Acetophenone	202	Not soluble

CONCEPT CHECK 14.2

■ Boiling Points

Arrange the compounds pentane, 2-butanol, and butanone in order of increasing boiling points. Explain.

ANSWER

The only attractions between molecules of alkanes such as pentane are weak dispersion forces. With no dipole–dipole attractions or hydrogen bonds, pentane has the lowest boiling point of the three compounds. With a polar carbonyl group, butanone has dipole–dipole attractions but no hydrogen bonds. Butanone has a higher boiling point than pentane. Molecules of 2-butanol can form hydrogen bonds with other butanol molecules. The 2-butanol would have the highest boiling point of the three compounds. The actual boiling points are pentane (36 °C), butanone (80 °C), and 2-butanol (100 °C).

SAMPLE PROBLEM 14.3

■ Boiling Point and Solubility

Would you expect ethanol (CH_3—CH_2—OH) to have a higher or lower boiling point than ethanal (CH_3—CHO)? Explain.

SOLUTION

Ethanol would have a higher boiling point because its molecules can hydrogen bond with each other, whereas molecules of ethanal cannot.

STUDY CHECK

If acetone molecules cannot hydrogen bond with each other, why is acetone soluble in water?

QUESTIONS AND PROBLEMS

Physical Properties of Aldehydes and Ketones

14.13 Which compound in each of the following pairs would have the higher boiling point? Explain.

a. $CH_3-CH_2-CH_3$ or $CH_3-\overset{\overset{\displaystyle O}{\|}}{C}-H$

b. propanal or pentanal
c. butanal or 1-butanol

14.14 Which compound in each of the following pairs would have the higher boiling point? Explain.

a. (structure: $\overset{OH}{\wedge\wedge}$) or (structure: $\overset{O}{\wedge\wedge}$)

b. pentane or butanone
c. propanone or pentanone

14.15 Which compound in each of the following pairs would be more soluble in water? Explain.

a. $CH_3-\overset{\overset{\displaystyle O}{\|}}{C}-CH_2-CH_3$ or $CH_3-\overset{\overset{\displaystyle O}{\|}}{C}-\overset{\overset{\displaystyle O}{\|}}{C}-CH_3$

b. propane or acetaldehyde
c. acetone or 2-pentanone

14.16 Which compound in each of the following pairs would be more soluble in water? Explain.

a. $CH_3-CH_2-CH_3$ or CH_3-CH_2-CHO
b. propanone or 3-hexanone
c. propane or propanone

14.17 Would you expect an aldehyde with a formula of $C_8H_{16}O$ to be soluble in water? Explain.

14.18 Would you expect an aldehyde with a formula of C_3H_6O to be soluble in water? Explain.

14.3 Oxidation and Reduction of Aldehydes and Ketones

In Chapter 13, we saw that aldehydes produced by the oxidation of primary alcohols oxidize readily to carboxylic acids. In fact, they oxidize so easily that aldehydes exposed to the air in the laboratory quickly form carboxylic acids. In contrast, ketones produced by the oxidation of secondary alcohols do not undergo further oxidation. Let's review examples of the oxidation reactions of primary and secondary alcohols that form aldehydes and ketones.

LEARNING GOAL

Draw the condensed structural formulas of reactants and products for the oxidation or reduction of aldehydes and ketones.

MC TUTORIAL
Oxidation–Reduction Reactions of Aldehydes and Ketones

$$CH_3-CH_2-OH \xrightarrow{\text{Oxidation}} CH_3-\overset{\overset{\displaystyle O}{\|}}{C}-H \xrightarrow{\text{Further oxidation}} CH_3-\overset{\overset{\displaystyle O}{\|}}{C}-OH$$

Ethanol (1°)   Ethanal   Ethanoic acid

$$CH_3-\overset{OH}{\underset{|}{CH}}-CH_3 \xrightarrow{\text{Oxidation}} CH_3-\overset{\overset{\displaystyle O}{\|}}{C}-CH_3 \xrightarrow{\text{Further oxidation}} \text{no reaction}$$

2-Propanol (2°)   Propanone

Tollens' Test

The ease of oxidation of aldehydes allows certain mild oxidizing agents to oxidize the aldehyde functional group without oxidizing other functional groups such as alcohols or ethers. In the laboratory, **Tollens' test** may be used to distinguish between aldehydes and ketones. Tollens' reagent, a solution of Ag^+ ($AgNO_3$) and ammonia, oxidizes aldehydes, but not ketones. The silver ion is reduced to metallic silver, which forms a layer called a "silver mirror" on the inside of the container:

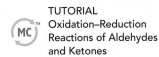

$$CH_3-\overset{\overset{\displaystyle O}{\|}}{C}-H + 2Ag^+ \xrightarrow{[O]} 2Ag(s) + CH_3-\overset{\overset{\displaystyle O}{\|}}{C}-OH$$

Acetaldehyde   Tollens' reagent   Silver mirror   Acetic acid

Commercially, a similar process is used to make mirrors by applying a solution of $AgNO_3$ and ammonia on glass with a spray gun. (See Figure 14.4.)

FIGURE 14.4 In Tollens' test, a "silver mirror" forms when the oxidation of an aldehyde reduces silver ions to metallic silver. The silvery surface of a mirror is formed in a similar way.

Q What is the product of the oxidation of an aldehyde?

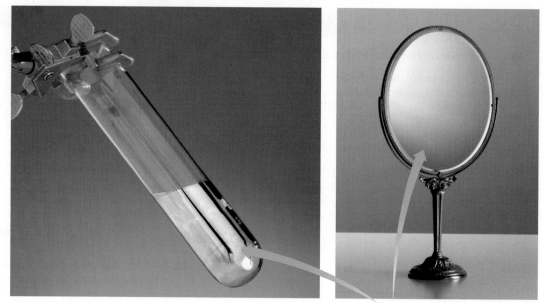

$$Ag^+ + 1e^- \longrightarrow Ag(s)$$

Cu^{2+} $Cu_2O(s)$

FIGURE 14.5 The blue Cu^{2+} in Benedict's solution forms a brick-red solid of Cu_2O in a positive test for many sugars and aldehydes with adjacent hydroxyl groups.

Q Which test tube indicates that glucose is present?

Another test, called **Benedict's test**, gives a positive test with compounds that have an aldehyde functional group and an adjacent hydroxyl group. When Benedict's solution containing Cu^{2+} ($CuSO_4$) ions is added to this type of aldehyde and heated, a brick-red solid of Cu_2O forms. (See Figure 14.5.) The test is negative with simple aldehydes and ketones:

$$CH_3-\overset{\overset{\displaystyle OH}{|}}{CH}-\overset{\overset{\displaystyle O}{\|}}{C}-H + 2Cu^{2+} \longrightarrow Cu_2O(s) + CH_3-\overset{\overset{\displaystyle OH}{|}}{CH}-\overset{\overset{\displaystyle O}{\|}}{C}-OH$$

2-Hydroxypropanal   Benedict's reagent   Brick-red solid   2-Hydroxypropanoic acid

Because many sugars such as glucose contain this type of aldehyde grouping, Benedict's reagent can be used to determine the presence of glucose in blood or urine:

D-Glucose

$$\begin{array}{c} \overset{\displaystyle O}{\overset{\displaystyle \|}{C}}-H \\ H-C-OH \\ HO-C-H \\ H-C-OH \\ H-C-OH \\ CH_2OH \end{array} \quad + \quad 2Cu^{2+} \quad \longrightarrow \quad \begin{array}{c} O\diagup OH \\ C \\ H-C-OH \\ HO-C-H \\ H-C-OH \\ H-C-OH \\ CH_2OH \end{array} \quad + \quad Cu_2O(s)$$

Benedict's (blue)   (brick red)

D-Glucose   D-Gluconic acid

SAMPLE PROBLEM 14.4

■ **Alcohol Oxidation**

Draw the condensed structural formula of the alcohol needed to give each of the following oxidation products:

a. $CH_3-\overset{\overset{\displaystyle O}{\|}}{C}-CH_2-CH_3$ **b.** $CH_3-\overset{\overset{\displaystyle CH_3}{|}}{CH}-\overset{\overset{\displaystyle O}{\|}}{C}-H$ **c.** $CH_3-\overset{\overset{\displaystyle O}{\|}}{C}-OH$

SOLUTION

a. A secondary alcohol oxidizes to a ketone:

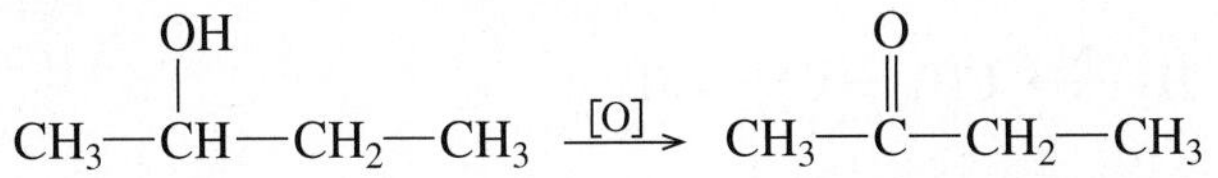

$$CH_3-\underset{\underset{OH}{|}}{CH}-CH_2-CH_3 \xrightarrow{[O]} CH_3-\underset{\underset{O}{\|}}{C}-CH_2-CH_3$$

b. A primary alcohol oxidizes to an aldehyde with a mild oxidizing agent:

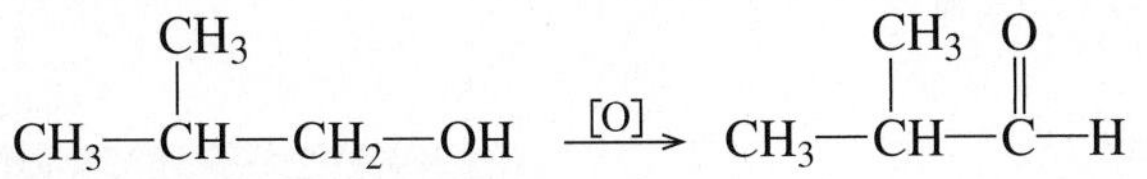

$$CH_3-\underset{\underset{CH_3}{|}}{CH}-CH_2-OH \xrightarrow{[O]} CH_3-\underset{\underset{CH_3}{|}}{CH}-\underset{\underset{O}{\|}}{C}-H$$

c. A primary alcohol oxidizes to an aldehyde, which oxidizes further to a carboxylic acid:

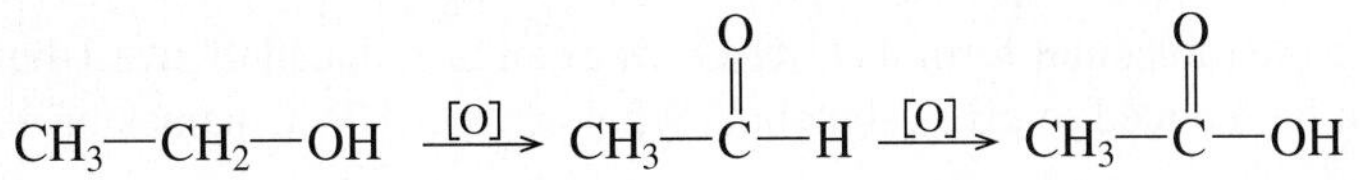

$$CH_3-CH_2-OH \xrightarrow{[O]} CH_3-\underset{\underset{O}{\|}}{C}-H \xrightarrow{[O]} CH_3-\underset{\underset{O}{\|}}{C}-OH$$

STUDY CHECK

What is the IUPAC name of the alcohol that oxidized to cyclohexanone?

SAMPLE PROBLEM 14.5

■ **Tollens' Test**

Draw the condensed structural formula of the product of oxidation, if any, when Tollens' reagent is added to each of the following compounds:

a. propanal   **b.** propanone   **c.** 2-methylbutanal

SOLUTION

Tollens' reagent will oxidize aldehydes but not ketones.

a. 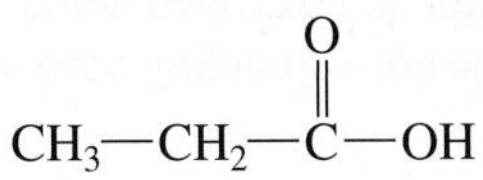 $CH_3-CH_2-\underset{\underset{O}{\|}}{C}-OH$ **b.** no reaction   **c.** 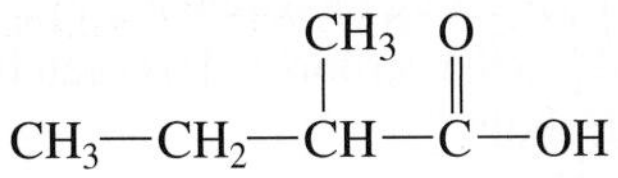 $CH_3-CH_2-\underset{\underset{CH_3}{|}}{CH}-\underset{\underset{O}{\|}}{C}-OH$

STUDY CHECK

Why does a silver mirror form when Tollens' reagent is added to a test tube containing benzaldehyde?

Reduction of Aldehydes and Ketones

Aldehydes and ketones are reduced by sodium borohydride ($NaBH_4$) or hydrogen (H_2). **Reduction** decreases the number of carbon–oxygen bonds by the addition of hydrogen or the loss of oxygen. Aldehydes are reduced to primary alcohols, and ketones are reduced to secondary alcohols. A catalyst such as nickel, platinum, or palladium is needed for hydrogenation.

Aldehydes Reduce to Primary Alcohols

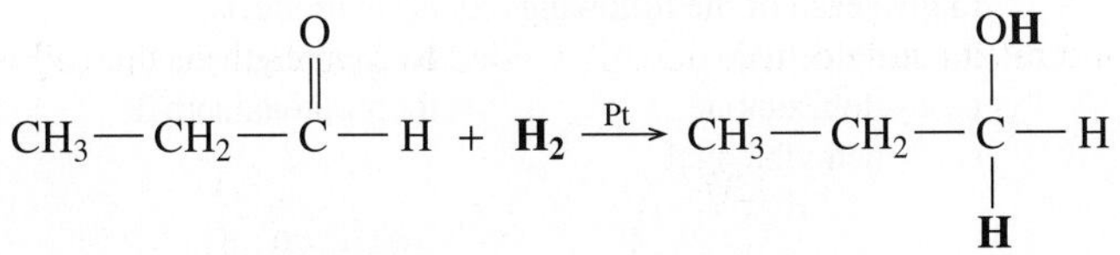

$$CH_3-CH_2-\underset{\underset{O}{\|}}{C}-H + H_2 \xrightarrow{Pt} CH_3-CH_2-\underset{\underset{\underset{H}{|}}{|}}{\overset{\overset{OH}{|}}{C}}-H$$

Propionaldehyde   1-Propanol (1° alcohol)

Ketones Reduce to Secondary Alcohols

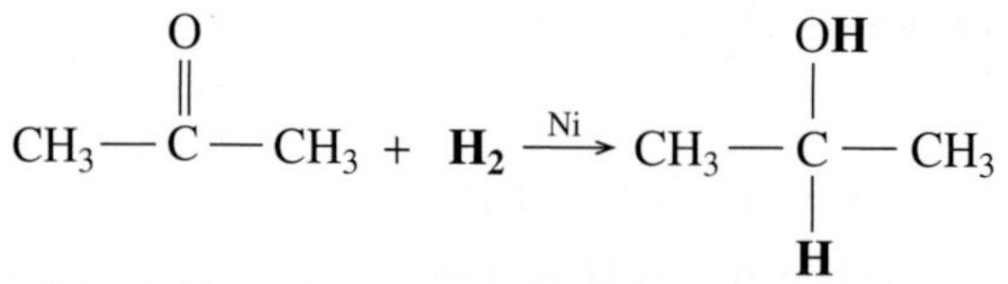

$$CH_3-\overset{\overset{\displaystyle O}{\|}}{C}-CH_3 + H_2 \xrightarrow{Ni} CH_3-\overset{\overset{\displaystyle OH}{|}}{\underset{\underset{\displaystyle H}{|}}{C}}-CH_3$$

Dimethyl ketone   2-Propanol (2° alcohol)

CONCEPT CHECK 14.3

■ **Reduction of Aldehydes and Ketones**

Two isomers have the molecular formula C_4H_8O. One can be reduced to give 1-butanol, and the other can be reduced to give 2-butanol. What are the IUPAC names of the two isomers?

ANSWER

When an aldehyde is reduced, the product is a primary (1°) alcohol. The aldehyde that would be reduced to 1-butanol would have four carbons with an aldehyde group on the beginning carbon, which is named butanal.

When a ketone is reduced, the product is a secondary (2°) alcohol. The ketone that would be reduced to 2-butanol would have four carbons with a keto group on carbon 2, which is named butanone. Thus, the two isomers with molecular formula C_4H_8O are butanal and butanone.

SAMPLE PROBLEM 14.6

■ **Reduction of Carbonyl Groups**

Write an equation for the reduction of cyclopentanone in the presence of a nickel catalyst.

SOLUTION

The reacting molecule is a cyclic ketone that has five carbon atoms. Hydrogen atoms will add to the carbon and oxygen in the carbonyl group to form the corresponding secondary alcohol:

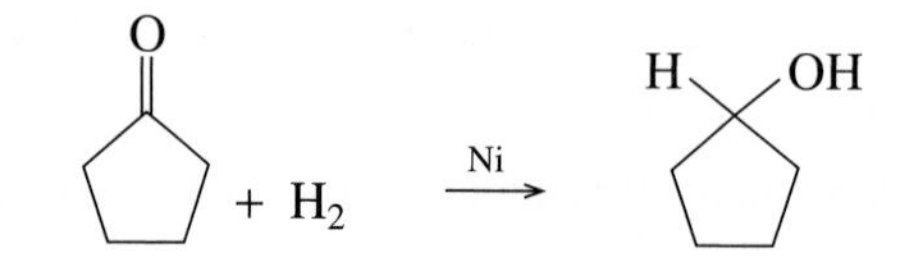

Cyclopentanone   Cyclopentanol

STUDY CHECK

What is the name of the product obtained from the hydrogenation of propionaldehyde?

QUESTIONS AND PROBLEMS

Oxidation and Reduction of Aldehydes and Ketones

14.19 Draw the condensed structural formula of the alcohol needed to give each of the following oxidation products:
a. formaldehyde
b. cyclopentanone
c. 2-butanone
d. benzaldehyde
e. 3-methylcyclohexanone

14.20 Draw the condensed structural formula of the alcohol needed to give each of the following oxidation products:
a. acetaldehyde
b. 3-methylbutanone
c. cyclohexanone
d. propionaldehyde
e. 3-methylbutanal

14.21 Draw the condensed structural formula of the aldehyde or ketone product when each of the following alcohols is oxidized [O] (if no reaction, write *none*):

a. $CH_3-CH_2-CH_2-CH_2-CH_2-OH$

b. $CH_3-CH_2-\overset{\displaystyle OH}{\underset{|}{CH}}-CH_3$

c. cyclohexanol with OH

d. $CH_3-\overset{\displaystyle OH}{\underset{|}{CH}}-CH_2-\overset{\displaystyle CH_3}{\underset{|}{CH}}-CH_3$

e. $CH_3-\overset{\displaystyle CH_3}{\underset{|}{CH}}-CH_2-CH_2-OH$

14.22 Draw the condensed structural formula of the aldehyde or ketone product when each of the following alcohols is oxidized [O] (if no reaction, write *none*):

a. cyclobutane$-CH_2-OH$

b. $CH_3-\overset{\displaystyle CH_3}{\underset{|}{CH}}-CH_2-\overset{}{CH}-OH$ with CH_3

c. $CH_3-CH_2-\overset{\displaystyle OH}{\underset{|}{\underset{|}{C}}}-CH_3$ with CH_3

d. $CH_3-\overset{\displaystyle OH}{\underset{|}{CH}}-\overset{}{\underset{|}{CH}}-CH_2-CH_3$ with OH

e. cyclobutane with OH

14.23 Give the condensed structural formula of the organic product formed when each of the following is reduced by hydrogen in the presence of a nickel catalyst:
a. butyraldehyde   **b.** acetone
c. 3-bromohexanal   **d.** 2-methyl-3-pentanone

14.24 Give the condensed structural formula of the organic product formed when each of the following is reduced by hydrogen in the presence of a nickel catalyst:
a. ethyl propyl ketone
b. formaldehyde
c. 3-chlorocyclopentanone
d. 2-pentanone

Addition Reactions of Aldehydes and Ketones

One of the most common reactions of aldehydes and ketones is the addition of polar molecules to the carbonyl group. The carbonyl group is reactive because of the polarity of the C=O double bond. In addition reactions, the partially negative part of the adding molecule bonds with the partially positively charged carbonyl carbon. The partially positive part, usually a proton, combines with the partially negatively charged carbonyl oxygen. This type of addition to the carbonyl group can be illustrated as follows:

LEARNING GOAL
Write the products of the addition of alcohols to aldehydes and ketones.

TUTORIAL
Addition of Polar Molecules to a Carbonyl Group

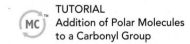

Carbonyl group of aldehyde or ketone   Adding molecule

In general, aldehydes are more reactive than ketones because the carbonyl carbon is more positive in aldehydes. Also, the presence of two alkyl groups in ketones makes it more difficult for a molecule to form bonds with the carbon in the carbonyl group.

Addition of Water

The components of water add to aldehydes and ketones to give carbonyl hydrates in the presence of acid or base. The partially negative —OH group bonds with the carbonyl carbon, while the —H bonds to the partially negative oxygen. In water, the simplest aldehyde, formaldehyde, forms its hydrate called *formalin*, which is used to preserve tissues. Other aldehydes form hydrates in water as well, but not with as high a percentage as formaldehyde. The carbonyl group in ketones also reacts with water, but their hydrates are not very stable:

$$
\underset{\substack{\text{H} \\ \\ \text{H}}}{\text{C}}{=}\text{O} \quad + \quad \text{H}_2\text{O} \quad \overset{\text{H}^+}{\rightleftharpoons} \quad \underset{\substack{\text{H} \quad \text{OH}}}{\overset{\text{H} \quad \text{OH}}{\text{C}}}
$$

Formaldehyde   Formalin

$$
\underset{\substack{\text{H}_3\text{C} \\ \\ \text{H}}}{\text{C}}{=}\text{O} \quad + \quad \text{H}_2\text{O} \quad \overset{\text{H}^+}{\rightleftharpoons} \quad \underset{\substack{\text{H} \quad \text{OH}}}{\overset{\text{H}_3\text{C} \quad \text{OH}}{\text{C}}}
$$

Acetaldehyde   Hydrate

Chloral, which is an aldehyde with chlorine atoms, forms a hydrate known as *chloral hydrate*, the substance in "knock out" drops:

$$
\underset{\substack{\text{Cl}_3\text{C} \\ \\ \text{H}}}{\text{C}}{=}\text{O} \quad + \quad \text{H}_2\text{O} \quad \rightleftharpoons \quad \underset{\substack{\text{H} \quad \text{OH}}}{\overset{\text{Cl}_3\text{C} \quad \text{OH}}{\text{C}}}
$$

Chloral   Chloral hydrate

Acetal Formation

MC TUTORIAL
Formation of Acetals

Similar to the addition of water to form hydrates, aldehydes and ketones react with alcohols in the presence of an acid catalyst to form **acetals**. (Ketal is an older term previously used for acetals from ketones.) In the acetal product, the two alkoxy groups are added to the carbonyl carbon and a molecule of water is eliminated:

$$
\underset{\text{Acetaldehyde}}{\text{CH}_3{-}\overset{\overset{\displaystyle\text{O}}{\|}}{\text{C}}{-}\text{H}} \quad + \quad \underset{\text{Methyl alcohol}}{2\text{CH}_3{-}\text{OH}} \quad \overset{\text{H}^+}{\rightleftharpoons} \quad \underset{\text{Acetaldehyde dimethyl acetal}}{\text{CH}_3{-}\underset{\underset{\displaystyle\text{O}{-}\text{CH}_3}{|}}{\overset{\overset{\displaystyle\text{O}{-}\text{CH}_3}{|}}{\text{C}}}{-}\text{H}} \quad + \quad \text{H}_2\text{O}
$$

$$
\underset{\text{Propanone}}{\text{CH}_3{-}\overset{\overset{\displaystyle\text{O}}{\|}}{\text{C}}{-}\text{CH}_3} \quad + \quad \underset{\text{Ethyl alcohol}}{2\text{CH}_3{-}\text{CH}_2{-}\text{OH}} \quad \overset{\text{H}^+}{\rightleftharpoons} \quad \underset{\text{Propanone diethyl acetal}}{\text{CH}_3{-}\underset{\underset{\displaystyle\text{O}{-}\text{CH}_2{-}\text{CH}_3}{|}}{\overset{\overset{\displaystyle\text{O}{-}\text{CH}_2{-}\text{CH}_3}{|}}{\text{C}}}{-}\text{CH}_3} \quad + \quad \text{H}_2\text{O}
$$

Cyclohexanone   Methyl alcohol   Cyclohexanone dimethyl acetal

Hemiacetal Intermediate

In the process of forming acetals, an intermediate called a **hemiacetal** forms when one of the two alcohol molecules adds to the carbonyl carbon. The hemiacetal has an —OH and an alkoxy group bonded to the same carbon atom. The term *hemi* indicates that the hemiacetal is halfway to an acetal. Most of the hemiacetal intermediates are unstable and difficult to isolate from the reaction mixture, which is indicated by the brackets around the hemiacetal structure. In the next step, the second alcohol is added to produce the more stable acetal. Acetals are stable and can be isolated from the reaction mixture:

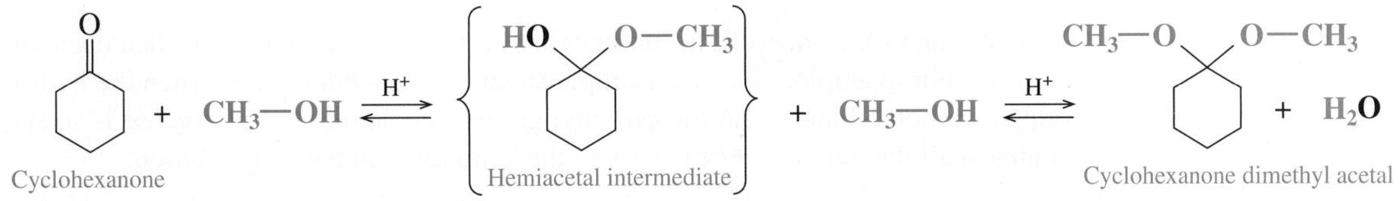

$$\underset{\text{Acetaldehyde}}{CH_3-\overset{\displaystyle O}{\overset{\|}{C}}-H} \; + \; \underset{\substack{\text{Methyl} \\ \text{alcohol}}}{CH_3-OH} \; \underset{}{\overset{H^+}{\rightleftharpoons}} \; \left\{ \underset{\substack{\text{Hemiacetal} \\ \text{intermediate}}}{CH_3-\overset{\displaystyle O-CH_3}{\underset{\displaystyle OH}{\overset{|}{\underset{|}{C}}}}-H} \right\} \; + \; CH_3-OH \; \overset{H^+}{\rightleftharpoons} \; \underset{\text{Acetaldehyde dimethyl acetal}}{CH_3-\overset{\displaystyle O-CH_3}{\underset{\displaystyle O-CH_3}{\overset{|}{\underset{|}{C}}}}-H} \; + \; H_2O$$

$$\underset{\text{Cyclohexanone}}{\text{(cyclohexanone structure)}} \; + \; CH_3-OH \; \overset{H^+}{\rightleftharpoons} \; \left\{ \underset{\text{Hemiacetal intermediate}}{\text{(hemiacetal structure } HO, O-CH_3)} \right\} \; + \; CH_3-OH \; \overset{H^+}{\rightleftharpoons} \; \underset{\text{Cyclohexanone dimethyl acetal}}{\text{(acetal structure } CH_3-O, O-CH_3)} \; + \; H_2O$$

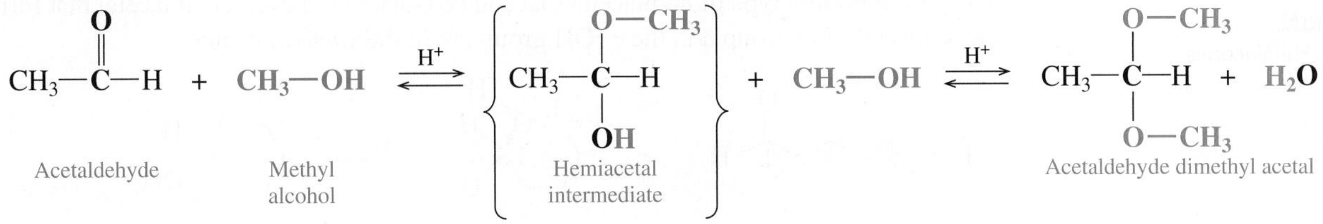

Both the step to the hemiacetal and the step to the acetal are reversible. As predicted by Le Châtelier's principle, the forward reaction to form the acetal is favored by removing water from the reaction mixture. The reverse reaction, which is the hydrolysis of an acetal, is favored by adding water to drive the equilibrium back to the ketone or aldehyde.

CONCEPT CHECK 14.4

■ Hemiacetals and Acetals

From the following descriptions, identify the compound as a hemiacetal or an acetal:

a. a molecule that contains a carbon atom attached to a hydroxyl group and an ethoxy group
b. a molecule that contains a carbon atom attached to two ethoxy groups
c. intermediate that forms when one molecule of an alcohol adds to a ketone
d. product that forms when two molecules of an alcohol add to an aldehyde

ANSWER

a. A hemiacetal contains a carbon atom attached to a hydroxyl group and an ethoxy group.
b. An acetal contains a carbon atom attached to two ethoxy groups.
c. A hemiacetal involves the addition of one molecule of an alcohol to a ketone.
d. An acetal involves the addition of two molecules of an alcohol to an aldehyde.

SAMPLE PROBLEM 14.7

■ Acetals

Draw the condensed structural formulas of the hemiacetal and acetal products when methanol adds to propionaldehyde.

SOLUTION

To form the hemiacetal, the hydrogen from the alcohol adds to the oxygen of the carbonyl group to form a new hydroxyl group. The remaining part of the alcohol adds to the carbon atom in the carbonyl group. The acetal forms when a second molecule of methanol is added to the carbonyl carbon atom:

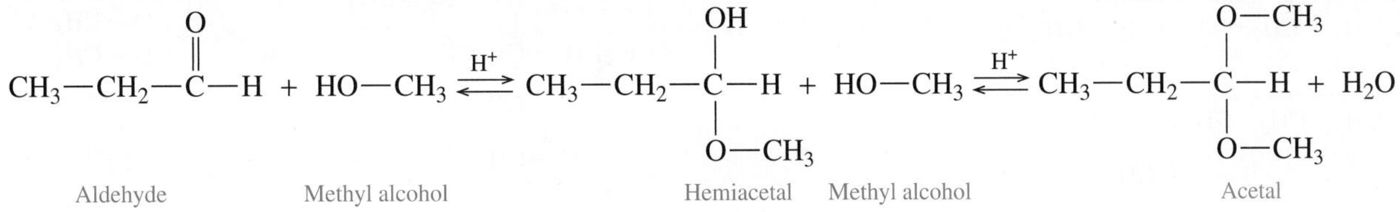

$$\underset{\text{Aldehyde}}{CH_3-CH_2-\overset{\displaystyle O}{\overset{\|}{C}}-H} + \underset{\text{Methyl alcohol}}{HO-CH_3} \overset{H^+}{\rightleftharpoons} \underset{\text{Hemiacetal}}{CH_3-CH_2-\overset{\displaystyle OH}{\underset{\displaystyle O-CH_3}{\overset{|}{\underset{|}{C}}}}-H} + \underset{\text{Methyl alcohol}}{HO-CH_3} \overset{H^+}{\rightleftharpoons} \underset{\text{Acetal}}{CH_3-CH_2-\overset{\displaystyle O-CH_3}{\underset{\displaystyle O-CH_3}{\overset{|}{\underset{|}{C}}}}-H} + H_2O$$

STUDY CHECK

What is the condensed structural formula of the acetal produced when methanol adds to propanone?

Cyclic Hemiacetals

MC TUTORIAL
Cyclic Hemiacetals

One very important type of hemiacetal that can be isolated is a cyclic hemiacetal that forms when the carbonyl group and the —OH group are in the *same* molecule:

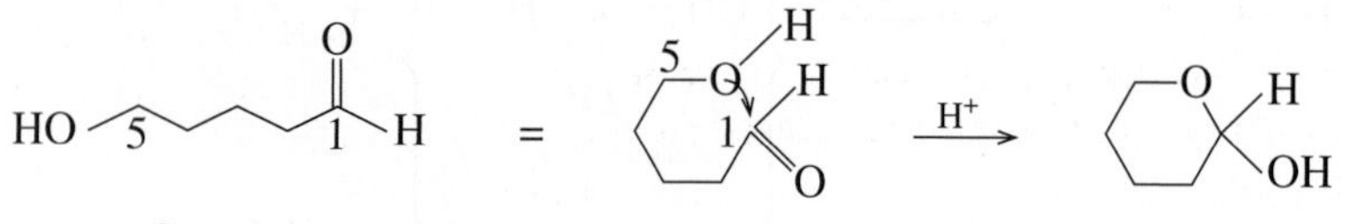

Open chain   Cyclic hemiacetal

The five- and six-atom cyclic hemiacetals and acetals are more stable than their open-chain structures. For example, glucose, a simple sugar, forms a hemiacetal when the hydroxyl group on carbon 5 bonds with the carbonyl group. The hemiacetal of glucose is so stable that almost all the glucose (99%) exists as the hemiacetal in aqueous solution:

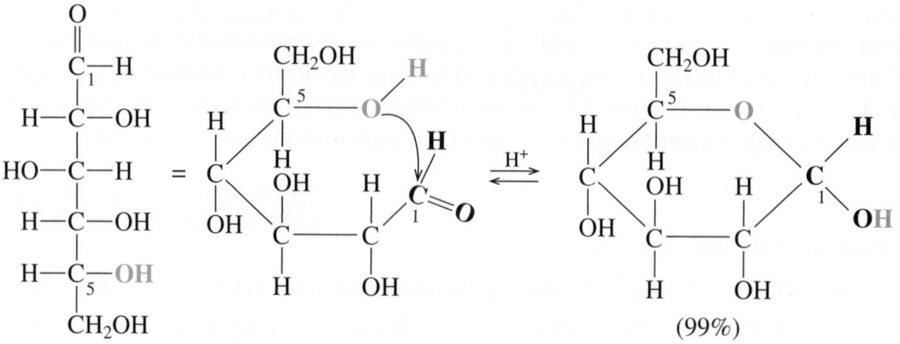

Glucose   Formation of cyclic hemiacetal   (99%)

We will discuss carbohydrates and their structures in Chapter 15.

An alcohol can add to the cyclic hemiacetal to form a cyclic acetal. This reaction is also very important in carbohydrate chemistry. It is the linkage used by glucose molecules to bond to other glucose molecules to form long chains:

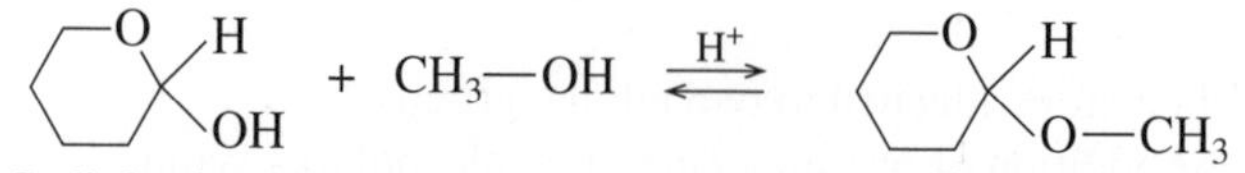

Cyclic hemiacetal   Cyclic acetal

QUESTIONS AND PROBLEMS

Addition Reactions of Aldehydes and Ketones

14.25 Draw the condensed structural formula of the organic product formed by the addition of water to each of the following:
a. acetaldehyde   b. formaldehyde

14.26 Draw the condensed structural formula of the organic product formed by the addition of water to each of the following:
a. propanal   b. propanone

14.27 Indicate whether each of the following structural formulas is a hemiacetal, acetal, or neither:
a. $CH_3—CH_2—O—CH_2—OH$

b. 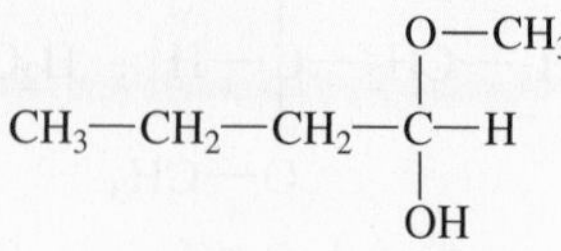 $CH_3—CH_2—CH_2—\overset{\overset{\displaystyle O—CH_3}{|}}{\underset{\underset{\displaystyle OH}{|}}{C}}—H$

c. $CH_3—\overset{\overset{\displaystyle O—CH_2—CH_3}{|}}{\underset{\underset{\displaystyle O—CH_2—CH_3}{|}}{C}}—CH_2—CH_3$

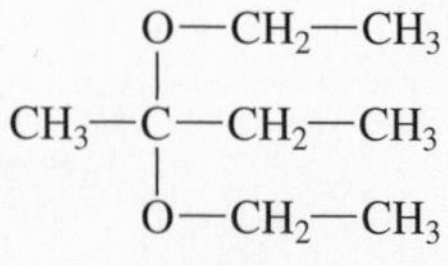

d.

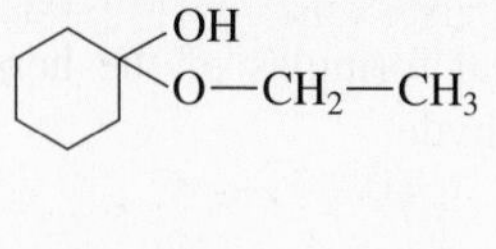

e. 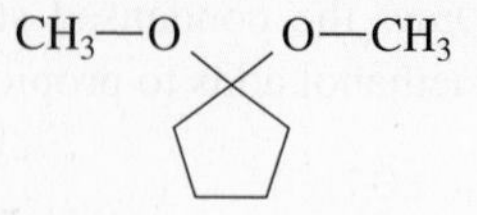 $CH_3—O$ $O—CH_3$

14.28 Indicate whether each of the following structural formulas is a hemiacetal, acetal, or neither:
a. $CH_3—CH_2—O—CH_2—CH_3$
b. $HO—CH_2—CH_2—O—CH_2—CH_2—O—CH_3$

c. 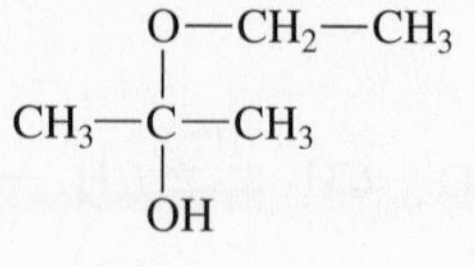 $CH_3—\overset{\overset{\displaystyle O—CH_2—CH_3}{|}}{\underset{\underset{\displaystyle OH}{|}}{C}}—CH_3$ d.

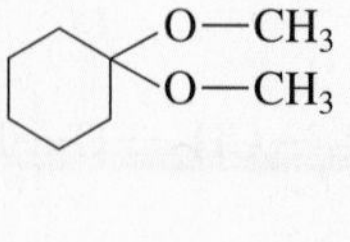

e.

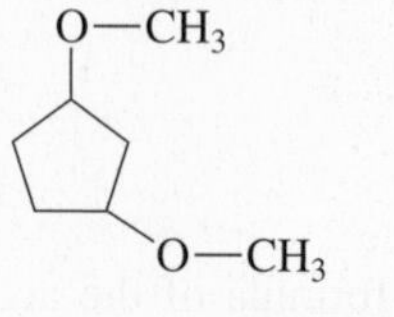

14.29 Draw the condensed structural formula of the hemiacetal formed by adding one methanol molecule to each of the following compounds:
  a. ethanal   **b.** propanone
  c. cyclopentanone   **d.** butanal

14.30 Draw the condensed structural formula of the hemiacetal formed by adding one ethanol molecule to each of the following compounds:

  a. propanal   **b.** 2-butanone
  c. cyclohexanone   **d.** formaldehyde

14.31 Draw the condensed structural formula of the acetal formed by adding a second methanol to the compounds in problem 14.29.

14.32 Draw the condensed structural formula of the acetal formed by adding a second ethanol to the compounds in problem 14.30.

14.5 Chiral Molecules

In the preceding chapters, we have looked at isomers. Let's review those now. Molecules are structural isomers when they have the same molecular formula but different bonding arrangements:

LEARNING GOAL
Identify chiral and achiral carbon atoms in an organic molecule.

Isomers

C_2H_6O CH_3—CH_2—OH CH_3—O—CH_3
            Ethanol   Dimethyl ether

$$C_3H_6O \qquad CH_3{-}CH_2{-}\overset{\displaystyle O}{\overset{\|}{C}}{-}H \qquad CH_3{-}\overset{\displaystyle O}{\overset{\|}{C}}{-}CH_3$$
            Propanal   Propanone

Another group of isomers called **stereoisomers** have identical molecular formulas, too, but they are not structural isomers. In stereoisomers, the atoms are bonded in the same sequence but differ in the way they are arranged in space.

Chirality

When stereoisomers have mirror images that are different, they are said to have "handedness." If you hold your right hand up to a mirror, you see its mirror image, which matches your left hand. (See Figure 14.6.)

If you turn your palms toward each other, you also have mirror images. If you look at the palms of your hands, your thumbs are on opposite sides. If you place your right hand over your left hand, you cannot match up all the parts of the hands: palms, backs, thumbs, and little fingers. The thumbs and little fingers can be matched, but then the palms and backs of your hands are facing each other. Your hands are mirror images that cannot be

FIGURE 14.6 The left and right hands are chiral because they have mirror images that cannot be superimposed on each other.
Q Why are your shoes chiral objects?

Left hand

Mirror image of right hand

Right hand

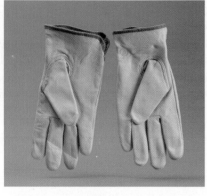

Chiral

Golf club, chiral

Achiral

Achiral

Chiral

Right-handed scissors, chiral

FIGURE 14.7 Everyday objects can be chiral or achiral.

Q Why are some of the above objects chiral and others achiral?

superimposed on each other. When organic molecules have mirror images but cannot be completely matched, we say that they are *nonsuperimposable*.

Objects such as hands that have nonsuperimposable mirror images are **chiral**. Left and right shoes are chiral; left- and right-handed golf clubs are chiral. When we think of how difficult it is to put a left-hand glove on our right hand, put a right shoe on our left foot, or use left-handed scissors if we are right handed, we begin to realize that certain properties of mirror images are very different.

Sometimes a mirror image can be superimposed on the original. For example, all parts of the mirror image of a plain drinking glass can be matched to the glass. When one mirror image can be superimposed on the other, the object is **achiral**. (See Figure 14.7.)

CONCEPT CHECK 14.5

■ **Everyday Chiral Objects**

Classify each of the following objects as chiral or achiral:

a. left ear
b. flip-flop beach sandal
c. plain golf ball

ANSWER

a. A left ear is chiral because it cannot be superimposed on the right ear.
b. The mirror image of a left flip-flop is the right flip-flop. They are chiral because they are not superimposable.
c. A golf ball is achiral because the mirror images are superimposable.

EXPLORE YOUR WORLD

Using Gumdrops and Toothpicks to Model Chiral Objects

Part 1: Achiral Objects

Obtain some toothpicks and several orange, yellow, green, purple, and black gumdrops. Place four toothpicks into the black gumdrop, making the ends of toothpicks form a tetrahedron. Attach gumdrops to the toothpicks: two orange, one green, and one yellow.

Using another black gumdrop, make a second model that is the mirror image of the original model. Now rotate one of the models, and try to superimpose it on the other model. Are the models superimposable? If achiral objects have superimposable mirror images, are these models chiral or achiral?

Part 2: Chiral Objects

Using one of the original models, replace one orange gumdrop with a purple gumdrop. Now there are four different colors of gumdrops attached to the black gumdrop. Make its mirror image by replacing one orange gumdrop with a purple one. Now rotate one of the models, and try to superimpose it on the other model. Are the models superimposable? If chiral objects have nonsuperimposable mirror images, are these models chiral or achiral?

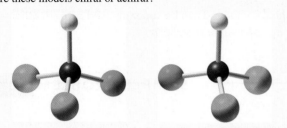

Chiral Carbon Atoms

A carbon compound is chiral if it has at least one carbon atom bonded to four different atoms or groups. This type of carbon atom is called a **chiral carbon** because there are two different ways that it can bond to four atoms or groups of atoms. The resulting structures are mirror images of each other. Let's look at the mirror images of a carbon bonded to four different atoms. (See Figure 14.8.) If we line up the hydrogen and iodine atoms in the mirror images, the bromine and chlorine atoms appear on opposite sides. No matter how we turn the models, we cannot align all four atoms at the same time. When stereoisomers cannot be superimposed, they are called **enantiomers**.

MC™ TUTORIAL
Chiral Carbon Atoms

Mirror

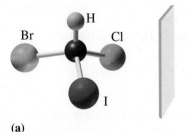

(a)

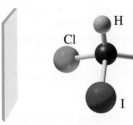

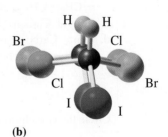

(b)

Limonene (lemons)

FIGURE 14.8 (a) The enantiomers of a chiral molecule are mirror images. **(b)** The enantiomers of a chiral molecule cannot be superimposed on each other.
Q Why is the carbon atom in this compound a chiral carbon?

Molecules in nature also have mirror images, and often one stereoisomer has a different biological effect than the other one. For some compounds, one enantiomer has a certain odor, and the other enantiomer has a completely different odor. For example, the compound limonene has one chiral carbon in the carbon ring indicated by an asterisk; limonene has two enantiomers. One enantiomer of limonene smells like lemons, while its mirror image has the odor of oranges. If two or more atoms bonded to a particular carbon are the same, the atoms can be aligned (superimposed), and the mirror images represent the same structure. (See Figure 14.9.)

Limonene (oranges)

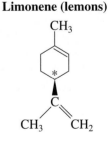

Rotate

Achiral
carbon atom

Mirror

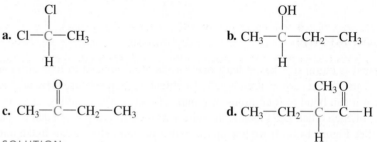

These are the same structures.

FIGURE 14.9 The mirror images of an achiral compound can be superimposed on each other.
Q Why can the mirror images of the compound be superimposed?

SAMPLE PROBLEM 14.8

■ **Chiral Carbons**

For each of the following, indicate whether the carbon in red is chiral or achiral:

a.
$$Cl-\overset{\overset{\displaystyle Cl}{|}}{\underset{\underset{\displaystyle H}{|}}{C}}-CH_3$$

b.
$$CH_3-\overset{\overset{\displaystyle OH}{|}}{\underset{\underset{\displaystyle H}{|}}{C}}-CH_2-CH_3$$

c.
$$CH_3-\overset{\overset{\displaystyle O}{||}}{C}-CH_2-CH_3$$

d.
$$CH_3-CH_2-\overset{\overset{\displaystyle CH_3}{|}}{\underset{\underset{\displaystyle H}{|}}{C}}-\overset{\overset{\displaystyle O}{||}}{C}-H$$

SOLUTION

a. Achiral. Two of the substituents on the carbon are the same (—Cl). A chiral carbon must be bonded to four different groups or atoms.
b. Chiral. Carbon 2 is bonded to four different groups: one —OH, one —CH₃, one —CH₂—CH₃, and one —H.
c. Achiral. Carbon 2 is bonded to only three groups, not four.
d. Chiral. Carbon 2 is bonded to four different groups: one —H, one —CH₃, one —CH₂—CH₃, and one —CHO.

STUDY CHECK

Circle the two chiral carbons in the structural formula of the carbohydrate erythrose:

$$HO-CH_2-\overset{\overset{\displaystyle OH}{|}}{CH}-\overset{\overset{\displaystyle OH}{|}}{CH}-\overset{\overset{\displaystyle O}{||}}{C}-H$$

Erythrose

Drawing Fischer Projections

Emil Fischer devised a simplified system for drawing stereoisomers that shows the arrangements of the atoms. Fischer received the Nobel Prize in Chemistry in 1902 for his contributions to carbohydrate and protein chemistry. Using his method, called a **Fischer**

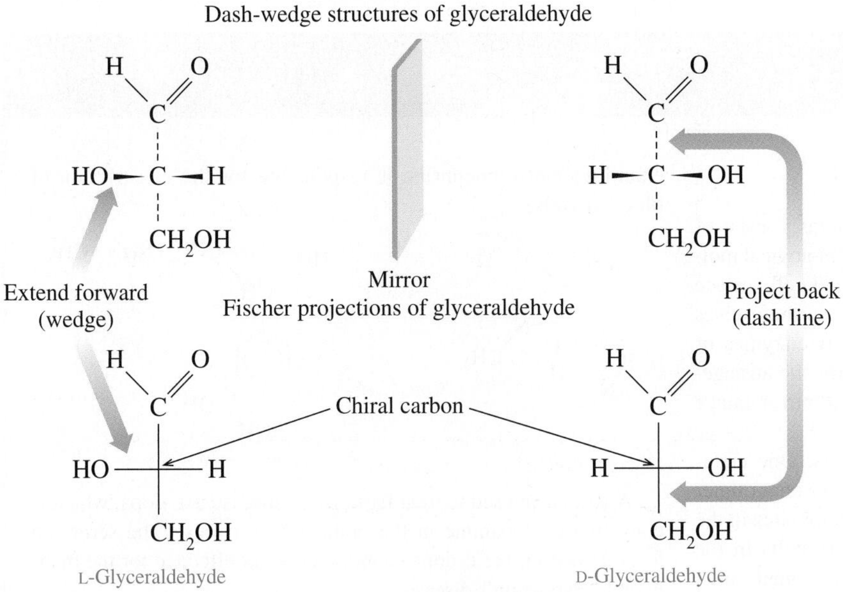

Dash-wedge structures of glyceraldehyde

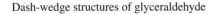

Extend forward
(wedge)

Mirror
Fischer projections of glyceraldehyde

Project back
(dash line)

L-Glyceraldehyde

Chiral carbon

D-Glyceraldehyde

FIGURE 14.10 In a Fischer projection, the chiral carbon atom is at the center with horizontal lines for bonds that extend toward the viewer and vertical lines for bonds that point away.

Q Why does glyceraldehyde have only one chiral carbon atom?

projection, the carbon chain is written vertically with the most highly oxidized carbon at the top. Horizontal lines represent bonds that project forward in the three-dimensional structure. Vertical lines represent bonds that project backward. Each intersection of lines represents a carbon atom that is usually chiral.

For glyceraldehyde, the carbonyl group, which is the most highly oxidized group in the molecule, is written at the top. The letter L is assigned to the left-handed stereoisomer, which has the —OH group on the left of the chiral carbon. The letter D is assigned to the right-handed structure, where the —OH is on the right of the chiral carbon. Today, the "D- and L-" system is used primarily to identify the enantiomers of carbohydrates and amino acids. Let's look at how glyceraldehyde, the simplest sugar, is converted from a three-dimensional view to a Fischer projection. (See Figure 14.10.)

Fischer projections can also be written for compounds that have two or more chiral carbons. For example, in the following mirror images, the chiral carbon atom at each intersection is bonded to four different groups. To draw the mirror image, the positions of the substituents on the horizontal lines are reversed:

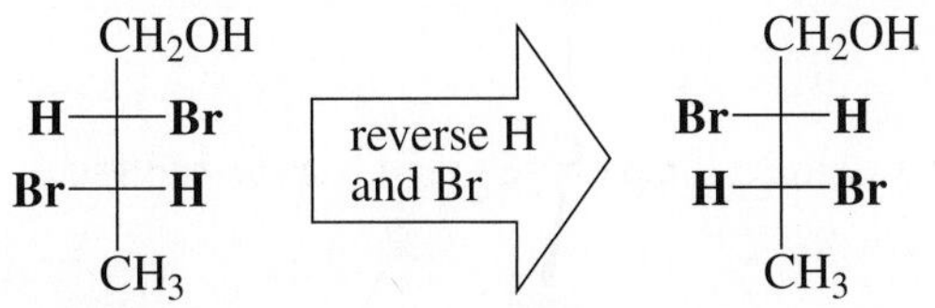

reverse H
and Br

We can also draw the mirror image of the carbohydrate erythrose by changing the sides of the —OH groups on the two chiral carbons:

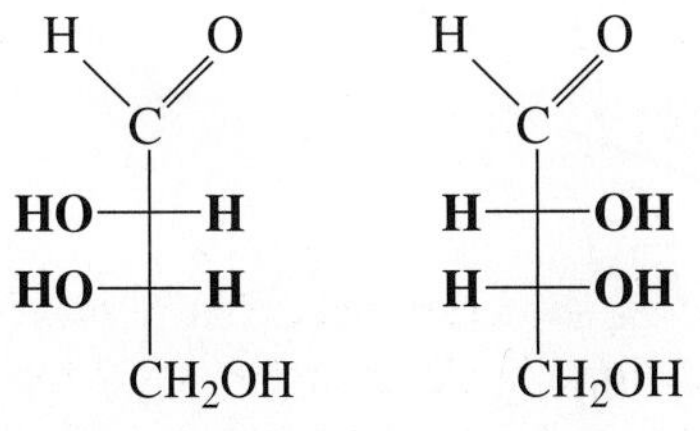

L-Erythrose

D-Erythrose

HEALTH NOTE

Enantiomers in Biological Systems

Most compounds that are active in biological systems consist of only one enantiomer. Rarely are both enantiomers of biological molecules active. This happens because the enzymes and cell surface receptors on which metabolic reactions take place are themselves chiral. Thus, only one enantiomer interacts with its enzymes or receptors; the other is inactive. The chiral receptor fits the arrangement of the substituents in only one enantiomer; its mirror image does not fit properly. (See Figure 14.11.)

A substance called *carvone* has two enantiomers. One enantiomer gives the odor of spearmint oil, while the other enantiomer produces the odor of caraway seeds. The chiral receptor sites in the olfactory cells in the nasal cavity and the gustatory cells in the taste buds on the tongue fit the shape of only one enantiomer. Thus, our senses of smell and taste are responsive to the chirality of molecules.

Enantiomers of Carvone

From spearmint oil   From caraway seeds

In the brain, one enantiomer of LSD affects the production of serotonin, affecting sensory perception and possibly leading to hallucinations. However, its enantiomer produces little effect in the brain. The behavior of nicotine and epinephrine (adrenaline) also depends upon only one of their enantiomers. For example, one enantiomer of nicotine is more toxic than the other. Only one enantiomer of epinephrine is responsible for the constriction of blood vessels.

Nicotine   Adrenalin (epinephrine)

A substance used to treat Parkinson's disease is L-dopa, which is converted to dopamine in the brain, where it raises the serotonin level. However, the D-dopa enantiomer is not effective for the treatment of Parkinson's disease.

L-Dopa, anti-Parkinsonian drug   D-Dopa has no biological effect

For many drugs, only one of the enantiomers is biologically active. However, for many years, drugs have been produced that were mixtures of their enantiomers. Today, drug researchers are using *chiral technology* to produce the active enantiomers of chiral drugs. Chiral catalysts are being designed that direct the formation of just one enantiomer rather than both. The benefits of producing only the active enantiomer include using a lower dose, enhancing activity, reducing interactions with other drugs, and eliminating possible harmful side effects from the inactive enantiomer. Several active enantiomers are now being produced such as L-dopa and the active enantiomer of the popular analgesic ibuprofen used in Advil, Motrin, and Nuprin.

Ibuprofen

FIGURE 14.11 (a) The substituents on the biologically active enantiomer bind to all the sites on a chiral receptor; (b) its enantiomer does not bind properly and is not active biologically.

Q Why doesn't the mirror image of the active enantiomer fit into a chiral receptor site?

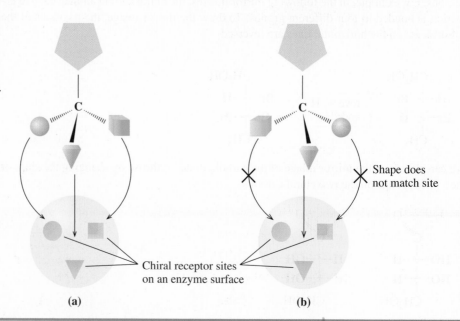

Shape does not match site

Chiral receptor sites on an enzyme surface

(a)   (b)

SAMPLE PROBLEM 14.9

■ Fischer Projections

Determine if each Fischer projection is chiral or achiral. If chiral, identify it as the D or L isomer and draw the mirror image.

a. 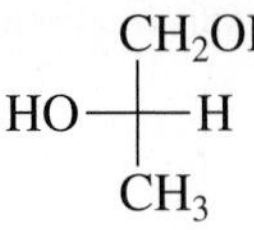
$$\begin{array}{c} CH_2OH \\ HO-\!\!\!\!\!\!\!\!-\!\!\!\!H \\ CH_3 \end{array}$$
b.
$$\begin{array}{c} CH_3 \\ HO-\!\!\!\!\!\!\!\!-\!\!\!\!H \\ CH_3 \end{array}$$
c.
$$\begin{array}{c} CHO \\ H-\!\!\!\!\!\!\!\!-\!\!\!\!OH \\ CH_3 \end{array}$$

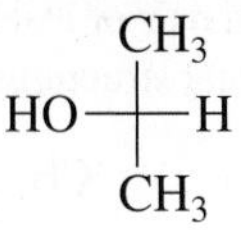

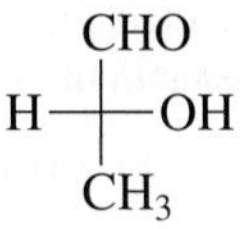

SOLUTION

a. Chiral. The carbon at the intersection that is attached to four different substituents is the L isomer because the —OH is on the left. Its mirror image is written by reversing the —H and —OH:

$$\begin{array}{c} CH_2OH \\ H-\!\!\!\!\!\!\!\!-\!\!\!\!OH \\ CH_3 \end{array}$$

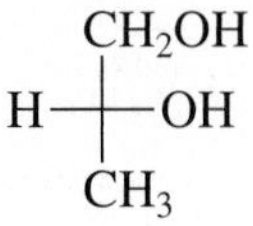

b. Achiral. The carbon atom at the intersection is attached to two identical groups (—CH₃).
c. Chiral. The carbon atom at the intersection is attached to four different substituents. It is the D isomer because the —OH is on the right. The mirror image is written by reversing the —H and —OH:

$$\begin{array}{c} CHO \\ HO-\!\!\!\!\!\!\!\!-\!\!\!\!H \\ CH_3 \end{array}$$

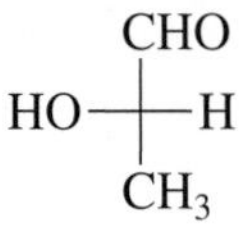

STUDY CHECK

Draw the Fischer projections for the D and L stereoisomers of 2-hydroxypropanal.

QUESTIONS AND PROBLEMS

Chiral Molecules

14.33 Identify each of the following structures as chiral or achiral. If chiral, indicate the chiral carbon.

a.
$$\begin{array}{c} OH \\ | \\ CH_3-CH-CH_3 \end{array}$$
b.
$$\begin{array}{c} Br \\ | \\ CH_3-CH-CH_2-CH_3 \end{array}$$

c.
$$\begin{array}{cc} CH_3 & O \\ | & \| \\ CH_3-CH-C-H \end{array}$$
d.
$$\begin{array}{c} O \\ \| \\ CH_3-CH_2-C-CH_3 \end{array}$$

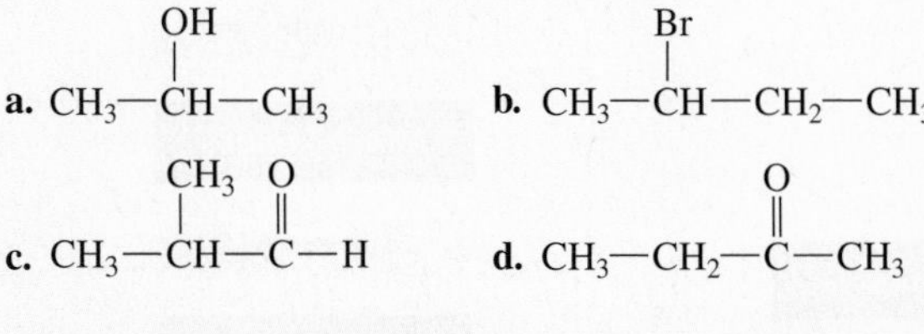

14.34 Identify each of the following structures as chiral or achiral. If chiral, indicate the chiral carbon.

a.
$$\begin{array}{cc} Cl & Cl \\ | & | \\ CH_3-C-CH_2-CH-CH_3 \\ | \\ CH_3 \end{array}$$

b.
$$\begin{array}{c} Br \\ | \\ CH_3-C=CH-CH_3 \end{array}$$
c.
$$\begin{array}{cc} OH & OH \\ | & | \\ CH_3-C-CH-CH_3 \\ | \\ OH \end{array}$$

d.
$$\begin{array}{c} Cl \\ | \\ Br-CH_2-CH-CH_3 \end{array}$$

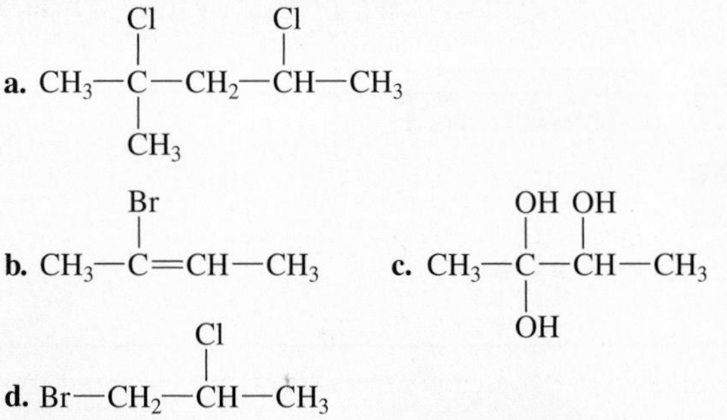

14.35 Identify the chiral carbon in each of the following naturally occurring compounds:
a. citronellol, one enantiomer has the geranium odor

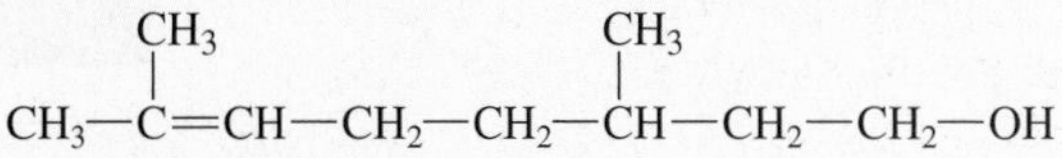

$$\begin{array}{cc} CH_3 & CH_3 \\ | & | \\ CH_3-C=CH-CH_2-CH_2-CH-CH_2-CH_2-OH \end{array}$$

b. alanine, amino acid

$$\begin{array}{cc} CH_3 & O \\ | & \| \\ H_2N-CH-C-OH \end{array}$$

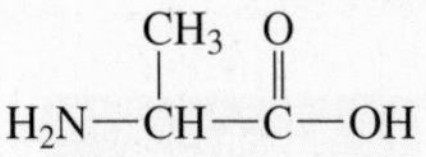

14.36 Identify the chiral carbon in each of the following naturally occurring compounds:
a. amphetamine (Benzedrine), stimulant, treatment of hyperactivity

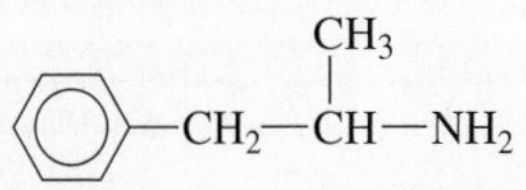

$$\begin{array}{c} CH_3 \\ | \\ \langle\!\!\bigcirc\!\!\rangle-CH_2-CH-NH_2 \end{array}$$

b. Norepinephrine, increases blood pressure and nerve transmission

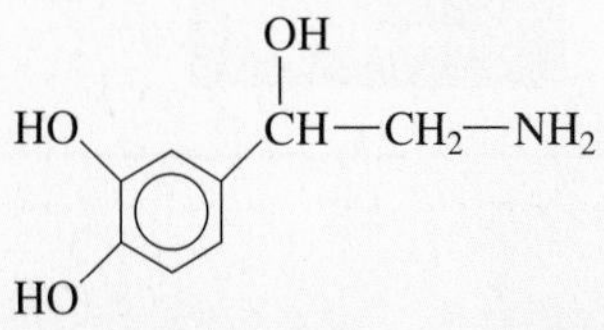

$$\begin{array}{c} OH \\ | \\ HO-\langle\!\!\bigcirc\!\!\rangle-CH-CH_2-NH_2 \\ HO \end{array}$$

14.37 Draw the Fischer projection for each of the following dash-wedge structures:

a.
```
        H
        |
        C
       ⁄ ⋮ ＼
     HO  CH₃ Br
```

b.
```
       CH₃
        |
        C
       ⁄  ＼
     Cl    Br
         OH
```

c.
```
       CHO
        |
        C
       ⁄  ＼
     HO    H
         CH₂CH₃
```

14.38 Draw the Fischer projection for each of the following dash-wedge structures:

a.
```
       CHO
        |
        C
       ⁄ ⋮ ＼
     HO   Br
        CH₂OH
```

b.
```
       CHO
        |
        C
      ⋮    ＼
     H      OH
        CH₂OH
```

c.
```
       CHO
        |
        C
       ⁄    ＼
     HO      H
        CH₂OH
```

14.39 Indicate whether each pair of Fischer projections represent enantiomers or identical structures:

a.
$$
\begin{array}{c} CH_3 \\ Br-\!\!\!\!-Cl \\ CH_3 \end{array}
\quad \text{and} \quad
\begin{array}{c} CH_3 \\ Cl-\!\!\!\!-Br \\ CH_3 \end{array}
$$

b.
$$
\begin{array}{c} CHO \\ HO-\!\!\!\!-H \\ CH_3 \end{array}
\quad \text{and} \quad
\begin{array}{c} CHO \\ H-\!\!\!\!-OH \\ CH_3 \end{array}
$$

c.
$$
\begin{array}{c} CH_3 \\ Cl-\!\!\!\!-Br \\ H \end{array}
\quad \text{and} \quad
\begin{array}{c} CH_3 \\ Br-\!\!\!\!-Cl \\ H \end{array}
$$

d.
$$
\begin{array}{c} COOH \\ H-\!\!\!\!-OH \\ CH_3 \end{array}
\quad \text{and} \quad
\begin{array}{c} COOH \\ HO-\!\!\!\!-H \\ CH_3 \end{array}
$$

14.40 Indicate whether each pair of Fischer projections represent enantiomers or identical structures:

a.
$$
\begin{array}{c} CH_2OH \\ Br-\!\!\!\!-Cl \\ CH_3 \end{array}
\quad \text{and} \quad
\begin{array}{c} CH_2OH \\ Cl-\!\!\!\!-Br \\ CH_3 \end{array}
$$

b.
$$
\begin{array}{c} CHO \\ H-\!\!\!\!-H \\ CH_3 \end{array}
\quad \text{and} \quad
\begin{array}{c} CHO \\ H-\!\!\!\!-H \\ CH_3 \end{array}
$$

c.
$$
\begin{array}{c} CH_3 \\ H-\!\!\!\!-OH \\ CH_2CH_3 \end{array}
\quad \text{and} \quad
\begin{array}{c} CH_3 \\ HO-\!\!\!\!-H \\ CH_2CH_3 \end{array}
$$

d.
$$
\begin{array}{c} COOH \\ H-\!\!\!\!-NH_2 \\ CH_3 \end{array}
\quad \text{and} \quad
\begin{array}{c} COOH \\ H_2N-\!\!\!\!-H \\ CH_3 \end{array}
$$

CONCEPT MAP

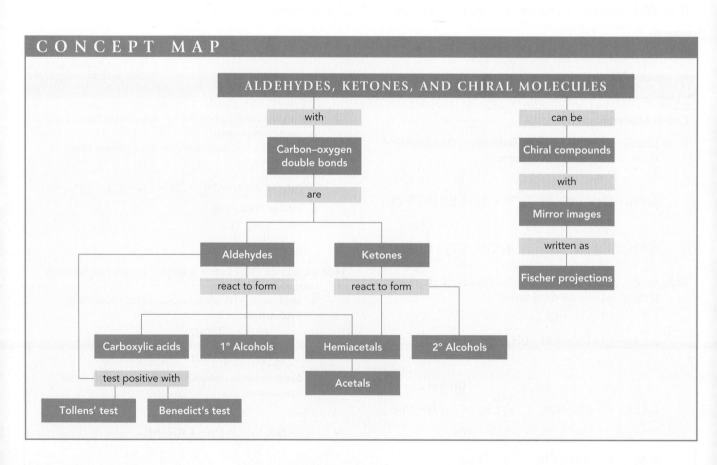

CHAPTER REVIEW

14.1 Aldehydes and Ketones
LEARNING GOAL: *Identify compounds with the carbonyl group as aldehydes and ketones. Give the IUPAC and common names for aldehydes and ketones; draw their condensed structural formulas.*
Aldehydes and ketones contain a carbonyl group (C=O), which consists of a double bond between a carbon and an oxygen atom. However, in contrast to the C=C double bond, the C=O is strongly polar. In aldehydes, the carbonyl group appears at the end of carbon chains attached to at least one hydrogen atom. In ketones, the carbonyl group occurs between two alkyl or aromatic groups. In the IUPAC system, the *e* in the corresponding alkane is replaced with *al* for aldehydes and *one* for ketones. For ketones with more than four carbon atoms in the main chain, the carbonyl group is numbered to show its location. Many of the simple aldehydes and ketones use common names. Many aldehydes and ketones are found in biological systems, flavorings, and drugs.

14.2 Physical Properties of Aldehydes and Ketones
LEARNING GOAL: *Compare the boiling points and solubility of aldehydes and ketones to those of alkanes and alcohols.*
Because they contain a polar carbonyl group, aldehydes and ketones have higher boiling points than alkanes and ethers of similar molar mass. Their boiling points are lower than alcohols because aldehydes and ketones cannot hydrogen bond with each other. However, aldehydes and ketones can hydrogen bond with water molecules, which makes carbonyl compounds with one to four carbon atoms soluble in water.

14.3 Oxidation and Reduction of Aldehydes and Ketones
LEARNING GOAL: *Draw the condensed structural formulas of reactants and products for the oxidation or reduction of aldehydes and ketones.*

Primary alcohols can be oxidized to aldehydes, whereas secondary alcohols can oxidize to ketones. Aldehydes are easily oxidized to carboxylic acids, but ketones do not oxidize further. Aldehydes, but not ketones, react with Tollens' reagent to give "silver mirrors." In Benedict's test, aldehydes with adjacent hydroxyl groups reduce blue Cu^{2+} to give a brick-red Cu_2O solid. The reduction of aldehydes with hydrogen produces primary alcohols, while ketones are reduced to secondary alcohols.

14.4 Addition Reactions of Aldehydes and Ketones
LEARNING GOAL: *Write the products of the addition of alcohols to aldehydes and ketones.*
Water and alcohols can add to the carbonyl group of aldehydes and ketones. The addition of one alcohol forms a hemiacetal, while the addition of two alcohols forms an acetal. Hemiacetals are not usually stable, except for cyclic hemiacetals, which are the most common form of simple sugars such as glucose.

14.5 Chiral Molecules
LEARNING GOAL: *Identify chiral and achiral carbon atoms in an organic molecule.*
Chiral molecules are molecules with mirror images that cannot be superimposed on each other. These types of stereoisomers are called enantiomers. A chiral molecule must have at least one chiral carbon, which is a carbon bonded to four different atoms or groups of atoms. The Fischer projection is a simplified way to draw the arrangements of atoms by placing the carbon atoms at the intersection of vertical and horizontal lines. The names of the mirror images are labeled D or L to differentiate between enantiomers of carbohydrates and amino acids.

SUMMARY OF NAMING

Structure	Family	IUPAC Name	Common Name
H—C(=O)—H	Aldehyde	Methanal	Formaldehyde
CH_3—C(=O)—CH_3	Ketone	Propanone	Acetone; Dimethyl ketone

SUMMARY OF REACTIONS

OXIDATION OF ALDEHYDES TO CARBOXYLIC ACIDS

$$CH_3-C(=O)-H \xrightarrow{[O]} CH_3-C(=O)-OH$$
Acetaldehyde → Acetic acid

REDUCTION OF ALDEHYDES TO PRIMARY ALCOHOLS

$$CH_3-C(=O)-H + H_2 \xrightarrow{Ni} CH_3-CH_2-OH$$
Acetaldehyde → Ethanol

REDUCTION OF KETONES TO SECONDARY ALCOHOLS

$$CH_3-C(=O)-CH_3 + H_2 \xrightarrow{Ni} CH_3-CH(OH)-CH_3$$
Acetone → 2-Propanol

ADDITION OF WATER TO ALDEHYDES

$$\underset{\text{Formaldehyde}}{\overset{H}{\underset{H}{>}}C=O} + H_2O \overset{H^+}{\rightleftharpoons} \underset{\text{Formalin}}{\overset{H}{\underset{H}{}}C\overset{OH}{\underset{OH}{}}}$$

$$\underset{\text{Acetaldehyde}}{\overset{H_3C}{\underset{H}{>}}C=O} + H_2O \overset{H^+}{\rightleftharpoons} \underset{\text{Hydrate}}{\overset{H_3C}{\underset{H}{}}C\overset{OH}{\underset{OH}{}}}$$

ADDITION OF ALCOHOLS TO FORM HEMIACETALS AND ACETALS
FROM ALDEHYDES

$$\underset{\text{Formaldehyde}}{H-\overset{O}{\overset{\|}{C}}-H} + \underset{\text{Methanol}}{CH_3-OH} \overset{H^+}{\rightleftharpoons} \left\{ \underset{\text{Hemiacetal}}{H-\overset{O-CH_3}{\underset{OH}{\overset{|}{C}}}-H} \right\} + CH_3-OH \overset{H^+}{\rightleftharpoons} \underset{\text{Acetal}}{H-\overset{O-CH_3}{\underset{O-CH_3}{\overset{|}{C}}}-H} + H_2O$$

FROM KETONES

$$\underset{\text{Acetone}}{CH_3-\overset{O}{\overset{\|}{C}}-CH_3} + \underset{\text{Methanol}}{CH_3-OH} \overset{H^+}{\rightleftharpoons} \left\{ \underset{\text{Hemiacetal}}{CH_3-\overset{O-CH_3}{\underset{OH}{\overset{|}{C}}}-CH_3} \right\} + CH_3-OH \overset{H^+}{\rightleftharpoons} \underset{\text{Acetal}}{CH_3-\overset{O-CH_3}{\underset{O-CH_3}{\overset{|}{C}}}-CH_3} + H_2O$$

■ KEY TERMS

acetal The product of the addition of two alcohols to an aldehyde or ketone.

achiral Molecules with mirror images that are superimposable.

aldehyde An organic compound with a carbonyl functional group and at least one hydrogen attached to the carbon in the carbonyl group.

Benedict's test A test for aldehydes with adjacent hydroxyl groups in which Cu^{2+} ($CuSO_4$) ions in Benedict's reagent are reduced to a brick-red solid of Cu_2O.

chiral Objects or molecules that have nonsuperimposable mirror images.

chiral carbon A carbon atom that is bonded to four different atoms or groups.

enantiomers Stereoisomers that are mirror images that cannot be superimposed.

Fischer projection A system for drawing stereoisomers; carbon atoms are shown at intersections of horizontal lines for bonds

projecting forward and vertical lines for bonds projecting backward. The most highly oxidized carbon is at the top.

hemiacetal The product of the addition of one alcohol to the double bond of the carbonyl group in aldehydes and ketones.

ketone An organic compound in which the carbonyl functional group is bonded to two alkyl or aromatic groups.

reduction A decrease in the number of carbon–oxygen bonds by the addition of hydrogen to a carbonyl bond. Aldehydes are reduced to primary alcohols; ketones to secondary alcohols.

stereoisomers Isomers that have atoms bonded in the same order but with different arrangements in space.

Tollens' test A test for aldehydes in which Ag^+ in Tollens' reagent is reduced to metallic silver, which forms a "silver mirror" on the walls of the container.

■ UNDERSTANDING THE CONCEPTS

14.41 Which of the following will give a positive Tollens' test?

a. $CH_3-CH_2-\overset{O}{\overset{\|}{C}}-H$

b. $CH_3-\overset{O}{\overset{\|}{C}}-H$

c. $CH_3-O-CH_2-CH_3$

d. $CH_3-CH_2-CH_2-OH$

e. $CH_3-\overset{OH}{\overset{|}{C}H}-CH_3$

f. $\overset{O}{\overset{\|}{C}}-H$ (cyclopropyl)

UNDERSTANDING THE CONCEPTS **535**

14.42 Citronellal, a constituent of oil of citronella as well as lemon and lemon grass, is used in perfumes and as an insect repellent:

$$CH_3-\underset{\underset{CH_3}{|}}{C}=CH-CH_2-CH_2-\underset{\underset{CH_3}{|}}{CH}-CH_2-\overset{\overset{O}{\|}}{C}-H$$

a. Complete the IUPAC name

_____, _____-di_____ - _____-octenal.
b. What does the *en* in octenal signify?
c. What does the *al* in octenal signify?
d. Write the balanced equation for the combustion of citronellal when burned in a candle to repel insects.

14.43 Identify the functional groups in each of the following:

a. **almonds**

b. **vanilla extract or vanilla beans**

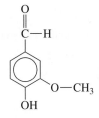

c. **cinnamon sticks**

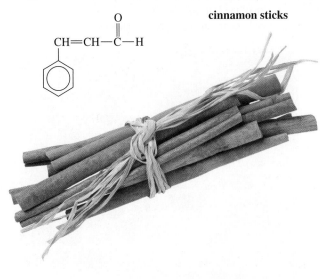

d. **mint leaves**

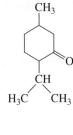

e.

$$CH_3-\overset{\overset{O}{\|}}{C}-\overset{\overset{O}{\|}}{C}-CH_3$$

butter

Match each of the preceding formulas with the following names:

1. 2,3-butanedione
2. benzaldehyde
3. 2-isopropyl-5-methylcyclohexanone
4. cinnamaldehyde
5. 4-hydroxy-3-methoxybenzaldehyde

14.44 Draw the condensed structural formula and line-bond formula for each of the following:

a. 2-heptanone, an alarm pheromone of bees

b. 2,6-dimethyl-3-heptanone, communication pheromone of bees

c. *trans*-2-hexenal, an alarm pheromone of ants

d. 2,6-dimethyl-5-heptenal, communication pheromone of ants

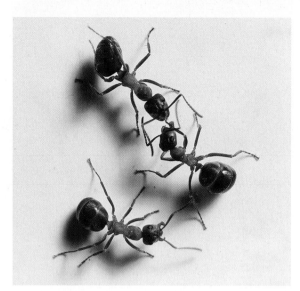

ADDITIONAL QUESTIONS AND PROBLEMS

For instructor-assigned homework, go to www.masteringchemistry.com.

14.45 Write the isomers for the carbonyl compounds of C_4H_8O.

14.46 Why does the $C=O$ double bond have a dipole, whereas the $C=C$ does not?

14.47 Give the IUPAC and common names (if any) for each of the following compounds:

a.

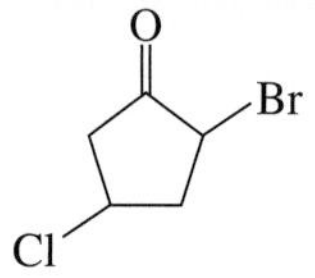

b. 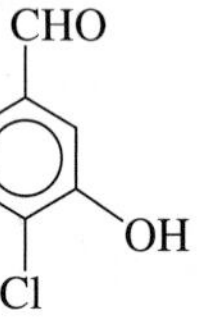 CHO

c. Cl—CH$_2$—CH$_2$—C(=O)—H

d. CH$_3$—CH$_2$—C(=O)—CH$_2$—CH(Cl)—CH$_3$

e. CH$_3$—CH(Cl)—C(=O)—CH$_2$—CH$_3$

14.48 Give the IUPAC and common names (if any) for each of the following compounds:

a. CH$_3$—CH$_2$—C(=O)—CH$_3$

b.

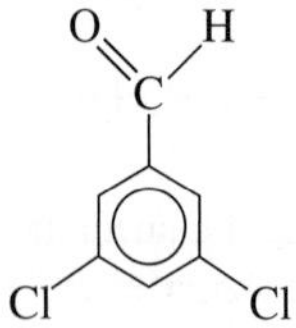

c.

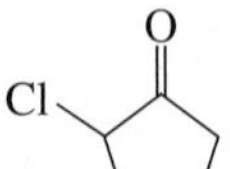

d. CH$_3$—CH(CH$_3$)—CH(CH$_3$)—CH$_2$—C(=O)—H

e.

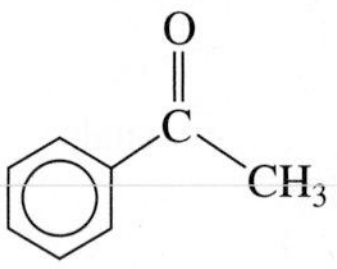

14.49 Draw the condensed structural formula of each of the following:

a. 3-methylcyclopentanone   **b.** 4-chlorobenzaldehyde

c. 3-chloropropionaldehyde   **d.** ethyl methyl ketone

e. 3-methylhexanal

14.50 Draw the condensed structural formula of each of the following:

a. propionaldehyde   **b.** 2-chlorobutanal

c. 2-methylcyclohexanone   **d.** 3,5-dimethylhexanal

e. 3-bromocyclopentanone

14.51 Which of the following compounds are soluble in water?

a. CH$_3$—CH$_2$—CH$_2$—CH$_3$

b. CH$_3$—CH$_2$—C(=O)—H   **c.** CH$_3$—C(=O)—CH$_3$

d. CH$_3$—CH$_2$—CH$_2$—OH

e. CH$_3$—CH$_2$—C(=O)—CH$_2$—CH$_2$—CH$_3$

14.52 Which of the following compounds are soluble in water?

a. CH$_3$—CH$_2$—C(=O)—CH$_3$ **b.** H—C(=O)—H

c. CH$_3$—C(=O)—H

d. CH$_3$—CH$_2$—CH$_3$

e. CH$_3$—CH$_2$—CH(CH$_3$)—CH$_2$—CH$_2$—C(=O)—H

14.53 In each of the following pairs of compounds, select the compound with the higher boiling point:

a. 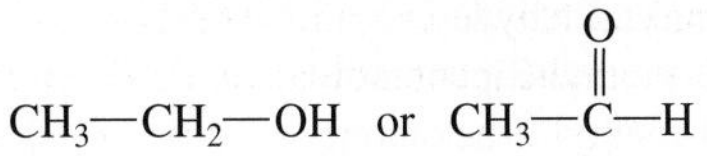 $CH_3—CH_2—OH$ or $CH_3—\overset{\overset{O}{\|}}{C}—H$

b. $CH_3—CH_2—CH_2—CH_3$ or $CH_3—CH_2—\overset{\overset{O}{\|}}{C}—H$

c. $CH_3—CH_2—CH_2—OH$ or $CH_3—\overset{\overset{O}{\|}}{C}—CH_3$

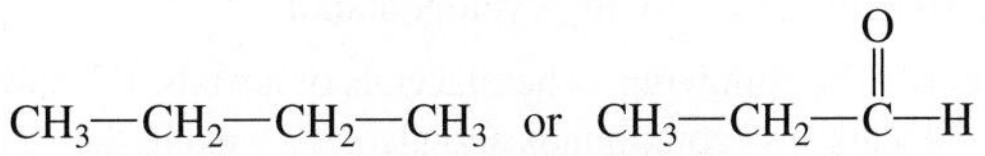

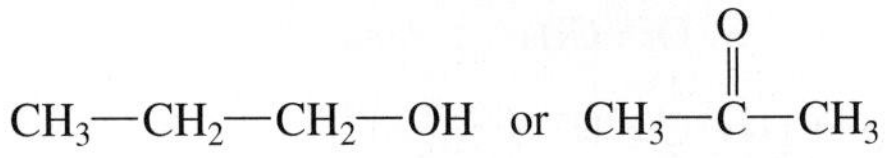

14.54 In each of the following pairs of compounds, select the compound with the higher boiling point:

a. 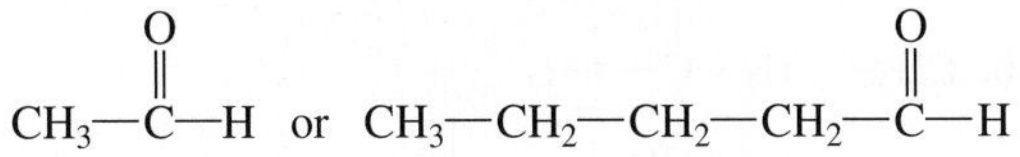 $CH_3—\overset{\overset{O}{\|}}{C}—H$ or $CH_3—CH_2—CH_2—CH_2—\overset{\overset{O}{\|}}{C}—H$

b. $CH_3—CH_2—CH_2—CH_3$ or $CH_3—\overset{\overset{O}{\|}}{C}—CH_3$

c. $CH_3—CH_2—\overset{\overset{O}{\|}}{C}—H$ or $CH_3—\overset{\overset{OH}{|}}{CH}—CH_3$

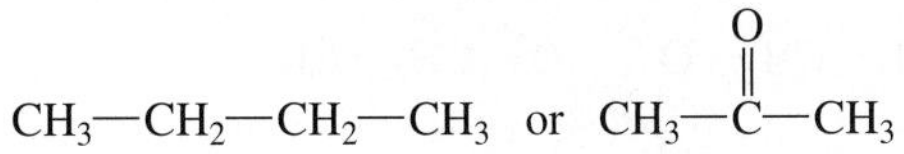

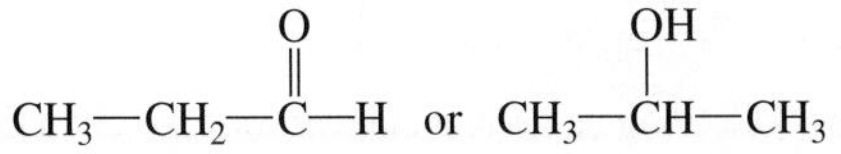

14.55 Identify the chiral carbons, if any, in each of the following compounds:

a. 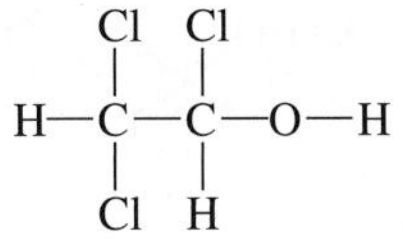 $H—\overset{\overset{Cl}{|}}{\underset{\underset{Cl}{|}}{C}}—\overset{\overset{Cl}{|}}{\underset{\underset{H}{|}}{C}}—O—H$

b. $CH_3—\overset{\overset{H}{|}}{C}=\overset{\overset{CH_3}{|}}{C}—CH_3$

c. $HO—CH_2—\overset{\overset{OH}{|}}{CH}—CH_2—OH$

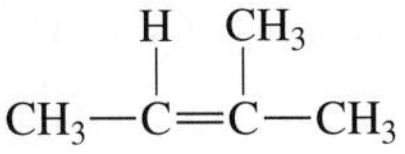

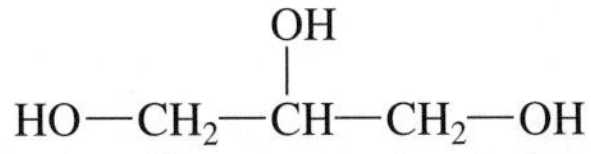

d. 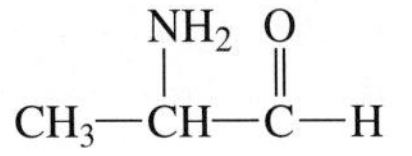 $CH_3—\overset{\overset{NH_2}{|}}{CH}—\overset{\overset{O}{\|}}{C}—H$

e. 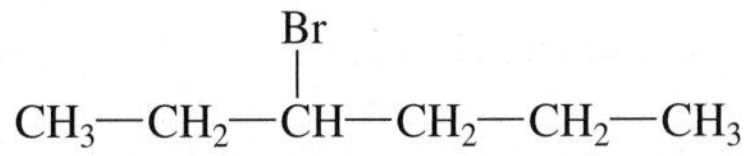 $CH_3—CH_2—\overset{\overset{Br}{|}}{CH}—CH_2—CH_2—CH_3$

f. 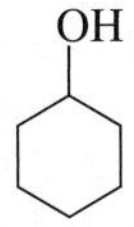 cyclohexane with OH

14.56 Identify the chiral carbons, if any, in each of the following compounds:

a. 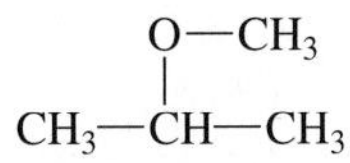 $CH_3—\overset{\overset{O—CH_3}{|}}{CH}—CH_3$

b. 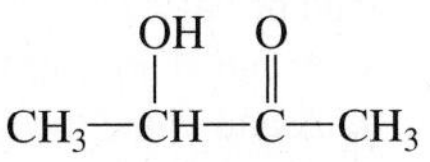 $CH_3—\overset{\overset{OH}{|}}{CH}—\overset{\overset{O}{\|}}{C}—CH_3$

c. $CH_3—\overset{\overset{OH}{|}}{\underset{\underset{OH}{|}}{C}}—CH_3$

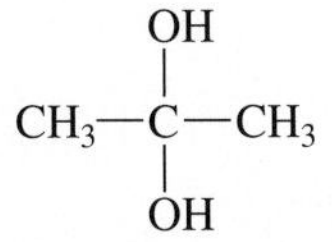

d. 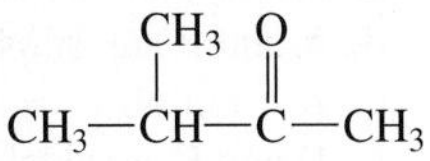 $CH_3—\overset{\overset{CH_3}{|}}{CH}—\overset{\overset{O}{\|}}{C}—CH_3$

e. 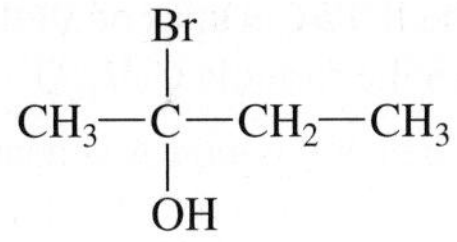 $CH_3—\overset{\overset{Br}{|}}{\underset{\underset{OH}{|}}{C}}—CH_2—CH_3$

f. 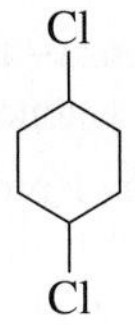 cyclohexane with Cl and Cl

14.57 Identify each of the following pairs of Fischer projections as enantiomers or identical compounds:

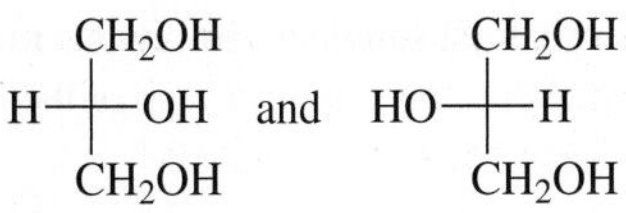

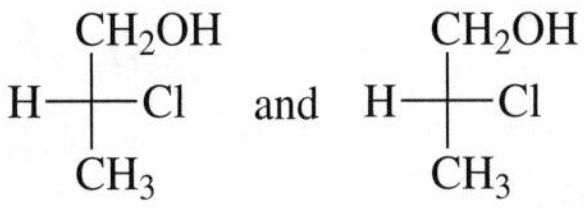

a. 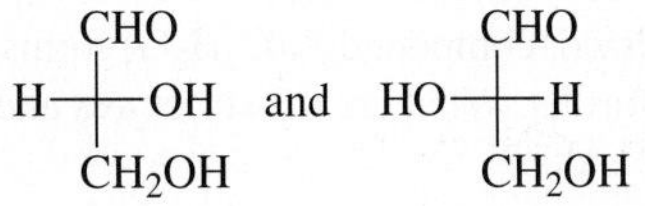 H—CHO/OH/CH₂OH and HO—CHO/H/CH₂OH

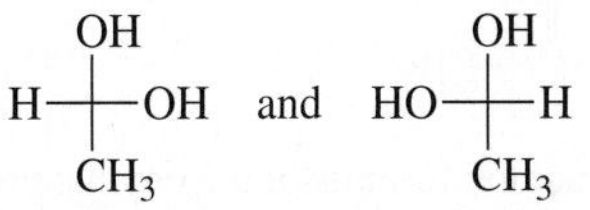

14.58 Identify each of the following pairs of Fischer projections as enantiomers or identical compounds:

a. 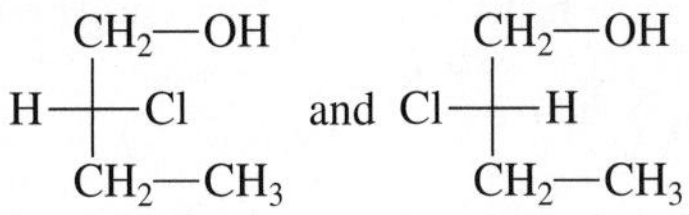 enantiomers/identical with CH₂—OH ... CH₂—CH₃
b. 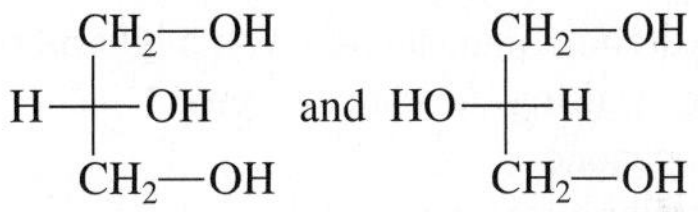 ... CH₂—OH ... CH₂—OH
c. 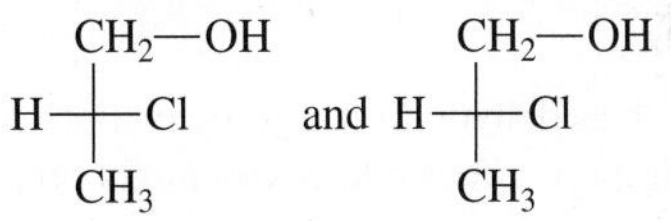 ... CH₃ ... CH₃
d. 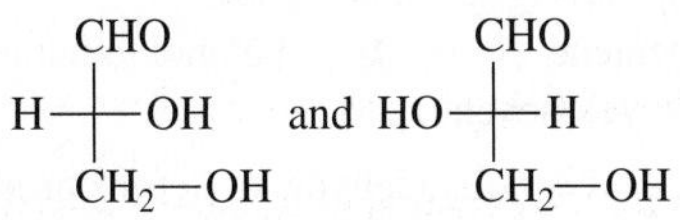 CHO ... CH₂—OH

14.59 Draw the condensed structural formula of the organic product when each of the following is oxidized:

a. $CH_3—CH_2—CH_2—OH$

b. 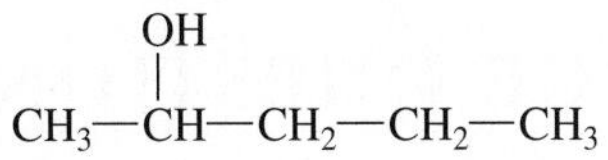 $CH_3—\overset{\overset{OH}{|}}{CH}—CH_2—CH_2—CH_3$

c. 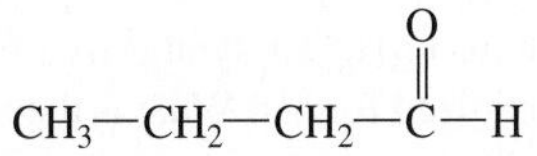 $CH_3—CH_2—CH_2—\overset{\overset{O}{\|}}{C}—H$

d. 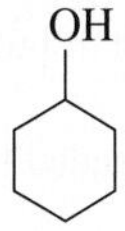 cyclohexanol (OH)

14.60 Draw the condensed structural formula of the organic product when each of the following is oxidized:

a. 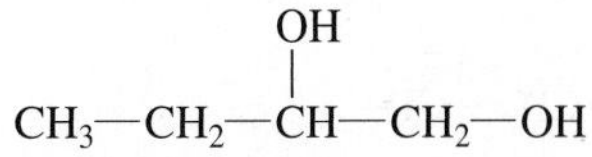 $CH_3—CH_2—\overset{\overset{OH}{|}}{CH}—CH_2—OH$

b. 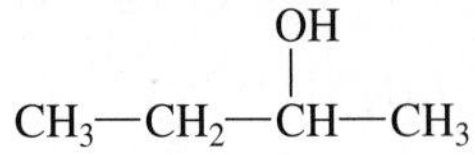 $CH_3—CH_2—\overset{\overset{OH}{|}}{CH}—CH_3$

c. 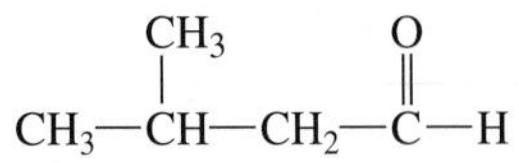 $CH_3—\overset{\overset{CH_3}{|}}{CH}—CH_2—\overset{\overset{O}{\|}}{C}—H$

d. 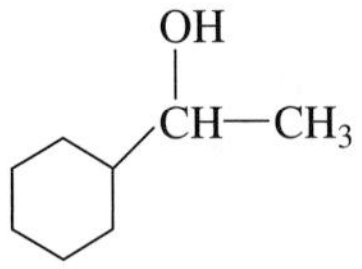 cyclohexane with $\overset{\overset{OH}{|}}{CH}—CH_3$

14.61 Draw the condensed structural formula of the organic product when hydrogen and a nickel catalyst reduce each of the following:

a. $CH_3-\overset{\overset{\displaystyle O}{\|}}{C}-CH_3$

b. $CH_2-\overset{\overset{\displaystyle O}{\|}}{C}-H$

c. $CH_3-\overset{\overset{\displaystyle CH_3}{|}}{CH}-CH_2-\overset{\overset{\displaystyle O}{\|}}{C}-CH_3$

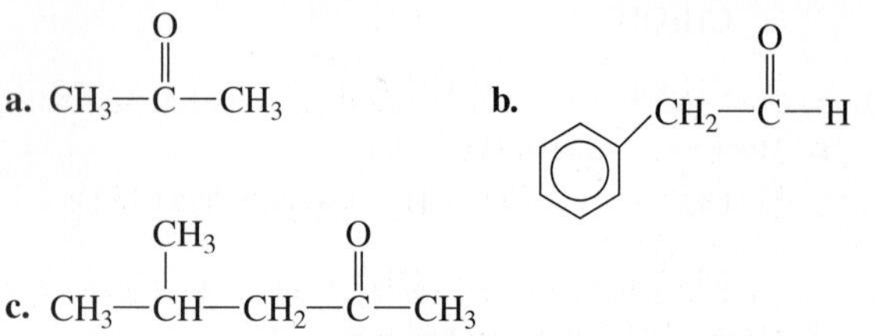

14.62 Draw the condensed structural formula of the organic product when hydrogen and a nickel catalyst reduce each of the following:

a. $CH_3-\overset{\overset{\displaystyle O}{\|}}{C}-H$

b. cyclopentanone with CH₃

c. $H-\overset{\overset{\displaystyle O}{\|}}{C}-H$

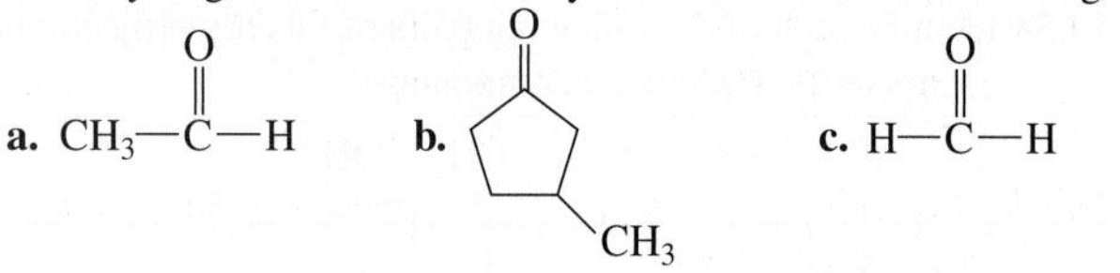

14.63 Using reactions such as dehydration, hydrogenation, oxidation, reduction, and hydration, indicate how you might prepare the following from the starting substance given:
a. propene to propanone
b. butanal to 1,2-dibromobutane
c. butanal to butanone

14.64 Using reactions such as dehydration, hydrogenation, oxidation, reduction, and hydration, indicate how you might prepare the following from the starting substance given:
a. pentanal to 1-pentene   b. 1-butanol to butanone
c. cyclohexene to cyclohexanone

14.65 Give the name of the alcohol, aldehyde, or ketone product for each of the following:
a. oxidation of 1-propanol   b. oxidation of 2-pentanol
c. reduction of 2-butanone   d. oxidation of cyclohexanol

14.66 Give the name of the alcohol, aldehyde, or ketone product for each of the following:
a. reduction of butyraldehyde
b. oxidation of 3-methyl-2-pentanol
c. reduction of 4-methyl-2-hexanone
d. oxidation of 3-methylcyclopentanol

14.67 Identify the following as hemiacetals or acetals. Give the names of the carbonyl compounds and alcohols used in their synthesis.

a. $CH_3-CH_2-\overset{\overset{\displaystyle O-CH_3}{|}}{\underset{\underset{\displaystyle O-CH_3}{|}}{C}}-H$

b. $CH_3-CH_2-\overset{\overset{\displaystyle O-CH_2-CH_3}{|}}{\underset{\underset{\displaystyle OH}{|}}{C}}-CH_3$

c. CH_3-CH_2-O $O-CH_2-CH_3$

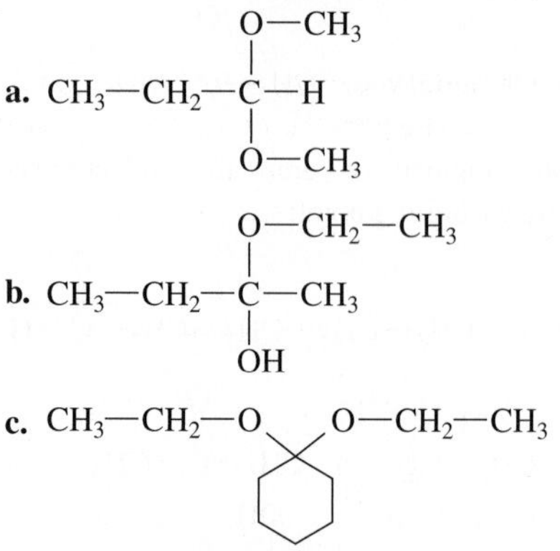

14.68 Identify the following as hemiacetals or acetals. Give the names of the carbonyl compounds and alcohols used in their synthesis.

a. $CH_3-CH_2-\overset{\overset{\displaystyle O-CH_3}{|}}{\underset{\underset{\displaystyle OH}{|}}{C}}-H$

b. HO $O-\overset{\overset{\displaystyle CH_3}{|}}{CH}-CH_3$

c. $CH_3-\overset{\overset{\displaystyle O-CH_2-CH_2-CH_3}{|}}{\underset{\underset{\displaystyle O-CH_2-CH_2-CH_3}{|}}{C}}-H$

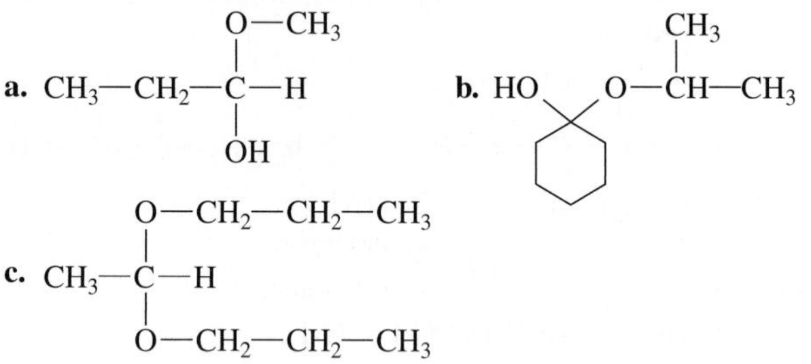

CHALLENGE QUESTIONS

14.69 A compound with the formula C_4H_8O is synthesized from 2-butanol and cannot be oxidized further. What is the structure and name of the compound?

14.70 a. Write the balanced equation for the reduction of butanone using a Pt catalyst.
b. How many milliliters of H_2 gas at STP are needed to reduce 1.56 g of butanone?

14.71 Use the following structures to answer the true/false questions below:

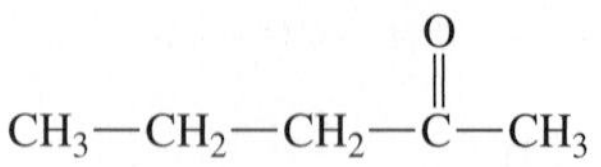

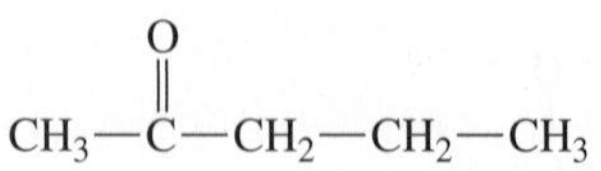

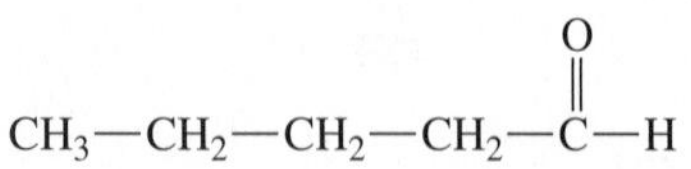

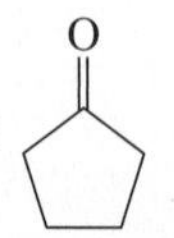

A $CH_3-CH_2-\overset{\overset{\displaystyle O}{\|}}{C}-CH_2-CH_3$

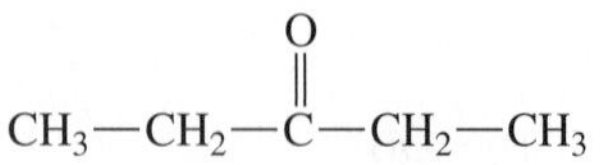

B $CH_3-CH_2-CH_2-\overset{\overset{\displaystyle O}{\|}}{C}-CH_3$

C $CH_3-\overset{\overset{\displaystyle O}{\|}}{C}-CH_2-CH_2-CH_3$

D $CH_3-CH_2-CH_2-CH_2-\overset{\overset{\displaystyle O}{\|}}{C}-H$

E

F $\overset{\overset{\displaystyle O}{\|}}{C}-H$

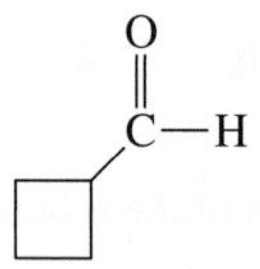

True or False?
a. **A** and **B** are isomers.
b. **A** and **C** are the same compound.
c. **B** and **C** are the same compound.
d. **E** and **F** are isomers.
e. **A** is chiral.
f. **D** and **F** are aldehydes.
g. **B** and **E** are ketones.

14.72 Draw the structures and give the IUPAC names of all the aldehydes and ketones that have the formula $C_5H_{10}O$.

14.73 Compound A is 1-propanol. When compound A is heated with strong acid, it dehydrates to form compound B (C_3H_6). When compound A is oxidized, compound C (C_3H_6O) forms. What are the structures and names of compounds A, B, and C?

14.74 Compound X is 2-propanol. When compound X is heated with strong acid, it dehydrates to form compound Y (C_3H_6). When compound X is oxidized, compound Z (C_3H_6O) forms, which cannot be oxidized further. What are the structures and names of compounds X, Y, and Z?

ANSWERS

ANSWERS TO STUDY CHECKS

14.1 propanal (IUPAC), propionaldehyde (common)

14.2 ethyl propyl ketone

14.3 The oxygen atom in the carbonyl group of acetone hydrogen bonds with water molecules.

14.4 cyclohexanol

14.5 The oxidation of benzaldehyde reduces Ag^+ to metallic silver, which forms a silvery coating on the walls of the test tube.

14.6 1-propanol

14.7 CH_3—$\overset{\overset{\displaystyle O-CH_3}{|}}{\underset{\underset{\displaystyle O-CH_3}{|}}{C}}$—$CH_3$

14.8 HO—CH_2—$\overset{\overset{\displaystyle OH}{|}}{CH}$—$\overset{\overset{\displaystyle OH}{|}}{CH}$—$\overset{\overset{\displaystyle O}{||}}{C}$—$H$

14.9

CHO	CHO
H——OH	HO——H
CH₃	CH₃
D-2-Hydroxypropanal	L-2-Hydroxypropanal

ANSWERS TO SELECTED QUESTIONS AND PROBLEMS

14.1 a. ketone   **b.** aldehyde
    c. ketone   **d.** aldehyde

14.3 a. (1) isomers   **b.** (1) isomers
    c. (2) the same compound

14.5 a. propanal
    b. 2-methyl-3-pentanone
    c. 3-bromobutanal
    d. 2-pentanone
    e. 3-methylcyclohexanone
    f. 4-chlorobenzaldehyde

14.7 a. acetaldehyde
    b. methyl propyl ketone
    c. formaldehyde

14.9 a. CH_3—$\overset{\overset{\displaystyle O}{||}}{C}$—$H$ **b.** CH_3—$\overset{\overset{\displaystyle O}{||}}{C}$—$CH_2$—$\overset{\overset{\displaystyle CH_3}{|}}{CH}$—$CH_3$

    c. CH_3—$\overset{\overset{\displaystyle Br}{|}}{CH}$—$\overset{\overset{\displaystyle Br}{|}}{CH}$—$\overset{\overset{\displaystyle O}{||}}{C}$—$H$

    d. CH_3—$\overset{\overset{\displaystyle O}{||}}{C}$—$CH_2$—$CH_2$—$CH_2$—$CH_3$

    e. CH_3—CH_2—$\overset{\overset{\displaystyle CH_3}{|}}{CH}$—$CH_2$—$\overset{\overset{\displaystyle O}{||}}{C}$—$H$

14.11

CHO (on benzene ring with OCH₃ para)

14.13 a. CH_3—$\overset{\overset{\displaystyle O}{||}}{C}$—$H$ has a higher boiling point because it has a polar carbonyl group.
    b. Pentanal has a higher molar mass and thus a higher boiling point.
    c. 1-Butanol has a higher boiling point because it can hydrogen bond with other 1-butanol molecules.

14.15 a. CH_3—$\overset{\overset{\displaystyle O}{||}}{C}$—$\overset{\overset{\displaystyle O}{||}}{C}$—$CH_3$, more hydrogen bonding
    b. acetaldehyde, hydrogen bonding
    c. acetone, lower number of carbon atoms

14.17 No. The long carbon chain diminishes the effect of the carbonyl group.

14.19 a. CH_3—OH **b.** cyclopentane with OH

    c. CH_3—CH_2—$\overset{\overset{\displaystyle OH}{|}}{CH}$—$CH_3$

    d. CH_2—OH (on benzene ring)   **e.** cyclohexane with OH and CH₃

14.21 a. CH_3—CH_2—CH_2—CH_2—$\overset{\overset{\displaystyle O}{||}}{C}$—$H$

    b. CH_3—CH_2—$\overset{\overset{\displaystyle O}{||}}{C}$—$CH_3$ **c.** cyclohexanone

    d. CH_3—$\overset{\overset{\displaystyle O}{||}}{C}$—$CH_2$—$\overset{\overset{\displaystyle CH_3}{|}}{CH}$—$CH_3$

    e. CH_3—$\overset{\overset{\displaystyle CH_3}{|}}{CH}$—$CH_2$—$\overset{\overset{\displaystyle O}{||}}{C}$—$H$

14.23 a. CH_3—CH_2—CH_2—CH_2—OH
    b. CH_3—$\overset{\overset{\displaystyle OH}{|}}{CH}$—$CH_3$

    c. CH_3—CH_2—CH_2—$\overset{\overset{\displaystyle Br}{|}}{CH}$—$CH_2$—$CH_2$—$OH$

    d. CH_3—$\overset{\overset{\displaystyle CH_3}{|}}{CH}$—$\underset{\underset{\displaystyle OH}{|}}{CH}$—$CH_2$—$CH_3$

14.25 a. CH_3—$\overset{\overset{\displaystyle OH}{|}}{\underset{\underset{\displaystyle OH}{|}}{C}}$—$H$ **b.** H—$\overset{\overset{\displaystyle OH}{|}}{\underset{\underset{\displaystyle OH}{|}}{C}}$—$H$

14.27 a. hemiacetal   **b.** hemiacetal   **c.** acetal
d. hemiacetal   **e.** acetal

14.29 a.
$$CH_3-\underset{\underset{OH}{|}}{\overset{\overset{O-CH_3}{|}}{C}}-H$$
b.
$$CH_3-\underset{\underset{OH}{|}}{\overset{\overset{O-CH_3}{|}}{C}}-CH_3$$

c. (cyclopentane ring with HO and O—CH₃ substituents)
d.
$$CH_3-CH_2-CH_2-\underset{\underset{OH}{|}}{\overset{\overset{O-CH_3}{|}}{C}}-H$$

14.31 a.
$$CH_3-\underset{\underset{O-CH_3}{|}}{\overset{\overset{O-CH_3}{|}}{C}}-H$$
b.
$$CH_3-\underset{\underset{O-CH_3}{|}}{\overset{\overset{O-CH_3}{|}}{C}}-CH_3$$

c. CH₃—O   O—CH₃ (cyclopentane ring)

d.
$$CH_3-CH_2-CH_2-\underset{\underset{O-CH_3}{|}}{\overset{\overset{O-CH_3}{|}}{C}}-H$$

14.33 a. achiral

b. chiral
$$CH_3-\overset{\overset{Br}{|}}{CH}-CH_2-CH_3$$ (Br, Chiral carbon)

c. achiral
d. achiral

14.35 a.
$$CH_3-\overset{\overset{CH_3}{|}}{C}=CH-CH_2-CH_2-\overset{\overset{CH_3}{|}}{CH}-CH_2-CH_2-OH$$ (CH₃ Chiral carbon)

b.
$$H_2N-\overset{\overset{CH_3}{|}}{CH}-\overset{\overset{O}{||}}{C}-OH$$
Chiral carbon

14.37 a.
HO—|—Br
CH₃ (with H on top)
b. Cl—|—Br
OH (with CH₃ on top)
c. HO—|—H
CH₂CH₃ (with CHO on top)

14.39 a. identical   **b.** enantiomers
c. enantiomers   **d.** enantiomers

14.41 a, b, and f

14.43 a. aldehyde, aromatic
b. aldehyde, ether, phenol, aromatic
c. aldehyde, alkene, aromatic
d. ketone, cycloalkane
e. ketone
a. 2   **b.** 5   **c.** 4   **d.** 3   **e.** 1

14.45

$$CH_3-CH_2-CH_2-\overset{\overset{O}{||}}{C}-H \qquad CH_3-\overset{\overset{CH_3}{|}}{CH}-\overset{\overset{O}{||}}{C}-H \qquad CH_3-CH_2-\overset{\overset{O}{||}}{C}-CH_3$$

14.47 a. 2-bromo-4-chlorocyclopentanone
b. 4-chloro-3-hydroxybenzaldehyde
c. 3-chloropropanal; 3-chloropropionaldehyde
d. 5-chloro-3-hexanone
e. 2-chloro-3-pentanone

14.49 a. (cyclopentanone ring with CH₃)   **b.** CHO (benzene ring with Cl)

c.
$$Cl-CH_2-CH_2-\overset{\overset{O}{||}}{C}-H$$

d.
$$CH_3-CH_2-\overset{\overset{O}{||}}{C}-CH_3$$

e.
$$CH_3-CH_2-CH_2-\overset{\overset{CH_3}{|}}{CH}-CH_2-\overset{\overset{O}{||}}{C}-H$$

14.51 b, c, and d

14.53 a. CH₃—CH₂—OH

b.
$$CH_3-CH_2-\overset{\overset{O}{||}}{C}-H$$

c. CH₃—CH₂—CH₂—OH

14.55 a.
$$H-\overset{\overset{Cl}{|}}{\underset{\underset{Cl}{|}}{C}}-\overset{\overset{Cl}{|}}{\underset{\underset{H}{|}}{C}}-O-H$$ **b.** none   **c.** none

d.
$$CH_3-\overset{\overset{NH_2}{|}}{CH}-\overset{\overset{O}{||}}{C}-H$$

e.
$$CH_3-CH_2-\overset{\overset{Br}{|}}{CH}-CH_2-CH_2-CH_3$$ **f.** none

14.57 a. enantiomers   **b.** identical
c. identical   **d.** identical

14.59 a.
$$CH_3-CH_2-\overset{\overset{O}{||}}{C}-H \xrightarrow[\text{oxidation}]{\text{Further}} CH_3-CH_2-\overset{\overset{O}{||}}{C}-OH$$

b.
$$CH_3-\overset{\overset{O}{||}}{C}-CH_2-CH_2-CH_3$$

c.
$$CH_3-CH_2-CH_2-\overset{\overset{O}{||}}{C}-OH$$

d. (cyclohexanone ring)

14.61 a.
$$CH_3-\overset{\overset{OH}{|}}{CH}-CH_3$$

b. (benzene ring)—CH₂—CH₂—OH

c.
$$CH_3-\overset{\overset{CH_3}{|}}{CH}-CH_2-\overset{\overset{OH}{|}}{CH}-CH_3$$

14.63 a. $CH_3-CH=CH_2 + H_2O \xrightarrow{H^+} CH_3-\overset{OH}{\underset{|}{CH}}-CH_3 \xrightarrow{[O]} CH_3-\overset{O}{\overset{||}{C}}-CH_3$

Propene   Propanone

b. $CH_3-CH_2-CH_2-\overset{O}{\overset{||}{C}}-H + H_2 \xrightarrow{Ni} CH_3-CH_2-CH_2-CH_2-OH \xrightarrow[\text{Heat}]{H^+}$

Butanal

$CH_3-CH_2-CH=CH_2 + Br_2 \longrightarrow CH_3-CH_2-\overset{Br}{\underset{|}{CH}}-CH_2-Br$

1,2-Dibromobutane

c. $CH_3-CH_2-CH_2-\overset{O}{\overset{||}{C}}-H + H_2 \xrightarrow{Ni} CH_3-CH_2-CH_2-CH_2-OH \xrightarrow[\text{Heat}]{H^+}$

Butanal

$CH_3-CH_2-CH=CH_2 + H_2O \xrightarrow{H^+} CH_3-CH_2-\overset{OH}{\underset{|}{CH}}-CH_3 \xrightarrow{[O]} CH_3-CH_2-\overset{O}{\overset{||}{C}}-CH_3$

Butanone

14.65 a. propanal   **b.** 2-pentanone
c. 2-butanol   **d.** cyclohexanone

14.67 a. acetal; propanal and methanol
b. hemiacetal; butanone and ethanol
c. acetal; cyclohexanone and ethanol

14.69 $CH_3-\overset{CH_3}{\underset{|}{CH}}-\overset{O}{\overset{||}{C}}-H$ 2-methylpropanal

14.71 a. true   **b.** false   **c.** true   **d.** true
e. false   **f.** true   **g.** true

14.73 $CH_3-CH_2-CH_2-OH$ A. 1-propanol
$CH_3-CH=CH_2$ B. propene

$CH_3-CH_2-\overset{O}{\overset{||}{C}}-H$ C. propanal

15 Carbohydrates

"We use a refractometer to measure sugar content in a small sample of juices from the grapes in different areas of the vineyard," says Leslie Bucher, laboratory director at Bouchaine Winery. "We also measure the alcohol content during fermentation and run tests for sulfur, pH, and total acid."

As grapes ripen, there is an increase in the sugars, which are the monosaccharides fructose and glucose. The sugar content is affected by soil conditions and the amount of sun and water. When the grapes are ripe and sugar content is at a desirable level, they are harvested. During fermentation, enzymes from yeast convert about half the sugar to ethanol, and half to carbon dioxide. Grapes harvested with 22.5% sugar will ferment to produce a wine with 12.5–13.5% alcohol content.

Mastering**CHEMISTRY**™

Visit **www.masteringchemistry.com** for self-study materials and instructor-assigned homework.

C arbohydrates are the most abundant of all the organic compounds in nature. In plants, energy from the Sun converts carbon dioxide and water into the carbohydrate glucose. Many of the glucose molecules are made into long-chain polymers of starch that store energy or into cellulose to build the structural framework of the plant. About 65% of the foods in our diet consist of carbohydrates. Each day we utilize carbo- hydrates known as *starches* in foods such as bread, pasta, potatoes, and rice. Other carbohydrates called *disaccharides* include sucrose (table sugar) and lactose in milk. During di- gestion and cellular metabolism, carbohydrates are converted into glucose, which is oxidized further in our cells to provide our bodies with energy and to provide the cells with carbon atoms for building molecules of proteins, lipids, and nucleic acids. Cellulose has other important uses, too. The wood in our furniture, the pages in this book, and the cotton in our clothing are made of cellulose.

15.1 Carbohydrates

Carbohydrates such as table sugar, lactose in milk, and cellulose are all made of car- bon, hydrogen, and oxygen. Simple sugars, which have formulas of $C_n(H_2O)_n$, were once thought to be hydrates of carbon, thus the name *carbohydrate*. In a series of reac- tions called *photosynthesis*, energy from the Sun is used to combine the carbon atoms from carbon dioxide (CO_2) and the hydrogen and oxygen atoms of water into the carbo- hydrate glucose:

$$6CO_2 + 6H_2O + \text{energy} \underset{\text{Respiration}}{\overset{\text{Photosynthesis}}{\rightleftharpoons}} \underset{\text{Glucose}}{C_6H_{12}O_6} + 6O_2$$

In the body, glucose is oxidized in a series of metabolic reactions known as *respiration*, which releases chemical energy to do work in the cells. Carbon dioxide and water are pro- duced and returned to the atmosphere. The combination of photosynthesis and respiration is called the *carbon cycle*, in which energy from the Sun is stored in plants by photosynthe- sis and made available to us when the carbohydrates in our diets are metabolized. (See Figure 15.1.)

Types of Carbohydrates

The simplest carbohydrates are the **monosaccharides**. A monosaccharide cannot be split or hydrolyzed into smaller carbohydrates. One of the most common carbohydrates, glu- cose, $C_6H_{12}O_6$, is a monosaccharide. A **disaccharide** consists of two monosaccharide units joined together. Likewise, a disaccharide can be split into two monosaccharide units. For example, ordinary table sugar, sucrose, $C_{12}H_{22}O_{11}$, is a disaccharide that can be split by water (hydrolysis) in the presence of an acid or an enzyme to give one molecule of glu- cose and one molecule of another monosaccharide, fructose:

$$\underset{\text{Sucrose}}{C_{12}H_{22}O_{11}} + H_2O \xrightarrow{\text{H}^+ \text{ or enzyme}} \underset{\text{Glucose}}{C_6H_{12}O_6} + \underset{\text{Fructose}}{C_6H_{12}O_6}$$

LEARNING GOAL

Classify a monosaccharide as an aldose or ketose, and indicate the number of carbon atoms.

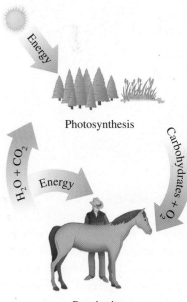

FIGURE 15.1 During photosyn- thesis, energy from the Sun com- bines CO_2 and H_2O to form glucose ($C_6H_{12}O_6$) and O_2. During respiration in the body, carbohy- drates are oxidized to CO_2 and H_2O, while energy is produced.

Q What are the reactants and products of respiration?

SELF STUDY ACTIVITY
Carbohydrates

Polysaccharides are carbohydrates that are naturally occurring polymers containing many monosaccharide units. In the presence of an acid or an enzyme, a polysaccharide can be completely hydrolyzed to yield many molecules of monosaccharide:

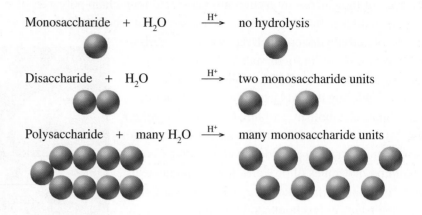

Monosaccharides

TUTORIAL
Types of Carbohydrates

Monosaccharides are simple sugars that have a chain of three to eight carbon atoms, one in a carbonyl group and the rest attached to hydroxyl groups. There are two types of monosaccharide structures. In an **aldose**, the carbonyl group is on the first carbon (—CHO); a **ketose** contains the carbonyl group on the second carbon atom as a ketone (C=O):

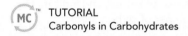
TUTORIAL
Carbonyls in Carbohydrates

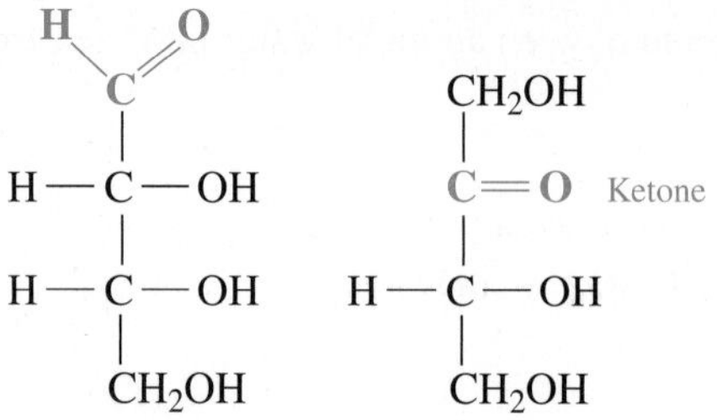

Aldehyde

H   O
 \\   //
   C
   |
H — C — OH
   |
H — C — OH
   |
   CH₂OH

Erythrose,
an aldose

CH₂OH
 |
C = O   Ketone
 |
H — C — OH
 |
CH₂OH

Erythrulose,
a ketose

A monosaccharide with three carbon atoms is a *triose*, one with four carbon atoms is a *tetrose*, a *pentose* has five carbons, and a *hexose* contains six carbons. We can use both classification systems to indicate the type of carbonyl group and the number of carbon atoms. An aldopentose is a five-carbon monosaccharide that is an aldehyde; a ketohexose would be a six-carbon monosaccharide that is a ketone:

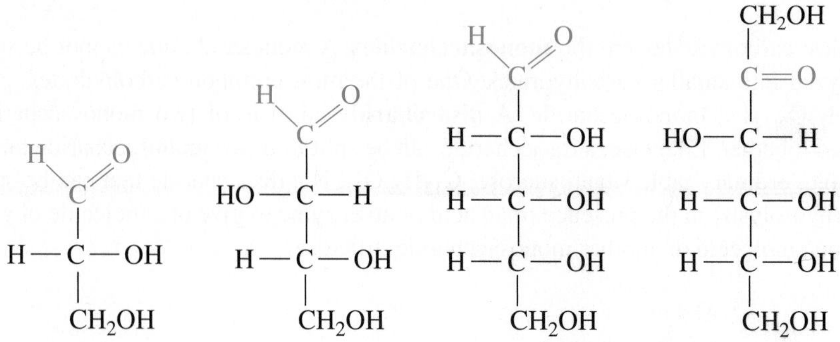

H   O
 \\   //
   C
   |
H — C — OH
   |
   CH₂OH

Glyceraldehyde
(aldotriose)

H   O
 \\   //
   C
   |
HO — C — H
   |
H — C — OH
   |
   CH₂OH

Threose
(aldotetrose)

H   O
 \\   //
   C
   |
H — C — OH
   |
H — C — OH
   |
H — C — OH
   |
   CH₂OH

Ribose
(aldopentose)

CH₂OH
 |
C = O
 |
HO — C — H
 |
H — C — OH
 |
H — C — OH
 |
CH₂OH

Fructose
(ketohexose)

CONCEPT CHECK 15.1

■ Monosaccharides

Classify each of the following monosaccharides to indicate their carbonyl group and number of carbon atoms:

a.

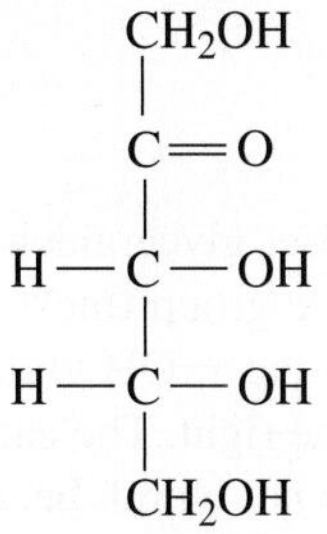

$$CH_2OH$$
$$C=O$$
$$H-C-OH$$
$$H-C-OH$$
$$CH_2OH$$
Ribulose

b.

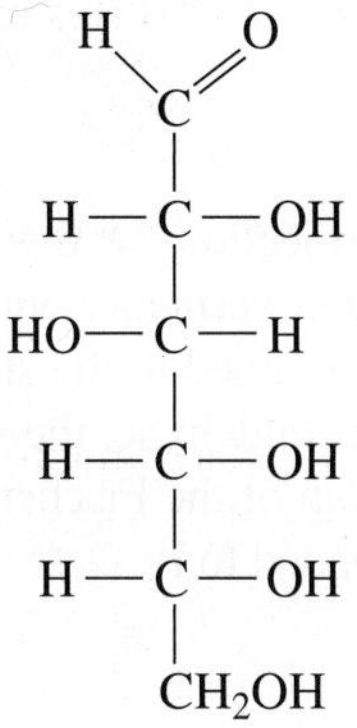

H   O
 \\ //
  C
$$H-C-OH$$
$$HO-C-H$$
$$H-C-OH$$
$$H-C-OH$$
$$CH_2OH$$
Glucose

ANSWER

a. Ribulose has five carbon atoms, which makes it a pentose. The ketone (keto) group makes it a ketopentose.

b. Glucose has six carbon atoms, which makes it a hexose. The aldehyde (aldo) group makes it an aldohexose.

QUESTIONS AND PROBLEMS

Carbohydrates

15.1 What reactants are needed for photosynthesis and respiration?

15.2 What is the relationship between photosynthesis and respiration?

15.3 What is a monosaccharide? A disaccharide?

15.4 What is a polysaccharide?

15.5 What functional groups are found in all monosaccharides?

15.6 What is the difference between an aldose and a ketose?

15.7 What are the functional groups and number of carbons in a ketopentose?

15.8 What are the functional groups and number of carbons in an aldohexose?

15.9 Classify each of the following monosaccharides as an aldose or ketose:

a. 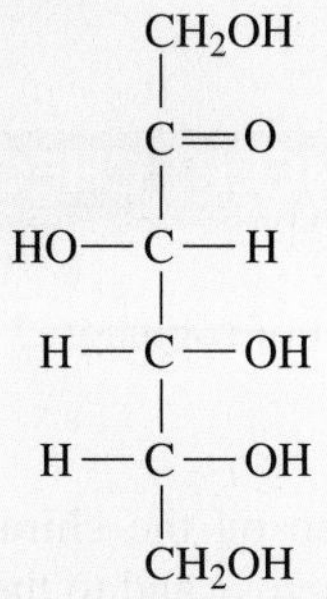
$$CH_2OH$$
$$C=O$$
$$HO-C-H$$
$$H-C-OH$$
$$H-C-OH$$
$$CH_2OH$$
Fructose

b. 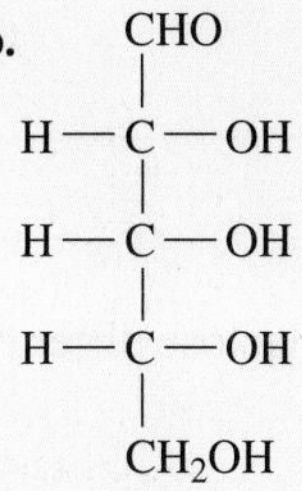
$$CHO$$
$$H-C-OH$$
$$H-C-OH$$
$$H-C-OH$$
$$CH_2OH$$
Ribose

c. 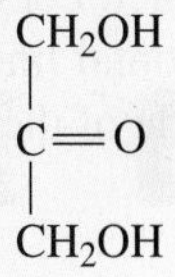
$$CH_2OH$$
$$C=O$$
$$CH_2OH$$
Dihydroxyacetone

d. 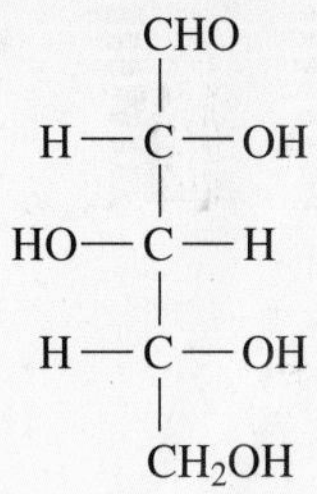
$$CHO$$
$$H-C-OH$$
$$HO-C-H$$
$$H-C-OH$$
$$CH_2OH$$
Xylose

e. 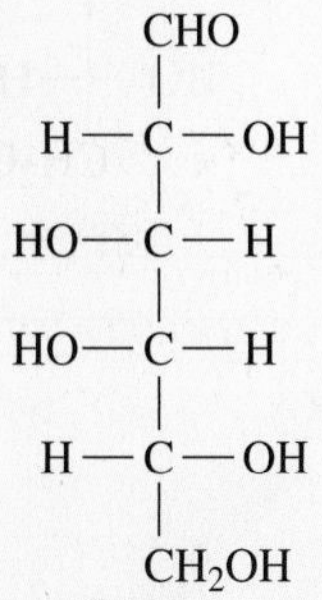
$$CHO$$
$$H-C-OH$$
$$HO-C-H$$
$$HO-C-H$$
$$H-C-OH$$
$$CH_2OH$$
Galactose

15.10 Classify each of the monosaccharides in problem 15.9 according to the number of carbon atoms in the chain.

15.2 Fischer Projections of Monosaccharides

In Chapter 14, we learned that chiral compounds exist as mirror images that cannot be superimposed. Many monosaccharides exist as mirror images.

Fischer Projections

Let's take a look again at the Fischer projection for the simplest aldose, glyceraldehyde. By convention, the carbon chain is written vertically with the aldehyde group (most oxidized carbon) at the top. The letter L is assigned to the stereoisomer if the —OH group is on the left of the chiral carbon. In D-glyceraldehyde, the —OH is on the right. The carbon atom in the —CH2OH group at the bottom of the Fischer projection is not chiral, because it does not have four different groups bonded to it:

Most of the carbohydrates we will study have carbon chains with five or six carbon atoms. Because there are several chiral carbons, the chiral carbon *farthest* from the carbonyl group is used to determine the D or L isomer. The following are the Fischer projections for the D and L isomers of ribose, a five-carbon monosaccharide, and glucose, a six-carbon monosaccharide. In each of the mirror images, it is important to understand that the —OH groups on all the chiral carbon atoms are reversed from one side to the other. For example, in L-ribose, the —OH groups are all written on the left side of the horizontal lines. In the mirror image, D-ribose, the —OH groups are all written on the right side of the horizontal lines.

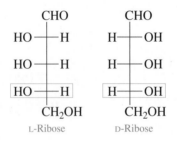 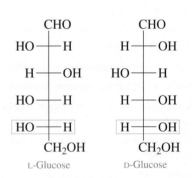

CONCEPT CHECK 15.2

■ **Fischer Projections**

How does the Fischer projection of D-galactose differ from that of D-glucose?

ANSWER
In the Fischer projections, the direction of the —OH group on the chiral carbon atoms differs only at carbon 4, extending to the left in D-galactose and to the right in D-glucose.

SAMPLE PROBLEM **15.1**

■ **Identifying D and L Isomers of Sugars**

Identify the following Fischer projection as D- or L-ribose:

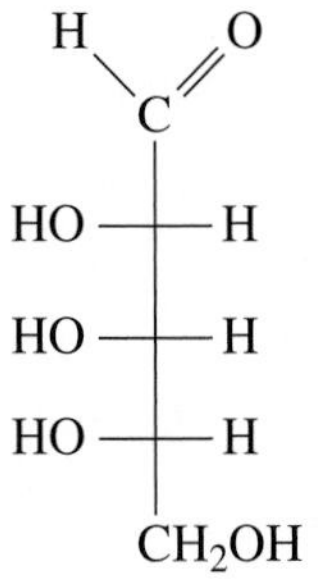

$$
\begin{array}{c}
\text{H}\diagdown \text{C} \diagup \text{O} \\
\text{HO} - \!\!\!\!\!\!-\text{H} \\
\text{HO} - \!\!\!\!\!\!-\text{H} \\
\text{HO} - \!\!\!\!\!\!-\text{H} \\
\text{CH}_2\text{OH}
\end{array}
$$

SOLUTION

In ribose, carbon 4 is the chiral atom farthest from the carbonyl group. Because the hydroxyl group on carbon 4 is on the left, this is L-ribose:

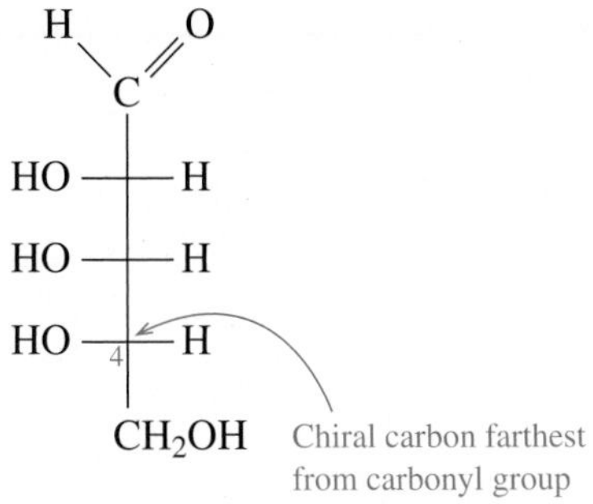

$$
\begin{array}{c}
\text{H}\diagdown \text{C} \diagup \text{O} \\
\text{HO} - \!\!\!\!\!\!-\text{H} \\
\text{HO} - \!\!\!\!\!\!-\text{H} \\
\text{HO} - \!\!\!\!\!\!-\text{H} \\
\text{CH}_2\text{OH}
\end{array}
$$

Chiral carbon farthest from carbonyl group

STUDY CHECK

Draw the Fischer projection for D-ribose.

Some Important Monosaccharides

The hexoses glucose, galactose, and fructose are important monosaccharides. Although we can draw Fischer projections for D and L isomers, the D isomers are commonly found in nature and used in the cells of the body. The Fischer projections for the D isomers are written as follows:

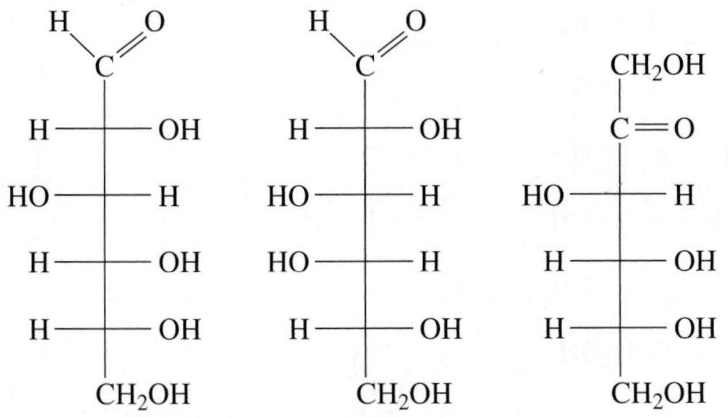

D-Glucose	D-Galactose	D-Fructose
$\begin{array}{c} \text{H}-\text{C}=\text{O} \\ \text{H}-\text{OH} \\ \text{HO}-\text{H} \\ \text{H}-\text{OH} \\ \text{H}-\text{OH} \\ \text{CH}_2\text{OH} \end{array}$	$\begin{array}{c} \text{H}-\text{C}=\text{O} \\ \text{H}-\text{OH} \\ \text{HO}-\text{H} \\ \text{HO}-\text{H} \\ \text{H}-\text{OH} \\ \text{CH}_2\text{OH} \end{array}$	$\begin{array}{c} \text{CH}_2\text{OH} \\ \text{C}=\text{O} \\ \text{HO}-\text{H} \\ \text{H}-\text{OH} \\ \text{H}-\text{OH} \\ \text{CH}_2\text{OH} \end{array}$

The most common hexose, D-**glucose**, $C_6H_{12}O_6$, also known as dextrose and blood sugar, is found in fruits, vegetables, corn syrup, and honey. It is a building block of the disaccharides sucrose, lactose, and maltose, and polysaccharides such as starch, cellulose, and glycogen.

In the body, glucose normally occurs at a concentration of 70–90 mg/dL (1 dL = 100 mL) of blood. Excess glucose is converted to glycogen and stored in the liver and muscle. When the amount of glucose exceeds what is needed for energy or glycogen, the excess glucose is converted to fat, which can be stored in unlimited amounts:

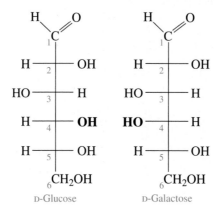

Glycogen (liver and muscle)

Fat ⇌ Glucose
     Excess

Urine CO_2 + H_2O + energy
                    Metabolism

Galactose is an aldohexose that is obtained as a hydrolysis product of the disaccharide lactose, a sugar found in milk and milk products. Galactose is important in the cellular membranes of the brain and nervous system. The only difference in the Fischer projections of D-glucose and D-galactose is the arrangement of the —OH group on carbon 4:

D-Glucose   D-Galactose

In a condition called *galactosemia*, an enzyme needed to convert galactose to glucose is missing. The accumulation of galactose in the blood and tissues can lead to cataracts, mental retardation, and cirrhosis. The treatment for galactosemia is the removal of all galactose-containing foods, mainly milk and milk products, from the diet. If this is done for an infant immediately after birth, the damaging effects of galactose accumulation can be avoided.

In contrast to glucose and galactose, **fructose** is a ketohexose. The structure of fructose differs from glucose at carbons 1 and 2 by the location of the carbonyl group:

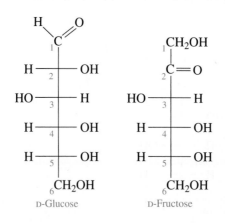

D-Glucose   D-Fructose

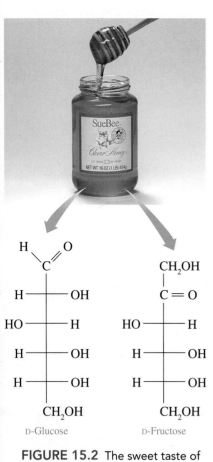

D-Glucose   D-Fructose

FIGURE 15.2 The sweet taste of honey is due to the monosaccharides D-glucose and D-fructose.

Q What are some differences in the Fischer projections of D-glucose and D-fructose?

Fructose is the sweetest of the carbohydrates, twice as sweet as sucrose (table sugar). This characteristic makes fructose popular with dieters because less fructose, and therefore fewer calories, is needed to provide a pleasant taste. After fructose enters the bloodstream, it is converted to its isomer, glucose. (See Figure 15.2.) Fructose, also

HEALTH NOTE

Hyperglycemia and Hypoglycemia

In the body, glucose normally occurs at a concentration of 70–90 mg/dL (1 dL = 100 mL) of blood. However, the amount of glucose in the blood depends on the time that has passed since eating. In the first hour after a meal, the level of glucose rises to about 130 mg/dL of blood and then decreases over the next 2–3 hours as it is used in the tissues.

A doctor may order a glucose tolerance test to evaluate the body's ability to return to normal glucose concentration in response to the ingestion of a specified amount of glucose. The patient fasts for 12 hours and then drinks a solution containing glucose. A blood sample is taken immediately, followed by more blood samples each half-hour for 2 hours, and then every hour for a total of 5 hours. If the blood glucose exceeds 140 mg/dL in plasma and remains high, hyperglycemia may be indicated. The term *glyc* or *gluco* refers to "sugar." The prefix *hyper* means above or over, *hypo* means below or under, and the suffix *emia* means "in the blood." Thus, the blood sugar level in *hyperglycemia* is above normal and below normal in *hypoglycemia*.

An example of a disease that can cause hyperglycemia is diabetes mellitus, which occurs when the pancreas is unable to produce sufficient quantities of insulin. As a result, glucose levels in the body fluids can rise as

high as 350 mg/dL in plasma. Symptoms of diabetes in people under the age of 40 include thirst, excessive urination, increased appetite, and weight loss. In older adults, diabetes is sometimes a consequence of excessive weight gain.

When a person is hypoglycemic, the blood glucose level rises and then decreases rapidly to levels as low as 40 mg/dL plasma. In some cases, hypoglycemia is caused by overproduction of insulin by the pancreas. Low blood glucose can cause dizziness, general weakness, and muscle tremors. A diet may be prescribed that consists of several small meals high in protein and low in carbohydrate. Some hypoglycemic patients are finding success with diets that include more complex carbohydrates rather than simple sugars.

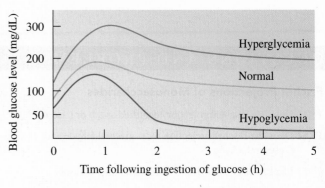

called levulose and fruit sugar, is found in fruit juices and honey. Fructose is also obtained as one of the hydrolysis products of sucrose, the disaccharide known as table sugar.

SAMPLE PROBLEM 15.2

■ Monosaccharides

Ribulose has the following Fischer projection:

```
        CH2OH
         |
         C=O
         |
   H ────┼──── OH
         |
   H ────┼──── OH
         |
        CH2OH
```

a. Identify the compound as D- or L-ribulose.
b. Draw the Fischer projection of its mirror image.

SOLUTION

a. The compound is D-ribulose because the —OH is on the right side of the chiral carbon farthest from the carbonyl group.

b. To draw the mirror image, all the —OH groups on the chiral carbon atoms are written on the opposite side. L-Ribulose has the following Fischer projection:

$$
\begin{array}{c}
\text{CH}_2\text{OH} \\
| \\
\text{C}=\text{O} \\
\text{HO}\!\!-\!\!|\!\!-\!\!\text{H} \\
\text{HO}\!\!-\!\!|\!\!-\!\!\text{H} \\
\text{CH}_2\text{OH}
\end{array}
$$

STUDY CHECK

What type of carbohydrate is ribulose?

QUESTIONS AND PROBLEMS

Fischer Projections of Monosaccharides

15.11 How is a Fischer projection identified as a D or L isomer?

15.12 Draw the Fischer projection for D-glyceraldehyde and L-glyceraldehyde.

15.13 Identify each of the following as the D or L isomer:

a.
$$
\begin{array}{c}
\text{CHO} \\
\text{HO}\!\!-\!\!|\!\!-\!\!\text{H} \\
\text{H}\!\!-\!\!|\!\!-\!\!\text{OH} \\
\text{CH}_2\text{OH}
\end{array}
$$
Threose

b.
$$
\begin{array}{c}
\text{CH}_2\text{OH} \\
| \\
\text{C}=\text{O} \\
\text{HO}\!\!-\!\!|\!\!-\!\!\text{H} \\
\text{H}\!\!-\!\!|\!\!-\!\!\text{OH} \\
\text{CH}_2\text{OH}
\end{array}
$$
Xylulose

c.
$$
\begin{array}{c}
\text{CHO} \\
\text{H}\!\!-\!\!|\!\!-\!\!\text{OH} \\
\text{H}\!\!-\!\!|\!\!-\!\!\text{OH} \\
\text{HO}\!\!-\!\!|\!\!-\!\!\text{H} \\
\text{HO}\!\!-\!\!|\!\!-\!\!\text{H} \\
\text{CH}_2\text{OH}
\end{array}
$$
Mannose

d.
$$
\begin{array}{c}
\text{CHO} \\
\text{H}\!\!-\!\!|\!\!-\!\!\text{OH} \\
\text{H}\!\!-\!\!|\!\!-\!\!\text{OH} \\
\text{H}\!\!-\!\!|\!\!-\!\!\text{OH} \\
\text{H}\!\!-\!\!|\!\!-\!\!\text{OH} \\
\text{CH}_2\text{OH}
\end{array}
$$
Allose

15.14 Identify each of the following as the D or L isomer:

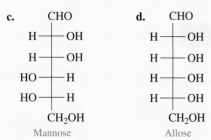

a.
$$
\begin{array}{c}
\text{CH}_2\text{OH} \\
| \\
\text{C}=\text{O} \\
\text{H}\!\!-\!\!|\!\!-\!\!\text{OH} \\
\text{H}\!\!-\!\!|\!\!-\!\!\text{OH} \\
\text{CH}_2\text{OH}
\end{array}
$$
Ribulose

b.
$$
\begin{array}{c}
\text{CH}_2\text{OH} \\
| \\
\text{C}=\text{O} \\
\text{HO}\!\!-\!\!|\!\!-\!\!\text{H} \\
\text{H}\!\!-\!\!|\!\!-\!\!\text{OH} \\
\text{HO}\!\!-\!\!|\!\!-\!\!\text{H} \\
\text{CH}_2\text{OH}
\end{array}
$$
Sorbose

c.
$$
\begin{array}{c}
\text{CHO} \\
\text{H}\!\!-\!\!|\!\!-\!\!\text{OH} \\
\text{HO}\!\!-\!\!|\!\!-\!\!\text{H} \\
\text{H}\!\!-\!\!|\!\!-\!\!\text{OH} \\
\text{H}\!\!-\!\!|\!\!-\!\!\text{OH} \\
\text{CH}_2\text{OH}
\end{array}
$$
Glucose

d.
$$
\begin{array}{c}
\text{CHO} \\
\text{HO}\!\!-\!\!|\!\!-\!\!\text{H} \\
\text{HO}\!\!-\!\!|\!\!-\!\!\text{H} \\
\text{HO}\!\!-\!\!|\!\!-\!\!\text{H} \\
\text{CH}_2\text{OH}
\end{array}
$$
Ribose

15.15 Draw the Fischer projections for the mirror images for **a–d** in problem 15.13.

15.16 Draw the Fischer projections for the mirror images for **a–d** in problem 15.14.

15.17 Draw the Fischer projections for D-glucose and L-glucose.

15.18 Draw the Fischer projections for D-fructose and L-fructose.

15.19 How does the Fischer projection for D-galactose differ from D-glucose?

15.20 How does the Fischer projection for D-fructose differ from D-glucose?

15.21 Identify the monosaccharide that fits each of the following descriptions:
a. also called blood sugar
b. not metabolized in galactosemia
c. also called fruit sugar

15.22 Identify the monosaccharide that fits each of the following descriptions:
a. high blood levels in diabetes
b. obtained as a hydrolysis product of lactose
c. the sweetest of the monosaccharides

15.3 | Haworth Structures of Monosaccharides

In Chapter 14, we saw that an aldehyde group reacts with one alcohol molecule to form a hemiacetal. This same reaction occurs when a carbonyl group and an —OH group are in the *same* molecule, which forms a *cyclic hemiacetal*. While the carbonyl group in the open chain could react with several of the —OH groups, the most stable form of pentoses and hexoses are their hemiacetals with five- or six-atom rings. For the aldohexose in the following diagram, the oxygen atom in the hydroxyl group on carbon 5 forms a bond with the carbonyl carbon 1 to produce a heterocyclic six-atom ring containing an oxygen atom and an —OH group on carbon 1:

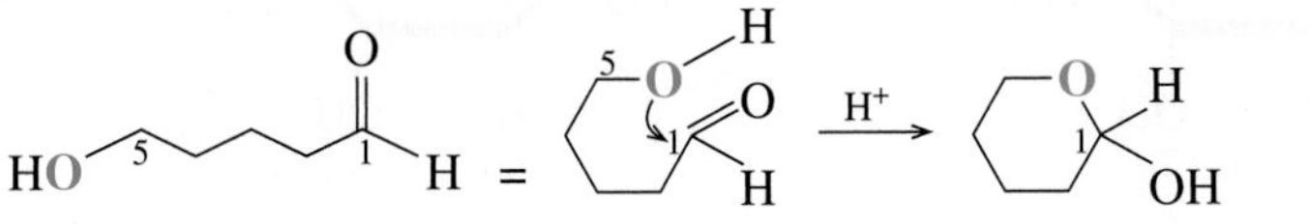

LEARNING GOAL

Draw and identify the Haworth structures of monosaccharides.

(MC) **TUTORIAL**
Drawing Cyclic Sugars

Open chain   Heterocyclic hemiacetal

Drawing Haworth Structures for Cyclic Forms

Let's look at how we draw the **Haworth structure**, a representation of the cyclic hemi- acetals of the monosaccharides for some D isomers, starting with the open-chain structure of D-glucose. Traditionally, Fischer projections represent the chiral carbon intersections of vertical and horizontal lines. In this text, we will show the carbon chain when it helps understanding.

STEP 1 **Turn the open-chain structure of D-glucose clockwise.** This places the —OH groups on the right of the vertical open chain below the carbon atoms and the —OH group on the left of the open chain above its carbon atom:

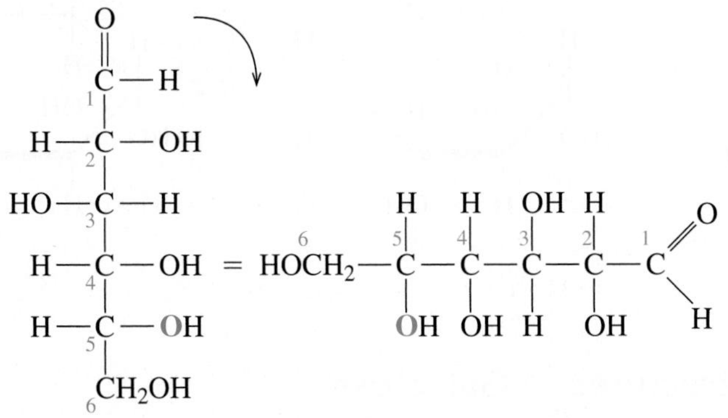

D-Glucose (open chain)

STEP 2 **Fold the carbon chain into a hexagon by moving carbon 5 above carbon 3.** In all D-monosaccharides including D-glucose, the —CH₂OH group (carbon 6) is placed above carbon 5, and the —OH group on carbon 5 is written next to the car- bonyl carbon. To complete the Haworth structure, draw a bond from the oxygen of the —OH group to the carbonyl carbon:

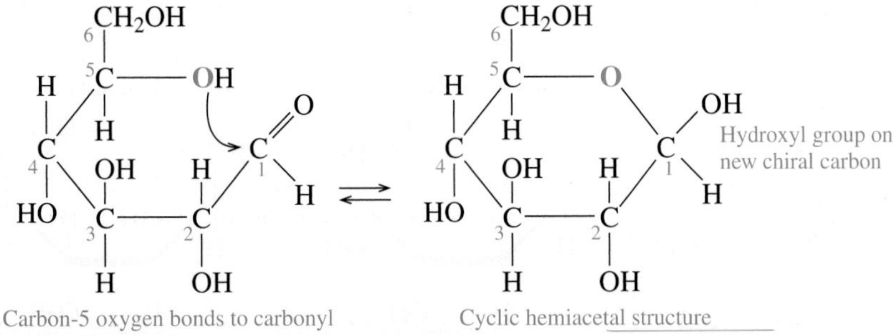

Carbon-5 oxygen bonds to carbonyl   Cyclic hemiacetal structure

STEP 3   **In the Haworth structure for the hemiacetal, the —OH group forms on carbon 1.**   In the Haworth structure, the corners of the ring represent carbon atoms. There are two ways to draw the —OH on carbon 1, either up or down, which gives two isomers called **anomers**. The —OH group is drawn down in the α (alpha) anomer and up in the β (beta) anomer:

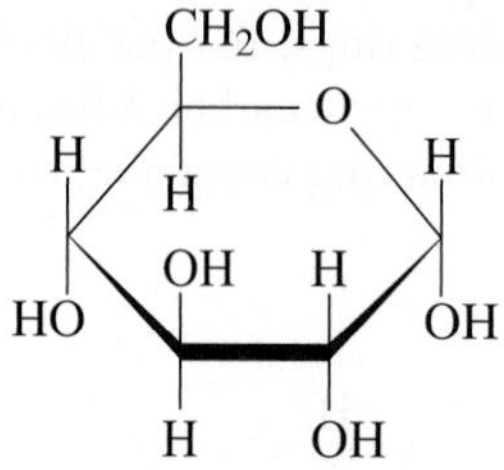

α-D-Glucose 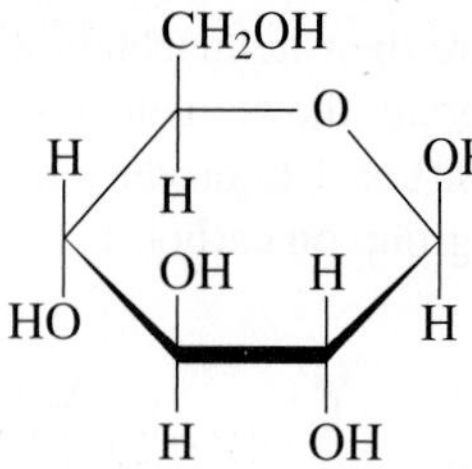 β-D-Glucose

Mutarotation of α- and β-D-glucose

In aqueous solution, the Haworth structure of α-D-glucose opens and closes to form β-D-glucose. In this process called **mutarotation**, each anomer converts to the open chain and back again. As the ring opens and closes, the hydroxyl (—OH) group on carbon 1 forms either the α or the β anomer. At equilibrium, a glucose solution contains a mixture of 36% of the α anomer and 64% of the β anomer. Although the open chain is an essential part of mutarotation, only a trace amount of the open chain is present at any given time:

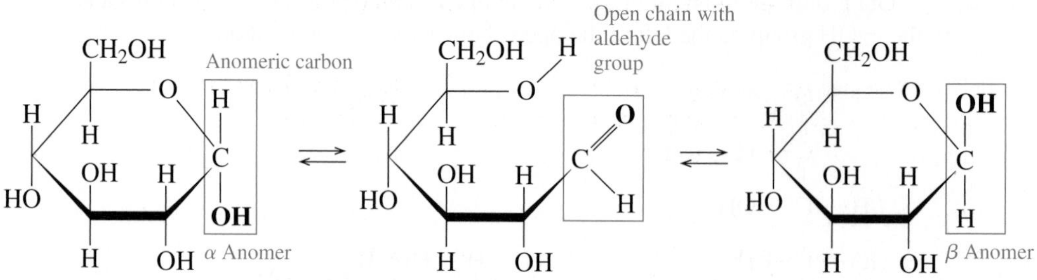

α-D-Glucose
(36% in equilibrium mixture)

D-Glucose
open chain (trace)

β-D-Glucose
(64% in equilibrium mixture)

Haworth Structures of Galactose

Galactose is an aldohexose that differs from glucose only in the arrangement of the —OH group on carbon 4. Thus, its Haworth structure is similar to glucose, except that in galactose the —OH on carbon 4 is up. Galactose also exists as α and β anomers and undergoes mutarotation via the open-chain form in aqueous solution:

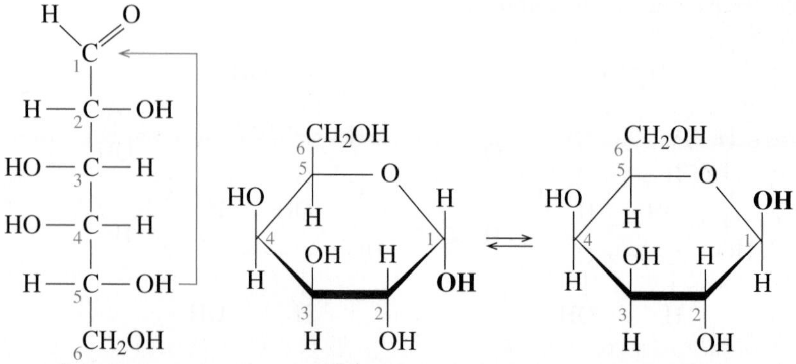

D-Galactose α-D-Galactose β-D-Galactose

Haworth Structures of Fructose

In contrast to glucose and galactose, fructose is a ketohexose. The Haworth structure for fructose is a stable five-atom ring. The hemiacetal forms when the hydroxyl group on carbon 5 reacts with the ketone group on carbon 2. In fructose, the anomeric carbon, which is carbon 2, is bonded to —CH_2OH and a hydroxyl group (—OH). Mutarotation of the anomeric carbon 2 gives α and β anomers:

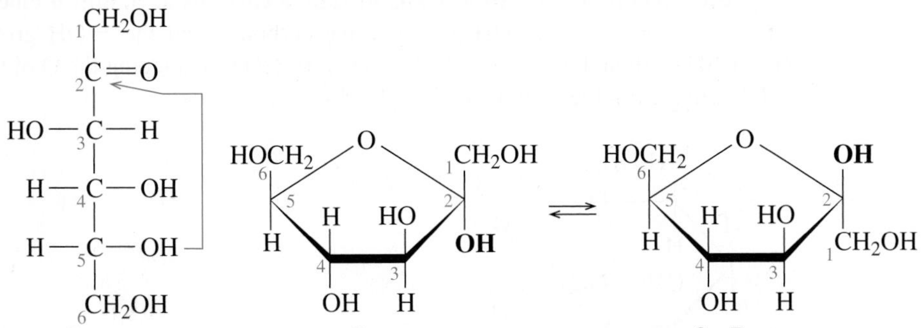

D-Fructose α-D-Fructose β-D-Fructose

■ Anomers

a. Why is the Haworth structure of D-galactose a hemiacetal?
b. What is the difference between α and β anomers of D-galactose?

ANSWER

a. D-galactose consists of both a carbonyl group as the aldehyde and several hydroxyl groups. A stable six-atom cyclic structure forms when the hydroxyl group on carbon 5 reacts with the carbonyl group at carbon 1. The resulting structure is a cyclic hemiacetal.
b. When the hemiacetal forms, an —OH appears on carbon 1. Two isomers called *anomers* are possible because the —OH can form above or below the ring. In the α anomer, the —OH is drawn down, and for the β anomer, the —OH is drawn up.

SAMPLE PROBLEM 15.3

■ Drawing Haworth Structures for Sugars

D-Mannose, a carbohydrate found in immunoglobulins, has the following open-chain structure. Draw the Haworth structure for β-D-mannose anomer:

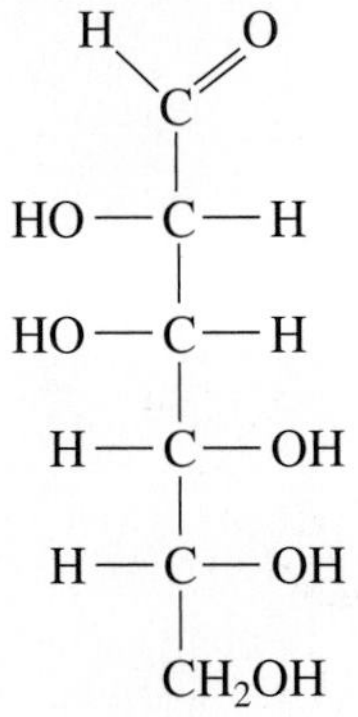

D-Mannose

Guide to Drawing Haworth Structures

> **STEP 1**
> Turn the open-chain structure clockwise 90°.

> **STEP 2**
> Fold the chain into a hexagon and bond the O on carbon 5 to the carbon of the carbonyl group.

> **STEP 3**
> Draw the new —OH group on carbon 1 down to give the α anomer or up to give the β anomer.

SOLUTION

STEP 1   Turn the open-chain structure to the right.

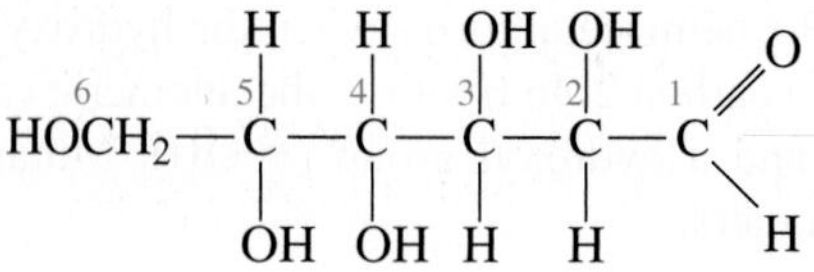

$$HOCH_2 \overset{\overset{H}{|}}{\underset{\underset{OH}{|}}{C}} \overset{\overset{H}{|}}{\underset{\underset{OH}{|}}{C}} \overset{\overset{OH}{|}}{\underset{\underset{H}{|}}{C}} \overset{\overset{OH}{|}}{\underset{\underset{H}{|}}{C}} \overset{O}{\underset{H}{C}}$$

STEP 2   Fold the carbon chain into a hexagon (move carbons 4, 5, and 6 clockwise). Draw the —CH₂OH group above carbon 5 and the —OH group next to the carbonyl. Complete the Haworth structure by bonding the O of the —OH group with the C of the carbonyl group:

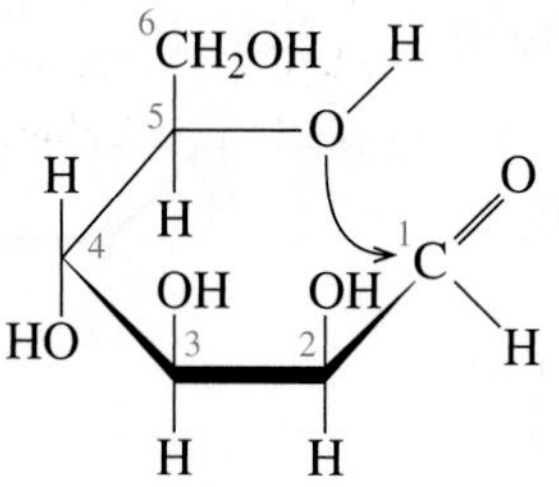

STEP 3   In the Haworth structure, draw the hydroxyl group on carbon 1 up to make the β-D-mannose anomer:

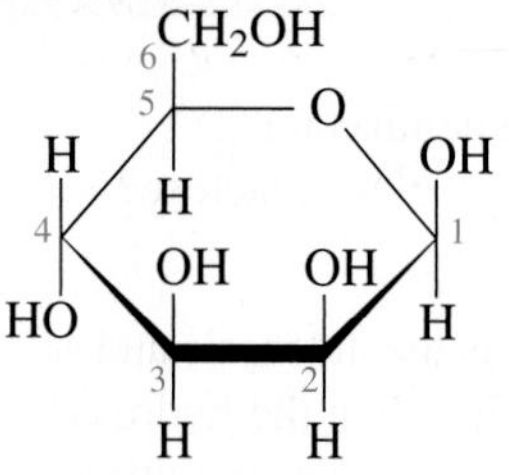

β-D-Mannose

STUDY CHECK

Draw the Haworth structure for α-D-glucose.

QUESTIONS AND PROBLEMS

Haworth Structures of Monosaccharides

15.23 Name the kind and number of atoms in the ring portion of the Haworth structure of glucose.

15.24 Name the kind and number of atoms in the ring portion of the Haworth structure of fructose.

15.25 Draw the Haworth structures for the α and β anomers of D-glucose.

15.26 Draw the Haworth structures for the α and β anomers of D-fructose.

15.27 Identify each of the following Haworth structures as the α or β anomer:

a. 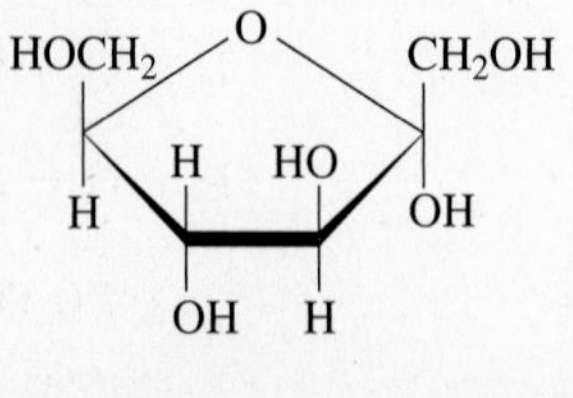 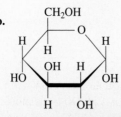   b.

15.28 Identify each of the following Haworth structures as the α or β anomer:

a.

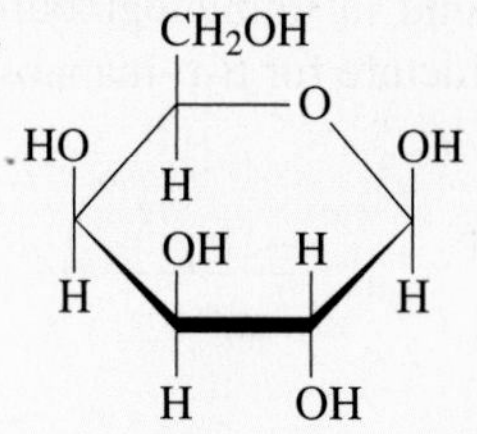

b.

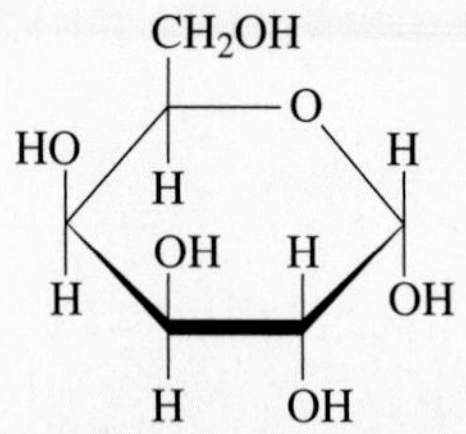

15.4 Chemical Properties of Monosaccharides

Monosaccharides contain functional groups that can undergo chemical reactions. In an aldose, the aldehyde group can be oxidized to a carboxylic acid. The carbonyl group in both an aldose and a ketose can be reduced to give a hydroxyl group. The hydroxyl groups can react with other compounds to form a variety of derivatives that are important in biological structures.

LEARNING GOAL

Identify the products of oxidation or reduction of monosaccharides; determine whether a carbohydrate is a reducing sugar.

Oxidation of Monosaccharides

Although monosaccharides exist mostly in cyclic form, a small amount of the open-chain structure is always present, which provides an aldehyde group. When Benedict's reagent is added, the aldehyde group is oxidized and Cu^{2+} is reduced to Cu^+, which forms a brick-red precipitate of Cu_2O. Monosaccharides, including all the aldohexoses, that reduce another substance are called **reducing sugars**.

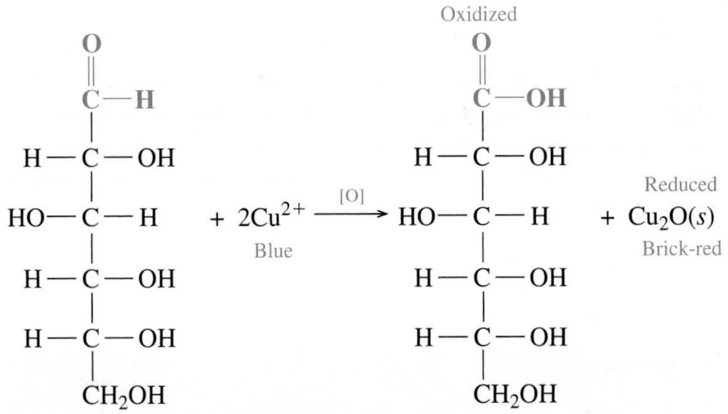

Open chain of D-Glucose, a reducing sugar

D-Gluconic acid

Fructose, a ketohexose, is also a reducing sugar. Usually a ketone cannot be oxidized. However, in a basic Benedict's solution, a rearrangement moves the carbonyl group from carbon 2 to carbon 1. As a result, this rearrangement converts fructose to glucose, which provides an aldehyde group that can be oxidized:

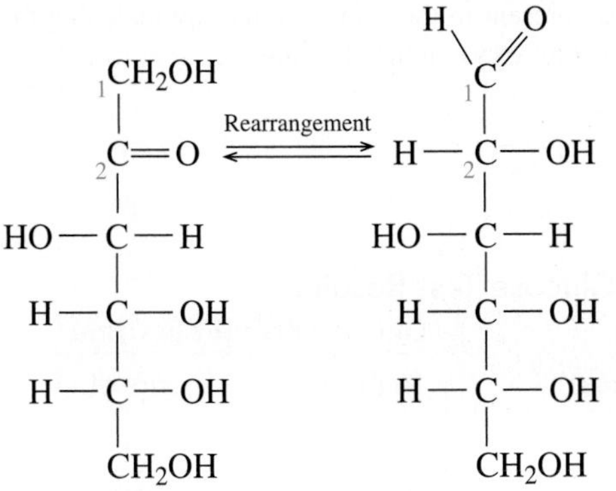

D-Fructose
(ketose)

D-Glucose
(aldose)

Reduction of Monosaccharides

The reduction of the carbonyl group in monosaccharides produces sugar alcohols, which are also called *alditols*. D-Glucose is reduced to D-glucitol, better known as *sorbitol*. D-Mannose

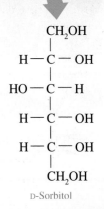

D-Sorbitol

is reduced to give D-mannitol. The sugar alcohols are named by changing the *ose* ending of the monosaccharide to *itol*.

$$
\begin{array}{ccc}
\text{D-Glucose} & \xrightarrow{\ H_2\ } & \text{D-Glucitol or D-Sorbitol}
\end{array}
$$

D-Glucose:
O=C—H
H—C—OH
HO—C—H
H—C—OH
H—C—OH
CH₂OH

D-Glucitol or D-Sorbitol:
CH₂OH
H—C—OH
HO—C—H
H—C—OH
H—C—OH
CH₂OH

CASE STUDY
Diabetes and Blood Glucose

Sugar alcohols such as sorbitol, xylitol from xylose, and mannitol from mannose are used as sweeteners in many sugar-free products such as diet drinks and sugarless gum, as well as products for people with diabetes. However, there are some side effects of these sugar substitutes. Some people experience some discomfort, such as gas and diarrhea, from the ingestion of sugar alcohols. The development of cataracts in diabetics is attributed to the accumulation of sorbitol in the lens of the eye.

HEALTH NOTE

Testing for Glucose in Urine

Normally, blood glucose flows through the kidneys and is reabsorbed into the bloodstream. However, if the blood level exceeds about 160 mg of glucose/dL of blood, the kidneys cannot reabsorb it all, and glucose spills over into the urine, a condition known as glucosuria. A symptom of diabetes mellitus is a high level of glucose in the urine.

Benedict's test can be used to determine the presence of glucose in urine. The amount of copper(I) oxide (Cu_2O) formed is proportional to the concentration of reducing sugar present in the urine. Low to moderate levels of reducing sugar turn the solution green; solutions with high glucose levels turn Benedict's yellow or brick-red. Table 15.1 lists some colors associated with the concentration of glucose in the urine.

In another clinical test that is more specific for glucose, the enzyme glucose oxidase is used. The oxidase enzyme converts glucose to gluconic acid and hydrogen peroxide (H_2O_2). The peroxide produced reacts with a dye in the test strip to produce different colors. The level of glucose present in the urine is found by matching the color produced to a color chart on the container.

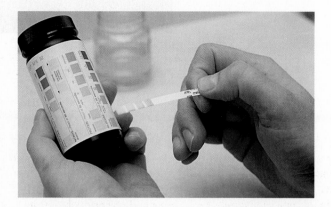

TABLE 15.1 Glucose Test Results

Color (of Benedict's test)	Glucose Present in Urine	
	% (m/v)	mg/dL
Blue	0	0
Blue-green	0.25	250
Green	0.50	500
Yellow	1.00	1000
Brick-red	2.00	2000

CONCEPT CHECK 15.4

■ Reducing Sugars
a. Why is D-glucose a *reducing sugar*?
b. In a laboratory test using Benedict's reagent, a sample of urine turns brick-red. According to Table 15.1, what might this test result indicate?

ANSWER
a. The aldehyde in D-glucose is easily oxidized by Benedict's reagent. A carbohydrate that reduces Cu^{2+} to Cu^+ is called a reducing sugar.
b. This result indicates a high level of reducing sugar (probably glucose) in the urine. One common cause of this condition is diabetes mellitus.

QUESTIONS AND PROBLEMS

Chemical Properties of Monosaccharides

15.29 Draw the product xylitol produced from the reduction of D-xylose:

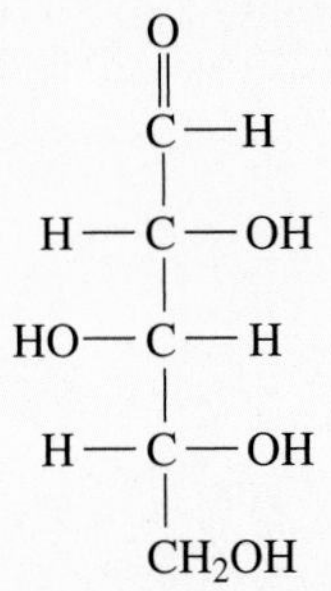

D-Xylose

15.30 Draw the product mannitol produced from the reduction of D-mannose:

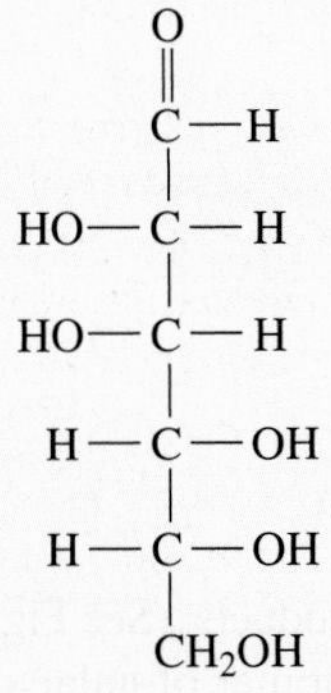

D-Mannose

15.31 Write the oxidation and reduction products of D-arabinose. What is the name of the sugar alcohol produced by reduction?

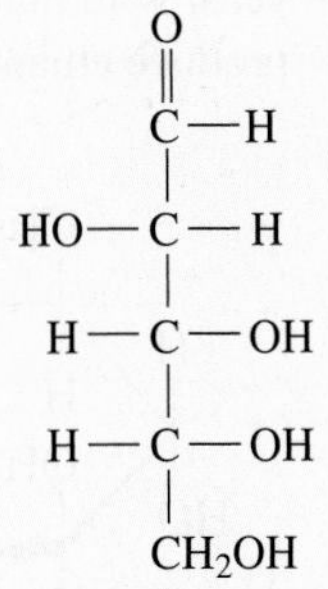

D-Arabinose

15.32 Write the oxidation and reduction products of D-ribose. What is the name of the sugar alcohol produced by reduction?

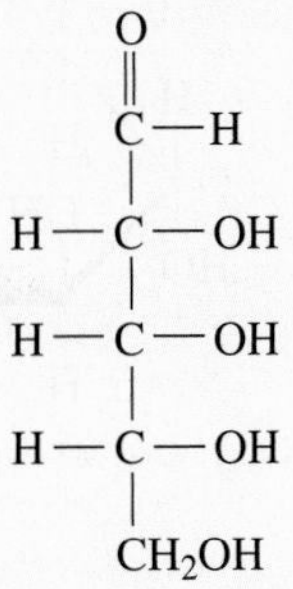

D-Ribose

15.5 Disaccharides

A disaccharide is composed of two monosaccharides linked together. When monosaccharides combine, they form an acetal. The reaction occurs between the anomeric hydroxyl group as a hemiacetal and one of the hydroxyl groups as the alcohol on a second monosaccharide. The most common disaccharides are maltose, lactose, and sucrose. Their

LEARNING GOAL

Describe the monosaccharide units and glycosidic bonds in disaccharides.

EXPLORE YOUR WORLD

Sugar and Sweeteners

Add a tablespoon of sugar to a glass of water and stir. Taste. Add more tablespoons of sugar, stir, and taste. If you have other carbohydrates such as fructose, honey, cornstarch, arrowroot, or flour, add some of each to separate glasses of water and stir. If you have some artificial sweeteners, add a few drops of the sweetener or a package, if solid, to a glass of water. Taste each.

QUESTIONS

1. Which substance is the most soluble in water?
2. Place the substances in order from the one that tastes least sweet to the sweetest.
3. How does your list compare to Table 15.2?
4. How does the sweetness of sucrose compare with the artificial sweeteners?
5. Check the labels of food products in your kitchen. Look for sugars such as sucrose and fructose or artificial sweeteners such as aspartame or sucralose on the label. How many grams of sugar are in a serving of the food?

hydrolysis, by an acid or an enzyme (maltase, lactase, and sucrase), gives the following monosaccharides:

$$\text{Maltose} + H_2O \xrightarrow{\;H^+ \text{ or maltase}\;} \text{glucose} + \text{glucose}$$

$$\text{Lactose} + H_2O \xrightarrow{\;H^+ \text{ or lactase}\;} \text{glucose} + \text{galactose}$$

$$\text{Sucrose} + H_2O \xrightarrow{\;H^+ \text{ or sucrase}\;} \text{glucose} + \text{fructose}$$

Maltose, or malt sugar, is a disaccharide. A **glycosidic bond** between two glucose molecules forms when one glucose acting as a hemiacetal reacts with a hydroxyl group in another glucose. In maltose, the glycosidic bond that joins the two glucose molecules is an α-1,4 linkage, which shows that the —OH on carbon 1 of α-D-glucose is bonded to carbon 4 of the second glucose. In maltose, the —OH group on carbon 1 gives α and β anomers. Maltose is a reducing sugar because the hemiacetal —OH on carbon 1 opens and closes, which provides an aldehyde group. Maltose is used in cereals, candies, and the brewing of beverages. When maltose from the starches in barley and other grains is hydrolyzed by yeast with maltase enzyme, glucose is obtained. This glucose can undergo fermentation to produce ethanol:

α-D-Glucose $\quad+\quad$ α-D-Glucose

α-1,4-Glycosidic bond $\quad+\ H_2O$ $\quad\alpha$ Anomer

α-Maltose, a disaccharide

Lactose, milk sugar, is a disaccharide found in milk and milk products. (See Figure 15.3.) The bond in lactose is a β-1,4-glycosidic bond because the β anomer of galactose forms a bond with the hydroxyl group on carbon 4 of glucose. In lactose, the —OH group on the hemiacetal carbon 1 gives α and β anomers. Lactose is a reducing sugar because the hemiacetal on carbon 1 provides an open chain with an aldehyde group that can be oxidized.

Lactose makes up 6–8% of human milk and about 4–5% of cow's milk, and it is used in products that attempt to duplicate mother's milk. Some people do not produce sufficient quantities of the enzyme needed to hydrolyze lactose, and the sugar remains undigested, causing abdominal cramps and diarrhea. In some commercial milk products, an enzyme called lactase is added to break down lactose.

Sucrose consists of an α-D-glucose and β-D-fructose molecule joined by an α,β-1,2-glycosidic bond. (See Figure 15.4.) Unlike maltose and lactose, the glycosidic bond

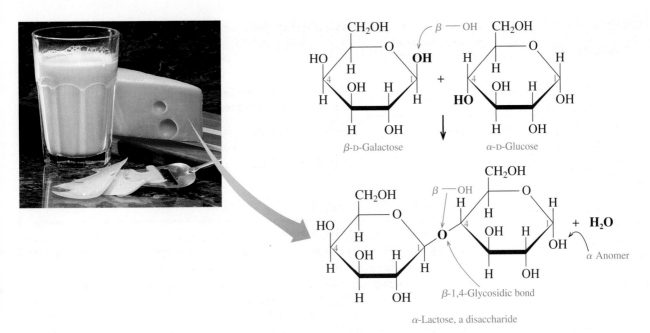

FIGURE 15.3 α-Lactose, a disaccharide found in milk and milk products, contains β-D-galactose and α-D-glucose.
Q What type of glycosidic bond links β-D-galactose and α-D-glucose in α-lactose?

in sucrose is between carbon 1 of glucose and carbon 2 of fructose. Thus, sucrose does not have a hemiacetal on carbon 1 and cannot form an open chain. Sucrose cannot react with Benedict's reagent and is not a reducing sugar.

The sugar we use to sweeten our cereal, coffee, and tea is sucrose. Most of the sucrose for table sugar comes from sugar cane (20% by mass) or sugar beets (15% by mass). Both the raw and refined forms of sugar are sucrose. Some estimates indicate that each person in the United States consumes an average of 68 kg (150 lb) of sucrose every year either by itself or in a variety of food products. In the body, the enzyme sucrase hydrolyzes sucrose to glucose and fructose.

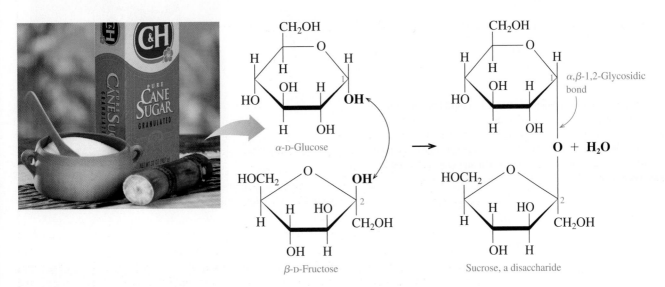

FIGURE 15.4 Sucrose, a disaccharide obtained from sugar beets and sugar cane, contains α-D-glucose and β-D-fructose.
Q Why is sucrose a nonreducing sugar?

HEALTH NOTE

How Sweet Is My Sweetener?

Although many of the monosaccharides and disaccharides taste sweet, they differ considerably in their degree of sweetness. Dietetic foods contain sweeteners that are noncarbohydrate or carbohydrates that are sweeter than sucrose. Some examples of sweeteners compared with sucrose are shown in Table 15.2.

Sucralose is made from sucrose by replacing some of the hydroxyl groups with chlorine atoms:

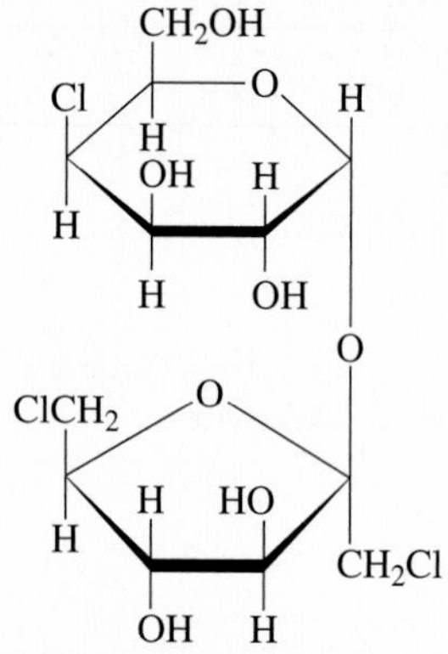

Sucralose

Aspartame, which is marketed as NutraSweet, is used in a large number of sugar-free products. It is a noncarbohydrate sweetener made of aspartic acid and a methyl ester of phenylalanine. It does have some caloric value, but it is so sweet that only a very small quantity is needed. However, phenylalanine, one of the breakdown products, poses a danger to anyone who cannot metabolize it properly, a condition called phenylketonuria (PKU):

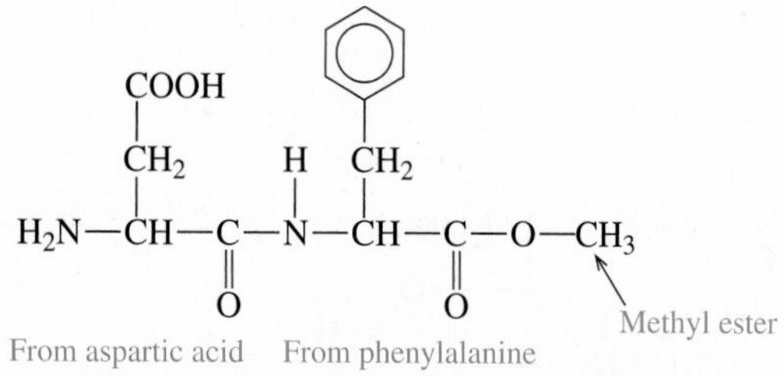

From aspartic acid   From phenylalanine   Methyl ester
Aspartame (NutraSweet)

Another artificial sweetener, Neotame, is a modification of the aspartame structure. The addition of a large alkyl group to the amine group prevents enzymes from breaking the amide bond between aspartic acid and phenylalanine. Thus, phenylalanine is not produced when Neotame is used as a sweetener. Very small amounts of Neotame are needed because it is about 10 000 times sweeter than sucrose:

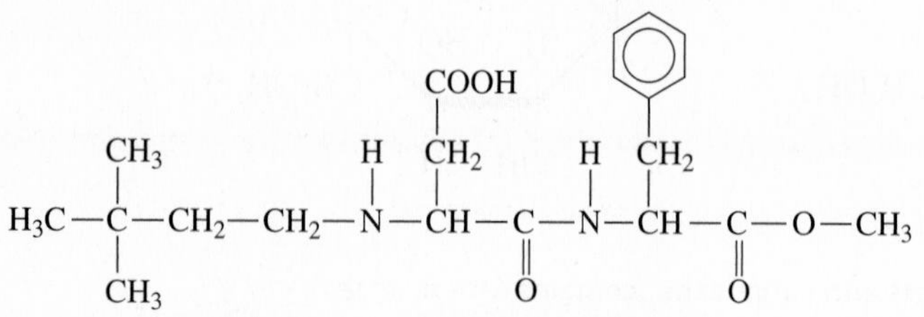

Large alkyl group to modify Aspartame   Neotame

TABLE 15.2 Relative Sweetness of Sugars and Artificial Sweeteners

	Sweetness Relative to Sucrose (= 100)
Monosaccharides	
Galactose	30
Glucose	75
Fructose	175
Disaccharides	
Lactose	16
Maltose	33
Sucrose	100 = reference standard
Sugar Alcohols (Polyols)	
Sorbitol	60
Maltitol	80
Xylitol	100
Artificial Sweeteners (Noncarbohydrate)	
Aspartame	18 000
Saccharin	45 000
Sucralose	60 000
Neotame	1 000 000

Saccharin has been used as a noncarbohydrate artificial sweetener for the past 25 years. The use of saccharin has been banned in Canada because studies indicate that it may cause bladder tumors. However, it is still approved for use by the FDA in the United States.

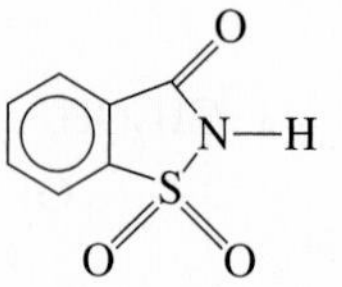

Saccharin

HEALTH NOTE

Blood Types and Carbohydrates

Every individual's blood can be typed as one of four blood groups: A, B, AB, and O. Although there is some variation among ethnic groups in the United States, the incidence of blood types in the general population is about 43% O, 40% A, 12% B, and 5% AB.

The blood types A, B, and O are determined by saccharides attached to the surface of red blood cells. In type O, the end saccharides are *N*-acetylglucosamine, galactose, and fucose. These same three end saccharides also occur in type A and type B blood. In type A, the galactose is bonded to *N*-acetylgalactosamine. In type B, the galactose is bonded to another galactose. Thus, blood types A and B are determined by an end *N*-acetylgalactosamine (type A) or an end galactose (type B). In type AB, both sequences are at the ends of the saccharide chains. The structures of these monosaccharides are as follows:

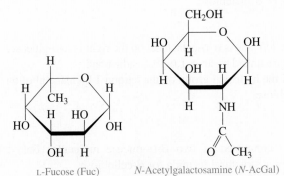

N-Acetylglucosamine (*N*-AcGlu)   D-Galactose (Gal)

L-Fucose (Fuc)   N-Acetylgalactosamine (*N*-AcGal)

Terminal saccharide that determines blood type

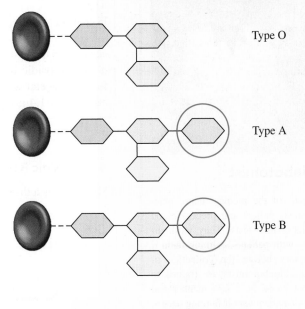

Type O

Type A

Type B

Red blood cell surface

N-Acetylglucosamine   *N*-Acetylgalactosamine

Fucose   Galactose

Table 15.3 summarizes the compatibility of blood groups for transfusion.

TABLE 15.3 Compatibility of Blood Groups

Blood Type	Antibodies Against	Can Receive
A	B	A, O
B	A	B, O
AB[a]	None	A, B, AB, O
O[b]	A, B	O

[a]AB universal recipient
[b]O universal donor

A person with type A blood produces antibodies against type B, whereas a person with type B blood produces antibodies against type A. Type AB blood produces no antibodies, whereas type O produces antibodies against both types A and B. Thus, if a person with type A blood receives a transfusion of type B blood, factors in the recipient's blood will cause the donor's red blood cells to clump together, or agglutinate.

People with type O can donate to individuals with all blood types; they are universal donors. However, a type O person can receive only type O blood. People with type AB blood can receive all blood types because they do not have antibodies for types A and B; they are universal recipients.

CONCEPT CHECK 15.5

■ Glycosidic Bonds

Why is the glycosidic bond in maltose called an α-1,4-glycosidic bond whereas in lactose it is called a β-1,4-glycosidic bond?

ANSWER

In maltose, the hydroxyl group on the hemiacetal (carbon 1) is down, which makes it the α anomer. When the hydroxyl group from the α anomer of one glucose forms an acetal with the hydroxyl group on carbon 4 of another glucose, the glycosidic bond is an α-1,4-glycosidic bond. In lactose, a hydroxyl group from the β anomer of galactose forms an acetal with the hydroxyl group on carbon 4 of glucose. Then the glycosidic bond is a β-1,4-glycosidic bond.

SAMPLE PROBLEM 15.4

■ Glycosidic Bonds in Disaccharides

Melebiose is a disaccharide that is 30 times sweeter than sucrose:

a. What are the monosaccharide units in melebiose?
b. What type of glycosidic bond links the monosaccharides?
c. Identify the structure as α- or β-melebiose.

SOLUTION

a. The monosaccharide on the left side is α-D-galactose; on the right is α-D-glucose.
b. The monosaccharide units are linked by an α-1,6-glycosidic bond.
c. The downward position of the hydroxyl group on the carbon 1 hemiacetal of the D-glucose makes it α-melebiose.

STUDY CHECK

Cellobiose is a disaccharide composed of two β-D-glucose molecules linked by a β-1,4-glycosidic linkage. Draw a structural formula for β-cellobiose.

QUESTIONS AND PROBLEMS

Disaccharides

15.33 Give the monosaccharide units produced by hydrolysis, the type of glycosidic bond, and the identity of the disaccharide including the α or β anomer for each of the following:

15.34 Give the monosaccharide units produced by hydrolysis, the type of glycosidic bond, and the identity of the disaccharide including the α or β anomer for each of the following:

a.

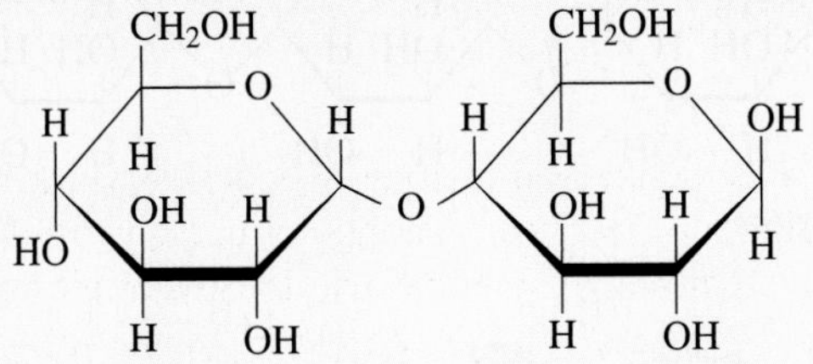

b.

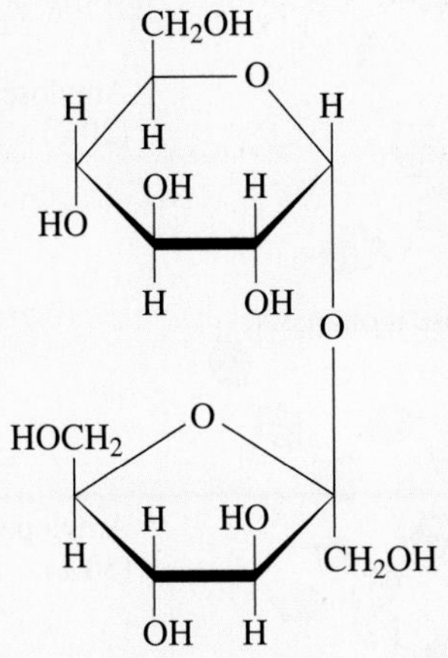

15.35 Indicate whether each disaccharide in problem 15.33 is a reducing sugar or not.

15.36 Indicate whether each disaccharide in problem 15.34 is a reducing sugar or not.

15.37 Identify the disaccharide that fits each of the following descriptions:
  a. ordinary table sugar
  b. found in milk and milk products
  c. also called malt sugar
  d. hydrolysis gives galactose and glucose

15.38 Identify the disaccharide that fits each of the following descriptions:
  a. not a reducing sugar
  b. composed of two glucose units
  c. also called milk sugar
  d. hydrolysis gives glucose and fructose

15.6 Polysaccharides

A **polysaccharide** is a polymer of many monosaccharides joined together. Four biologically important polysaccharides—amylose, amylopectin, cellulose, and glycogen—are all polymers of D-glucose that differ only in the type of glycosidic bonds and the amount of branching in the molecule.

Starch, a storage form of glucose in plants, is found as insoluble granules in rice, wheat, potatoes, beans, and cereals. Starch is composed of two kinds of polysaccharides, amylose and amylopectin. **Amylose**, which makes up about 20% of starch, consists of 250 to 4000 α-D-glucose molecules connected by α-1,4-glycosidic bonds in a continuous chain. Sometimes called a straight-chain polymer, polymers of amylose are actually coiled in helical fashion.

Amylopectin, which makes up as much as 80% of plant starch, is a branched-chain polysaccharide. Like amylose, α-1,4-glycosidic bonds connect the glucose molecules. However, at about every 25 glucose units, there is a branch of glucose molecules attached by an α-1,6-glycosidic bond between carbon 1 of the branch and carbon 6 in the main chain. (See Figure 15.5.)

Starches hydrolyze easily in water and acid to give shorter glucose chains called *dextrins*, which then hydrolyze to maltose and finally glucose. In our bodies, these complex carbohydrates are digested by the enzymes amylase (in saliva) and maltase. The glucose obtained usually provides about 50% of our nutritional calories.

LEARNING GOAL

Describe the structural features of amylose, amylopectin, glycogen, and cellulose.

MC **SELF STUDY ACTIVITY**
Polymers

Amylose, amylopectin $\xrightarrow{\text{H}^+ \text{ or amylase}}$ dextrins $\xrightarrow{\text{H}^+ \text{ or amylase}}$ maltose $\xrightarrow{\text{H}^+ \text{ or maltase}}$ many D-glucose units

Glycogen, or animal starch, is a polymer of glucose that is stored in the liver and muscle of animals. It is hydrolyzed in our cells at a rate that maintains the blood level of glucose and provides energy between meals. The structure of glycogen is very similar to that of amylopectin, found in plants, except that glycogen is more highly branched. In glycogen, α-1,4-glycosidic bonds join the glucose units, and branches occurring about every 10 to 15 glucose units are attached by α-1,6-glycosidic bonds.

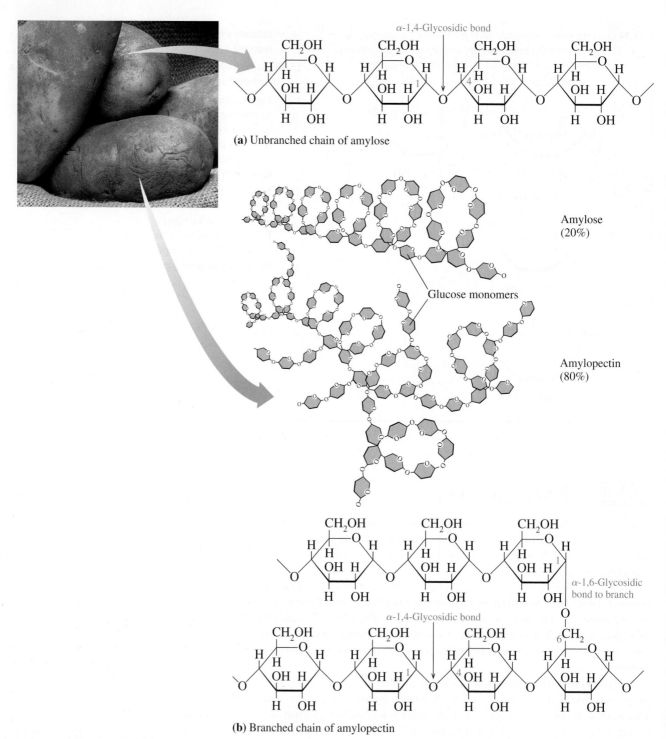

(a) Unbranched chain of amylose

Amylose (20%)

Glucose monomers

Amylopectin (80%)

(b) Branched chain of amylopectin

FIGURE 15.5 The structure of amylose **(a)** is a straight-chain polysaccharide of glucose units, and amylopectin **(b)** is a branched chain of glucose.

Q What are the two types of glycosidic bonds that link glucose molecules in amylopectin?

Cellulose is the major structural material of wood and plants. Cotton is almost pure cellulose. In cellulose, glucose molecules form a long unbranched chain similar to that of amylose. However, β-1,4-glycosidic bonds link the glucose units in cellulose. The β isomers do not form coils like the α isomers but are aligned in parallel rows that are held in place by hydrogen bonds between hydroxyl groups in adjacent chains. This arrangement makes cellulose insoluble in water and gives a rigid structure to the cell walls in wood and fiber that is more resistant to hydrolysis than the starches. (See Figure 15.6.)

Humans have an enzyme called α-amylase in saliva and pancreatic juices that hydrolyzes the α-1,4-glycosidic bonds of the starches but not the β-1,4-glycosidic bonds

Cellulose

β-1,4-Glycosidic bond

FIGURE 15.6 The polysaccharide cellulose is composed of β-1,4-glycosidic bonds.
Q Why are humans unable to digest cellulose?

of cellulose. Thus, humans cannot digest cellulose. Animals such as horses, cows, and goats can obtain glucose from cellulose because their digestive systems contain bacteria that provide enzymes such as cellulase to hydrolyze β-1,4-glycosidic bonds.

Iodine Test

In the **iodine test**, iodine (I_2) is used to test for the presence of starch. The unbranched helical shape of the polysaccharide amylose in starch interacts with iodine to form a deep blue-black complex. Amylopectin, cellulose, and glycogen produce reddish-purple and brown colors. Such colors do not develop when iodine is added to samples of mono- or disaccharides.

SAMPLE PROBLEM 15.5

■ Structures of Polysaccharides

Identify the polysaccharide described by each of the following:

a. a polysaccharide that is stored in the liver and muscle tissues
b. an unbranched polysaccharide containing β-1,4-glycosidic bonds
c. a starch containing α-1,4- and α-1,6-glycosidic bonds

SOLUTION

a. glycogen   **b.** cellulose   **c.** amylopectin, glycogen

STUDY CHECK

Amylose and amylopectin are both glucose polymers. How do they differ?

QUESTIONS AND PROBLEMS

Polysaccharides

15.39 Describe the similarities and differences in the following:
  a. amylose and amylopectin
  b. amylopectin and glycogen

15.40 Describe the similarities and differences in the following:
  a. amylose and cellulose
  b. cellulose and glycogen

15.41 Give the name of one or more polysaccharides that matches each of the following descriptions:
  a. not digestible by humans
  b. the storage form of carbohydrates in plants

  c. contains only α-1,4-glycosidic bonds
  d. the most highly branched polysaccharide

15.42 Give the name of one or more polysaccharides that matches each of the following descriptions:
  a. the storage form of carbohydrates in animals
  b. contains only β-1,4-glycosidic bonds
  c. contains both α-1,4- and α-1,6-glycosidic bonds
  d. produces maltose during digestion

CONCEPT MAP

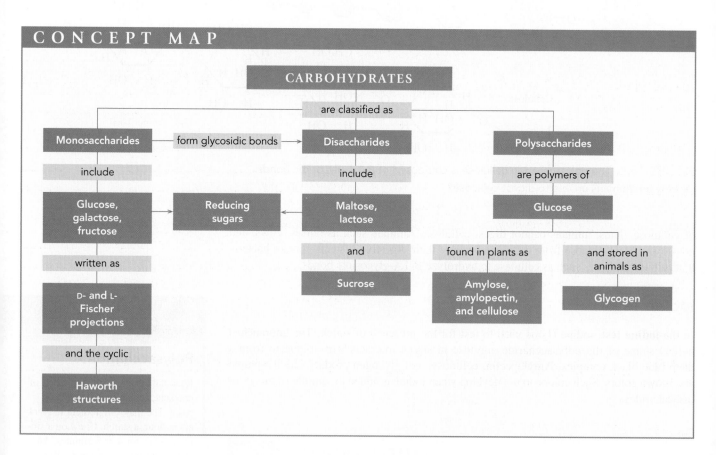

CHAPTER REVIEW

15.1 Carbohydrates

LEARNING GOAL: *Classify a monosaccharide as an aldose or ketose, and indicate the number of carbon atoms.*
Carbohydrates are classified as monosaccharides (simple sugars), disaccharides (two monosaccharide units), and polysaccharides (many monosaccharide units). Monosaccharides are polyhydroxy aldehydes (aldoses) or ketones (ketoses). Monosaccharides are also classified by their number of carbon atoms: *triose, tetrose, pentose,* or *hexose.*

15.2 Fischer Projections of Monosaccharides

LEARNING GOAL: *Use Fischer projections to draw the D or L isomers of glucose, galactose, and fructose.*

Chiral molecules can exist in two different forms, which are mirror images of each other. In a Fischer projection (straight chain), the prefixes D- and L- are used to distinguish between the mirror images. In D isomers, the —OH is on the right of the chiral carbon farthest from the carbonyl carbon; it is on the left in L isomers. Important monosaccharides are the aldohexoses glucose and galactose and the ketohexose fructose.

15.3 Haworth Structures of Monosaccharides

LEARNING GOAL: *Draw and identify the Haworth structures of monosaccharides.*
The predominant form of monosaccharides is the cyclic arrangement of five or six atoms. The cyclic structure forms by a reaction between

an —OH (usually the one on carbon 5 in hexoses) with the carbonyl group of the same molecule. The mutarotation of the hydroxyl group on carbon 1 (or 2 in fructose) gives α and β anomers of the cyclic monosaccharide.

15.4 Chemical Properties of Monosaccharides
LEARNING GOAL: *Identify the products of oxidation or reduction of monosaccharides; determine whether a carbohydrate is a reducing sugar.*
The aldehyde group in an aldose can be oxidized to a carboxylic acid, while the carbonyl group in an aldose or a ketose can be reduced to give a hydroxyl group. Monosaccharides that are reducing sugars have an aldehyde group in the open chain that is oxidized.

15.5 Disaccharides
LEARNING GOAL: *Describe the monosaccharide units and glycosidic bonds in disaccharides.*

Disaccharides are two monosaccharide units joined together by a glycosidic bond. In the most common disaccharides maltose, lactose, and sucrose, there is at least one glucose unit.

15.6 Polysaccharides
LEARNING GOAL: *Describe the structural features of amylose, amylopectin, glycogen, and cellulose.*
Polysaccharides are polymers of monosaccharide units. Amylose is an unbranched chain of glucose with α-1,4-glycosidic bonds, and amylopectin is a branched polymer of glucose with α-1,4- and α-1,6-glycosidic bonds. Glycogen, the storage form of glucose in animals, is similar to amylopectin with more branching. Cellulose is also a polymer of glucose, but in cellulose the glycosidic bonds are β-1,4-bonds rather than α-1,4-bonds in amylose.

SUMMARY OF CARBOHYDRATES

Carbohydrate	Food Sources	
Monosaccharides		
Glucose	Fruit juices, honey, corn syrup	
Galactose	Lactose hydrolysis	
Fructose	Fruit juices, honey, sucrose hydrolysis	
Disaccharides		**Monosaccharides**
Maltose	Germinating grains, starch hydrolysis	Glucose + glucose
Lactose	Milk, yogurt, ice cream	Glucose + galactose
Sucrose	Sugar cane, sugar beets	Glucose + fructose
Polysaccharides		
Amylose	Rice, wheat, grains, cereals	Unbranched polymer of glucose joined by α-1,4-glycosidic bonds
Amylopectin	Rice, wheat, grains, cereals	Branched polymer of glucose joined by α-1,4- and α-1,6-glycosidic bonds
Glycogen	Liver, muscles	Highly branched polymer of glucose joined by α-1,4- and α-1,6-glycosidic bonds
Cellulose	Plant fiber, bran, beans, celery	Unbranched polymer of glucose joined by β-1,4-glycosidic bonds

SUMMARY OF REACTIONS

FORMATION OF DISACCHARIDES

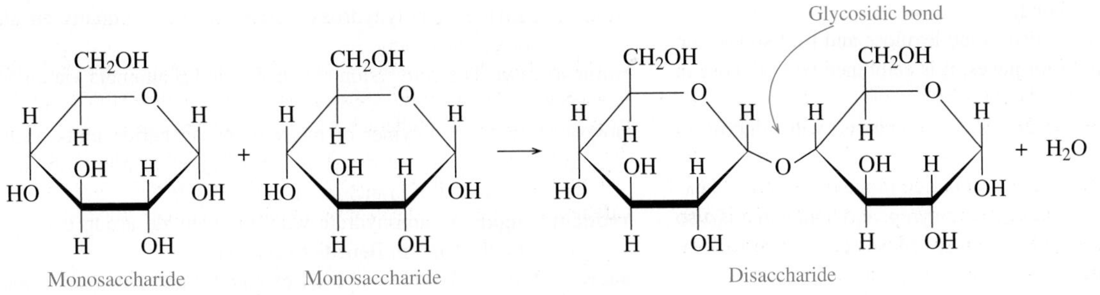

Monosaccharide + Monosaccharide → Disaccharide + H_2O

OXIDATION AND REDUCTION OF MONOSACCHARIDES

$$
\begin{array}{ccc}
CH_2OH & CHO & COOH \\
H-C-OH & H-C-OH & H-C-OH \\
HO-C-H & HO-C-H & HO-C-H \\
H-C-OH & H-C-OH & H-C-OH \\
H-C-OH & H-C-OH & H-C-OH \\
CH_2OH & CH_2OH & CH_2OH \\
\text{D-Glucitol} & \text{D-Glucose} & \text{D-Gluconic acid}
\end{array}
$$

$\xleftarrow{\text{Reduction}}$ $\xrightarrow{\text{Oxidation}}$

HYDROLYSIS OF DISACCHARIDES

Sucrose + H_2O $\xrightarrow{\;H^+ \text{ or sucrase}\;}$ glucose + fructose

Lactose + H_2O $\xrightarrow{\;H^+ \text{ or lactase}\;}$ glucose + galactose

Maltose + H_2O $\xrightarrow{\;H^+ \text{ or maltase}\;}$ glucose + glucose

HYDROLYSIS OF POLYSACCHARIDES

Amylose, amylopectin $\xrightarrow{\;H^+ \text{ or enzymes}\;}$ many D-glucose units

■ KEY TERMS

aldose A monosaccharide that contains an aldehyde group.

amylopectin A branched-chain polymer of starch composed of glucose units joined by α-1,4- and α-1,6-glycosidic bonds.

amylose An unbranched polymer of starch composed of glucose units joined by α-1,4-glycosidic bonds.

anomers The isomers of cyclic hemiacetals of monosaccharides that have a hydroxyl group on carbon 1 (or carbon 2). In the α anomer, the —OH is drawn downward; in the β anomer, the —OH is up.

carbohydrate A simple or complex sugar composed of carbon, hydrogen, and oxygen.

cellulose An unbranched polysaccharide composed of glucose units linked by β-1,4-glycosidic bonds that cannot be hydrolyzed by the human digestive system.

disaccharide A carbohydrate composed of two monosaccharides joined by a glycosidic bond.

fructose A monosaccharide, also called levulose and fruit sugar, that is found in honey and fruit juices; it is combined with glucose in sucrose.

galactose A monosaccharide that occurs combined with glucose in lactose.

glucose The most prevalent monosaccharide in the diet. An aldohexose found in fruits, vegetables, corn syrup, and honey that is also known as blood sugar and dextrose. Most polysaccharides are polymers of glucose.

glycogen A polysaccharide formed in the liver and muscles for the storage of glucose as an energy reserve. It is composed of glucose in a highly branched polymer joined by α-1,4- and α-1,6-glycosidic bonds.

glycosidic bond The bond that forms when the hydroxyl group of one monosaccharide reacts with the hydroxyl group of another monosaccharide; it is the type of bond that links monosaccharide units in di- or polysaccharides.

Haworth structure The cyclic structure that represents the closed chain of a monosaccharide.

iodine test A test for amylose that forms a blue-black color after iodine is added to the sample.

ketose A monosaccharide that contains a ketone group.

lactose A disaccharide consisting of glucose and galactose found in milk and milk products.

maltose A disaccharide consisting of two glucose units; it is obtained from the hydrolysis of starch and germinating grains.

monosaccharide A polyhydroxy compound that contains an aldehyde or ketone group.

mutarotation The conversion between α and β anomers via an open chain.

polysaccharide A polymer of many monosaccharide units, usually glucose. Polysaccharides differ in the types of glycosidic bonds and the amount of branching in the polymer.

reducing sugar A carbohydrate with an aldehyde group capable of reducing the Cu^{2+} in Benedict's reagent.

sucrose A disaccharide composed of glucose and fructose; a nonreducing sugar, commonly called table sugar or "sugar."

UNDERSTANDING THE CONCEPTS

15.43 Isomaltose, obtained from the breakdown of starch, has the following Haworth structure:

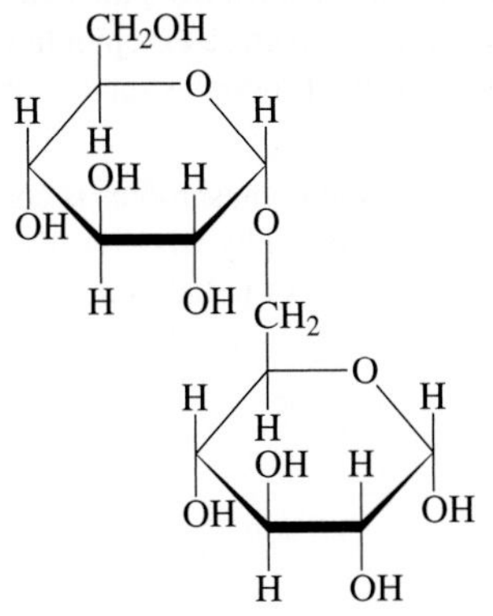

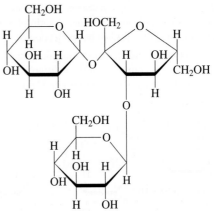

a. Is isomaltose a mono-, di-, or polysaccharide?
b. What are the monosaccharides in isomaltose?
c. What is the glycosidic link in isomaltose?
d. Is this the α or β form of isomaltose?
e. Would isomaltose be a reducing sugar?

15.44 Sophorose, a carbohydrate found in certain types of beans, has the following Haworth structure:

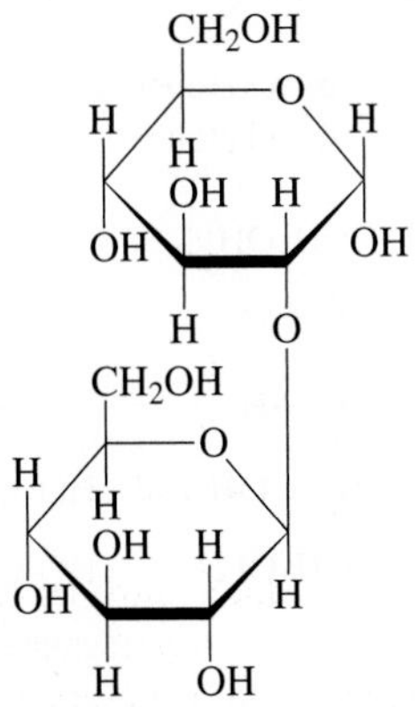

a. Is sophorose a mono-, di-, or polysaccharide?
b. What are the monosaccharides in sophorose?
c. What is the glycosidic link in sophorose?
d. Is this the α or β anomer of sophorose?
e. Is sophorose a reducing sugar?

15.45 Melezitose, a carbohydrate found in tree sap, has the following Haworth structure:

a. Is melezitose a mono-, di-, tri-, or polysaccharide?
b. What are the monosaccharides in melezitose?

15.46 What are the disaccharides and polysaccharides present in each of the following?

(a)   (b)

(c)   (d)

ADDITIONAL QUESTIONS AND PROBLEMS

*For instructor-assigned homework, go to **www.masteringchemistry.com**.*

15.47 What are the differences in the Fischer projections of D-fructose and D-galactose?

15.48 What are the differences in the Fischer projections of D-glucose and D-fructose?

15.49 What are the differences in the Fischer projections of D-galactose and L-galactose?

15.50 What are the differences in the Haworth structures of α-D-glucose and β-D-glucose?

15.51 Consider the sugar D-gulose:

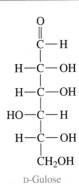

D-Gulose

a. Draw the Fischer projection for L-gulose.
b. Draw the Haworth structures for α- and β-D-gulose.

15.52 Consider the open-chain structure for D-gulose in question 15.51.
   a. Draw the structure and give the name of the product formed by the reduction of D-gulose.
   b. Draw the structure and give the name of the product formed by the oxidation of D-gulose.

15.53 D-Sorbitol, a sweetener found in seaweed and berries, contains only hydroxyl functional groups. When D-sorbitol is oxidized, it forms D-glucose. Draw the Fischer projection of D-sorbitol.

15.54 Raffinose is a trisaccharide found in Australian manna and in cottonseed meal. It is composed of three different monosaccharides. Identify the monosaccharides in raffinose.

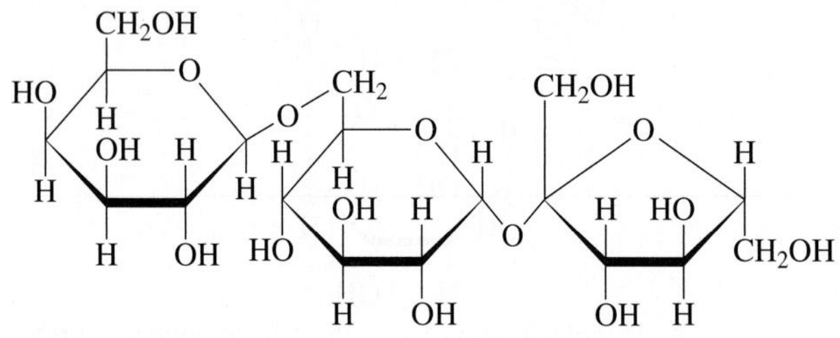

15.55 If α-galactose is dissolved in water, β-galactose is eventually present. Explain how this occurs.

15.56 Why are lactose and maltose considered reducing sugars, but sucrose is not?

15.57 β-Cellobiose is a disaccharide obtained from the hydrolysis of cellulose. It is quite similar to maltose except it has a β-1,4-glycosidic bond. Draw the Haworth structure of β-cellobiose.

15.58 The disaccharide trehalose found in mushrooms is composed of two α-D-glucose molecules joined by an α-1,1-glycosidic bond. Draw the Haworth structure of trehalose.

CHALLENGE QUESTIONS

15.59 Gentiobiose is found in saffron.
   a. Gentiobiose contains two glucose molecules linked by a β-1,6-glycosidic bond. Draw the Haworth structure of α-gentiobiose.
   b. Would gentiobiose be a reducing sugar? Explain.

15.60 Identify the open-chain formula that matches each of the following:
   a. L-mannose   **b.** a ketopentose
   c. an aldopentose   **d.** a ketohexose

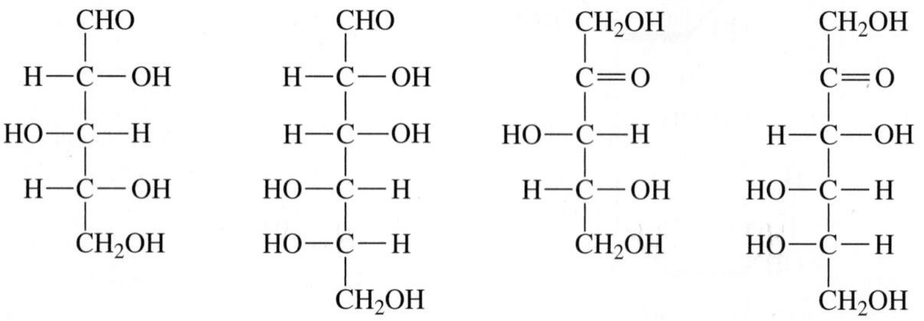

ANSWERS

ANSWERS TO STUDY CHECKS

15.1

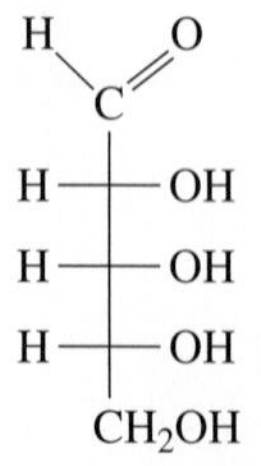

15.2 Ribulose is a ketopentose.

15.3

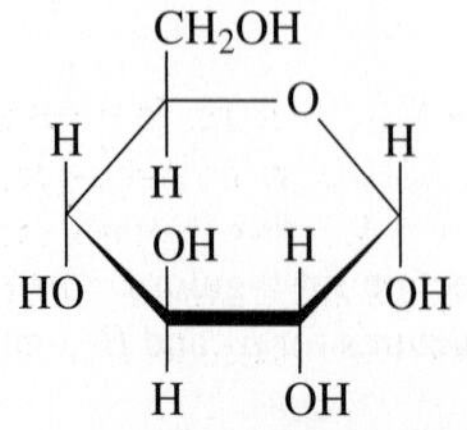

15.4

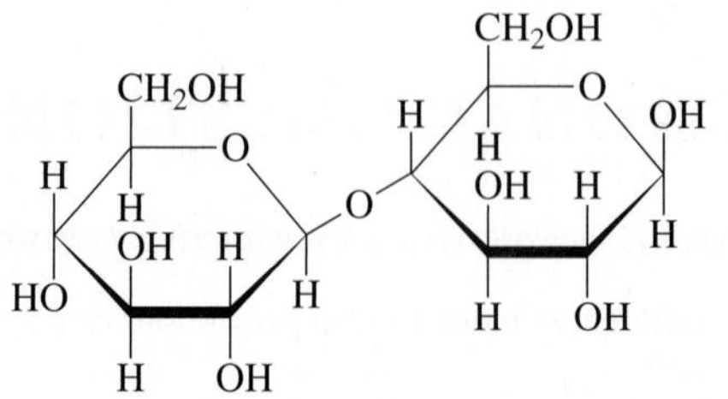

15.5 Both amylose and amylopectin contain glucose units connected by α-1,4-glycosidic bonds. However, in amylopectin, branches of glucose units are connected by α-1,6-glycosidic bonds about every 25 glucose units on the chain.

ANSWERS TO SELECTED QUESTIONS AND PROBLEMS

15.1 Photosynthesis requires CO_2, H_2O, and the energy from the Sun. Respiration requires O_2 from the air and glucose from our foods.

15.3 Monosaccharides can be a chain of three to eight carbon atoms, one in a carbonyl group as an aldehyde or ketone, and the rest attached to hydroxyl groups. A monosaccharide cannot be split or hydrolyzed into smaller carbohydrates. A disaccharide consists of two monosaccharide units joined together that can be split.

15.5 Hydroxyl groups are found in all monosaccharides along with a carbonyl on the first or second carbon.

15.7 A ketopentose contains hydroxyl and ketone functional groups and has five carbon atoms.

15.9 **a.** ketose   **b.** aldose   **c.** ketose
d. aldose   **e.** aldose

15.11 In the D isomer, the —OH on the chiral carbon atom at the bottom of the chain is on the right side, whereas in the L isomer, the —OH appears on the left side.

15.13 **a.** D   **b.** D   **c.** L   **d.** D

15.15 **a.**

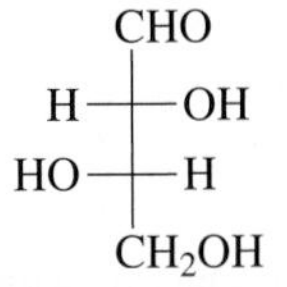

CHO
H—OH
HO—H
CH₂OH

b.

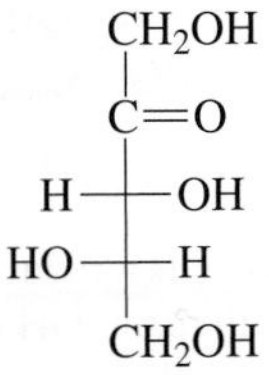

CH₂OH
C=O
H—OH
HO—H
CH₂OH

c.

CHO
HO—H
HO—H
H—OH
H—OH
CH₂OH

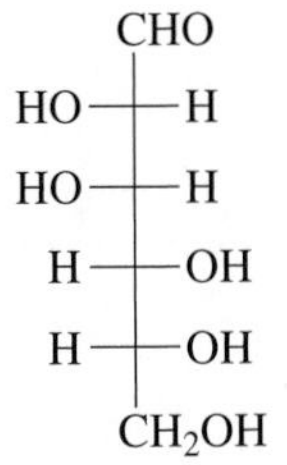

d.

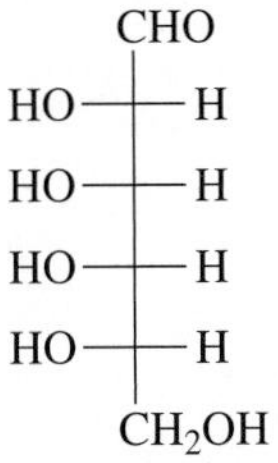

CHO
HO—H
HO—H
HO—H
HO—H
CH₂OH

15.17

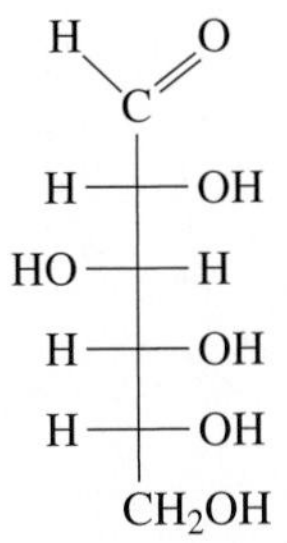

D-Glucose

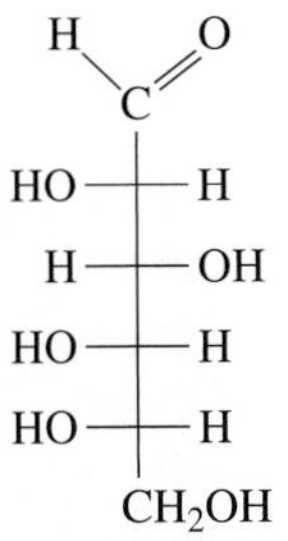

H—OH
HO—H
H—OH
H—OH
CH₂OH

L-Glucose

HO—H
H—OH
HO—H
HO—H
CH₂OH

15.19 In D-galactose, the hydroxyl on carbon four extends to the left. In D-glucose, this hydroxyl goes to the right.

15.21 **a.** glucose   **b.** galactose   **c.** fructose

15.23 In the cyclic structure of glucose, there are five carbon atoms and an oxygen atom.

15.25

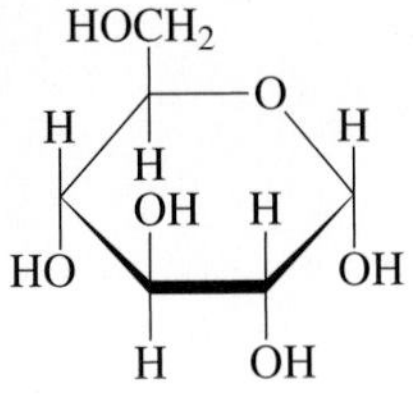

α-D-Glucose

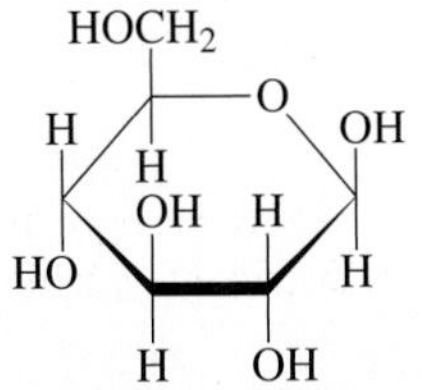

β-D-Glucose

15.27 **a.** α anomer   **b.** α anomer

15.29

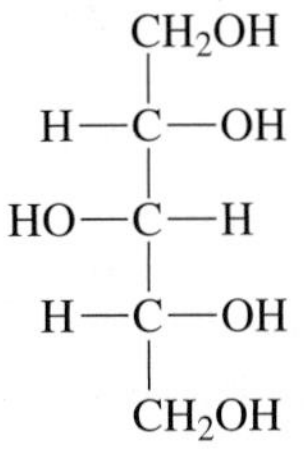

CH₂OH
H—C—OH
HO—C—H
H—C—OH
CH₂OH

Xylitol

15.31 Oxidation product:

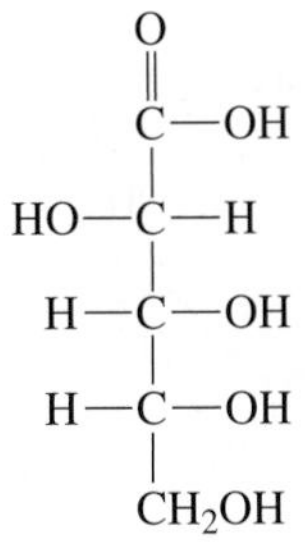

O
‖
C—OH
HO—C—H
H—C—OH
H—C—OH
CH₂OH

Reduction product (sugar alcohol):

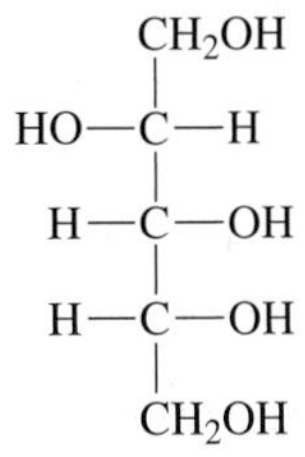

CH₂OH
HO—C—H
H—C—OH
H—C—OH
CH₂OH

D-Arabitol

15.33 **a.** galactose and glucose, β-1,4-glycosidic bond, β-lactose
b. glucose and glucose, α-1,4-glycosidic bond, α-maltose

15.35 **a.** reducing sugar
b. reducing sugar

15.37 **a.** sucrose   **b.** lactose
c. maltose   **d.** lactose

15.39 **a.** Amylose is an unbranched polymer of glucose units joined by α-1,4-glycosidic bonds; amylopectin is a branched polymer of glucose joined by α-1,4- and α-1,6-glycosidic bonds.
b. Amylopectin, which is produced in plants, is a branched polymer of glucose, joined by α-1,4- and α-1,6-glycosidic bonds. Glycogen, which is produced in animals, is a highly branched polymer of glucose, joined by α-1,4- and α-1,6-glycosidic bonds.

15.41 **a.** cellulose   **b.** amylose, amylopectin
c. amylose   **d.** glycogen

15.43 **a.** disaccharide   **b.** α-D-glucose
c. α-1,6-glycosidic bond
d. α   **e.** yes

15.45 **a.** trisaccharide
b. 2 glucose and 1 fructose

15.47 D-Fructose is a ketohexose, whereas D-galactose is an aldohexose. In galactose, the —OH on carbon 4 is on the left; in fructose, the —OH is on the right.

15.49 D-Galactose is the mirror image of L-galactose. In D-galactose, the —OH groups on carbon 2 and 5 are on the right side, but they are on the left for carbon 3 and 4. In L-galactose, the —OH groups are reversed; carbons 2 and 5 have —OH on the left, and carbons 3 and 4 have —OH on the right.

15.51 a.

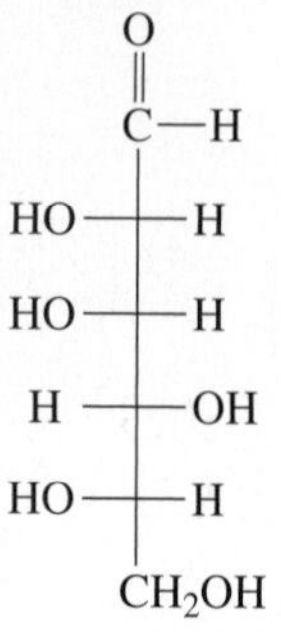

L-Gulose

b.

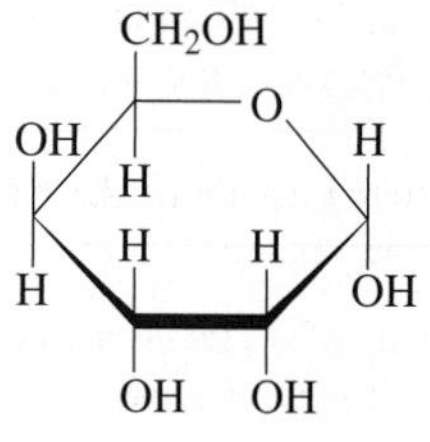

α-D-Gulose 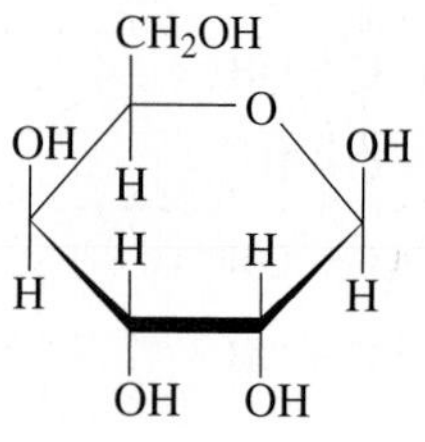   β-D-Gulose

15.53

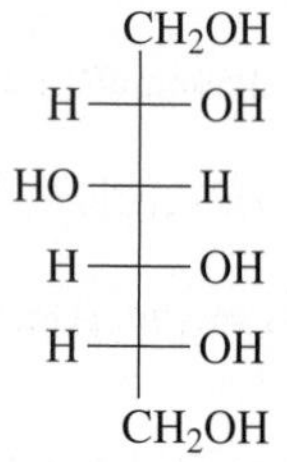

15.55 When the α-galactose forms an open-chain structure, it can close to form either α- or β-galactose.

15.57

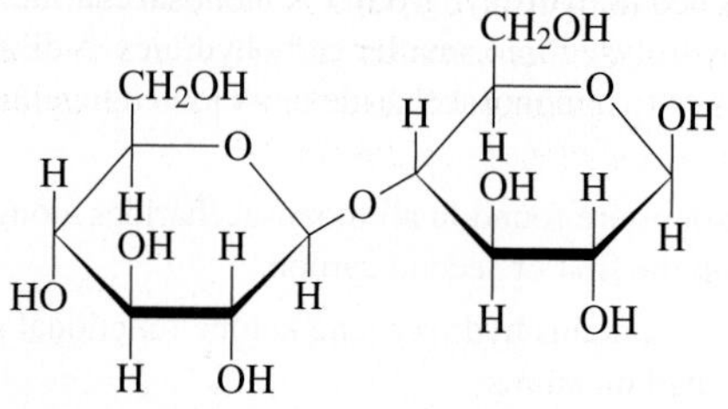

15.59 a.

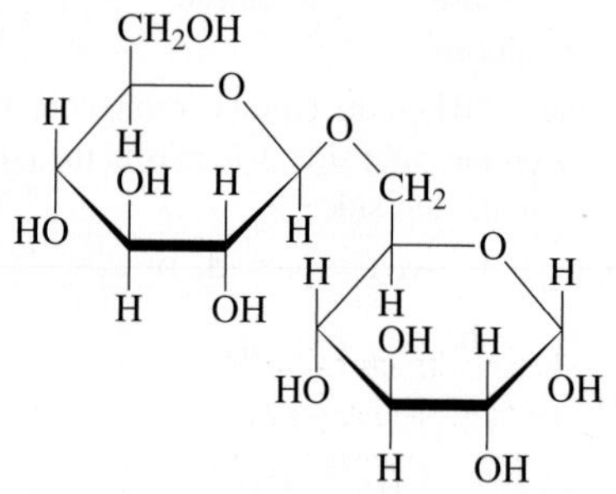

b. Yes. Gentiobiose is a reducing sugar. The ring with the hemiacetal with the —OH group can open up to form an aldehyde that can be oxidized.

COMBINING IDEAS FROM CHAPTERS 11 TO 15

CI.25 A compound called butylated hydroxytoluene, or BHT, has been added to cereal and other foods since 1947 as an antioxidant. Its IUPAC name is 1-hydroxy-2,6-dimethylethyl-4-methylbenzene. The formula of the alkyl group dimethylethyl is

$$CH_3-\underset{\underset{CH_3}{\mid}}{\overset{\overset{CH_3}{\mid}}{C}}-$$

a. Draw the condensed structural formula of BHT.
b. BHT is produced from 4-methylphenol and 2-methylpropene. Draw the condensed structural formulas of these reactants.
c. What are the molecular formula and molar mass of BHT?
d. The FDA (Food and Drug Administration) allows a maximum of 50. ppm of BHT added to cereal. How many mg of BHT could be added to a box of cereal that contains 15 oz of dry cereal?

CI.26 Used in "sunless" tanning lotions, the compound 1,3-dihydroxy-2-propanone, or dihydroxyacetone (DHA), darkens the skin without sun. DHA reacts with amino acids in the dead cells in the outer surface of the skin. A typical drugstore lotion contains 4.0 % (mass/volume) DHA.

a. Draw the condensed structural formula of DHA.
b. What are the functional groups in DHA?
c. What are the molecular formula and molar mass of DHA?
d. Why is DHA a ketotriose?
e. A bottle of sunless tanning lotion contains 177 mL of lotion. How many milligrams of DHA are in a bottle?

CI.27 Acetone (propanone), a clear liquid solvent with an acrid odor, is used to remove nail polish, paints, and resins. It has a low boiling point and is highly flammable.

a. Draw the condensed structural formula of propanone.
b. What are the molecular formula and molar mass of propanone?
c. Draw the condensed structural formula of the alcohol that can be oxidized to produce propanone.

CI.28 Acetone (propanone) has a density of 0.786 g/mL and a heat of combustion of 428 kcal/mole. Use your answers to problem CI.27 to solve the following:
a. Write the equation for the complete combustion reaction of propanone.
b. How much heat, in kilojoules, is released if 2.58 g of propanone reacts with oxygen?
c. How many grams of oxygen gas are needed to react with 15.0 mL of propanone?
d. How many liters of carbon dioxide gas are produced at STP in part c?

CI.29 Panose is a trisaccharide that is being considered as a possible sweetener by the food industry.

a. What are the monosaccharides, A, B, and C, in panose?
b. What type of bond connects the monosaccharides A and B?
c. What type of bond connects the monosaccharides B and C?
d. Is the structure drawn as α or β panose?
e. Why would panose be a reducing sugar?

CI.30 Ionone is a compound that gives violets their aroma. The small edible purple flowers of violets are used on salads and to make teas. An antioxidant called anthocyanin produces the blue and purple colors of violets. Liquid ionone has a density of 0.935 g/mL.

a. What functional groups are present in ionone?
b. Is the double bond on the side chain cis or trans?
c. What are the molecular formula and molar mass of ionone?
d. How many moles are in 2.00 mL of ionone?
e. When ionone reacts with hydrogen in the presence of a platinum catalyst, hydrogen adds to the double bonds and converts the ketone group to an alcohol. What is the condensed structural formula and molecular formula of the product?
f. How many mL of hydrogen gas are needed at STP to completely react 5.0 mL of ionone?

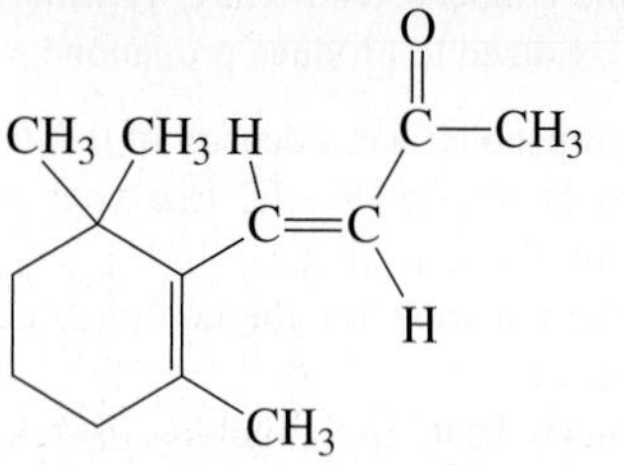

Ionone

■ ANSWERS

CI.25 a.

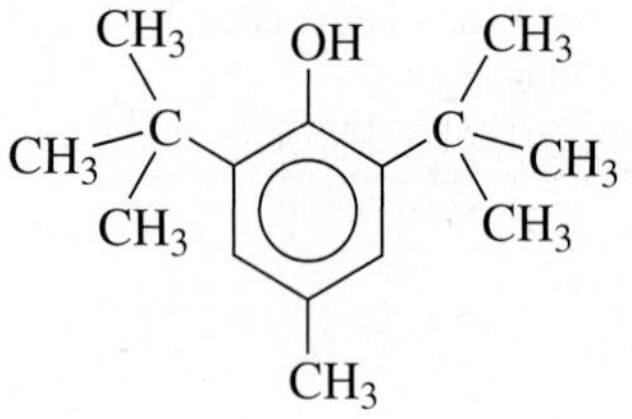

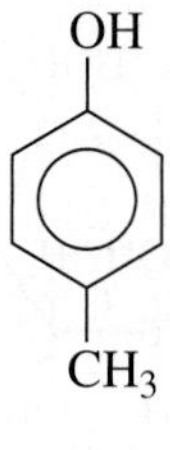

4-Methylphenol 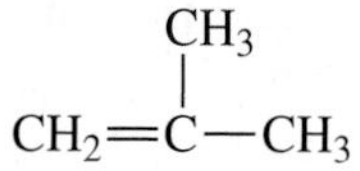   2-Methylpropene

c. $C_{15}H_{24}O$; 220. g/mole

d. 21 mg

CI.27 a. $CH_3-\overset{\overset{\displaystyle O}{\|}}{C}-CH_3$

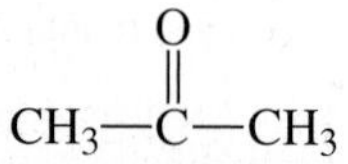

b. C_3H_6O; 58.0 g/mole

c. $CH_3-\overset{\overset{\displaystyle OH}{|}}{CH}-CH_3$

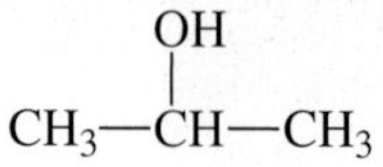

CI.29 a. A, B, and C are all glucose.
b. An α-1,6-glycosidic bond links A and B.
c. An α-1,4-glycosidic bond links B and C.
d. β panose
e. Panose is a reducing sugar because the hydroxyl group on the anomeric carbon 1 of structure C allows glucose (structure C) to form the aldehyde.

COMBINING IDEAS FROM CHAPTERS 11 TO 15

CI.25 A compound called butylated hydroxytoluene, or BHT, has been added to cereal and other foods since 1947 as an antioxidant. Its IUPAC name is 1-hydroxy-2,6-dimethylethyl-4-methylbenzene. The formula of the alkyl group dimethylethyl is

$$CH_3-\overset{\overset{\displaystyle CH_3}{|}}{\underset{\underset{\displaystyle CH_3}{|}}{C}}-$$

a. Draw the condensed structural formula of BHT.
b. BHT is produced from 4-methylphenol and 2-methylpropene. Draw the condensed structural formulas of these reactants.
c. What are the molecular formula and molar mass of BHT?
d. The FDA (Food and Drug Administration) allows a maximum of 50. ppm of BHT added to cereal. How many mg of BHT could be added to a box of cereal that contains 15 oz of dry cereal?

CI.26 Used in "sunless" tanning lotions, the compound 1,3-dihydroxy-2-propanone, or dihydroxyacetone (DHA), darkens the skin without sun. DHA reacts with amino acids in the dead cells in the outer surface of the skin. A typical drugstore lotion contains 4.0 % (mass/volume) DHA.

a. Draw the condensed structural formula of DHA.
b. What are the functional groups in DHA?
c. What are the molecular formula and molar mass of DHA?
d. Why is DHA a ketotriose?
e. A bottle of sunless tanning lotion contains 177 mL of lotion. How many milligrams of DHA are in a bottle?

CI.27 Acetone (propanone), a clear liquid solvent with an acrid odor, is used to remove nail polish, paints, and resins. It has a low boiling point and is highly flammable.

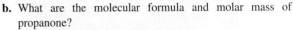

a. Draw the condensed structural formula of propanone.
b. What are the molecular formula and molar mass of propanone?
c. Draw the condensed structural formula of the alcohol that can be oxidized to produce propanone.

CI.28 Acetone (propanone) has a density of 0.786 g/mL and a heat of combustion of 428 kcal/mole. Use your answers to problem CI.27 to solve the following:
a. Write the equation for the complete combustion reaction of propanone.
b. How much heat, in kilojoules, is released if 2.58 g of propanone reacts with oxygen?
c. How many grams of oxygen gas are needed to react with 15.0 mL of propanone?
d. How many liters of carbon dioxide gas are produced at STP in part **c**?

CI.29 Panose is a trisaccharide that is being considered as a possible sweetener by the food industry.

a. What are the monosaccharides, A, B, and C, in panose?
b. What type of bond connects the monosaccharides A and B?
c. What type of bond connects the monosaccharides B and C?
d. Is the structure drawn as α or β panose?
e. Why would panose be a reducing sugar?

CI.30 Ionone is a compound that gives violets their aroma. The small edible purple flowers of violets are used on salads and to make teas. An antioxidant called anthocyanin produces the blue and purple colors of violets. Liquid ionone has a density of 0.935 g/mL.

a. What functional groups are present in ionone?
b. Is the double bond on the side chain cis or trans?
c. What are the molecular formula and molar mass of ionone?
d. How many moles are in 2.00 mL of ionone?
e. When ionone reacts with hydrogen in the presence of a platinum catalyst, hydrogen adds to the double bonds and converts the ketone group to an alcohol. What is the condensed structural formula and molecular formula of the product?
f. How many mL of hydrogen gas are needed at STP to completely react 5.0 mL of ionone?

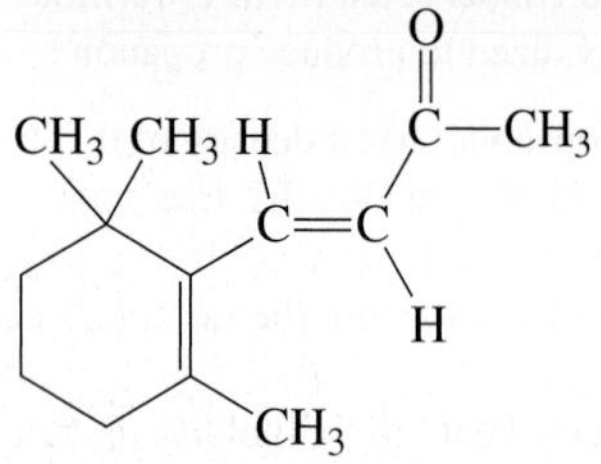

Ionone

■ ANSWERS

CI.25 a.

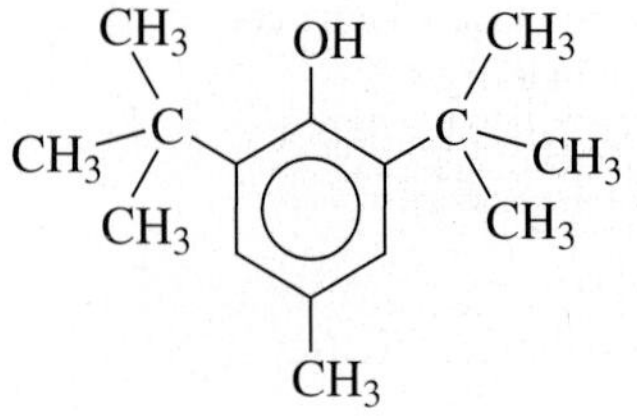

4-Methylphenol

b.

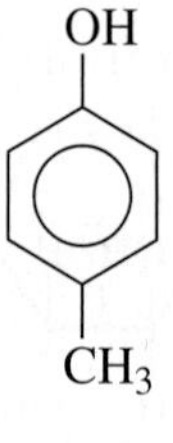

4-Methylphenol 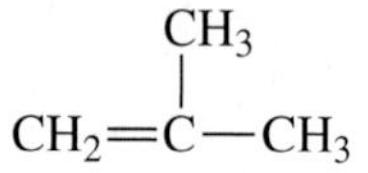   2-Methylpropene

c. $C_{15}H_{24}O$; 220. g/mole

d. 21 mg

CI.27 a. $CH_3-\overset{\overset{\displaystyle O}{\|}}{C}-CH_3$

b. C_3H_6O; 58.0 g/mole

c. $CH_3-\overset{\overset{\displaystyle OH}{|}}{CH}-CH_3$

CI.29 a. A, B, and C are all glucose.
b. An α-1,6-glycosidic bond links A and B.
c. An α-1,4-glycosidic bond links B and C.
d. β panose
e. Panose is a reducing sugar because the hydroxyl group on the anomeric carbon 1 of structure C allows glucose (structure C) to form the aldehyde.

Carboxylic Acids and Esters

16

"There are many carboxylic acids, including the alpha hydroxy acids, that are found today in skin products," says Dr. Ken Peterson, pharmacist and cosmetic chemist, Oakland, California. *"When you take a carboxylic acid called a fatty acid and react it with a strong base, you get a salt called soap. Soap has a high pH because the weak fatty acid and the strong base won't have a neutral pH of 7. If you take soap and drop its pH down to 7, you will convert the soap to the fatty acid. When I create fragrances, I use my nose and my chemistry background to identify and break down the reactions that produce good scents. Many fragrances are esters, which form when an alcohol reacts with a carboxylic acid. For example, the ester that smells like pineapple is made from ethanol and butyric acid."*

Mastering**CHEMISTRY**™

Visit **www.masteringchemistry.com**
for self-study materials and instructor-
assigned homework.

Carboxylic acids are similar to the weak acids we studied in Chapter 10. They have a sour or tart taste, produce hydronium ions in water, and neutralize bases. You encounter carboxylic acids when you taste the vinegar in a salad dressing, which is a solution of acetic acid and water, or experience the sour taste of citric acid in a grapefruit or lemon. When a carboxylic acid combines with an alcohol, an ester and water are produced. Fats and oils are esters of glycerol and fatty acids, which are long-chain carboxylic acids. Esters produce the pleasant aromas and flavors of many fruits, such as bananas, strawberries, and oranges.

16.1 Carboxylic Acids

LEARNING GOAL

Give the common names, IUPAC names, and condensed structural formulas of carboxylic acids.

In Chapter 14, we described the carbonyl group (C=O) as the functional group in aldehydes and ketones. In a **carboxylic acid**, a hydroxyl group is attached to the carbonyl group, forming a **carboxyl group**. The carboxyl functional group may be attached to an alkyl group or an aromatic group.

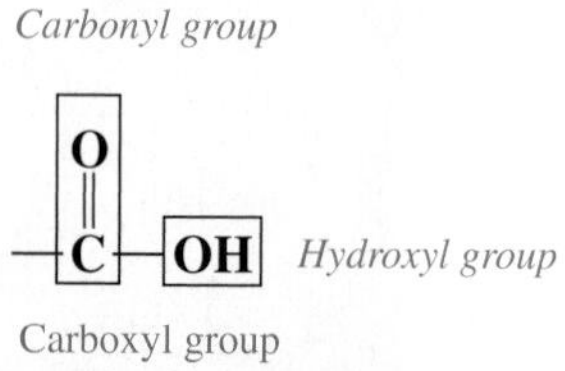

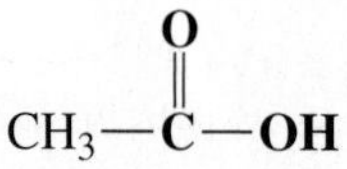
Acetic acid

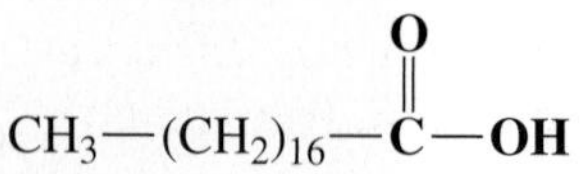
Stearic acid (a fatty acid in fats and oils)

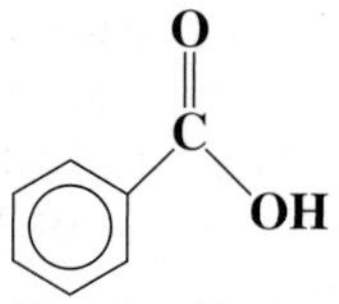
Benzoic acid (aromatic acid)

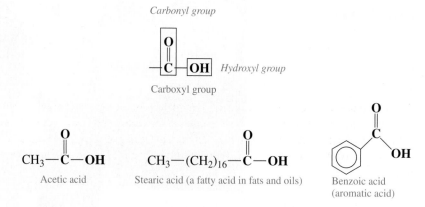

The carboxyl group can be written in several different ways. For example, the condensed structural formula and line-bond formula for propanoic acid can be written as follows:

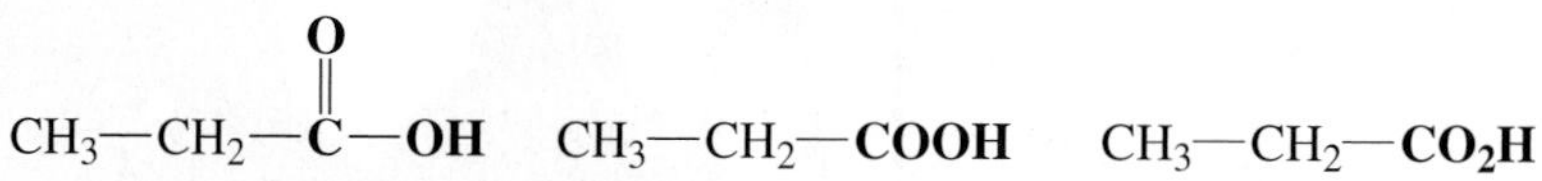
Some condensed structural formulas for propanoic acid

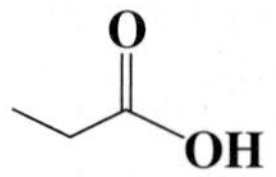
Line-bond formula

SELF STUDY ACTIVITY Carboxylic Acids

Naming Carboxylic Acids

The IUPAC names of carboxylic acids use the alkane names of the corresponding carbon chains.

STEP 1 **Identify the carbon chain containing the carboxyl group and replace the *e* of the alkane name with *oic acid*.** The carboxylic acid of benzene is named benzoic acid.

STEP 2 **Give the location and names of substituents on the main chain.** Number the carbon chain beginning with the carboxyl carbon as 1:

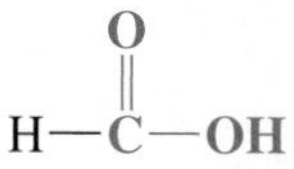
Methanoic acid

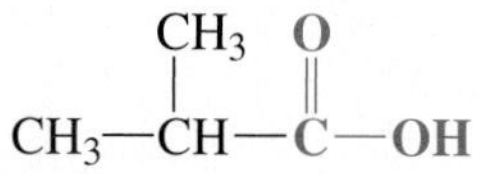
2-Methylpropanoic acid

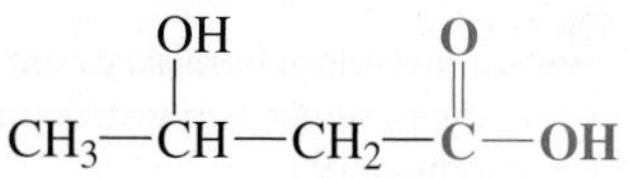
3-Hydroxybutanoic acid

For benzoic acid, where the carboxyl group is bonded to carbon 1, the ring is numbered to give the lowest possible numbers. As with other aromatic compounds, the prefixes *ortho*, *meta*, and *para* may be used to show the position of one other substituent:

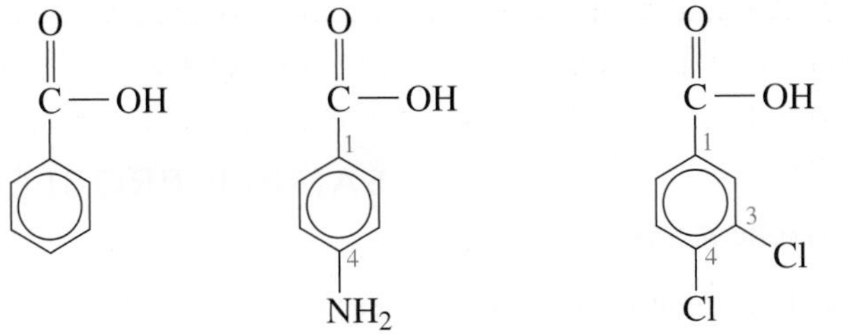

Benzoic acid	4-Aminobenzoic acid (*p*-aminobenzoic acid)	3,4-Dichlorobenzoic acid

Many carboxylic acids are still named by their common names, which are derived from their natural sources. In Chapter 14, we named aldehydes using the prefixes that represent the typical sources of carboxylic acids.

When using the common names, the Greek letters alpha (α), beta (β), and gamma (γ) are assigned to the carbons adjacent to the carboxyl carbon:

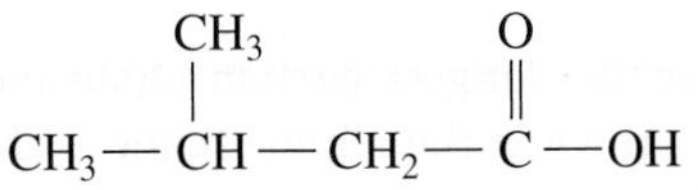

$$CH_3-CH-CH_2-C-OH$$

IUPAC	4	3	2	1
Common	γ	β	α	

Formic acid is injected under the skin during bee or red ant stings and other insect bites. Acetic acid is the oxidation product of the ethanol in wines and apple cider. The resulting solution of acetic acid and water is known as vinegar. Propionic acid is obtained from the fats of dairy products. Butyric acid gives the foul odor to rancid butter. (See Table 16.1.)

TABLE 16.1   Names and Natural Sources of Some Carboxylic Acids

Condensed Structural Formula	IUPAC Name	Common Name	
$H-C-OH$	Methanoic acid	Formic acid	
CH_3-C-H	Ethanoic acid	Acetic acid	
CH_3-CH_2-C-OH	Propanoic acid	Propionic acid	
$CH_3-CH_2-CH_2-C-OH$	Butanoic acid	Butyric acid	

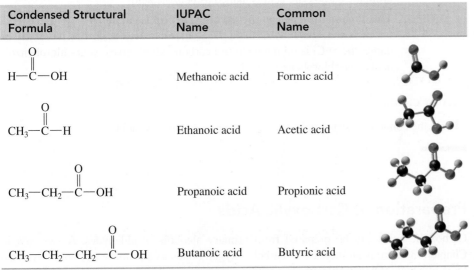

CONCEPT CHECK 16.1

Naming Carboxylic Acids

Why can the following condensed structural formula be named as propanoic acid or propionic acid?

$$CH_3-CH_2-C-OH$$

TUTORIAL
Naming and Drawing
Carboxylic Acids

ANSWER

The longest carbon chain containing the carboxyl group has three carbon atoms. In the IUPAC system, the *e* in propane is replaced by *oic acid*, to give the name propanoic acid. It has the common name propionic acid.

SAMPLE PROBLEM **16.1**

■ **Naming Carboxylic Acids**

Give the IUPAC and common name, if any, for each of the following carboxylic acids:

a.

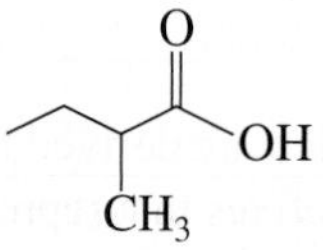

b.

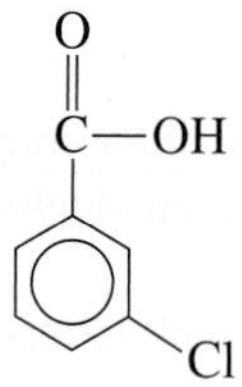

SOLUTION

a. STEP 1 In the IUPAC system, name the longest carbon chain containing the carboxyl group by replacing the *e* in the alkane name with *oic acid*. A carboxylic acid with four carbon atoms is named butanoic acid; the common name is butyric acid.

STEP 2 Give the location and names of the substituents on the carbon chain by counting the carboxyl carbon as carbon 1. With a methyl group on the second carbon, the IUPAC name is 2-methylbutanoic acid. For the common name, the Greek letter α specifies the carbon atom next to the carboxyl carbon, α-methylbutyric acid.

b. STEP 1 In the IUPAC system, name the longest carbon chain containing the carboxyl group by replacing the *e* in the alkane name with *oic acid*. An aromatic carboxylic acid is named as benzoic acid.

STEP 2 The carbon attached to the carboxyl group is carbon 1. With the —Cl on carbon 3, the IUPAC name is 3-chlorobenzoic acid. For the common name, the —Cl is on the *meta* (*m*) carbon, which gives *meta*-chlorobenzoic acid or *m*-chlorobenzoic acid.

STUDY CHECK

Draw the condensed structural formula of 3-phenylpropanoic acid.

Guide to Naming Carboxylic Acids

STEP 1
For nonaromatics, identify the carbon chain containing carboxyl group and replace the *e* in the alkane name by *oic acid*.

STEP 2
Give the location and names of substituents on the main chain.

Preparation of Carboxylic Acids

Carboxylic acids can be prepared from primary alcohols or aldehydes. As we saw in Chapter 13, there is an increase in carbon–oxygen bonds as a primary alcohol is oxidized to an aldehyde. Oxidation continues easily as oxygen is added to yield a carboxylic acid. For example, when ethyl alcohol in wine is exposed to oxygen in the air, vinegar is produced. The oxidation process converts the ethyl alcohol (primary alcohol) to acetaldehyde, and then to acetic acid, the carboxylic acid in vinegar. (See Figure 16.1.)

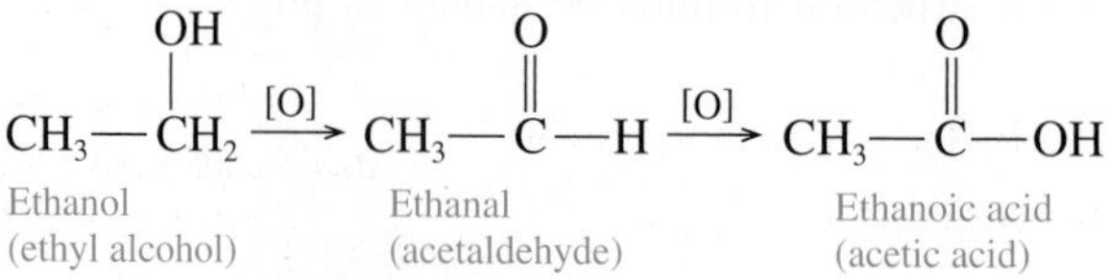

FIGURE 16.1 Vinegar is a 5% solution of acetic acid and water.

Q What is the IUPAC name for acetic acid?

$$CH_3-CH_2 \xrightarrow{[O]} CH_3-C-H \xrightarrow{[O]} CH_3-C-OH$$

Ethanol (ethyl alcohol)   Ethanal (acetaldehyde)   Ethanoic acid (acetic acid)

HEALTH NOTE

Alpha Hydroxy Acids

Alpha hydroxy acids (AHAs) are naturally occurring carboxylic acids found in fruits, milk, and sugar cane. Cleopatra reportedly bathed in sour milk to smooth her skin. Dermatologists use products with high concentrations (20–70%) of AHAs to remove acne scars and in skin peels to reduce irregular pigmentation and age spots. Lower concentrations (8–10%) of AHAs are added to skin care products for the purpose of smoothing fine lines, improving skin texture, and cleansing pores. Several different alpha hydroxy acids may be found in skin care products singly or in combination. Glycolic acid and lactic acid are most frequently used.

Recent studies indicate that products with AHAs increase sensitivity of the skin to sun and UV radiation. It is recommended that a sunscreen with a sun protection factor (SPF) of at least 15 be used when treating the skin with products that include AHAs. Products containing AHAs at concentrations under 10% and pH values greater than 3.5 are generally considered safe. However, the Food and Drug Administration (FDA) has reports of AHAs causing skin irritation including blisters, rashes, and discoloration of the skin. The FDA does not require product

safety reports from cosmetic manufacturers, although they are responsible for marketing safe products. The FDA advises that you test any product containing AHAs on a small area of skin before you use it on a large area.

Alpha Hydroxy Acid (Source)	Structure
Glycolic acid (sugar cane, sugar beet)	$HO-CH_2-\overset{\overset{O}{\|}}{C}-OH$
Lactic acid (sour milk)	$CH_3-\overset{\overset{OH}{\|}}{CH}-\overset{\overset{O}{\|}}{C}-OH$
Tartaric acid (grapes)	$HO-\overset{\overset{O}{\|}}{C}-\overset{\overset{OH}{\|}}{CH}-\overset{\overset{OH}{\|}}{CH}-\overset{\overset{O}{\|}}{C}-OH$
Malic acid (apples, grapes)	$HO-\overset{\overset{O}{\|}}{C}-CH_2-\overset{\overset{OH}{\|}}{CH}-\overset{\overset{O}{\|}}{C}-OH$
Citric acid (citrus fruits: lemons, oranges, grapefruit)	CH_2-COOH $HO-C-COOH$ CH_2-COOH

SAMPLE PROBLEM 16.2

■ Preparation of Carboxylic Acids

Write an equation for the oxidation of 1-propanol and name each product.

SOLUTION

A primary alcohol oxidizes to an aldehyde, which can oxidize further to a carboxylic acid:

$$CH_3-CH_2-CH_2-OH \xrightarrow{[O]} CH_3-CH_2-\overset{\overset{O}{\|}}{C}-H \xrightarrow{[O]} CH_3-CH_2-\overset{\overset{O}{\|}}{C}-OH$$

1-Propanol (propyl alcohol)   Propanal (propionaldehyde)   Propanoic acid (propionic acid)

STUDY CHECK

Draw the condensed structural formula of the carboxylic acid produced by the oxidation of 1-butanol.

QUESTIONS AND PROBLEMS

Carboxylic Acids

16.1 What carboxylic acid is responsible for the pain of an ant sting?

16.2 What carboxylic acid is found in vinegar?

16.3 Explain the differences in the condensed structural formulas of propanal and propanoic acid.

16.4 Explain the differences in the condensed structural formulas of benzaldehyde and benzoic acid.

16.5 Give the IUPAC and common name (if any) for each of the following carboxylic acids:

a. $CH_3-\overset{O}{\overset{\|}{C}}-OH$

b. (structure) $\diagup\diagdown\diagup\overset{O}{\overset{\|}{\diagdown}}OH$

c. $CH_3-\overset{Cl}{\underset{|}{CH}}-\overset{O}{\overset{\|}{C}}-OH$

d. (structure with CH_3 branch) OH

e. (benzene ring with $\overset{O}{\overset{\|}{C}}-OH$, HO and OH substituents)

f. $CH_3-\overset{Br}{\underset{|}{CH}}-CH_2-CH_2-\overset{O}{\overset{\|}{C}}-OH$

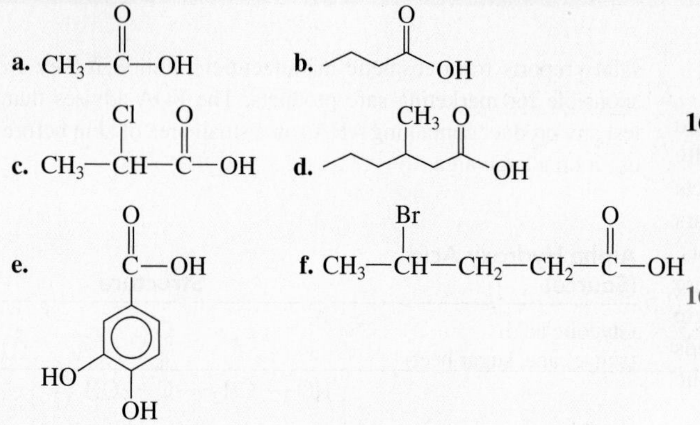

16.6 Give the IUPAC and common name (if any) for each of the following carboxylic acids:

a. $H-\overset{O}{\overset{\|}{C}}-OH$

b. (structure) $\overset{O}{\overset{\|}{\diagdown}}OH$ with Br

c. (benzene ring) $\overset{O}{\overset{\|}{C}}-OH$

d. (benzene ring with Cl) $\overset{O}{\overset{\|}{C}}-OH$

e. $CH_3-\overset{CH_3}{\underset{|}{CH}}-CH_2-\overset{O}{\overset{\|}{C}}-OH$

f. $Cl-CH_2-\overset{O}{\overset{\|}{C}}-OH$

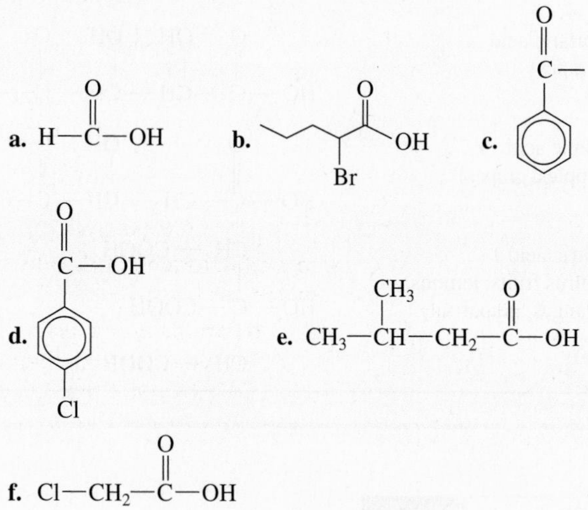

16.7 Draw the condensed structural formula of each of the following carboxylic acids:
a. propionic acid   b. benzoic acid
c. 2-chloroethanoic acid   d. 3-hydroxypropanoic acid
e. α-methylbutyric acid   f. 3,5-dibromoheptanoic acid

16.8 Draw the condensed structural formula of each of the following carboxylic acids:
a. butyric acid   b. 3-ethylbenzoic acid
c. α-hydroxyacetic acid   d. 2,4-dibromobutanoic acid
e. m-methylbenzoic acid   f. 4,4-dibromohexanoic acid

16.9 Draw the condensed structural formula of the carboxylic acid formed by the oxidation of each of the following:

a. CH_3-OH b. $CH_3-\overset{O}{\overset{\|}{C}}-H$

c. $CH_3-\overset{CH_3}{\underset{|}{CH}}-CH_2-CH_2-OH$

d. (cyclopentane) $-CH_2-CH_2-OH$

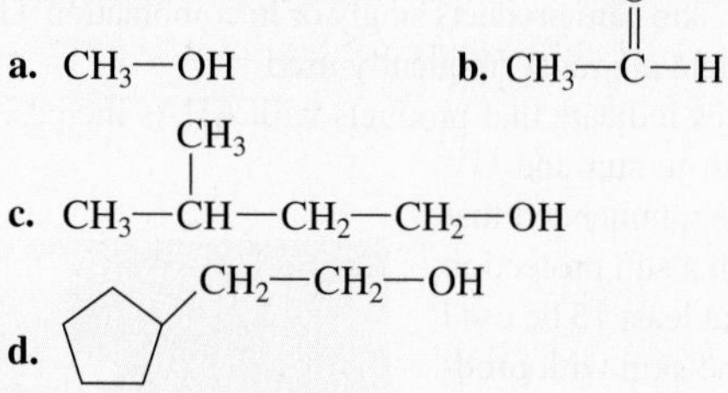

16.10 Draw the condensed structural formula of the carboxylic acid formed by the oxidation of each of the following:

a. $CH_3-CH_2-CH_2-CH_2-CH_2-CH_2-OH$

b. $CH_3-CH_2-CH_2-CH_2-\overset{O}{\overset{\|}{C}}-H$

c. $CH_3-\overset{CH_3}{\underset{|}{CH}}-CH_2-\overset{O}{\overset{\|}{C}}-H$

d. (benzene ring) $-CH_2-CH_2-OH$

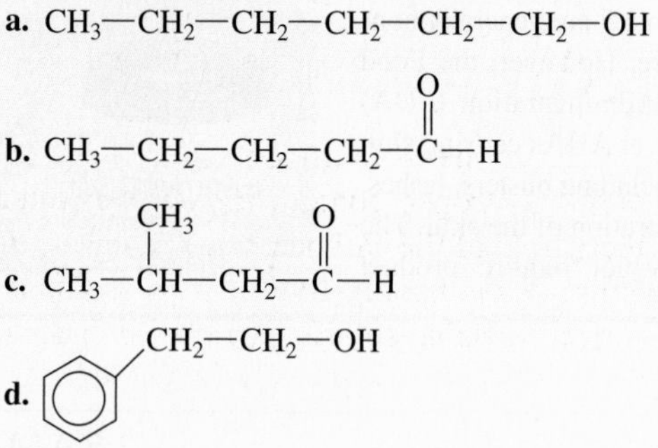

16.2 Properties of Carboxylic Acids

Carboxylic acids are among the most polar organic compounds because the functional group consists of two polar groups: a hydroxyl (—OH) group and a carbonyl (C=O) group:

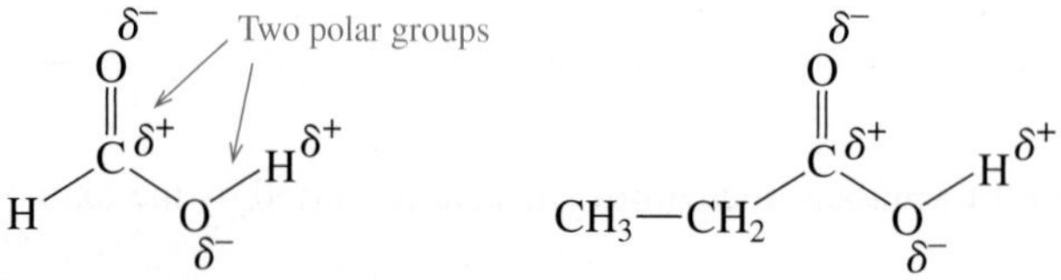

The —OH group is similar to the functional group in alcohols, and the C=O double bond is similar to that of aldehydes and ketones.

Boiling Points

The polar —OH group allows carboxylic acids to form several hydrogen bonds with other carboxylic acid molecules as well as with water. This effect of hydrogen bonds gives carboxylic acids higher boiling points than alcohols, ketones, and aldehydes of similar mass:

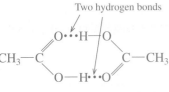

Compound	Propanal	1-Propanol	Ethanoic acid
Molar mass	58	60	60
Bp	49 °C	97 °C	118 °C

An important reason for the higher boiling points of carboxylic acids is that two carboxylic acids form hydrogen bonds between their carboxyl groups, resulting in a *dimer*. As a dimer, the mass of the carboxylic acid is effectively doubled, which means that a higher temperature is required to reach the boiling point:

Two hydrogen bonds

$$CH_3-C \overset{O\cdots H-O}{\underset{O-H\cdots O}{}} C-CH_3$$

A dimer of two ethanoic acid molecules

Solubility in Water

Carboxylic acids with one to four carbons are very soluble in water because the carboxyl group forms hydrogen bonds with several water molecules. (See Figure 16.2.) However, as the length of the carbon chain increases, the nonpolar portion reduces solubility. Carboxylic acids having five or more carbons are not very soluble in water. Table 16.2 lists boiling point, solubility, and acid dissociation constant for some selected carboxylic acids.

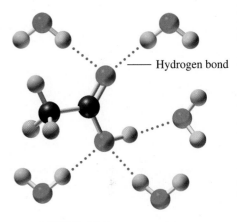
Hydrogen bond

FIGURE 16.2 Acetic acid forms hydrogen bonds with water molecules.

Q Why do the atoms in the carboxyl group hydrogen bond with water molecules?

TABLE 16.2 **Properties of Selected Carboxylic Acids**

IUPAC name	Bp (°C)	Soluble in water?	Acid Dissociation Constants (25 °C)
Methanoic acid	101	Yes	1.8×10^{-4}
Ethanoic acid	118	Yes	1.8×10^{-5}
Propanoic acid	141	Yes	1.3×10^{-5}
Butanoic acid	164	Yes	1.5×10^{-5}
Pentanoic acid	187	Slightly	1.5×10^{-5}
Hexanoic acid	205	Slightly	1.4×10^{-5}
Benzoic acid	250	Slightly	6.5×10^{-5}

CONCEPT CHECK 16.2

■ Boiling Points

Propanal (bp 49 °C) and ethanoic acid (bp 118 °C) have similar molar masses. Explain why ethanoic acid has a higher boiling point than propanal.

ANSWER

In the liquid state, hydrogen bonds between the carboxyl groups of two ethanoic acid molecules form a dimer. As a dimer, the molar mass of ethanoic acid is essentially doubled, which requires higher temperatures to form a gas. Ethanal does not form hydrogen bonds in the liquid state.

SAMPLE PROBLEM **16.3**

■ Properties of Carboxylic Acids

Put the following organic compounds in order of increasing boiling points: butanoic acid, pentane, and 2-butanol.

SOLUTION

The boiling point increases when the molecules of a compound can form hydrogen bonds or have dipole–dipole attractions. The alkane has the lowest boiling point because alkanes cannot hydrogen bond. Alcohols and carboxylic acids have higher boiling points than alkanes because they form hydrogen bonds. However, carboxylic acids can form stable dimers to increase their effective molar mass and therefore their boiling points.

Pentane < 2-butanol < butanoic acid

STUDY CHECK

Why would methanoic acid (molar mass 46, bp 101 °C) have a higher boiling point than ethanol (molar mass 46, bp 78 °C)?

Acidity of Carboxylic Acids

One of the most important properties of carboxylic acids is their ionization in water, which makes them weak acids (Chapter 10). In the ionization, a carboxylic acid donates a proton to a water molecule to produce an anion called a **carboxylate ion** and a hydronium ion:

$$CH_3-\overset{\overset{\displaystyle O}{\|}}{C}-OH \ + \ H_2O \ \rightleftharpoons \ CH_3-\overset{\overset{\displaystyle O}{\|}}{C}-O^- \ + \ H_3O^+$$

Carboxylic acid   Carboxylate ion   Hydronium
(acetic acid)   (acetate ion)   ion

Carboxylic acids are more acidic than other organic compounds, including phenols. Only a small percentage (~1%) of the carboxylic acid molecules in a dilute solution are ionized, which means that most of the acid is not ionized. The acid dissociation constants of most carboxylic acids are between 10^{-4} to 10^{-5}, as seen in Table 16.2.

SAMPLE PROBLEM **16.4**

■ Ionization of Carboxylic Acids in Water

Write the equation for the ionization of propionic acid in water.

SOLUTION

The ionization of propionic acid produces a carboxylate ion and a hydronium ion:

$$CH_3-CH_2-\overset{\overset{\displaystyle O}{\|}}{C}-OH \ + \ H_2O \ \rightleftharpoons \ CH_3-CH_2-\overset{\overset{\displaystyle O}{\|}}{C}-O^- \ + \ H_3O^+$$

STUDY CHECK

Write an equation for the ionization of formic acid in water.

Neutralization of Carboxylic Acids

Because carboxylic acids are weak acids, they are completely neutralized by strong bases such as NaOH and KOH. The products are water and a **carboxylic acid salt**, which is a carboxylate ion and the metal ion from the base. The carboxylate ion is named by replacing the *ic acid* ending of the acid name with *ate*.

$$H-\overset{\overset{\displaystyle O}{\|}}{C}-OH + NaOH \longrightarrow H-\overset{\overset{\displaystyle O}{\|}}{C}-O^-Na^+ + H_2O$$

Methanoic acid   Sodium methanoate
(formic acid)   (sodium formate)

Benzoic acid + KOH $\longrightarrow$ Potassium benzoate + H$_2$O

Benzoic acid   Potassium benzoate

Sodium propionate, a preservative, is added to bread, cheeses, and bakery items to inhibit the spoilage of the food by microorganisms. Sodium benzoate, an inhibitor of mold and bacteria, is added to juices, margarine, relishes, salads, and jams. Monosodium glutamate (MSG) is added to meats, fish, vegetables, and bakery items to enhance flavor, although it causes headaches in some people. (See Figure 16.3.)

FIGURE 16.3 Preservatives and flavor enhancers in soups and seasonings are often carboxylic acids or their salts.

Q What is the carboxylic acid salt produced by the neutralization of butanoic acid and lithium hydroxide?

$$CH_3-CH_2-\overset{\overset{\displaystyle O}{\|}}{C}-O^-Na^+$$

Sodium propionate

Sodium benzoate

$$HO-\overset{\overset{\displaystyle O}{\|}}{C}-\overset{\overset{\displaystyle NH_2}{|}}{CH}-CH_2-CH_2-\overset{\overset{\displaystyle O}{\|}}{C}-O^-Na^+$$

Monosodium glutamate

Carboxylic acid salts are ionic compounds with strong attractions between ions of metals such as Li^+, Na^+, and K^+ and the negatively charged carboxylate ion. Like most salts, the carboxylic acid salts are solids at room temperature, have high melting points, and are usually soluble in water.

SAMPLE PROBLEM 16.5

■ Neutralization of a Carboxylic Acid

Write the equation for the neutralization of propanoic acid (propionic acid) with sodium hydroxide.

SOLUTION

The neutralization of an acid with a base produces the salt of the acid and water:

$$CH_3-CH_2-\overset{\overset{\displaystyle O}{\|}}{C}-OH + NaOH \longrightarrow CH_3-CH_2-\overset{\overset{\displaystyle O}{\|}}{C}-O^-Na^+ + H_2O$$

Propanoic acid   Sodium propanoate
(propionic acid)   (sodium propionate)

STUDY CHECK

What carboxylic acid will give potassium butanoate (potassium butyrate) when it is neutralized by KOH?

HEALTH NOTE

Carboxylic Acids in Metabolism

Several carboxylic acids are part of the metabolic processes within our cells. For example, during glycolysis, a molecule of glucose is broken down into two molecules of pyruvic acid, or actually its carboxylate ion pyruvate. During strenuous exercise when oxygen levels are low (anaerobic), pyruvic acid is reduced to give lactic acid or the lactate ion. The buildup of lactate ion in muscle leads to fatigue and pain.

$$CH_3-\overset{\overset{O}{\|}}{C}-\overset{\overset{O}{\|}}{C}-OH \ + \ 2H \ \xrightarrow{\text{Reduction}}$$

Pyruvic acid

$$CH_3-\overset{\overset{OH}{|}}{CH}-\overset{\overset{O}{\|}}{C}-OH$$

Lactic acid

In the citric acid cycle, also called the Krebs cycle, di- and tricarboxylic acids are oxidized and decarboxylated (loss of CO_2) to produce energy for the cell. These carboxylic acids are normally referred to by their common names. At the start of the citric acid cycle, citric acid with six carbons is converted to five-carbon α-ketoglutaric acid. Citric acid is also the acid that gives the sour tastes to citrus fruits such as lemons and grapefruits.

$$
\begin{array}{ccc}
\text{COOH} & & \text{COOH} \\
| & & | \\
\text{CH}_2 & & \text{CH}_2 \\
| & & | \\
\text{HO}-\text{C}-\text{COOH} & \xrightarrow{[O]} & \text{CH}_2 \quad + \ CO_2 \\
| & & | \\
\text{CH}_2 & & \text{C}=\text{O} \\
| & & | \\
\text{COOH} & & \text{COOH}
\end{array}
$$

Citric acid α-Ketoglutaric acid

The citric acid cycle continues as α-ketoglutaric acid loses CO_2 to give a four-carbon succinic acid. Then a series of reactions converts succinic acid to oxaloacetic acid. We see that some of the functional groups we have studied along with reactions such as hydration and oxidation are part of the metabolic processes that take place in our cells.

$$
\begin{array}{ccc}
\text{COOH} & & \text{COOH} \\
| & & | \\
\text{CH}_2 & \xrightarrow{[O]} & \text{C}-\text{H} \\
| & & \| \\
\text{CH}_2 & & \text{H}-\text{C} \quad \xrightarrow{H_2O} \\
| & & | \\
\text{COOH} & & \text{COOH}
\end{array}
$$

Succinic acid   Fumaric acid

$$
\begin{array}{ccc}
\text{COOH} & & \text{COOH} \\
| & & | \\
\text{HO}-\text{C}-\text{H} & \xrightarrow{[O]} & \text{C}=\text{O} \\
| & & | \\
\text{CH}_2 & & \text{CH}_2 \\
| & & | \\
\text{COOH} & & \text{COOH}
\end{array}
$$

Malic acid   Oxaloacetic acid

At the pH of the aqueous environment in the cells, the carboxylic acids are ionized, which means it is actually the carboxylate ions that take part in the reactions of citric acid cycle. For example, in water, succinic acid is in equilibrium with its carboxylate ion succinate.

$$
\begin{array}{ccc}
\text{COOH} & & \text{COO}^- \\
| & & | \\
\text{CH}_2 & & \text{CH}_2 \\
| & + \ 2H_2O \ \rightleftharpoons & | \quad + \ 2H_3O^+ \\
\text{CH}_2 & & \text{CH}_2 \\
| & & | \\
\text{COOH} & & \text{COO}^-
\end{array}
$$

Succinic acid   Succinate ion

QUESTIONS AND PROBLEMS

Properties of Carboxylic Acids

16.11 Identify the compound in each of the following pairs that has the higher boiling point. Explain.
 a. ethanoic acid (acetic acid) or butanoic acid
 b. 1-propanol or propanoic acid
 c. butanone or butanoic acid

16.12 Identify the compound in each of the following pairs that has the higher boiling point. Explain.
 a. propanone (acetone) or propanoic acid
 b. propanoic acid or hexanoic acid
 c. ethanol or ethanoic acid (acetic acid)

16.13 Identify the compound in each of the following groups that is the most soluble in water. Explain.
 a. propanoic acid, hexanoic acid, benzoic acid
 b. pentane, 1-butanol, propanoic acid

16.14 Identify the compound in each of the following groups that is the most soluble in water. Explain.
 a. butanone, butanoic acid, butane
 b. acetic acid, pentanoic acid, octanoic acid

16.15 Write an equation for the ionization of each of the following carboxylic acids in water:

a. H—C(=O)—OH   b. CH₃—CH₂—C(=O)—OH
c. acetic acid

16.16 Write an equation for the ionization of each of the following carboxylic acids in water:
 a. CH₃—CH(CH₃)—C(=O)—OH
 b. α-hydroxyacetic acid
 c. butanoic acid

16.17 Write an equation for the reaction of each of the following carboxylic acids with NaOH:
 a. formic acid
 b. propanoic acid
 c. benzoic acid

16.18 Write an equation for the reaction of each of the following carboxylic acids with KOH:
 a. acetic acid
 b. 2-methylbutanoic acid
 c. p-chlorobenzoic acid

16.19 Give the IUPAC and common names, if any, of the carboxylic acid salts in problem 16.17.

16.20 Give the IUPAC and common names, if any, of the carboxylic acid salts in problem 16.18.

16.3 Esters

A carboxylic acid reacts with an alcohol to form an **ester** and water. In an ester, the —H of the carboxylic acid is replaced by an alkyl group. Fats and oils in our diets contain esters of long-chain carboxylic acids. The aromas and flavors of many fruits including bananas, oranges, and strawberries are because of esters.

LEARNING GOAL

Name an ester; write equations for the formation and hydrolysis of an ester.

TUTORIAL
Writing Esterification Equations

Carboxylic acid

CH₃—C(=O)—O—H
Ethanoic acid
(acetic acid)

Ester

CH₃—C(=O)—O—CH₃
Methyl ethanoate
(methyl acetate)

Esterification

In a reaction called **esterification**, an ester is produced when a carboxylic acid and an alcohol react in the presence of an acid catalyst (usually H₂SO₄). An excess of the alcohol reactant is used to favor the formation of the ester product. In this reaction, the —OH removed from the carboxylic acid and the —H removed from the alcohol combine to form water:

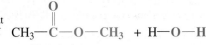

CH₃—C(=O)—O—H + H—O—CH₃ ⇌(H⁺, heat) CH₃—C(=O)—O—CH₃ + H—O—H
Ethanoic acid (acetic acid)   Methanol (methyl alcohol)   Methyl ethanoate (methyl acetate)

HEALTH NOTE

Salicylic Acid and Pain Relievers

Chewing on a piece of willow bark was used as a way to relieve pain for many centuries. By the 1800s, chemists discovered that salicylic acid was the agent in the bark responsible for the relief of pain. However, salicylic acid, which has both a carboxylic group and a hydroxyl group, irritates the stomach lining. A less irritating ester of salicylic acid and acetic acid, called acetylsalicylic acid or "aspirin," was prepared in 1899 by the Bayer chemical company in Germany. In some aspirin preparations, a buffer is added to neutralize the carboxylic acid group and lessen its irritation of the stomach. Aspirin is used as an analgesic (pain reliever), antipyretic (fever reducer), and anti-inflammatory agent. Many people take a daily low-dose aspirin, which has been found to lower the risk of heart attack and stroke.

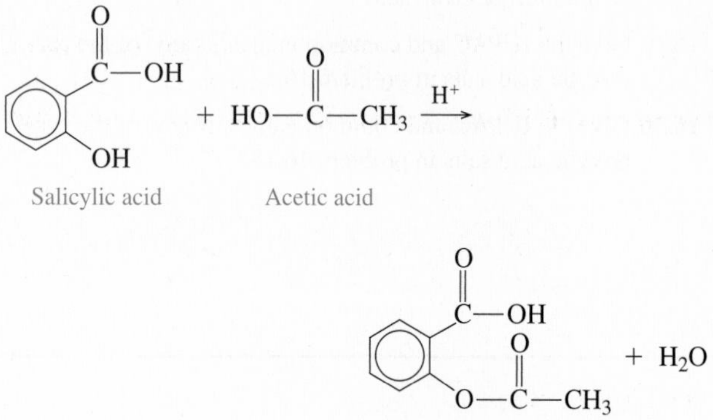

Salicylic acid   Acetic acid

Acetylsalicylic acid, aspirin

Oil of wintergreen, or methyl salicylate, has a spearmint odor and flavor. Because it can pass through the skin, methyl salicylate is used in skin ointments, where it acts as a counterirritant, producing heat to soothe sore muscles.

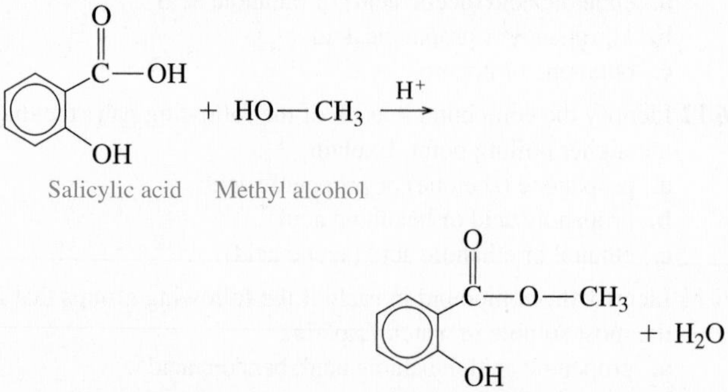

Salicylic acid   Methyl alcohol

Methyl salicylate
(oil of wintergreen)

For example, the ester responsible for the flavor and odor of pears can be prepared using acetic acid and 1-propanol. The equation for this esterification is written as follows:

$$CH_3-\overset{\overset{\displaystyle O}{\|}}{C}-OH \ + \ H-O-CH_2-CH_2-CH_3 \ \underset{}{\overset{H^+, \text{ heat}}{\rightleftharpoons}} \ CH_3-\overset{\overset{\displaystyle O}{\|}}{C}-O-CH_2-CH_2-CH_3 \ + \ H_2O$$

Ethanoic acid (acetic acid)   1-Propanol (propyl alcohol)   Propyl ethanoate (propyl acetate)

SAMPLE PROBLEM 16.6

■ Writing Esterification Equations

The ester that is present in apples and pineapples can be synthesized from butyric acid and methyl alcohol. What is the equation for the formation of the ester in apples?

SOLUTION

$$CH_3-CH_2-CH_2-\overset{\overset{\displaystyle O}{\|}}{C}-OH \ + \ H-O-CH_3 \ \overset{H^+, \text{ heat}}{\rightleftharpoons}$$

Butanoic acid (butyric acid)   Methanol (methyl alcohol)

$$CH_3-CH_2-CH_2-\overset{\overset{\displaystyle O}{\|}}{C}-O-CH_3 \ + \ H_2O$$

Methyl butanoate (methyl butyrate)

STUDY CHECK

What carboxylic acid and alcohol are needed to form the following ester, which gives flavor and odor to apricots? (*Hint*: Separate the O and C=O of the ester group and add —H and —OH to give the original alcohol and carboxylic acid.)

$$CH_3-CH_2-\overset{\overset{\displaystyle O}{\|}}{C}-O-CH_2-CH_2-CH_2-CH_2-CH_3$$

ENVIRONMENTAL NOTE

Plastics

Terephthalic acid (an acid with two carboxyl groups) is produced in large quantities for the manufacture of polyesters such as Dacron and plastics.

When terephthalic acid reacts with ethylene glycol, ester bonds can form on both ends of the molecules, allowing many molecules to combine until they have formed a long polymer known as a *polyester*:

$$\underset{\text{Terephthalic acid}}{HO-\overset{\overset{O}{\|}}{C}-\bigcirc-\overset{\overset{O}{\|}}{C}-OH} + \underset{\text{Ethylene glycol}}{HO-CH_2CH_2-OH} \longrightarrow$$

$$-O-\overset{\overset{O}{\|}}{C}-\bigcirc-\overset{\overset{O}{\|}}{C}-O-CH_2CH_2-O-\overset{\overset{O}{\|}}{C}-\bigcirc-\overset{\overset{O}{\|}}{C}-O-CH_2CH_2-O-$$

Ester bonds
A section of the polyester Dacron

Dacron polyester is used to make permanent press fabrics, carpets, and clothes. In medicine, artificial blood vessels and valves are made of Dacron, which is biologically inert and does not clot the blood. The polyester can also be made as a film called Mylar and as a plastic known as PETE (**p**oly**e**thylene**te**rephthalate). PETE is used for plastic soft drink bottles as well as for containers of salad dressings, shampoos, and dishwashing liquids.

Today PETE (recycling symbol "1") is the most widely recycled of all the plastics. In 1992, there were 365 million pounds (166 million kilograms) of PETE recycled. After it is separated from other plastics, PETE can be changed into other useful items, including polyester fabric for T-shirts and coats, fill for sleeping bags, doormats, and containers for tennis balls.

QUESTIONS AND PROBLEMS

Esters

16.21 Identify each of the following as an aldehyde, a ketone, a carboxylic acid, or an ester:

a. $CH_3-\overset{\overset{\displaystyle O}{\|}}{C}-H$

b. $CH_3-\overset{\overset{\displaystyle O}{\|}}{C}-O-CH_3$

c. $CH_3-CH_2-\overset{\overset{\displaystyle O}{\|}}{C}-CH_3$

d. $CH_3-CH_2-\overset{\overset{\displaystyle O}{\|}}{C}-O-H$

16.22 Identify each of the following as an aldehyde, a ketone, a carboxylic acid, or an ester:

a. 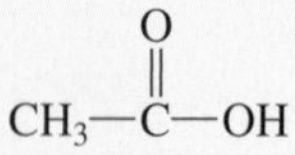 $CH_3-\overset{\overset{\displaystyle O}{\|}}{C}-OH$ b. $CH_3-\overset{\overset{\displaystyle O}{\|}}{C}-O-CH_2-CH_3$

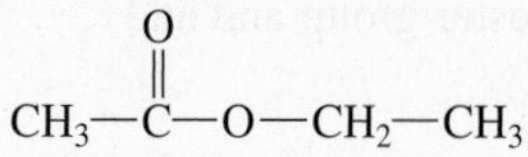

c. $CH_3-CH_2-\overset{\overset{\displaystyle O}{\|}}{C}-H$

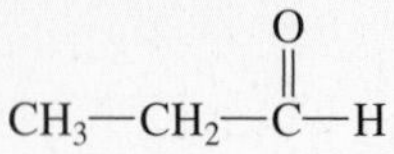

d. 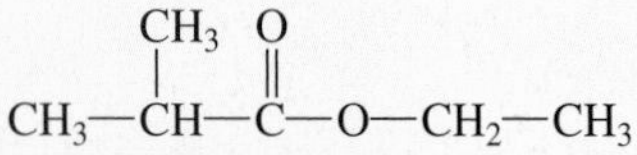 $CH_3-\overset{\overset{\displaystyle CH_3}{|}}{C}H-\overset{\overset{\displaystyle O}{\|}}{C}-O-CH_2-CH_3$

16.23 Draw the condensed structural formula of the ester formed when each of the following reacts with methyl alcohol:
  a. acetic acid   **b.** butyric acid   **c.** benzoic acid

16.24 Draw the condensed structural formula of the ester formed when each of the following reacts with methyl alcohol:
  a. formic acid
  b. propionic acid
  c. 2-methylpentanoic acid

16.25 Draw the condensed structural formula of the ester formed when each of the following react:

a. 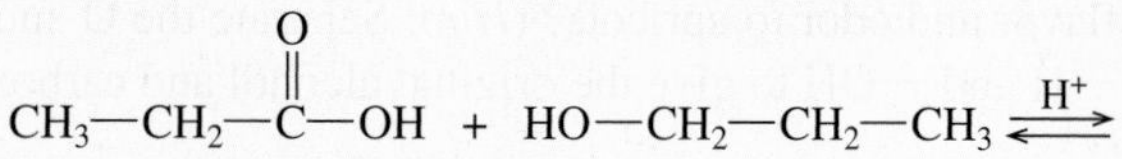 $CH_3-CH_2-\overset{\overset{\displaystyle O}{\|}}{C}-OH + HO-CH_2-CH_2-CH_3 \overset{H^+}{\rightleftharpoons}$

b.

$CH_3-CH_2-CH_2-CH_2-\overset{\overset{\displaystyle O}{\|}}{C}-OH + HO-\overset{\overset{\displaystyle CH_3}{|}}{C}H-CH_3 \overset{H^+}{\rightleftharpoons}$

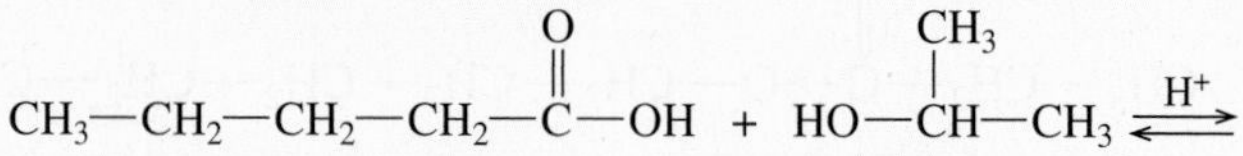

16.26 Draw the condensed structural formula of the ester formed when each of the following react:

a. 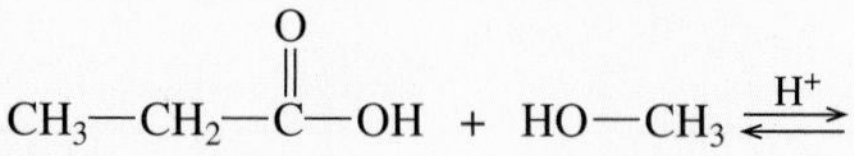 $CH_3-CH_2-\overset{\overset{\displaystyle O}{\|}}{C}-OH + HO-CH_3 \overset{H^+}{\rightleftharpoons}$

b. 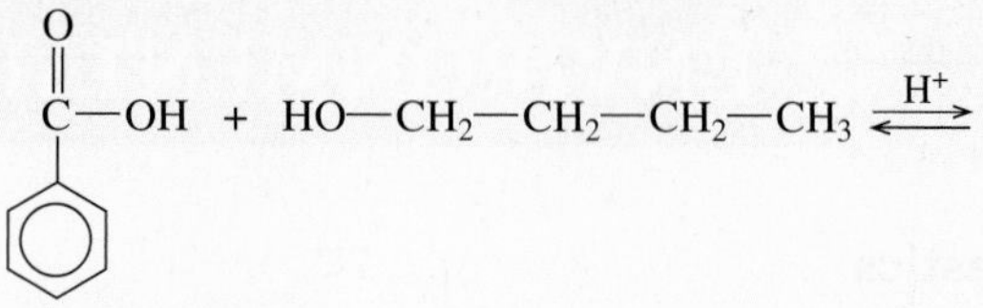 $\overset{\overset{\displaystyle O}{\|}}{C}-OH + HO-CH_2-CH_2-CH_2-CH_3 \overset{H^+}{\rightleftharpoons}$

16.4 Naming Esters

LEARNING GOAL

Write the IUPAC and common names for esters; draw condensed structural formulas.

The name of an ester consists of two words taken from the names of the alcohol and the acid. The first word indicates the *alkyl* part of the alcohol. The second word is the *carboxylate* name of the carboxylic acid. The IUPAC names of esters use the IUPAC names for the carbon chain of the acid, while the common names of esters use the common names of the acids. Let's take a look at the following ester, which has the odor and flavor of peppermint. We can separate the structure into two parts, one from the alcohol and one from the carbon chain of the acid. By writing and naming the alcohol and carboxylic acid that produced the ester, we can determine the name of the ester.

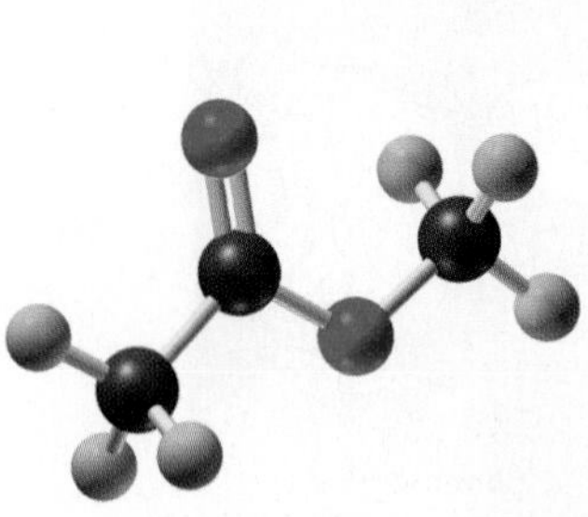

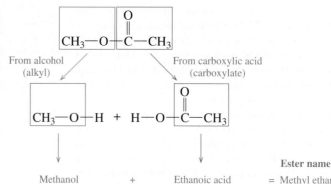

Methyl ethanoate
(methyl acetate)

	From alcohol (alkyl)		From carboxylic acid (carboxylate)	Ester name
IUPAC	Methanol	+	Ethanoic acid	= Methyl ethanoate
Common	Methyl alcohol	+	Acetic acid	= Methyl acetate

The following examples of some typical esters show the IUPAC as well as the common names of esters:

$CH_3-CH_2-O-\overset{\overset{\displaystyle O}{\|}}{C}-CH_3$ $CH_3-O-\overset{\overset{\displaystyle O}{\|}}{C}-CH_2-CH_3$ $CH_3-CH_2-O-\overset{\overset{\displaystyle O}{\|}}{C}-\bigcirc$

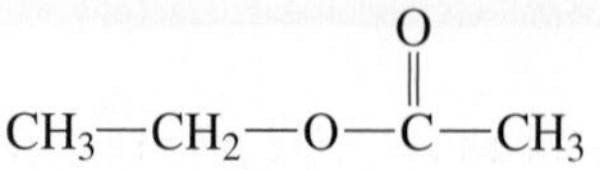

Ethyl ethanoate
(ethyl acetate)

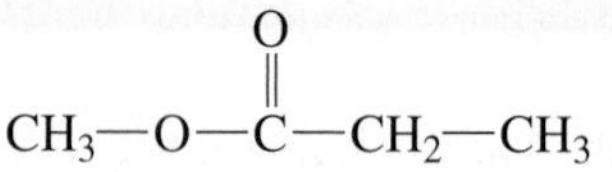

Methyl propanoate
(methyl propionate)

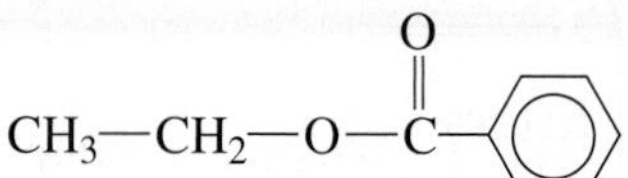

Ethyl benzoate

Many of the fragrances of perfumes and flowers and the flavors of fruits are due to esters. Small esters are volatile so we can smell them and soluble in water so we can taste them. Several of these are listed in Table 16.3.

TABLE 16.3 Some Esters in Fruits and Flavorings

Condensed Structural Formula and Name	Flavor/Odor
$CH_3-\overset{\overset{\textstyle O}{\|}}{C}-O-CH_2-CH_2-CH_3$ Propyl ethanoate (propyl acetate)	Pears
$CH_3-\overset{\overset{\textstyle O}{\|}}{C}-O-CH_2-CH_2-CH_2-CH_2-CH_3$ Pentyl ethanoate (pentyl acetate)	Bananas
$CH_3-\overset{\overset{\textstyle O}{\|}}{C}-O-CH_2-CH_2-CH_2-CH_2-CH_2-CH_2-CH_2-CH_3$ Octyl ethanoate (octyl acetate)	Oranges
$CH_3-CH_2-CH_2-\overset{\overset{\textstyle O}{\|}}{C}-O-CH_2-CH_3$ Ethyl butanoate (ethyl butyrate)	Pineapples
$CH_3-CH_2-CH_2-\overset{\overset{\textstyle O}{\|}}{C}-O-CH_2-CH_2-CH_2-CH_2-CH_3$ Pentyl butanoate (pentyl butyrate)	Apricots

CONCEPT CHECK 16.3

■ **Esterification**

The odor and flavor of apples is the ester from ethanol and pentanoic acid. What is the IUPAC name of the ester?

ANSWER

The first part of an ester name comes from the alkyl part of ethanol, which would be ethyl. The second part is obtained from the name of the carboxylic acid by replacing *ic acid* with *ate*. The name of the ester for apple flavor is ethyl pentanoate.

SAMPLE PROBLEM 16.7

 TUTORIAL
Naming Esters

■ **Naming Esters**

Write the IUPAC and common names of the following ester:

$$CH_3-CH_2-\overset{\overset{\textstyle O}{\|}}{C}-O-CH_2-CH_2-CH_3$$

SOLUTION

STEP 1   **Write the name of the carbon chain from the alcohol as an *alkyl* group.** The alcohol that is part of the ester is propanol, which is named as the alkyl group propyl.

STEP 2   **For the IUPAC name, replace the *ic acid* in the carboxylic acid name with *ate*.**   The carboxylic acid with three carbon atoms is propanoic acid. Replacing the *ic acid* with *ate* gives the IUPAC name of propyl propanoate.

Guide to Naming Esters

STEP 1
Write the name of the carbon chain from the alcohol as an *alkyl* group

STEP 2
Change the *ic acid* of the acid name to *ate*.

The common name of propionic acid gives the common name for the ester of propyl propionate:

From propanoic acid → propanoate   From propyl alcohol → propyl
(or propionic acid → propionate)

$$CH_3-CH_2-\overset{\overset{O}{\|}}{C}-O-CH_2-CH_2-CH_3$$

IUPAC name: propyl propanoate
Common name: propyl propionate

STUDY CHECK

Draw the condensed structural formula of ethyl heptanoate that gives odor and flavor to grapes.

QUESTIONS AND PROBLEMS

Naming Esters

16.27 Give the names of the carboxylic acid and alcohol needed to produce each of the following esters:

a. $H-\overset{\overset{O}{\|}}{C}-O-CH_3$ b. $CH_3-\overset{\overset{O}{\|}}{C}-O-CH_3$

c. $CH_3-CH_2-CH_2-\overset{\overset{O}{\|}}{C}-O-CH_3$

d. $CH_3-\overset{\overset{CH_3}{|}}{CH}-CH_2-\overset{\overset{O}{\|}}{C}-O-CH_2-CH_3$

16.28 Give the names of the carboxylic acid and alcohol needed to produce each of the following esters:

a. $CH_3-CH_2-\overset{\overset{O}{\|}}{C}-O-CH_2-CH_3$

b. $CH_3-CH_2-CH_2-CH_2-CH_2-\overset{\overset{O}{\|}}{C}-O-CH_3$

c. $CH_3-CH_2-\overset{\overset{O}{\|}}{\underset{\underset{CH_3}{|}}{CH}}-\overset{\overset{O}{\|}}{C}-O-CH_3$

d. $CH_3-CH_2-\overset{\overset{O}{\|}}{C}-O-CH_2-CH_2-CH_2-CH_3$

16.29 Name each of the following esters:

a. $CH_3-O-\overset{\overset{O}{\|}}{C}-H$

b. $CH_3-O-\overset{\overset{O}{\|}}{C}-CH_3$

c. $CH_3-O-\overset{\overset{O}{\|}}{C}-CH_2-CH_2-CH_3$

d. $CH_3-\overset{\overset{CH_3}{|}}{CH}-CH_2-\overset{\overset{O}{\|}}{C}-O-CH_2-CH_3$

16.30 Name each of the following esters:

a. $CH_3-CH_2-O-\overset{\overset{O}{\|}}{C}-CH_2-CH_2-CH_3$

b. $CH_3-O-\overset{\overset{O}{\|}}{C}-CH_2-CH_2-CH_2-CH_2-CH_3$

c. $CH_3-O-\overset{\overset{O}{\|}}{C}-CH_2-\overset{\overset{CH_3}{|}}{CH}-CH_3$

d. $CH_3-CH_2-\overset{\overset{O}{\|}}{C}-O-CH_2-CH_2-CH_2-CH_3$

16.31 Draw the condensed structural formula of each of the following esters:
a. methyl acetate
b. butyl formate
c. ethyl pentanoate
d. 2-bromopropyl propanoate

16.32 Draw the condensed structural formula of each of the following esters:
a. hexyl acetate
b. propyl propionate
c. ethyl 2-hydroxybutanoate
d. methyl benzoate

16.33 What is the ester responsible for the flavor and odor of each of the following fruits?
a. banana   b. orange   c. apricot

16.34 What flavor would you notice if you smelled or tasted each of the following?
a. ethyl butanoate   b. propyl acetate   c. octyl acetate

16.5 Properties of Esters

Esters have boiling points higher than those of alkanes but lower than those of alcohols and carboxylic acids of similar mass. Because ester molecules do not have hydroxyl groups, they cannot hydrogen bond to each other:

LEARNING GOAL
Describe the boiling points and solubility of esters; draw the condensed structural formulas of the hydrolysis products.

$$CH_3-CH_2-CH_2-CH_3 \quad CH_3-O-CH_2-CH_3 \quad CH_3-O-\overset{\overset{\displaystyle O}{\|}}{C}-H \quad CH_3-CH_2-CH_2-OH \quad CH_3-\overset{\overset{\displaystyle O}{\|}}{C}-OH$$

	Butane	Methoxyethane	Methyl methanoate	1-Propanol	Ethanoic acid
Type	Alkane	Ether	Ester	Alcohol	Carboxylic acid
Bp	0 °C	11 °C	32 °C	97 °C	118 °C
Mass	58	60	60	60	60

Increasing boiling points →

Solubility in Water

Esters with only a few carbon atoms are soluble in water. The partially negative oxygen of the carbonyl group forms hydrogen bonds with the partially positive hydrogen atoms of water molecules. The solubility of esters decreases as the number of carbon atoms increases.

Acid Hydrolysis of Esters

In **hydrolysis**, water splits apart esters when heated in the presence of a strong acid, usually H_2SO_4 or HCl. The products of acid hydrolysis are the carboxylic acid and alcohol. Therefore, hydrolysis is the reverse of the esterification reaction. However, in an application of Le Châtelier's principle, using a large quantity of water favors the formation of the carboxylic acid and alcohol products. When hydrolysis of biological compounds occurs in the cells, an enzyme replaces the acid as the catalyst. During hydrolysis, —OH from a water molecule bonds to the carbon atom in the carbonyl group of the ester to form the carboxylic acid:

TUTORIAL
Hydrolysis of Esters

$$CH_3-\overset{\overset{\displaystyle O}{\|}}{C}-O-CH_3 + H-OH \underset{}{\overset{H^+}{\rightleftharpoons}} CH_3-\overset{\overset{\displaystyle O}{\|}}{C}-O-H + CH_3-OH$$

Methyl ethanoate (methyl acetate) + Water ⇌ Ethanoic acid (acetic acid) + Methanol (methyl alcohol)

SAMPLE PROBLEM 16.8

■ Acid Hydrolysis of Esters

Aspirin that has been stored for a long time may undergo hydrolysis in the presence of water and heat. What are the hydrolysis products of aspirin? Why does a bottle of old aspirin smell like vinegar?

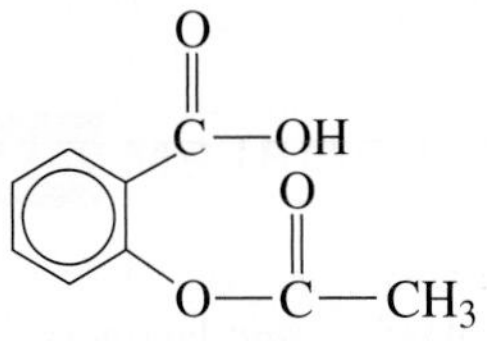

Aspirin (acetylsalicylic acid)

SOLUTION

To write the hydrolysis products, separate the compound at the ester bond. Complete the formula of the carboxylic acid by adding —OH (from water) to the carbonyl group and an —H to complete the alcohol. The acetic acid in the products gives the vinegar odor to a sample of aspirin that has hydrolyzed:

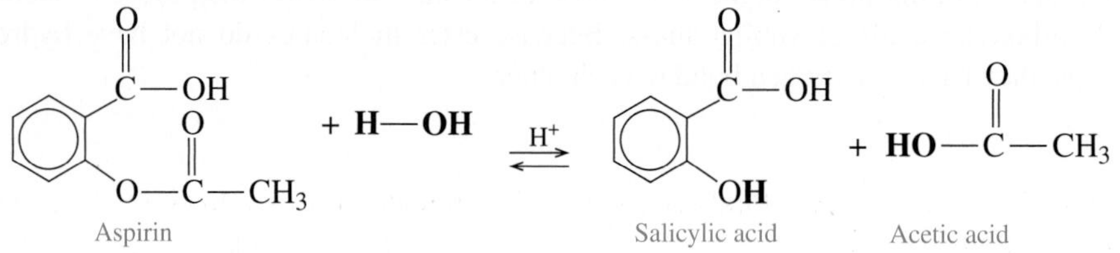

| Aspirin | Salicylic acid | Acetic acid |

STUDY CHECK

What are the names of the products from the acid hydrolysis of ethyl propanoate (ethyl propionate)?

Base Hydrolysis of Esters (Saponification)

When an ester undergoes hydrolysis with a strong base such as NaOH or KOH, the products are the carboxylic acid salt and the corresponding alcohol. The base hydrolysis reaction is also called **saponification**, which refers to the reaction of a long-chain fatty acid with NaOH to make soap. The carboxylic acid, which is produced in acid hydrolysis, is converted to its carboxylate ion by a strong base:

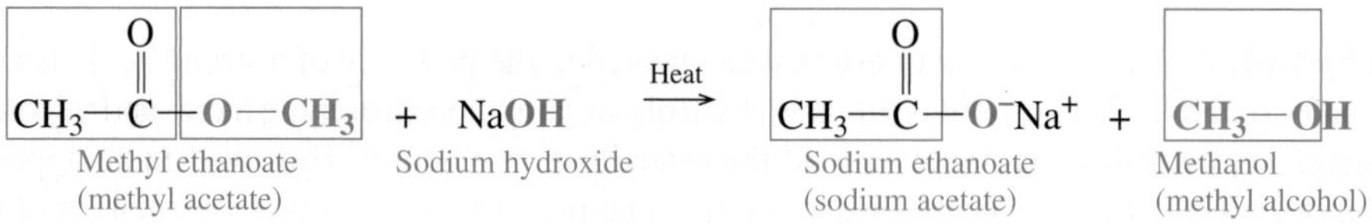

Methyl ethanoate   Sodium hydroxide   Sodium ethanoate   Methanol
(methyl acetate)   (sodium acetate)   (methyl alcohol)

CONCEPT CHECK 16.4

■ **Hydrolysis of Esters**

Ethyl methanoate has a fruity, lemon fragrance. Name the products of the following reactions of ethyl methanoate:

a. acid hydrolysis with HCl

b. saponification with KOH

ANSWER

a. The products of the acid hydrolysis of ethyl methanoate are the alcohol ethanol and a carboxylic acid methanoic acid.

b. The products of the base hydrolysis of ethyl methanoate with KOH are the alcohol ethanol and the carboxylic acid salt potassium methanoate.

SAMPLE PROBLEM 16.9

■ **Base Hydrolysis of Esters**

Ethyl acetate is a solvent widely used for fingernail polish, plastics, and lacquers. Write the equation of the hydrolysis of ethyl acetate by NaOH.

SOLUTION

The hydrolysis of ethyl acetate by NaOH gives the salt of acetic acid and ethyl alcohol:

$$CH_3-\overset{\overset{\displaystyle O}{\|}}{C}-O-CH_2-CH_3 \ + \ NaOH \ \xrightarrow{\text{Heat}} \ CH_3-\overset{\overset{\displaystyle O}{\|}}{C}-O^-Na^+ \ + \ HO-CH_2-CH_3$$

Ethyl ethanoate   Sodium ethanoate   Ethanol
(ethyl acetate)   (sodium acetate)   (ethyl alcohol)

STUDY CHECK

Draw the condensed structural formulas of the products from the hydrolysis of methyl benzoate by KOH.

ENVIRONMENTAL NOTE

Cleaning Action of Soaps

For many centuries, soaps were made by heating a mixture of animal fats (tallow) with lye, a basic solution obtained from wood ashes. In the soap-making process, fats, which are esters of long-chain carboxylic acids, undergo saponification with the strong base in lye.

Fatty acid

$$CH_3CH_2CH_2CH_2CH_2CH_2CH_2CH_2CH_2CH_2CH_2CH_2CH_2CH_2CH_2CH_2CH_2-\overset{\overset{\displaystyle O}{\|}}{C}-OH \ + \ NaOH \ \longrightarrow$$

Carboxylic acid salt ("soap")

$$CH_3CH_2CH_2CH_2CH_2CH_2CH_2CH_2CH_2CH_2CH_2CH_2CH_2CH_2CH_2CH_2CH_2-\overset{\overset{\displaystyle O}{\|}}{C}-O^-Na^+$$

Nonpolar tail   Polar head
(hydrophobic)   (hydrophilic)

Today soaps are also prepared from fats such as coconut oil. Perfumes are added to give a pleasant-smelling soap. Because a soap is the salt of a long-chain fatty acid, the two ends of a soap molecule have different polarities. The long carbon chain end is nonpolar and *hydrophobic* (water-fearing). It is soluble in nonpolar substances such as oil or grease, but it is not soluble in water. The carboxylate salt end is ionic and *hydrophilic* (water-loving). It is very soluble in water but not in oils or grease.

When soap is used to clean grease or oil, the nonpolar ends of the soap molecules dissolve in the nonpolar fats and oils that accompany dirt. The water-loving salt ends of the soap molecules extend outside where they can dissolve in water. The soap molecules coat the oil or grease, forming clusters called *micelles*. The ionic ends of the soap molecules provide polarity to the micelles, which makes them soluble in water. As a result, small globules of oil and fat coated with soap molecules are pulled into the water and rinsed away.

One of the problems of using soaps is that the carboxylate end reacts with ions in water such as Ca^{2+} and Mg^{2+} and forms insoluble substances.

$$2CH_3(CH_2)_{16}COO^- \ + \ Mg^{2+} \ \longrightarrow \ [CH_3(CH_2)_{16}COO^-]_2Mg^{2+}$$

Stearate ion   Magnesium   Magnesium stearate
               ion   (insoluble)

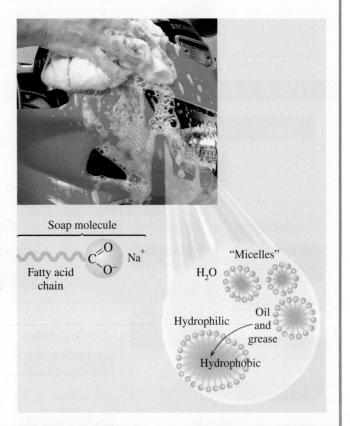

Soap molecule

Fatty acid chain $\overset{\displaystyle O}{C}\ O^-$ Na^+

"Micelles"

H_2O

Hydrophilic

Oil and grease

Hydrophobic

QUESTIONS AND PROBLEMS

Properties of Esters

16.35 For each of the following pairs of compounds, select the compound that has the higher boiling point:

a. $CH_3-\overset{\displaystyle O}{\overset{\|}{C}}-O-CH_3$ or $CH_3-\overset{\displaystyle O}{\overset{\|}{C}}-OH$

b. $CH_3-\overset{\displaystyle O}{\overset{\|}{C}}-O-CH_3$ or $CH_3-CH_2-CH_2-CH_2-OH$

c. $CH_3-CH_2-CH_2-CH_3$ or $CH_3-O-\overset{\displaystyle O}{\overset{\|}{C}}-CH_3$

16.36 For each of the following pairs of compounds, select the compound that has the higher boiling point:

a. $H-\overset{\displaystyle O}{\overset{\|}{C}}-O-CH_3$ or $CH_3-CH_2-CH_2-OH$

b. $CH_3-\overset{\displaystyle O}{\overset{\|}{C}}-O-CH_3$ or $CH_3-CH_2-\overset{\displaystyle O}{\overset{\|}{C}}-OH$

c. $CH_3-O-CH_2-CH_3$ or $CH_3-O-\overset{\displaystyle O}{\overset{\|}{C}}-H$

16.37 What are the products of the acid hydrolysis of an ester?

16.38 What are the products of the base hydrolysis of an ester?

16.39 Draw the condensed structural formulas of the products from the acid- or base-catalyzed hydrolysis of each of the following compounds:

a. $CH_3-CH_2-\overset{\displaystyle O}{\overset{\|}{C}}-O-CH_3 + NaOH \longrightarrow$

b. $CH_3-\overset{\displaystyle O}{\overset{\|}{C}}-O-CH_2-CH_2-CH_3 + H_2O \overset{H^+}{\rightleftharpoons}$

c. $CH_3-CH_2-CH_2-\overset{\displaystyle O}{\overset{\|}{C}}-O-CH_2-CH_3 + H_2O \overset{H^+}{\rightleftharpoons}$

d. $\langle \bigcirc \rangle-\overset{\displaystyle O}{\overset{\|}{C}}-O-CH_2-CH_3 + H_2O \overset{H^+}{\rightleftharpoons}$

e. $\langle \bigcirc \rangle-\overset{\displaystyle O}{\overset{\|}{C}}-O-CH_2-CH_3 + NaOH \longrightarrow$

16.40 Draw the condensed structural formulas of the products from the acid- or base-catalyzed hydrolysis of each of the following compounds:

a. $CH_3-CH_2-\overset{\displaystyle O}{\overset{\|}{C}}-O-CH_2-CH_2-CH_2-CH_3 + H_2O \overset{H^+}{\rightleftharpoons}$

b. $H-\overset{\displaystyle O}{\overset{\|}{C}}-O-CH_2-CH_3 + NaOH \longrightarrow$

c. $CH_3-CH_2-\overset{\displaystyle O}{\overset{\|}{C}}-O-CH_3 + H_2O \overset{H^+}{\rightleftharpoons}$

d. $CH_3-CH_2-\overset{\displaystyle O}{\overset{\|}{C}}-O-\langle \bigcirc \rangle + H_2O \overset{H^+}{\rightleftharpoons}$

e. $\langle \bigcirc \rangle-CH_2-\overset{\displaystyle O}{\overset{\|}{C}}-O-CH_2-CH_3 + NaOH \longrightarrow$

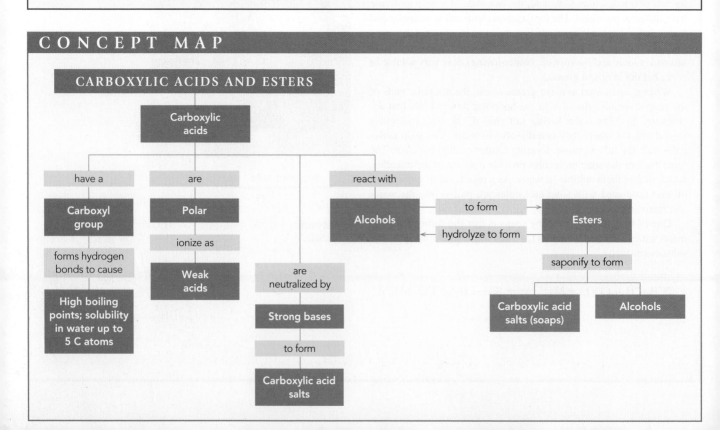

CONCEPT MAP

CARBOXYLIC ACIDS AND ESTERS

Carboxylic acids

- have a → **Carboxyl group** → forms hydrogen bonds to cause → **High boiling points; solubility in water up to 5 C atoms**
- are → **Polar** → ionize as → **Weak acids** → are neutralized by → **Strong bases** → to form → **Carboxylic acid salts**
- react with → **Alcohols** → to form → **Esters**
  - Esters → hydrolyze to form → Alcohols
  - Esters → saponify to form → **Carboxylic acid salts (soaps)** and **Alcohols**

CHAPTER REVIEW

16.1 Carboxylic Acids

LEARNING GOAL: *Give the common names, IUPAC names, and condensed structural formulas of carboxylic acids.*

A carboxylic acid contains the carboxyl functional group, which is a hydroxyl group connected to the carbonyl group.

16.2 Properties of Carboxylic Acids

LEARNING GOAL: *Describe the boiling points, solubility, and ionization of carboxylic acids in water.*

The carboxyl group contains polar bonds of O—H and C=O, which makes a carboxylic acid with one to four carbon atoms very soluble in water. As weak acids, carboxylic acids ionize slightly by donating a proton to water to form carboxylate and hydronium ions. Carboxylic acids are neutralized by base, producing the carboxylate salt and water.

16.3 Esters

LEARNING GOAL: *Name an ester; write equations for the formation and hydrolysis of an ester.*

In an ester, an alkyl or aromatic group has replaced the H of the hydroxyl group of a carboxylic acid. In the presence of a strong acid, a carboxylic acid reacts with an alcohol to produce an ester. A molecule of water is removed: —OH from the carboxylic acid, and —H from the alcohol molecule.

16.4 Naming Esters

LEARNING GOAL: *Write the IUPAC and common names for esters; draw condensed structural formulas.*

The names of esters consist of two words, one from the alcohol and the other from the carboxylic acid with the *ic acid* ending replaced by *ate*.

16.5 Properties of Esters

LEARNING GOAL: *Describe the boiling points and solubility of esters; draw the condensed structural formulas of the hydrolysis products.*

Esters undergo acid hydrolysis by adding water to yield the carboxylic acid and alcohol (or phenol). Base hydrolysis, or saponification, of an ester produces the carboxylate salt and an alcohol.

SUMMARY OF NAMING

Family	Condensed Structural Formula	IUPAC Name	Common Name
Carboxylic acid	CH_3—$\overset{\displaystyle O}{\overset{\|}{C}}$—OH	Ethanoic acid	Acetic acid
Carboxylic acid salt	CH_3—$\overset{\displaystyle O}{\overset{\|}{C}}$—$O^-Na^+$	Sodium ethanoate	Sodium acetate
Ester	CH_3—$\overset{\displaystyle O}{\overset{\|}{C}}$—O—$CH_3$	Methyl ethanoate	Methyl acetate

SUMMARY OF REACTIONS

IONIZATION OF A CARBOXYLIC ACID IN WATER

$$CH_3-\overset{\displaystyle O}{\overset{\|}{C}}-OH + H_2O \rightleftharpoons CH_3-\overset{\displaystyle O}{\overset{\|}{C}}-O^- + H_3O^+$$

Ethanoic acid (acetic acid)   Ethanoate ion (acetate ion)   Hydronium ion

NEUTRALIZATION OF A CARBOXYLIC ACID

$$CH_3-CH_2-\overset{\displaystyle O}{\overset{\|}{C}}-OH + NaOH \longrightarrow CH_3-CH_2-\overset{\displaystyle O}{\overset{\|}{C}}-O^-Na^+ + H_2O$$

Propanoic acid (propionic acid)   Sodium hydroxide   Sodium propanoate (sodium propionate)

ESTERIFICATION: CARBOXYLIC ACID AND AN ALCOHOL

$$CH_3-\overset{\displaystyle O}{\overset{\|}{C}}-OH + HO-CH_3 \overset{H^+}{\rightleftharpoons} CH_3-\overset{\displaystyle O}{\overset{\|}{C}}-O-CH_3 + H_2O$$

Ethanoic acid (acetic acid)   Methanol (methyl alcohol)   Methyl ethanoate (methyl acetate)

ACID HYDROLYSIS OF AN ESTER

$$CH_3-\overset{\overset{\displaystyle O}{\|}}{C}-O-CH_3 \;+\; H-OH \;\rightleftharpoons^{H^+}\; CH_3-\overset{\overset{\displaystyle O}{\|}}{C}-OH \;+\; H-O-CH_3$$

Methyl ethanoate (methyl acetate)   Ethanoic acid (acetic acid)   Methanol (methyl alcohol)

BASE HYDROLYSIS OF AN ESTER (SAPONIFICATION)

$$CH_3-CH_2-\overset{\overset{\displaystyle O}{\|}}{C}-O-CH_3 \;+\; NaOH \;\xrightarrow{\text{Heat}}\; CH_3-CH_2-\overset{\overset{\displaystyle O}{\|}}{C}-O^-Na^+ \;+\; H-O-CH_3$$

Methyl propanoate (methyl propionate)   Sodium hydroxide   Sodium propanoate (sodium propionate)   Methanol (methyl alcohol)

■ KEY TERMS

carboxyl group A functional group found in carboxylic acids composed of carbonyl and hydroxyl groups.

$$-\overset{\overset{\displaystyle O}{\|}}{C}-OH \qquad \text{Carboxyl group}$$

carboxylate ion The anion produced when a carboxylic acid donates a proton to water.

carboxylic acid An organic compound containing the carboxyl group.

carboxylic acid salt The product of neutralization of a carboxylic acid; a carboxylate ion and the metal ion from the base.

ester An organic compound in which an alkyl group replaces the hydrogen atom in a carboxylic acid.

esterification The formation of an ester from a carboxylic acid and an alcohol with the elimination of a molecule of water in the presence of an acid catalyst.

hydrolysis The splitting of a molecule by the addition of water. Esters hydrolyze to produce a carboxylic acid and an alcohol.

saponification The hydrolysis of an ester with a strong base to produce a salt of the carboxylic acid and an alcohol.

■ UNDERSTANDING THE CONCEPTS

16.41 Propyl acetate is the ester that gives the odor and flavor of pears.

a. What is the condensed structural formula of propyl acetate?
b. Write an equation for the formation of propyl acetate.
c. Write an equation for the acid hydrolysis of propyl acetate.
d. Write an equation for the base hydrolysis of propyl acetate with NaOH.
e. How many mL of 0.208 M NaOH are needed to completely hydrolyze (saponify) 1.58 g of propyl acetate?

16.42 Ethyl octanoate is a flavor component of mangos.

a. What is the condensed structural formula of ethyl octanoate?
b. Write an equation for the formation of ethyl octanoate.
c. Write an equation for the acid hydrolysis of ethyl octanoate.
d. Write an equation for the base hydrolysis of ethyl octanoate with NaOH.
e. How many mL of 0.315 M NaOH are needed to completely hydrolyze (saponify) 2.84 g of ethyl octanoate?

ADDITIONAL QUESTIONS AND PROBLEMS

*For instructor-assigned homework, go to **www.masteringchemistry.com**.*

16.43 Give the IUPAC and common names (if any) for each of the following compounds:

a. 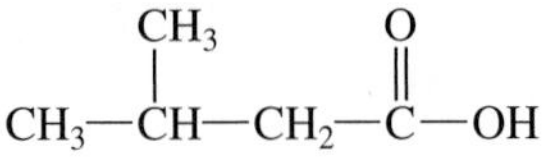 $CH_3-CH(CH_3)-CH_2-C(=O)-OH$

b. benzene ring $-C(=O)-O-CH_2-CH_3$

c. $CH_3-CH_2-O-C(=O)-CH_2-CH_3$

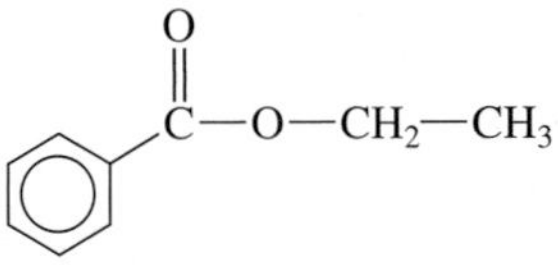

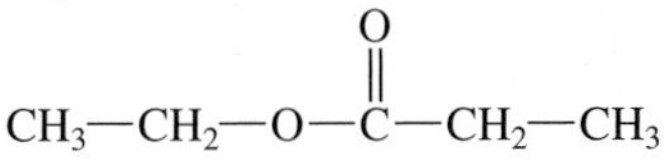

d. 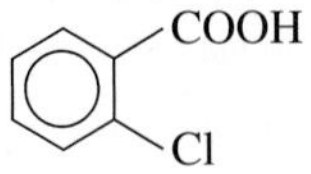 benzene ring with COOH and Cl

e. 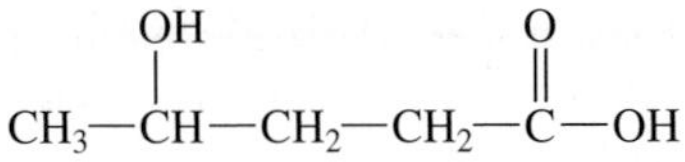 $CH_3-CH(OH)-CH_2-CH_2-C(=O)-OH$

f. 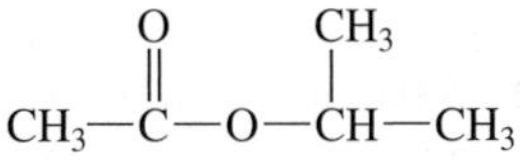 $CH_3-C(=O)-O-CH(CH_3)-CH_3$

16.44 Give the IUPAC and common names (if any) for each of the following compounds:

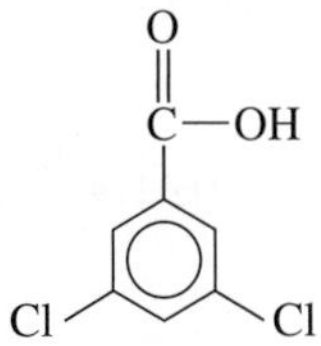

a. 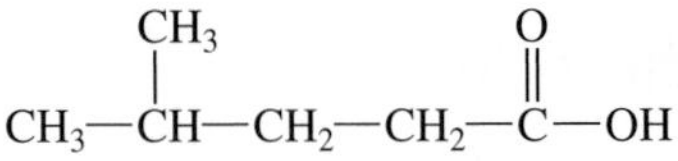 $CH_3-CH(CH_3)-CH_2-CH_2-C(=O)-OH$

b. benzene ring with $C(=O)-OH$ and two Cl

c. benzene ring $-C(=O)-O-CH_3$

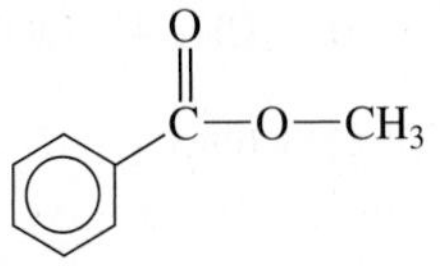

d. 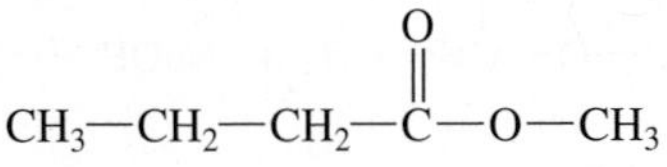 $CH_3-CH_2-CH_2-C(=O)-O-CH_3$

e. 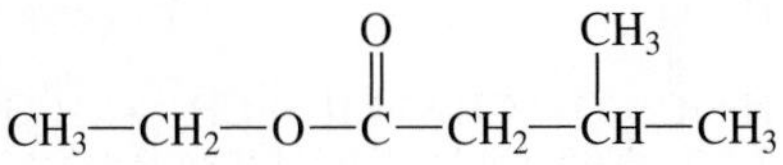 $CH_3-CH_2-O-C(=O)-CH_2-CH(CH_3)-CH_3$

f. 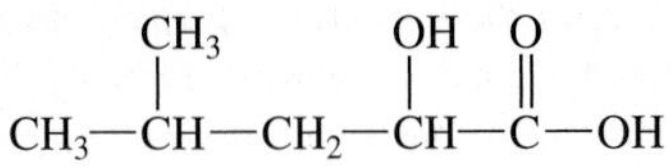 $CH_3-CH(CH_3)-CH_2-CH(OH)-C(=O)-OH$

16.45 Draw the condensed structural formulas of at least three carboxylic acids with the molecular formula $C_5H_{10}O_2$.

16.46 Draw the condensed structural formulas of at least three esters with the formula $C_4H_8O_2$.

16.47 Draw the condensed structural formula of each of the following:
a. methyl acetate
b. *p*-chlorobenzoic acid
c. β-chloropropionic acid

d. ethyl butanoate
e. 3-methylpentanoic acid
f. ethyl benzoate

16.48 Draw the condensed structural formula of each of the following:
a. α-bromobutyric acid
b. ethyl butyrate
c. 2-methyloctanoic acid
d. 3,5-dimethylhexanoic acid
e. propyl acetate
f. 3,4-dibromobenzoic acid

16.49 For each of the following pairs, identify the compound that would have the higher boiling point. Explain.

a. 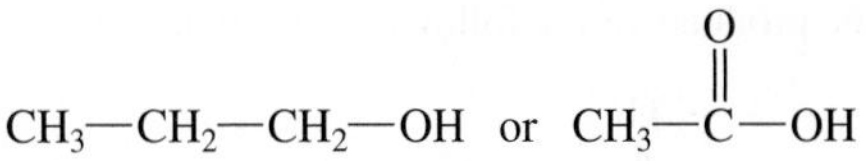 $CH_3-CH_2-CH_2-OH$ or $CH_3-C(=O)-OH$

b. $CH_3-CH_2-CH_2-CH_3$ or $CH_3-CH_2-C(=O)-OH$

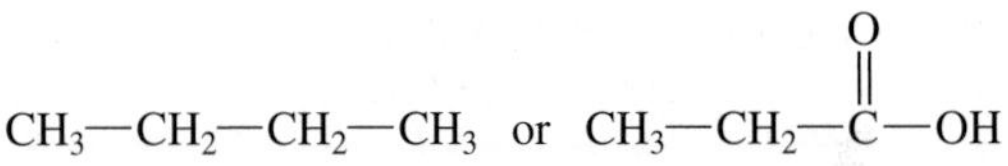

c. $CH_3-C(=O)-OH$ or $CH_3-CH_2-CH_2-C(=O)-OH$

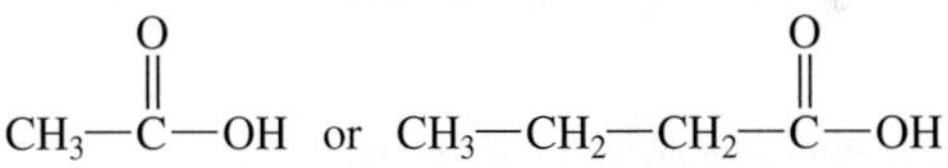

16.50 For each of the following pairs, identify the compound that would have the higher boiling point. Explain.

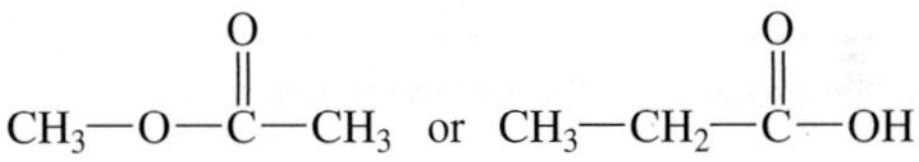

a. 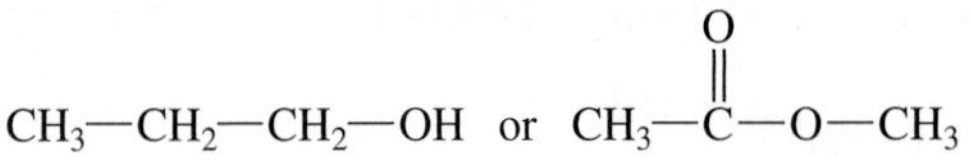 $CH_3-CH_2-CH_2-OH$ or $CH_3-C(=O)-O-CH_3$

b. $CH_3-O-C(=O)-CH_3$ or $CH_3-CH_2-C(=O)-OH$

c. $CH_3-C(=O)-O-CH_3$ or $CH_3-CH_2-CH_2-CH_3$

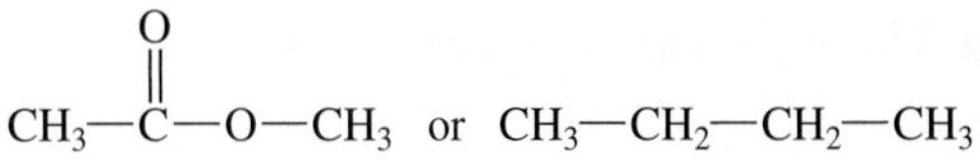

16.51 Why does acetic acid have a higher boiling point than either 1-propanol or methyl formate when they all have the same molar mass?

16.52 Propionic acid, 1-butanol, and butanal all have the same molar mass. The possible boiling points are 76 °C, 118 °C, and 141 °C. Match the compounds with the boiling points and explain your choice.

16.53 Which of the following compounds are soluble in water?

a. $CH_3-CH_2-CH_2-CH_2-CH_3$

b. 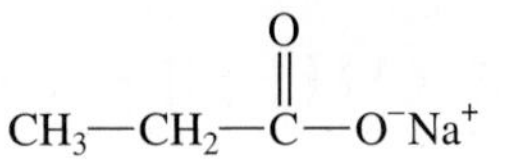 $CH_3-CH_2-C(=O)-O^-\,Na^+$

c. $CH_3-C(=O)-O-CH_3$

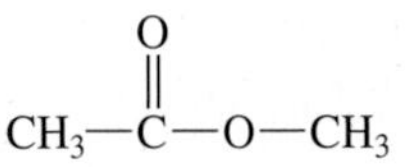

d. $CH_3-CH_2-CH_2-OH$

e. 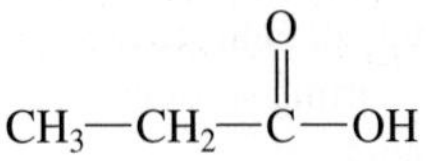 $CH_3-CH_2-C(=O)-OH$

16.54 Which of the following compounds are soluble in water?

a. $CH_3-CH_2-CH_2-\overset{\displaystyle O}{\overset{\|}{C}}-OH$

b. $CH_3-CH_2-\overset{\displaystyle O}{\overset{\|}{C}}-O-CH_2-CH_2-CH_3$

c. $CH_3-CH_2-CH_2-CH_3$

d. $CH_3-(CH_2)_8-CH_2-OH$

e. $CH_3-CH_2-CH_2-O-CH_2-CH_2-CH_3$

16.55 Draw the products of the following reactions:

a. $CH_3-CH_2-\overset{\displaystyle O}{\overset{\|}{C}}-OH + H_2O \rightleftharpoons$

b. $CH_3-CH_2-\overset{\displaystyle O}{\overset{\|}{C}}-OH + KOH \longrightarrow$

c. $CH_3-CH_2-\overset{\displaystyle O}{\overset{\|}{C}}-OH + CH_3-OH \overset{H^+}{\rightleftharpoons}$

d. 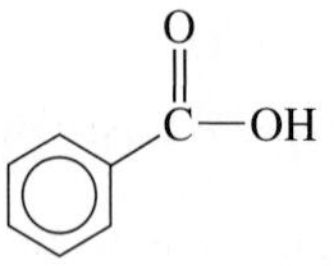 [benzene ring]$-\overset{\displaystyle O}{\overset{\|}{C}}-OH$ + $CH_3-CH_2-OH \overset{H^+}{\rightleftharpoons}$

16.56 Draw the products of the following reactions:

a. $CH_3-\overset{\displaystyle O}{\overset{\|}{C}}-OH + NaOH \longrightarrow$

b. $CH_3-\overset{\displaystyle O}{\overset{\|}{C}}-OH + H_2O \rightleftharpoons$

c. $CH_3-\overset{\displaystyle CH_3}{\underset{|}{CH}}-\overset{\displaystyle O}{\overset{\|}{C}}-OH + KOH \longrightarrow$

d. $CH_3-\overset{\displaystyle CH_3}{\underset{|}{CH}}-\overset{\displaystyle O}{\overset{\|}{C}}-OH + CH_3-OH \overset{H^+}{\rightleftharpoons}$

16.57 Give the IUPAC names of the carboxylic acid and alcohol needed to prepare each of the following esters:

a. $CH_3-\overset{\displaystyle CH_3}{\underset{|}{CH}}-CH_2-\overset{\displaystyle O}{\overset{\|}{C}}-O-CH_3$

b. 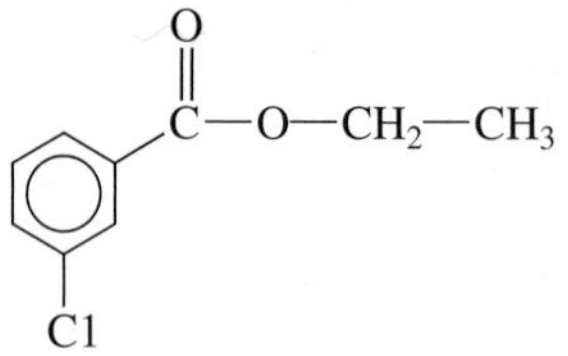 [benzene ring with Cl]$-\overset{\displaystyle O}{\overset{\|}{C}}-O-CH_2-CH_3$

c. $CH_3-(CH_2)_4-\overset{\displaystyle O}{\overset{\|}{C}}-O-CH_3$

16.58 Give the IUPAC names of the carboxylic acid and alcohol needed to prepare each of the following esters:

a. $CH_3-CH_2-CH_2-\overset{\displaystyle O}{\overset{\|}{C}}-O-CH_2-CH_3$

b. 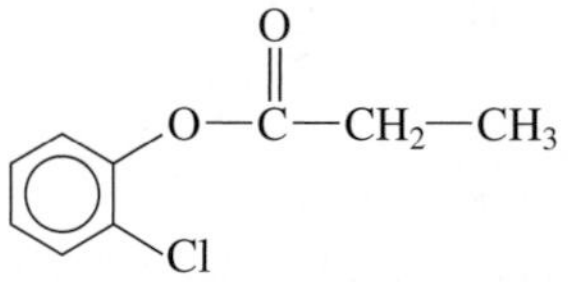 [benzene ring with Cl]$-O-\overset{\displaystyle O}{\overset{\|}{C}}-CH_2-CH_3$

c. $CH_3-\overset{\displaystyle CH_3}{\underset{|}{CH}}-\overset{\displaystyle CH_3}{\underset{|}{CH}}-\overset{\displaystyle O}{\overset{\|}{C}}-O-CH_3$

16.59 Draw the products of the following reactions:

a. $CH_3-CH_2-\overset{\displaystyle O}{\overset{\|}{C}}-O-\overset{\displaystyle CH_3}{\underset{|}{CH}}-CH_3 + H_2O \overset{H^+}{\rightleftharpoons}$

b. $CH_3-\overset{\displaystyle CH_3}{\underset{|}{CH}}-\overset{\displaystyle O}{\overset{\|}{C}}-O-CH_2-CH_2-CH_3 + NaOH \longrightarrow$

16.60 Draw the products of the following reactions:

a. $CH_3-CH_2-\overset{\displaystyle O}{\overset{\|}{C}}-O-\overset{\displaystyle CH_3}{\underset{|}{CH}}-CH_3 + NaOH \longrightarrow$

b. $CH_3-\overset{\displaystyle CH_3}{\underset{|}{CH}}-\overset{\displaystyle O}{\overset{\|}{C}}-O-CH_2-CH_2-CH_3 + H_2O \overset{H^+}{\rightleftharpoons}$

CHALLENGE QUESTIONS

16.61 Using the reactions we have studied, indicate how you might prepare the following from the starting substance given:
a. acetic acid from ethene
b. butyric acid from 1-butanol

16.62 Using the reactions we have studied, indicate how you might prepare the following from the starting substance given:
a. pentanoic acid from 1-pentanol
b. ethyl acetate from two molecules of ethanol

16.63 Methyl benzoate is not soluble in water; however, when it is heated with KOH, the ester forms soluble products. Write an equation for the reaction and explain what happens. When HCl is added to the product in solution, a white solid forms. What is the solid?

16.64 Hexanoic acid is not soluble in water. However, when hexanoic acid is added to a NaOH solution, a soluble product forms. Explain.

16.65 Salicylic acid could be named *o*-hydroxybenzoic acid.
   a. What two reactive functional groups are present?
   b. Draw the condensed structural formula of the ester product that forms when the hydroxyl group of salicylic acid reacts with acetic acid.

   c. Draw the condensed structural formula of methyl salicylate, oil of wintergreen, formed when salicylic acid forms an ester with methyl alcohol.

16.66 What volume (mL) of 0.100 M NaOH is needed to neutralize 3.00 g of benzoic acid?

ANSWERS

ANSWERS TO STUDY CHECKS

16.1

16.2 $CH_3-CH_2-CH_2-\overset{O}{\underset{\|}{C}}-OH$

16.3 Two methanoic acid molecules form a dimer, which gives an effective molar mass that is double that of the single acid molecule. Thus, a higher boiling point is required than for ethanol.

16.4 $H-\overset{O}{\underset{\|}{C}}-OH + H_2O \rightleftharpoons H-\overset{O}{\underset{\|}{C}}-O^- + H_3O^+$

16.5 butanoic acid, butyric acid

16.6 propanoic (propionic) acid and 1-pentanol

16.7
$CH_3-CH_2-CH_2-CH_2-CH_2-CH_2-\overset{O}{\underset{\|}{C}}-O-CH_2-CH_3$

16.8 propanoic (propionic) acid and ethanol

16.9
$+ CH_3-OH$

ANSWERS TO SELECTED QUESTIONS AND PROBLEMS

16.1 methanoic acid (formic acid)

16.3 Each compound contains three carbon atoms. They differ because propanal, an aldehyde, contains a carbonyl group bonded to a hydrogen. In propanoic acid, the carbonyl group connects to a hydroxyl group forming a carboxyl group.

16.5 **a.** ethanoic acid (acetic acid)
   b. butanoic acid (butyric acid)
   c. 2-chloropropanoic acid (α-chloropropionic acid)
   d. 3-methylhexanoic acid
   e. 3,4-dihydroxybenzoic acid
   f. 4-bromopentanoic acid

16.7
a. $CH_3-CH_2-\overset{O}{\underset{\|}{C}}-OH$ **b.**

c. $Cl-CH_2-\overset{O}{\underset{\|}{C}}-OH$

d. $HO-CH_2-CH_2-\overset{O}{\underset{\|}{C}}-OH$

e. $CH_3-CH_2-\underset{\underset{CH_3}{|}}{CH}-\overset{O}{\underset{\|}{C}}-OH$

f. $CH_3-CH_2-\underset{\underset{Br}{|}}{CH}-CH_2-\underset{\underset{Br}{|}}{CH}-CH_2-\overset{O}{\underset{\|}{C}}-OH$

16.9 **a.** $H-\overset{O}{\underset{\|}{C}}-OH$ **b.** $CH_3-\overset{O}{\underset{\|}{C}}-OH$

c. $CH_3-\underset{\underset{CH_3}{|}}{CH}-CH_2-\overset{O}{\underset{\|}{C}}-OH$

d.

16.11 a. Butanoic acid has a higher molar mass and would have a higher boiling point.
   b. Propanoic acid can form more hydrogen bonds and would have a higher boiling point.
   c. Butanoic acid can form hydrogen bonds and would have a higher boiling point.

16.13 a. Propanoic acid has the smaller alkyl group, which makes it more soluble.
   b. Propanoic acid forms more hydrogen bonds.

16.15 a. $H-\overset{O}{\underset{\|}{C}}-OH + H_2O \rightleftharpoons H-\overset{O}{\underset{\|}{C}}-O^- + H_3O^+$

   b. $CH_3-CH_2-\overset{O}{\underset{\|}{C}}-OH + H_2O \rightleftharpoons$
$CH_3-CH_2-\overset{O}{\underset{\|}{C}}-O^- + H_3O^+$

   c. $CH_3-\overset{O}{\underset{\|}{C}}-OH + H_2O \rightleftharpoons CH_3-\overset{O}{\underset{\|}{C}}-O^- + H_3O^+$

16.17 a. $H-\overset{O}{\underset{\|}{C}}-OH + NaOH \longrightarrow H-\overset{O}{\underset{\|}{C}}-O^-Na^+ + H_2O$

b. $CH_3-CH_2-\overset{\overset{\displaystyle O}{\|}}{C}-OH + NaOH \longrightarrow$

$$CH_3-CH_2-\overset{\overset{\displaystyle O}{\|}}{C}-O^-Na^+ + H_2O$$

c. $+ NaOH \longrightarrow$ $+ H_2O$

16.19 a. sodium methanoate, sodium formate
  b. sodium propanoate, sodium propionate
  c. sodium benzoate

16.21 a. aldehyde
  b. ester
  c. ketone
  d. carboxylic acid

16.23 a. $CH_3-\overset{\overset{\displaystyle O}{\|}}{C}-O-CH_3$

  b. $CH_3-CH_2-CH_2-\overset{\overset{\displaystyle O}{\|}}{C}-O-CH_3$

  c. $\overset{\overset{\displaystyle O}{\|}}{C}-O-CH_3$ (benzene ring)

16.25 a. $CH_3-CH_2-\overset{\overset{\displaystyle O}{\|}}{C}-O-CH_2-CH_2-CH_3$

  b. $CH_3-CH_2-CH_2-CH_2-\overset{\overset{\displaystyle O}{\|}}{C}-O-\overset{\overset{\displaystyle CH_3}{|}}{CH}-CH_3$

16.27 a. methanoic acid (formic acid) and methanol (methyl alcohol)
  b. ethanoic acid (acetic acid) and methanol (methyl alcohol)
  c. butanoic acid (butyric acid) and methanol (methyl alcohol)
  d. 3-methylbutanoic acid (β-methylbutyric acid) and ethanol (ethyl alcohol)

16.29 a. methyl methanoate (methyl formate)
  b. methyl ethanoate (methyl acetate)
  c. methyl butanoate (methyl butyrate)
  d. ethyl 3-methylbutanoate (ethyl β-methyl butyrate)

16.31

  a. $CH_3-\overset{\overset{\displaystyle O}{\|}}{C}-O-CH_3$

  b. $H-\overset{\overset{\displaystyle O}{\|}}{C}-O-CH_2-CH_2-CH_2-CH_3$

  c. $CH_3-CH_2-CH_2-CH_2-\overset{\overset{\displaystyle O}{\|}}{C}-O-CH_2-CH_3$

  d. $CH_3-CH_2-\overset{\overset{\displaystyle O}{\|}}{C}-O-CH_2-\overset{\overset{\displaystyle Br}{|}}{CH}-CH_3$

16.33 a. pentyl ethanoate (pentyl acetate)
  b. octyl ethanoate (octyl acetate)
  c. pentyl butanoate (pentyl butyrate)

16.35

  a. $CH_3-\overset{\overset{\displaystyle O}{\|}}{C}-OH$

  b. $CH_3-CH_2-CH_2-CH_2-OH$

  c. $CH_3-O-\overset{\overset{\displaystyle O}{\|}}{C}-CH_3$

16.37 The products of the acid hydrolysis of an ester are an alcohol and a carboxylic acid.

16.39 a. $CH_3-CH_2-\overset{\overset{\displaystyle O}{\|}}{C}-O^-Na^+$ and CH_3-OH

  b. $CH_3-\overset{\overset{\displaystyle O}{\|}}{C}-OH$ and $CH_3-CH_2-CH_2-OH$

  c. $CH_3-CH_2-CH_2-\overset{\overset{\displaystyle O}{\|}}{C}-OH$ and CH_3-CH_2-OH

  d. $\overset{\overset{\displaystyle O}{\|}}{C}-OH$ and CH_3-CH_2-OH (benzene ring)

  e. $\overset{\overset{\displaystyle O}{\|}}{C}-O^-Na^+$ and CH_3-CH_2-OH (benzene ring)

16.41 a. $CH_3-CH_2-CH_2-O-\overset{\overset{\displaystyle O}{\|}}{C}-CH_3$

  b. $CH_3-CH_2-CH_2-OH + HO-\overset{\overset{\displaystyle O}{\|}}{C}-CH_3 \xrightarrow[\;]{H^+, heat}$
  $CH_3-CH_2-CH_2-O-\overset{\overset{\displaystyle O}{\|}}{C}-CH_3 + H_2O$

  c. $CH_3-CH_2-CH_2-O-\overset{\overset{\displaystyle O}{\|}}{C}-CH_3 + H_2O \xrightleftharpoons[\;]{H^+}$
  $CH_3-CH_2-CH_2-OH + HO-\overset{\overset{\displaystyle O}{\|}}{C}-CH_3$

  d. $CH_3-CH_2-CH_2-O-\overset{\overset{\displaystyle O}{\|}}{C}-CH_3 + NaOH \xrightarrow{Heat}$
  $CH_3-CH_2-CH_2-OH + Na^+\ {}^-O-\overset{\overset{\displaystyle O}{\|}}{C}-CH_3$

  e. 74.5 mL of 0.208 M NaOH

16.43 a. 3-methylbutanoic acid, β-methylbutyric acid
  b. ethyl benzoate
  c. ethyl propanoate, ethyl propionate
  d. 2-chlorobenzoic acid, *ortho*-chlorobenzoic acid
  e. 4-hydroxypentanoic acid
  f. 2-propyl ethanoate, isopropyl acetate

16.45

$CH_3-CH_2-CH_2-CH_2-\overset{\overset{\displaystyle O}{\|}}{C}-OH$ $CH_3-CH_2-\overset{\overset{\displaystyle CH_3}{|}}{CH}-\overset{\overset{\displaystyle O}{\|}}{C}-OH$

$CH_3-\overset{\overset{\displaystyle CH_3}{|}}{CH}-CH_2-\overset{\overset{\displaystyle O}{\|}}{C}-OH$ $CH_3-\overset{\overset{\displaystyle CH_3}{|}}{\underset{\underset{\displaystyle CH_3}{|}}{C}}-\overset{\overset{\displaystyle O}{\|}}{C}-OH$

16.47 a. $CH_3-O-\overset{\overset{\displaystyle O}{\|}}{C}-CH_3$ **b.** (benzene ring with COOH at top and Cl at bottom)

c. $Cl-CH_2-CH_2-\overset{\overset{\displaystyle O}{\|}}{C}-OH$

d. $CH_3-CH_2-O-\overset{\overset{\displaystyle O}{\|}}{C}-CH_2-CH_2-CH_3$

e. $CH_3-CH_2-\overset{\overset{\displaystyle CH_3}{|}}{CH}-CH_2-\overset{\overset{\displaystyle O}{\|}}{C}-OH$

f. (benzene ring with $\overset{\overset{\displaystyle O}{\|}}{C}-O-CH_2-CH_3$)

16.49 a. Ethanoic acid has a higher boiling point than 1-propanol because two molecules of ethanoic acid hydrogen bond to form a dimer, which effectively doubles the molar mass and requires a higher temperature to reach the boiling point.
b. Propanoic acid forms hydrogen bonds, but butane does not.
c. Butanoic acid has a higher molar mass than ethanoic acid and requires a higher temperature to reach the boiling point.

16.51 The presence of two polar groups in the carboxyl group allows hydrogen bonding and the formation of a dimer that doubles the effective molar mass.

16.53 b, c, d, and **e** are all soluble in water

16.55 a. $CH_3-CH_2-\overset{\overset{\displaystyle O}{\|}}{C}-O^- + H_3O^+$

b. $CH_3-CH_2-\overset{\overset{\displaystyle O}{\|}}{C}-O^-K^+ + H_2O$

c. $CH_3-CH_2-\overset{\overset{\displaystyle O}{\|}}{C}-O-CH_3 + H_2O$

d. (benzene ring with $\overset{\overset{\displaystyle O}{\|}}{C}-O-CH_2-CH_3$) $+ H_2O$

16.57 a. 3-methylbutanoic acid and methanol
b. 3-chlorobenzoic acid and ethanol
c. hexanoic acid and methanol

16.59 a. $CH_3-CH_2-\overset{\overset{\displaystyle O}{\|}}{C}-OH$ and $HO-\overset{\overset{\displaystyle CH_3}{|}}{CH}-CH_3$

b. $CH_3-\overset{\overset{\displaystyle CH_3}{|}}{CH}-\overset{\overset{\displaystyle O}{\|}}{C}-O^-Na^+$ and $HO-CH_2-CH_2-CH_3$

16.61

a. $CH_2=CH_2 + H_2O \xrightarrow{H^+} CH_3-CH_2-OH \xrightarrow{[O]} CH_3-\overset{\overset{\displaystyle O}{\|}}{C}-OH$

b. $CH_3-CH_2-CH_2-CH_2-OH \xrightarrow{[O]} CH_3-CH_2-CH_2-\overset{\overset{\displaystyle O}{\|}}{C}-OH$

16.63 (benzene ring with $\overset{\overset{\displaystyle O}{\|}}{C}-O-CH_3$) $+ KOH \longrightarrow$

(benzene ring with $\overset{\overset{\displaystyle O}{\|}}{C}-O^-K^+$) $+ CH_3-OH$

In KOH solution, the ester undergoes saponification to form soluble salt of potassium benzoate. When acid is added to the soluble salt potassium benzoate, it is converted to insoluble benzoic acid.

16.65 a. phenol and carboxylic acid

b. (benzene ring with $O-\overset{\overset{\displaystyle O}{\|}}{C}-CH_3$ and $\overset{\underset{\displaystyle O}{\|}}{C}-OH$)

c. (benzene ring with OH and $\overset{\underset{\displaystyle O}{\|}}{C}-O-CH_3$)

17 Lipids

"In our toxicology lab, we measure the drugs in samples of urine or blood," says Penny Peng, assistant supervisor of chemistry, toxicology lab, Santa Clara Valley Medical Center. "But first we extract the drugs from the fluid and concentrate them so they can be detected in the machine we use. We extract the drugs by using different organic solvents such as methanol, ethyl acetate, or methylene chloride, and by changing the pH. We evaporate most of the organic solvent to concentrate any drugs it may contain. A small sample of the concentrate is placed into a machine called a gas chromatograph. As the gas moves over a column, the drugs in it are separated. From the results, we can identify as many as 10 to 15 different drugs from one urine sample."

Mastering CHEMISTRY™

Visit **www.masteringchemistry.com** for self-study materials and instructor-assigned homework.

When we talk of fats and oils, waxes, steroids, cholesterol, and fat-soluble vitamins, we are discussing lipids. Lipids are naturally occurring compounds that vary considerably in structure but share a common feature of being soluble in nonpolar solvents but not in water. Fats, which are one family of lipids, have many functions in the body, such as storing energy and protecting and insulating internal organs. Other types of lipids are found in nerve fibers and in hormones, which act as chemical messengers. Lipids are components of cell membranes. Because they are not soluble in water, they function to separate the internal contents of cells from the external environment.

Many people are concerned about the amounts of saturated fats and cholesterol in our diets. Researchers suggest that saturated fats and cholesterol are associated with diseases such as diabetes; cancers of the breast, pancreas, and colon; and atherosclerosis, a condition in which deposits of lipid materials (plaques) accumulate in the coronary blood vessels. In atherosclerosis, plaques restrict the flow of blood to the tissue, causing necrosis (death) of the tissue. In the heart, plaque accumulation could result in a *myocardial infarction* (heart attack).

The American Institute for Cancer Research (AICR) has recommended that our diet contain more fiber and starch by adding more vegetables, fruits, and whole grains and moderate amounts of foods with low levels of fat and cholesterol such as fish, poultry, lean meats, and low-fat dairy products. AICR also suggests that we limit our intake of foods high in fat and cholesterol such as eggs, nuts, french fries, fatty or organ meats, cheeses, butter, and coconut and palm oil.

17.1 Lipids

Lipids are a family of biomolecules that have the common property of being soluble in organic solvents but not in water. The word "lipid" comes from the Greek word *lipos*, meaning "fat" or "lard." Typically, the lipid content of a cell can be extracted using a nonpolar solvent such as ether or chloroform. Lipids are an important feature in cell membranes, fat-soluble vitamins, and steroid hormones.

LEARNING GOAL
Describe the classes of lipids.

Types of Lipids

Within the lipid family, there are specific structures that distinguish the different types of lipids. Lipids such as waxes, fats, oils, and glycerophospholipids are esters that can be hydrolyzed to give fatty acids along with other products, including an alcohol. Sphingolipids contain an alcohol called sphingosine, and glycosphingolipids contain a carbohydrate as well. Steroids do not contain fatty acids but are characterized by the steroid nucleus of four fused carbon rings. Steroids cannot be hydrolyzed. Figure 17.1 illustrates the types and general structures of lipids we will discuss in this chapter.

TUTORIAL
Classes of Lipids

SAMPLE PROBLEM 17.1

■ Classes of Lipids

What type of lipid does not contain fatty acids?

SOLUTION

The steroids are a group of lipids with no fatty acids.

STUDY CHECK

What type of lipid contains a carbohydrate?

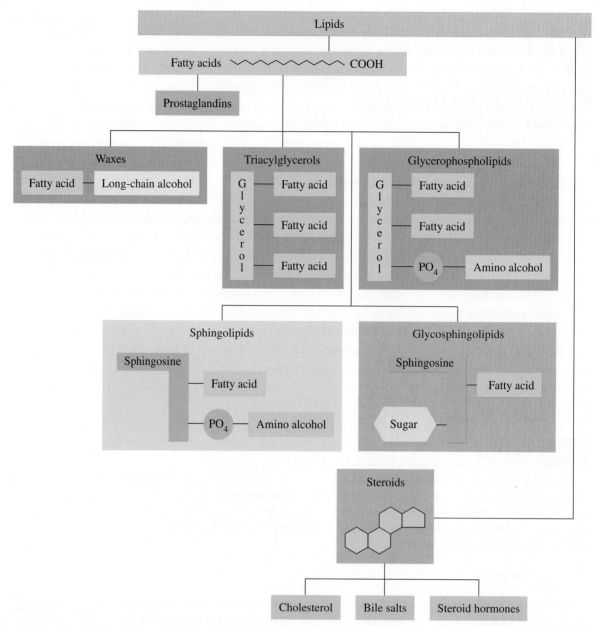

FIGURE 17.1 Structures for some classes of lipids that are naturally occurring compounds in cells and tissues.
Q What property do waxes, triacylglycerols, and steroids have in common?

QUESTIONS AND PROBLEMS

Lipids

17.1 What are some functions of lipids in the body?

17.2 What are some of the different kinds of lipids?

17.3 Lipids are not soluble in water. Are lipids polar or nonpolar molecules?

17.4 Which of the following solvents might be used to dissolve an oil stain?
a. water   **b.** CCl_4
c. diethyl ether   **d.** benzene
e. NaCl solution

17.2 Fatty Acids

LEARNING GOAL

Draw the condensed structural formula of a fatty acid and identify it as saturated or unsaturated.

The fatty acids are the simplest type of lipids and are found as components in more complex lipids. A **fatty acid** contains a long unbranched carbon chain attached to a carboxylic acid group at one end. Although the carboxylic acid part is hydrophilic, the long hydrophobic carbon chain makes long-chain fatty acids insoluble in water. Most naturally occurring fatty acids have an even number of carbon atoms, usually between 10 and 20. An example of a fatty acid is lauric acid, a 12-carbon acid found in coconut oil. In a simplified structure of a fatty acid called a line-bond formula, the carbon chain is written as a zigzag line that indicates the bonds between carbon atoms. In a zigzag line representation of a fatty acid, the ends and bends of the zigzag line are the carbon atoms. The structural formula of lauric acid can be written in several forms as follows:

Writing Formulas for Lauric Acid

Condensed structural formula

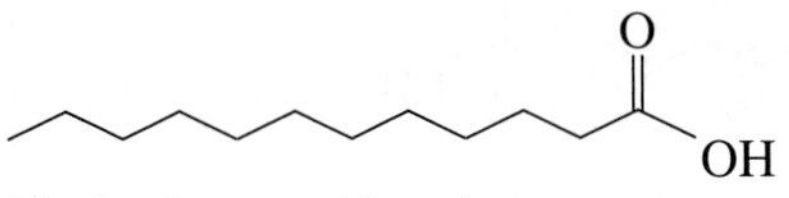

Line-bond structural formula

A **saturated fatty acid** contains only single carbon–carbon bonds, which makes the properties of a long-chain fatty acid similar to those of an alkane. In a **monounsaturated fatty acid**, the long carbon chain has one double bond, which makes its properties similar to those of an alkene. A **polyunsaturated fatty acid** has at least two carbon–carbon double bonds. Table 17.1 lists some of the typical fatty acids in lipids.

Cis and Trans Isomers of Unsaturated Fatty Acids

Unsaturated fatty acids can be written as cis and trans isomers in the same way as the cis and trans alkene structures we looked at in Chapter 12. For example, oleic acid, a monounsaturated fatty acid found in olives and corn, has one double bond at carbon 9. We can show its cis and trans structural formulas using the line-bond notation. The cis structure is the most prevalent isomer found in naturally occurring unsaturated fatty acids. In the cis isomer, the carbon chain has a "kink" at the double bond site. As we will see, the cis bond has a major impact on the properties of unsaturated fatty acids.

cis-Oleic acid
cis double bond

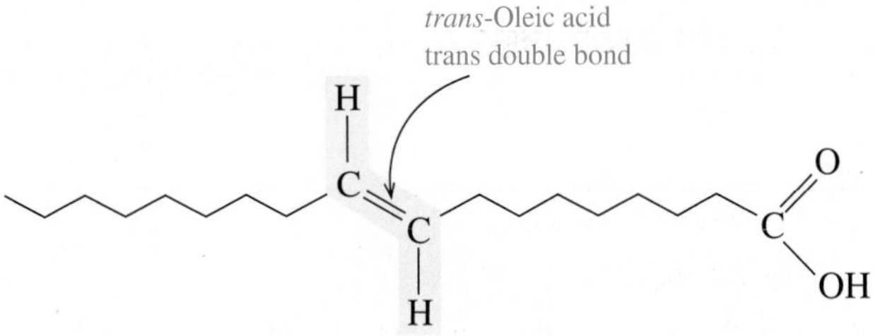

trans-Oleic acid
trans double bond

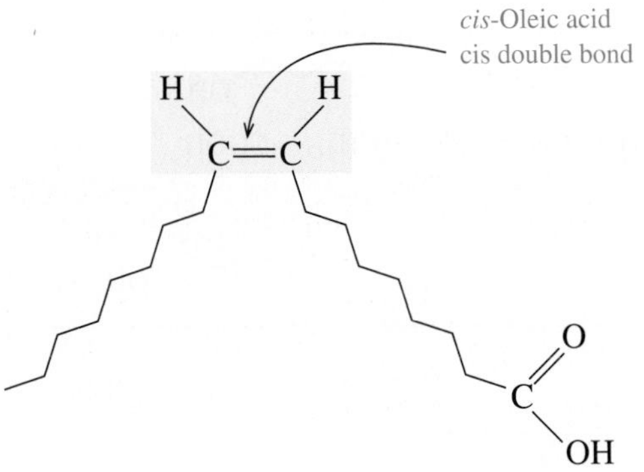

The human body is capable of synthesizing most fatty acids from carbohydrates or other fatty acids. However, humans do not synthesize sufficient amounts of polyunsaturated fatty acids, such as linoleic acid, linolenic acid, and arachidonic acid. Because these fatty acids must be obtained from the diet, they are known as *essential fatty acids*. In infants, a deficiency of essential fatty acids can cause skin dermatitis. However, the role of fatty acids in adult nutrition is not well understood. Adults do not usually have a deficiency of essential fatty acids.

TABLE 17.1   Structures and Melting Points of Common Fatty Acids

Name	Carbon Atoms	Source	Melting Point (°C)	Structures
Saturated Fatty Acids				
Lauric acid	12	Coconut	43	CH_3—$(CH_2)_{10}$—COOH 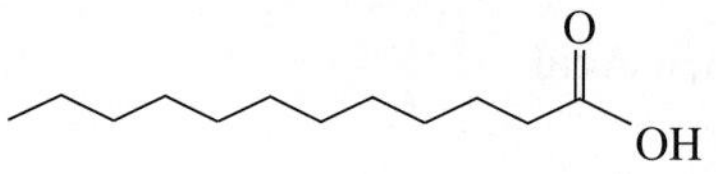
Myristic acid	14	Nutmeg	54	CH_3—$(CH_2)_{12}$—COOH 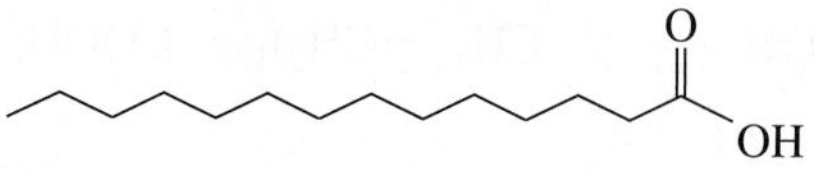
Palmitic acid	16	Palm	62	CH_3—$(CH_2)_{14}$—COOH 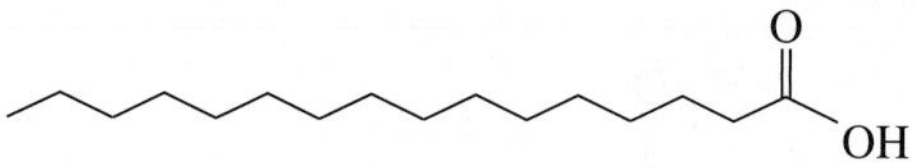
Stearic acid	18	Animal fat	69	CH_3—$(CH_2)_{16}$—COOH 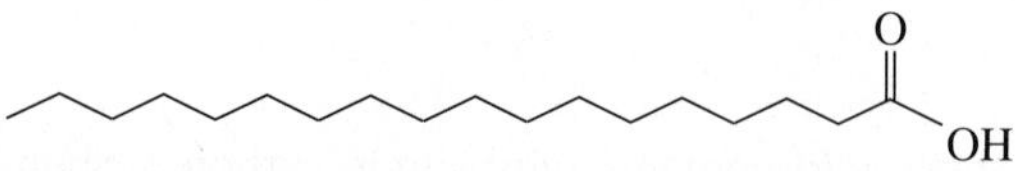
Monounsaturated Fatty Acids				
Palmitoleic acid	16	Butter	0	CH_3—$(CH_2)_5$—CH=CH—$(CH_2)_7$—COOH 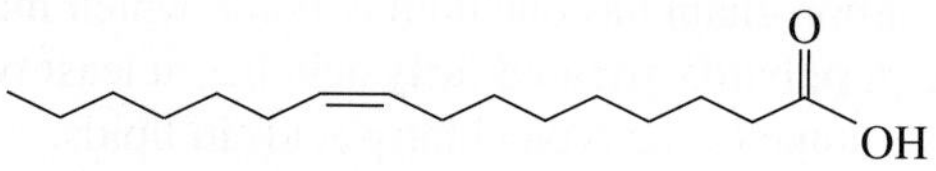
Oleic acid	18	Olives, corn	13	CH_3—$(CH_2)_7$—CH=CH—$(CH_2)_7$—COOH 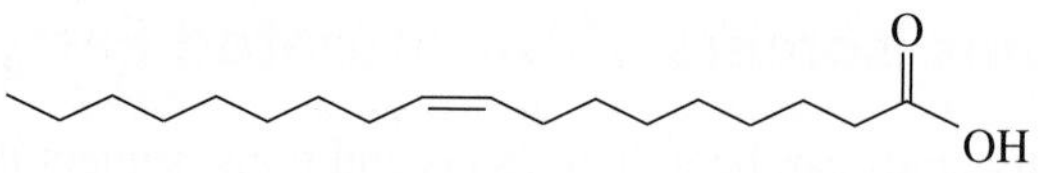
Polyunsaturated Fatty Acids				
Linoleic acid	18	Soybeans, sunflowers	−9	CH_3—$(CH_2)_4$—CH=CH—CH_2—CH=CH—$(CH_2)_7$—COOH 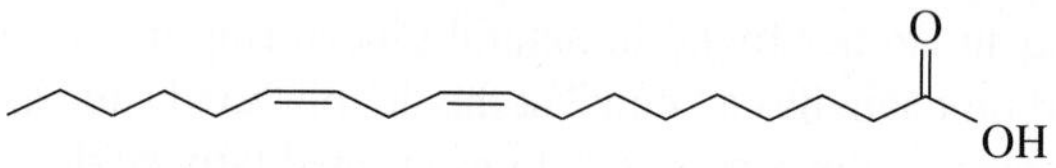
Linolenic acid	18	Corn	−17	CH_3—$(CH_2$—CH=CH$)_3$—$(CH_2)_7$—COOH 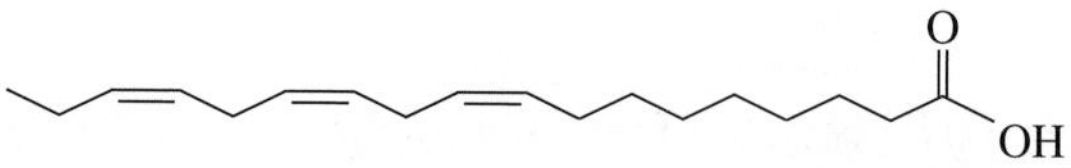
Arachidonic acid	20	Meat, eggs, fish	−50	CH_3—$(CH_2)_3$—$(CH_2$—CH=CH$)_4$—$(CH_2)_3$—COOH 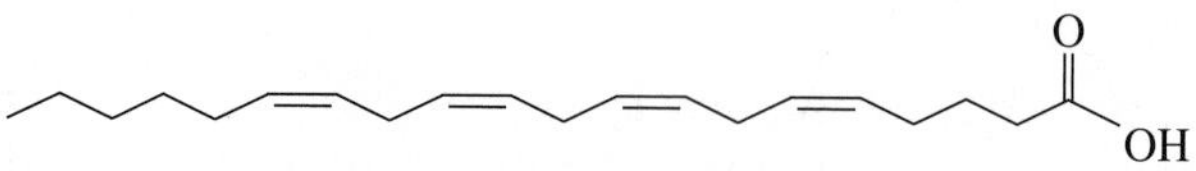

Properties of Fatty Acids

Saturated fatty acids fit close together in a regular pattern, which allows strong attractions to occur between the carbon chains. As a result, a significant amount of energy and high temperatures are required to separate the fatty acids and melt the fat. As the length of the carbon chain increases, more interactions occur between the carbon chains, which results in higher melting points. Saturated fatty acids are usually solids at room temperature.

In unsaturated fatty acids, the cis double bonds cause the carbon chain to bend or "kink," which gives the molecules an irregular shape. As a result, fewer interactions occur

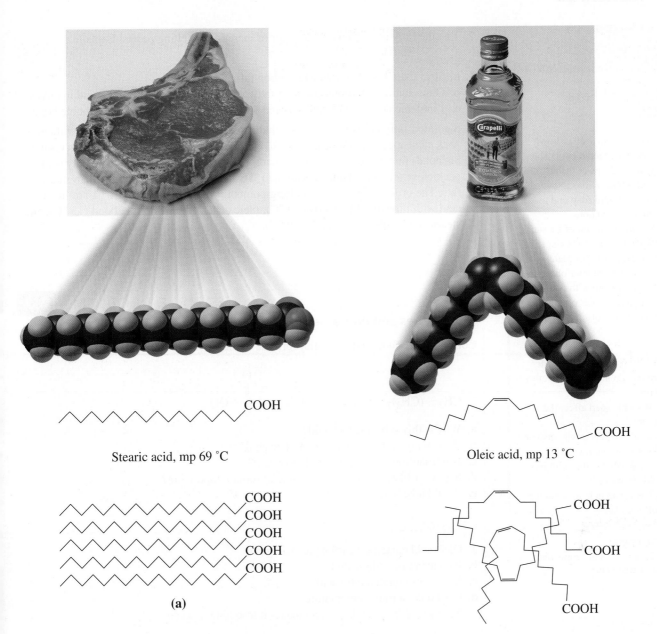

FIGURE 17.2 **(a)** In saturated fatty acids, the molecules fit closely together to give high melting points. **(b)** In unsaturated fatty acids, molecules cannot pack closely together, resulting in lower melting points.

Q Why does the cis double bond affect the melting points of unsaturated fatty acids?

between carbon chains. Consequently, less energy is required to separate the molecules, which makes the melting points of unsaturated fats lower than those of saturated fats. (See Figure 17.2.) Most unsaturated fats are liquid oils at room temperature.

We might think of saturated fatty acids as potato chips with matching shapes that stack close together in a container. Similarly, irregularly shaped chips would be like unsaturated fatty acids that do not pack close together.

CONCEPT CHECK 17.1

■ Fatty Acids

1. Using Table 17.1, identify the following:
   a. an 18-carbon fatty acid that is saturated
   b. a monounsaturated fatty acid found in olives
   c. an 18-carbon fatty acid with three double bonds

EXPLORE YOUR WORLD

Solubility of Fats and Oils

Place some water in a small bowl. Add a drop of a vegetable oil. Then add a few more drops of the oil. Record your observations. Now add a few drops of liquid soap and mix. Record your observations.

Place a small amount of fat such as margarine, butter, shortening, or vegetable oil on a dish or plate. Run water over it. Record your observations. Mix some soap with the fat substance and run water over it again. Record your observations.

QUESTIONS

1. Do the drops of oil in the water separate or do they come together? Explain.
2. How does the soap affect the oil layer?
3. Why don't the fats on the dish or plate wash off with water?
4. In general, what is the solubility of lipids in water?
5. Why does soap help to wash the fats off the plate?

TUTORIAL
Structures and Properties of Fatty Acids

---

2. List the fatty acids in part 1 in order of increasing melting points. Explain.

ANSWER

1. a. Stearic acid is a saturated 18-carbon fatty acid.
   b. Oleic acid is a monounsaturated fatty acid with one double bond found in olives.
   c. Linolenic acid is a polyunsaturated 18-carbon fatty acid with three double bonds.

2. Saturated fatty acids have carbon chains with only single bonds that allow them to pack close together and form molecular attractions. Unsaturated fats contain cis double bonds that place a "kink" in the carbon chain that does not allow the fatty acids to pack close together. Thus, unsaturated fats have lower melting points than saturated fats. The order of increasing melting points for the fatty acids in part 1 are linolenic acid with three double bonds (-9 °C), oleic acid with one double bond (13 °C), and stearic acid with single bonds (69 °C).

SAMPLE PROBLEM   17.2

■ Structures and Properties of Fatty Acids

Consider the condensed structural formula of oleic acid:

$$CH_3-(CH_2)_7-CH=CH-(CH_2)_7-\overset{\overset{\displaystyle O}{\|}}{C}-OH$$

a. Why is this substance an acid?
b. How many carbon atoms are in oleic acid?
c. Is it a saturated or unsaturated fatty acid?
d. Is it most likely to be solid or liquid at room temperature?
e. Would it be soluble in water?

SOLUTION

a. Oleic acid contains a carboxylic acid group.
b. It contains 18 carbon atoms.
c. It is an unsaturated fatty acid.
d. It is liquid at room temperature.
e. No, its long hydrocarbon chain makes it insoluble in water.

STUDY CHECK

Palmitoleic acid is a fatty acid with the following formula:

$$CH_3-(CH_2)_5-CH=CH-(CH_2)_7-\overset{\overset{\displaystyle O}{\|}}{C}-OH$$

a. How many carbon atoms are in palmitoleic acid?
b. Is it a saturated or unsaturated fatty acid?
c. Is it most likely to be solid or liquid at room temperature?

Prostaglandins

Prostaglandins (PGs) are hormone-like substances produced in low amounts in most cells of the body. The prostaglandins, also known as *eicosanoids*, are formed from arachidonic acid, the polyunsaturated fatty acid with 20 carbon atoms (*eicos* is the Greek word for 20). Swedish chemists first discovered prostaglandins and named them "prostaglandin E" (soluble in ether) and "prostaglandin F" (soluble in phosphate buffer, or *fosfat* in Swedish). The various kinds of prostaglandins differ by the substituents attached to the five-carbon ring. Prostaglandin E (PGE) has a ketone group on carbon 9, whereas prostaglandin F (PGF) has a hydroxyl group. The number of double bonds is shown as a subscript 1 or 2:

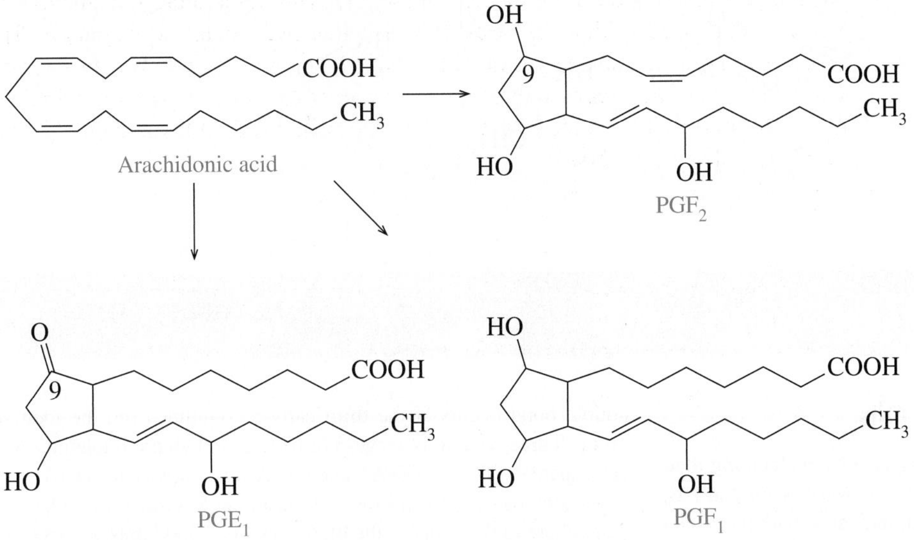

Although prostaglandins are broken down quickly, they have potent physiological effects. Some prostaglandins increase blood pressure, and others lower blood pressure. Other prostaglandins stimulate contraction and relaxation in the smooth muscle of the uterus during the birth process. When tissues are injured, arachidonic acid present in the blood is converted to prostaglandins such as PGE and PGF that produce inflammation and pain in the area:

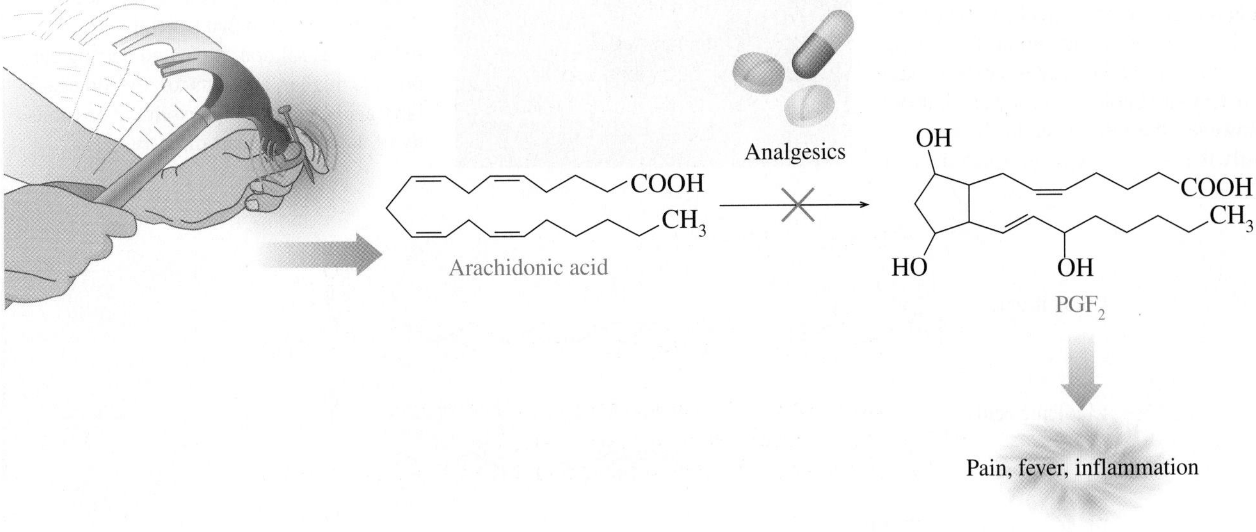

The treatment of pain, fever, and inflammation is based on inhibiting the enzymes that convert arachidonic acid to prostaglandins. Several nonsteroidal anti-inflammatory drugs (NSAIDs), such as aspirin, block the production of prostaglandins and in doing so decrease pain and inflammation and reduce fever (antipyretics). Ibuprofen has similar anti-inflammatory and analgesic effects. Other NSAIDs include naproxen (Aleve and Naprosyn), ketoprofen (Actron), and nabumetone (Relafen). Long-term use of such products can result in liver, kidney, and gastrointestinal damage. Some prostaglandins are being tested as inhibitors of gastric secretion for use in the treatment of stomach ulcers.

Aspirin (acetylsalicylic acid)   Ibuprofen (Advil®, Motrin®)   Naproxen (Aleve®, Naprosyn®)

HEALTH NOTE

Omega-3 Fatty Acids in Fish Oils

Over the past several decades, Americans have been changing their diets to include more polyunsaturated fats and fewer saturated fats. This change is a response to research that indicates that atherosclerosis and heart disease are associated with high levels of fats in the diet. However, the Inuit people of Alaska have a diet with high levels of polyunsaturated fats as well as high levels of blood cholesterol, but a very low occurrence of atherosclerosis and heart attacks. The fats in the Inuit diet are primarily polyunsaturated fats from fish rather than from land animals.

Both fish and vegetable oils have high levels of polyunsaturated fats. The fatty acids in vegetable oils are omega-6 acids, in which the first double bond occurs at carbon 6 counting from the end of the carbon chain. Two common omega-6 acids are linoleic acid and arachidonic acid. However, the fatty acids in the fish oils are mostly the omega-3 type, in which the first

double bond occurs at the third carbon counting from the methyl group. Three common omega-3 fatty acids in fish are linolenic acid, eicosapentaenoic acid (EPA), and docosahexaenoic acid (DHA).

In atherosclerosis and heart disease, cholesterol forms plaques that adhere to the walls of the blood vessels. Blood pressure rises as blood has to squeeze through a smaller opening in the blood vessel. As more plaque forms, there is also a possibility of blood clots blocking the blood vessels and causing a heart attack. Omega-3 fatty acids lower the tendency of blood platelets to stick together, thereby reducing the possibility of blood clots. However, high levels of omega-3 fatty acids can increase bleeding if the ability of the platelets to form blood clots is reduced too much. It does seem that a diet that includes fish such as salmon, tuna, and herring can provide higher amounts of the omega-3 fatty acids, which help lessen the possibility of developing heart disease.

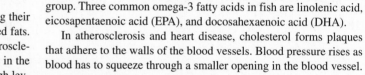

Linoleic acid

Omega-6 fatty acid

Linolenic acid

Omega-3 fatty acid

Eicosapentaenoic acid (EPA)

Docosahexaenoic acid (DHA)

QUESTIONS AND PROBLEMS

Fatty Acids

17.5 Describe some similarities and differences in the structures of a saturated fatty acid and an unsaturated fatty acid.

17.6 Stearic acid and linoleic acid both have 18 carbon atoms. Why does stearic acid melt at 69 °C, but linoleic acid melts at −9 °C?

17.7 Draw the line-bond formula of the following fatty acids:
  a. palmitic acid   **b.** oleic acid

17.8 Draw the line-bond formula of the following fatty acids:
  a. stearic acid   **b.** linoleic acid

17.9 Which of the following fatty acids are saturated and which are unsaturated?
  a. lauric acid   **b.** linolenic acid
  c. palmitoleic acid   **d.** stearic acid

17.10 Which of the following fatty acids are saturated and which are unsaturated?
  a. linoleic acid   **b.** palmitic acid
  c. myristic acid   **d.** oleic acid

17.11 How does the structure of a fatty acid with a cis double bond differ from the structure of a fatty acid with a trans double bond?

17.12 In each pair, identify the fatty acid with the lower melting point. Explain.
  a. myristic acid and stearic acid
  b. stearic acid and linoleic acid
  c. oleic acid and linolenic acid

17.13 What is the difference in the location of the first double bond in an omega-3 and an omega-6 fatty acid? (See Health Note "Omega-3 Fatty Acids in Fish Oils.")

17.14 a. What are some sources of omega-3 and omega-6 fatty acids? (See Health Note "Omega-3 Fatty Acids in Fish Oils.")
  b. How may omega-3 fatty acids help in lowering the risk of heart disease?

17.15 Compare the structures and functional groups of arachidonic acid and PGE_1.

17.16 Compare the structures and functional groups of PGE and PGF.

17.17 What are some effects of prostaglandins in the body?

17.18 How do nonsteroidal anti-inflammatory drugs reduce inflammation?

17.3 Waxes, Fats, and Oils

Waxes are found in many plants and animals. Coatings of carnauba wax on fruits and the leaves and stems of plants help to prevent loss of water and damage from pests. Waxes on the skin, fur, and feathers of animals and birds provide a waterproof coating. A **wax** is an ester of a saturated fatty acid and a long-chain alcohol, each containing from 14 to 30 carbon atoms.

The formulas of some common waxes are given in Table 17.2. Beeswax obtained from honeycombs and carnauba wax from palm trees are used to give a protective coating to furniture, cars, and floors. Jojoba wax is used in making candles and cosmetics such as lipstick. Lanolin, a mixture of waxes obtained from wool, is used in hand and facial lotions to aid retention of water, which softens the skin.

LEARNING GOAL

Draw the condensed structural formula of a wax, fat, or oil produced by the reaction of a fatty acid and an alcohol or glycerol.

TABLE 17.2 Some Typical Waxes

Type	Condensed Structural Formula	Source	Uses
Beeswax	$CH_3-(CH_2)_{14}-\overset{\overset{\textstyle O}{\|\|}}{C}-O-(CH_2)_{29}-CH_3$	Honeycomb	Candles, shoe polish, wax paper
Carnauba wax	$CH_3-(CH_2)_{24}-\overset{\overset{\textstyle O}{\|\|}}{C}-O-(CH_2)_{29}-CH_3$	Brazilian palm tree	Waxes for furniture, cars, floors, shoes
Jojoba wax	$CH_3-(CH_2)_{18}-\overset{\overset{\textstyle O}{\|\|}}{C}-O-(CH_2)_{19}-CH_3$	Jojoba	Candles, soaps, cosmetics

Fats and Oils: Triacylglycerols

In the body, fatty acids are stored as fats and oils known as **triacylglycerols**. These substances, also called *triglycerides*, are triesters of glycerol (a trihydroxy alcohol) and fatty acids. The general formula of a triacylglycerol follows:

$$
\begin{array}{l}
CH_2-O-\overset{\displaystyle O}{\overset{\|}{C}}\sim\sim\sim\sim\sim\sim\sim\sim \\[6pt]
CH-O-\overset{\displaystyle O}{\overset{\|}{C}}\sim\sim\sim\sim\sim\sim\sim\sim \\[6pt]
CH_2-O-\overset{\displaystyle O}{\overset{\|}{C}}\sim\sim\sim\sim\sim\sim\sim\sim
\end{array}
$$

Glycerol — Fatty acid / Fatty acid / Fatty acid

Triacylglycerol

MC™ **SELF STUDY ACTIVITY**
Triacylglycerols

In Chapter 16, we saw that esters are produced from the esterification reaction between a carboxylic acid and an alcohol. In a triacylglycerol, three hydroxyl groups on glycerol form ester bonds with the carboxyl groups of three fatty acids. For example, glycerol and three molecules of stearic acid form glyceryl tristearate, which is commonly named tristearin. In these complex molecules, bonds between carbon atoms may be omitted to give a condensed structure:

$$
\begin{array}{l}
CH_2-O-H + HO-\overset{\displaystyle O}{\overset{\|}{C}}-(CH_2)_{16}CH_3 \\[6pt]
CH-O-H + HO-\overset{\displaystyle O}{\overset{\|}{C}}-(CH_2)_{16}CH_3 \\[6pt]
CH_2-O-H + HO-\overset{\displaystyle O}{\overset{\|}{C}}-(CH_2)_{16}CH_3
\end{array}
\longrightarrow
\begin{array}{l}
CH_2-O-\overset{\displaystyle O}{\overset{\|}{C}}-(CH_2)_{16}CH_3 \\[6pt]
CH-O-\overset{\displaystyle O}{\overset{\|}{C}}-(CH_2)_{16}CH_3 + 3H_2O \\[6pt]
CH_2-O-\overset{\displaystyle O}{\overset{\|}{C}}-(CH_2)_{16}CH_3
\end{array}
$$

Ester bond

Glycerol   3 Stearic acid molecules   Glyceryl tristearate (tristearin, a fat)

Most fats and oils are mixed triacylglycerols that contain two or three different fatty acids. For example, a mixed triacylglycerol might be made from lauric acid, myristic acid, and palmitic acid. One possible structure for the mixed triacylglycerol follows:

$$
\begin{array}{l}
CH_2-O-\overset{\displaystyle O}{\overset{\|}{C}}-(CH_2)_{10}CH_3 \quad \text{Lauric acid} \\[6pt]
CH-O-\overset{\displaystyle O}{\overset{\|}{C}}-(CH_2)_{12}CH_3 \quad \text{Myristic acid} \\[6pt]
CH_2-O-\overset{\displaystyle O}{\overset{\|}{C}}-(CH_2)_{14}CH_3 \quad \text{Palmitic acid}
\end{array}
$$

A mixed triacylglycerol

Triacylglycerols are the major form of energy storage for animals. Animals that hibernate eat large quantities of plants, seeds, and nuts that contain high levels of fats and oils. Prior to hibernation, these animals, such as polar bears, gain as much as 14 kilograms a week. As the external temperature drops, the animal goes into hibernation. The body temperature drops to nearly freezing, and cellular activity, respiration, and heart rate are dramatically reduced. Animals that live in extremely cold climates will hibernate for 4–7 months. During this time, stored fat is their only source of energy.

CONCEPT CHECK 17.2

■ Triacylglycerols

Name the triacylglycerol that is formed by the esterification of glycerol with each of the following fatty acids:

a. $CH_3—(CH_2)_{12}—COOH$
b. $CH_3—(CH_2)_5—CH=CH—(CH_2)_7—COOH$

ANSWER

a. The saturated fatty acid with 14 carbon atoms is myristic acid. The triacylglycerol of glycerol and myristic acid is named glyceryl trimyristate or trimyristin (common).
b. The monounsaturated fatty acid with 16 carbon atoms is palmitoleic acid. The triacylglycerol of glycerol and palmitoleic acid is named glyceryl tripalmitoleate or tripalmitolein (common).

SAMPLE PROBLEM 17.3

■ Writing Structures for a Triacylglycerol

Draw the condensed structural formula of glyceryl tripalmitoleate (tripalmitolein).

SOLUTION

Glyceryl tripalmitoleate (tripalmitolein) is the triacylglycerol that contains ester bonds between glycerol and three palmitoleic acid molecules:

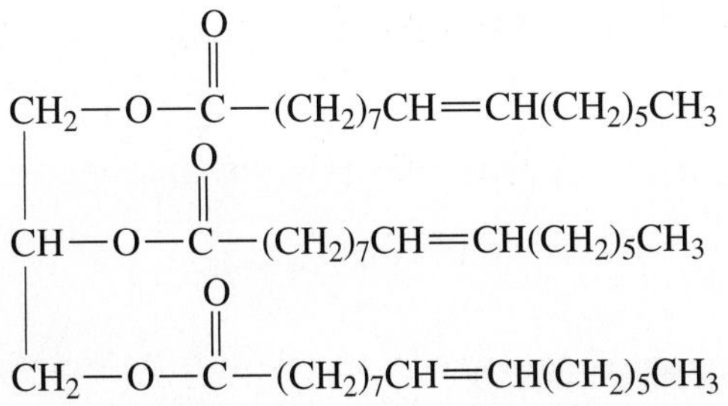

$$
\begin{array}{l}
\quad\quad\quad\quad\; O \\
\quad\quad\quad\quad\; \| \\
CH_2-O-C-(CH_2)_7CH=CH(CH_2)_5CH_3 \\
\;| \quad\quad\quad O \\
\quad\quad\quad\quad\; \| \\
CH-O-C-(CH_2)_7CH=CH(CH_2)_5CH_3 \\
\;| \quad\quad\quad O \\
\quad\quad\quad\quad\; \| \\
CH_2-O-C-(CH_2)_7CH=CH(CH_2)_5CH_3
\end{array}
$$

Glyceryl tripalmitoleate (tripalmitolein)

STUDY CHECK

Draw the condensed structural formula of the triacylglycerol containing three molecules of myristic acid.

Melting Points of Fats and Oils

A **fat** is a triacylglycerol that is solid at room temperature and usually comes from animal sources such as meat, whole milk, butter, and cheese.

An **oil** is a triacylglycerol that is usually a liquid at room temperature and is obtained from a plant source. Olive oil and peanut oil are monounsaturated because they contain large amounts of oleic acid. Oils from corn, cottonseed, safflowers, and sunflowers are polyunsaturated because they contain large amounts of fatty acids with two or more double bonds. (See Figure 17.3.) Palm oil and coconut oil are solids at room temperature because they consist mostly of saturated fatty acids.

The amounts of saturated, monounsaturated, and polyunsaturated fatty acids in some typical fats and oils are shown in Figure 17.4.

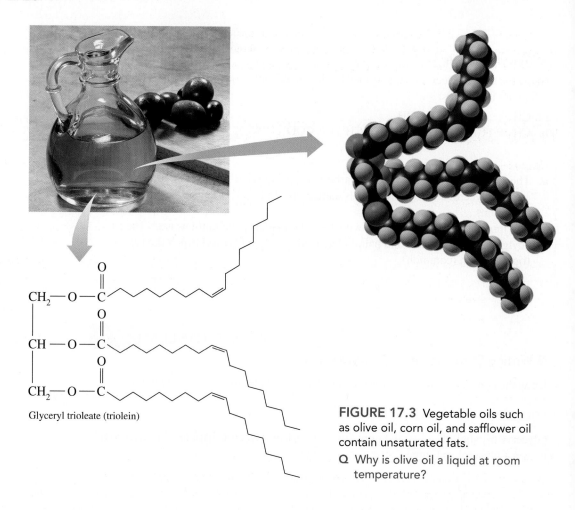

CH₂—O—C (with O double bond above C, attached to long unsaturated chain)

CH—O—C (with O double bond above C, attached to long unsaturated chain)

CH₂—O—C (with O double bond above C, attached to long unsaturated chain)

Glyceryl trioleate (triolein)

FIGURE 17.3 Vegetable oils such as olive oil, corn oil, and safflower oil contain unsaturated fats.

Q Why is olive oil a liquid at room temperature?

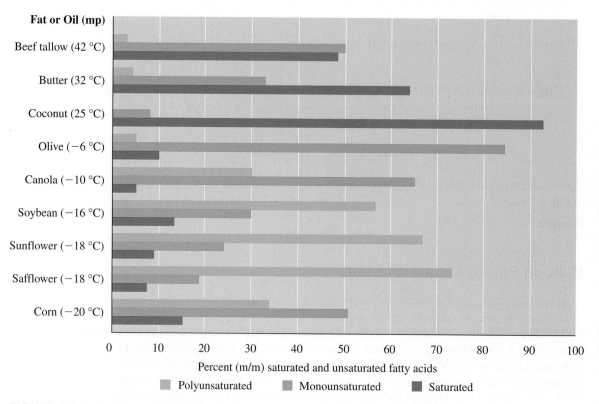

Fat or Oil (mp)

Beef tallow (42 °C)

Butter (32 °C)

Coconut (25 °C)

Olive (−6 °C)

Canola (−10 °C)

Soybean (−16 °C)

Sunflower (−18 °C)

Safflower (−18 °C)

Corn (−20 °C)

Percent (m/m) saturated and unsaturated fatty acids

■ Polyunsaturated   ■ Monounsaturated   ■ Saturated

FIGURE 17.4 Vegetable oils have low melting points because they have a higher percentage of unsaturated fatty acids than do animal fats.

Q Why is the melting point of butter higher than olive or canola oil?

Saturated fatty acids have higher melting points than unsaturated fatty acids because they pack together more tightly. Animal fats usually contain more saturated fatty acids than do vegetable oils. Therefore the melting points of animal fats are higher than those of vegetable oils.

QUESTIONS AND PROBLEMS

Waxes, Fats, and Oils

17.19 Draw the condensed structural formula of an ester in beeswax formed from myricyl alcohol, $CH_3(CH_2)_{29}OH$, and palmitic acid.

17.20 Draw the condensed structural formula of an ester in jojoba wax formed from arachidic acid, a 20-carbon saturated fatty acid, and 1-docosanol, $CH_3(CH_2)_{21}OH$.

17.21 Draw the condensed structural formula of a triacylglycerol that contains stearic acid and glycerol.

17.22 A mixed triacylglycerol contains two palmitic acid molecules and one oleic acid molecule. Draw two possible condensed structural formulas (isomers) for the compound.

17.23 Draw the condensed structural formula of glyceryl tripalmitate (tripalmitin).

17.24 Draw the condensed structural formula of glyceryl trioleate (triolein).

17.25 Safflower oil is polyunsaturated, whereas olive oil is monounsaturated. Explain.

17.26 Why does olive oil have a lower melting point than butter fat?

17.27 Why does coconut oil, a vegetable oil, have a melting point similar to fats from animal sources?

17.28 A label on a bottle of 100% sunflower seed oil states that it is lower in saturated fats than all the leading oils.
   a. How does the percentage of saturated fats in sunflower seed oil compare to that of safflower, corn, and canola oil? (See Figure 17.4.)
   b. Is the claim valid?

17.4 Chemical Properties of Triacylglycerols

The chemical reactions of the triacylglycerols (fats and oils) are the same as those we discussed for alkenes (Chapter 12) and esters (Chapter 16). Next, we will look at the hydrogenation and the hydrolysis and saponification of fats and oils.

LEARNING GOAL

Draw the structure of the product when a triacylglycerol is hydrogenated, hydrolyzed, or oxidized.

Hydrogenation

In the **hydrogenation** of an unsaturated fat, hydrogen is added to carbon–carbon double bonds to form carbon–carbon single bonds. The hydrogen gas is bubbled through the heated oil, typically in the presence of a nickel catalyst:

TUTORIAL
Hydrogenation and Hydrolysis of Triacylglycerols

$$-CH=CH- + H_2 \xrightarrow{Ni} \begin{array}{c} H\ \ H \\ | \ \ \ | \\ -C-C- \\ | \ \ \ | \\ H\ \ H \end{array}$$

For example, when hydrogen adds to all of the double bonds of glyceryl trioleate (triolein), the product is the saturated fat glyceryl tristearate (tristearin):

$$
\begin{array}{l}
CH_2-O-\overset{\displaystyle O}{\overset{\|}{C}}-(CH_2)_7CH=CH(CH_2)_7CH_3 \\[4pt]
| \qquad\quad O \\
CH-O-\overset{\displaystyle }{\overset{\|}{C}}-(CH_2)_7CH=CH(CH_2)_7CH_3 \ + \ 3H_2 \\[4pt]
| \qquad\quad O \\
CH_2-O-\overset{\displaystyle }{\overset{\|}{C}}-(CH_2)_7CH=CH(CH_2)_7CH_3
\end{array}
\xrightarrow{Ni}
\begin{array}{l}
CH_2-O-\overset{\displaystyle O}{\overset{\|}{C}}-(CH_2)_{16}CH_3 \\[4pt]
| \qquad\quad O \\
CH-O-\overset{\displaystyle }{\overset{\|}{C}}-(CH_2)_{16}CH_3 \\[4pt]
| \qquad\quad O \\
CH_2-O-\overset{\displaystyle }{\overset{\|}{C}}-(CH_2)_{16}CH_3
\end{array}
$$

Glyceryl trioleate (triolein)   Glyceryl tristearate (tristearin)

In commercial hydrogenation, the addition of hydrogen is stopped before all the double bonds in a liquid vegetable oil become completely saturated. Complete hydrogenation gives a very brittle product, whereas the partial hydrogenation of a liquid vegetable oil

HEALTH NOTE

Olestra: A Fat Substitute

In 1968, food scientists designed an artificial fat called *olestra* as a source of nutrition for premature babies. However, olestra could not be digested and was never used for that purpose. Later, scientists realized that olestra had the flavor and texture of a fat without the calories.

Olestra is manufactured by obtaining the fatty acids from the fats in cottonseed or soybean oils and bonding the fatty acids with the hydroxyl groups on sucrose. Chemically, olestra is composed of six to eight long-chain fatty acids attached by ester links to a sugar (sucrose) rather than to a glycerol molecule found in fats. This structure makes olestra a very large molecule that cannot be absorbed through the intestinal walls. The enzymes and bacteria in the intestinal tract are unable to break down the olestra molecule, and it travels through the intestinal tract undigested.

The large molecule of olestra also combines with fat-soluble vitamins (A, D, E, and K) as well as the carotenoids from the foods we eat before they can be absorbed through the intestinal wall. Carotenoids are plant pigments in fruits and vegetables that protect against cancer, heart disease, and macular degeneration, a form of blindness in the elderly. The FDA now requires manufacturers to add the four vitamins, but not the carotenoids, to olestra products. There have been reports of some adverse reactions, including diarrhea, abdominal cramps, and anal leakage, indicating that olestra may act as a laxative in some people. However, the manufacturers contend there is no direct proof that olestra is the cause of those effects.

Snack foods made with olestra are now in supermarkets nationwide. Since there are already low-fat snacks on the market, it remains to be seen whether olestra will have any significant effect on reducing the problem of obesity.

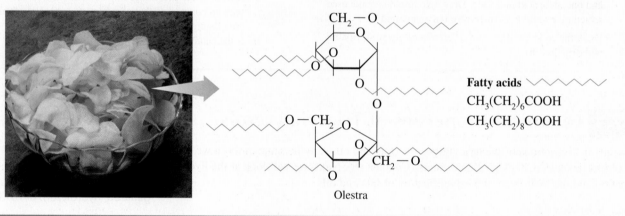

Fatty acids
$CH_3(CH_2)_6COOH$
$CH_3(CH_2)_8COOH$

Olestra

changes it to a soft, semisolid fat. As the semisolid fat becomes more saturated, the melting point increases, and the substance becomes more solid at room temperature. By controlling the amount of hydrogen, manufacturers can produce the various types of products on the market today, such as soft margarines, solid stick margarines, and solid shortenings. (See Figure 17.5.) Although these products now contain more saturated fatty acids than the original oils, they contain no cholesterol, unlike similar products from animal sources, such as butter and lard.

FIGURE 17.5 Many soft margarines, stick margarines, and solid shortenings are produced by the partial hydrogenation of vegetable oils.

Q How does hydrogenation change the structure of the fatty acids in the vegetable oils?

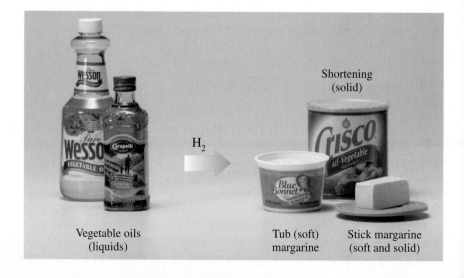

Vegetable oils
(liquids)

H_2

Shortening
(solid)

Tub (soft)
margarine

Stick margarine
(soft and solid)

HEALTH NOTE

Trans Fatty Acids and Hydrogenation

During the early 1900s, margarine became a popular replacement for highly saturated fats such as butter and lard. Margarine is produced by partially hydrogenating the unsaturated fats in vegetable oils such as safflower oil, corn oil, canola oil, cottonseed oil, and sunflower oil. Fats that are more saturated are more resistant to oxidation.

In vegetable oils, the unsaturated fats usually contain cis double bonds. As hydrogenation occurs, double bonds are converted to single bonds. However, a small amount of the cis double bonds are converted to trans double bonds, which causes a change in the overall structure of the fatty acids. If the label on a product states that the oils have been "partially hydrogenated," that product will also contain trans fatty acids. In the United States, it is estimated that 2–4% of our total calories comes from trans fatty acids.

The concern about trans fatty acids is that their altered structure may make them behave like saturated fatty acids in the body. During the 1980s, research indicated that trans fatty acids have an effect on blood cholesterol similar to that of saturated fats, although study results vary. Several studies reported that trans fatty acids raise the levels of LDL-cholesterol, low-density lipoproteins containing cholesterol that can accumulate in the arteries. (LDLs and HDLs are described in the section on lipoproteins later in the chapter.) Some studies also report that trans fatty acids lower HDL-cholesterol, high-density lipoproteins that carry cholesterol to the liver to be excreted. However, other studies did not report any decrease in HDL-cholesterol. In some American and European studies, an increased risk of breast cancer was associated with increased intake of trans fatty acids. However, these studies are not conclusive, and not all studies have supported such findings. Current evidence does not yet indicate that the intake of trans fatty acids is a significant risk factor for heart disease. The trans fatty acids controversy will continue to be debated as more research is done.

Foods containing trans fatty acids include milk, bread, fried foods, ground beef, baked goods, stick margarine, butter, soft margarine, cookies, crackers, and vegetable shortening. The American Heart Association recommends that margarine should have no more than 2 grams of saturated fat per tablespoon, and a liquid vegetable oil should be the first ingredient. They also recommend the use of soft margarine, which is only slightly hydrogenated and therefore has fewer trans fatty acids.

Many health organizations agree that fat should account for less than 30% of daily calories (the current average for Americans is 34%) and saturated fat should be less than 10% of total calories. Lowering the overall fat intake would also decrease the amount of trans fatty acids. The Food and Drug Administration and the U.S. Department of Agriculture are encouraging the use of new food labels to inform consumers of the fat content of food. Since the beginning of 2006, the amount of trans fats has been included on the Nutritional Facts panel on food products. The best advice may be to reduce total fat in the diet by using fats and oils sparingly, cooking with little or no fat, substituting olive oil or canola oil for other oils, and limiting the use of coconut oil and palm oil, which are high in saturated fatty acids.

There are several products on the market, including peanut butter and butterlike spreads, that have 0% trans fatty acids. On the labels, they state that their products are nonhydrogenated, which avoids the production of the undesirable trans fatty acid. However, in the list of natural vegetable oils, such as soy and canola oil, there is also palm oil. Because palm oil has a melting point of 30 °C, palm oil increases the overall melting point of the spread and gives a product that is solid at room temperature. However, palm oil contains high amounts of saturated fatty acids and has a similar effect in the body as do stearic acid (18 carbons) and fats derived from animal sources. Health experts recommend that we limit the amount of saturated fats, including palm oil, in our diets.

cis-Oleic acid

H_2/Ni

Ni catalyst

H_2 Isomerization

Addition of H_2

Undesired side product (*trans*-oleic acid)

Desired saturated product (stearic acid)

Oxidation of Unsaturated Fats

A fat or oil becomes rancid when its double bonds are oxidized in the presence of oxygen and microorganisms. The products are short-chain fatty acids and aldehydes that have disagreeable odors:

$$-CH{=}CH- \xrightarrow{[O]} \underset{\substack{\text{Short-chain}\\\text{aldehydes}}}{-\overset{\displaystyle O}{\overset{\|}{C}}-H \;+\; H-\overset{\displaystyle O}{\overset{\|}{C}}-} \xrightarrow{[O]} \underset{\substack{\text{Short-chain}\\\text{carboxylic acids}}}{-\overset{\displaystyle O}{\overset{\|}{C}}-OH \;+\; HO-\overset{\displaystyle O}{\overset{\|}{C}}-}$$

Unsaturated fatty acids

If a vegetable oil does not contain an antioxidant, it will oxidize rather easily. You can detect oil that has become rancid by its unpleasant odor. If oil is covered tightly and stored in a refrigerator, the process of oxidation can be slowed and the oil will last longer.

Oxidation also occurs in the oils that accumulate on the surface of the skin during heavy exercise.

At body temperature, microorganisms on the skin promote rapid oxidation of the oils as they are exposed to oxygen and water. The resulting short-chain aldehydes and fatty acids account for the body odor associated with working out and heavy perspiration.

Hydrolysis

Triacylglycerols are hydrolyzed (split by water) in the presence of strong acids such HCl or H_2SO_4 or digestive enzymes called *lipases*. The products of hydrolysis of the ester bonds are glycerol and three fatty acids. The polar glycerol is soluble in water, but the fatty acids with their long hydrocarbon chains are not.

Water adds to ester bonds

$$
\begin{array}{l}
CH_2-O{\vdots}\overset{\displaystyle O}{\overset{\|}{C}}-(CH_2)_{14}CH_3\\[4pt]
CH-O{\vdots}\overset{\displaystyle O}{\overset{\|}{C}}-(CH_2)_{14}CH_3 \;+\; \mathbf{3H_2O}\\[4pt]
CH_2-O{\vdots}\overset{\displaystyle O}{\overset{\|}{C}}-(CH_2)_{14}CH_3
\end{array}
\xrightarrow[\text{lipase}]{\substack{H^+\\ \text{or}}}
\begin{array}{l}
CH_2-OH\\[4pt]
CH-OH \;+\; \mathbf{3}HO-\overset{\displaystyle O}{\overset{\|}{C}}-(CH_2)_{14}CH_3\\[4pt]
CH_2-OH
\end{array}
$$

Glyceryl tripalmitate (tripalmitin) → Glycerol + 3 Palmitic acid molecules

Saponification

When a fat is heated with a strong base such as sodium hydroxide, saponification (base hydrolysis) of the fat gives glycerol and the sodium salts of the fatty acids, which are soaps. When NaOH is used, a solid soap is produced that can be molded into a desired shape; KOH produces a softer, liquid soap. Polyunsaturated oils produce softer soaps. Names like "coconut" or "avocado shampoo" tell you the sources of the oil used in the reaction:

Fat or oil + strong base $\longrightarrow$ glycerol + salts of fatty acids (soaps)

$$
\begin{array}{l}
CH_2-O-\overset{\displaystyle O}{\overset{\|}{C}}-(CH_2)_{14}CH_3\\[4pt]
CH-O-\overset{\displaystyle O}{\overset{\|}{C}}-(CH_2)_{14}CH_3 \;+\; \mathbf{3NaOH}\\[4pt]
CH_2-O-\overset{\displaystyle O}{\overset{\|}{C}}-(CH_2)_{14}CH_3
\end{array}
\longrightarrow
\begin{array}{l}
CH_2-OH\\[4pt]
CH-OH \;+\; \mathbf{3}Na^+\,{}^-O-\overset{\displaystyle O}{\overset{\|}{C}}-(CH_2)_{14}CH_3\\[4pt]
CH_2-OH
\end{array}
$$

Glyceryl tripalmitate (tripalmitin) → Glycerol + 3 Sodium palmitate (soap)

GREEN CHEMISTRY NOTE

Biodiesel as an Alternative Fuel

Biodiesel is a name of a nonpetroleum fuel that can be used in place of diesel fuel. Biodiesel is produced from renewable biological resources such as vegetable oils (primarily soybean), waste vegetable oils from restaurants, and some animal fats. Biodiesel is nontoxic and biodegradable.

Biodiesel is prepared from triacylglycerols and alcohols (usually ethanol) to form ethyl esters and glycerol. The glycerol that separates from the fat is used in soaps and other products. The reaction of triacylglycerols is catalyzed by a base such as NaOH or KOH at low temperatures to give a very high percentage of the fatty acid esters, which make up the biodiesel product.

Triacylglycerol + 3 ethanol $\longrightarrow$ 3 ethyl ester (biodiesel) + glycerol

In many cases, diesel engines need only slight modification to use biodiesel. Manufacturers of diesel cars, trucks, boats, and tractors have different suggestions for the percentage of biodiesel to use, ranging from 2% (B2) blended with standard diesel fuel to using 100% pure biodiesel (B100). For example, B20 is 20 percent by volume of biodiesel blended with 80 percent by volume petroleum diesel. In 2006, 9.8×10^{14} liters of biodiesel were used in the United States. Fuel stations in Europe and the United States are now stocking biodiesel fuel.

Compared to diesel fuel from petroleum, biodiesel burns in an engine to produce much lower levels of carbon dioxide emissions, particulates, unburned hydrocarbons, and polycyclic aromatic hydrocarbons that cause lung cancer. Because biodiesel has extremely low sulfur content, it does not contribute to the formation of the sulfur oxides that produce acid rain. The energy output from the combustion of biodiesel is almost the same as energy produced by petroleum diesel.

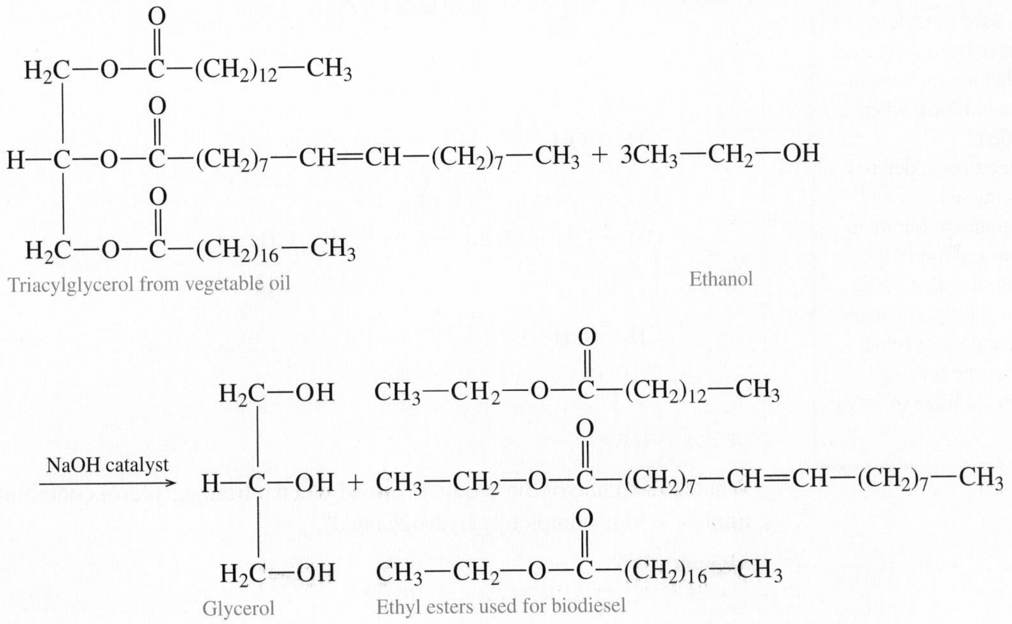

$$
\begin{array}{l}
H_2C-O-\overset{\displaystyle O}{\overset{\|}{C}}-(CH_2)_{12}-CH_3 \\[2mm]
H-\overset{|}{C}-O-\overset{\displaystyle O}{\overset{\|}{C}}-(CH_2)_7-CH=CH-(CH_2)_7-CH_3 \quad + \quad 3CH_3-CH_2-OH \\[2mm]
H_2C-O-\overset{\displaystyle O}{\overset{\|}{C}}-(CH_2)_{16}-CH_3
\end{array}
$$

Triacylglycerol from vegetable oil   Ethanol

$$\xrightarrow{\text{NaOH catalyst}}$$

$$
\begin{array}{l}
H_2C-OH \\[1mm]
H-\overset{|}{C}-OH \\[1mm]
H_2C-OH
\end{array}
\quad + \quad
\begin{array}{l}
CH_3-CH_2-O-\overset{\displaystyle O}{\overset{\|}{C}}-(CH_2)_{12}-CH_3 \\[2mm]
CH_3-CH_2-O-\overset{\displaystyle O}{\overset{\|}{C}}-(CH_2)_7-CH=CH-(CH_2)_7-CH_3 \\[2mm]
CH_3-CH_2-O-\overset{\displaystyle O}{\overset{\|}{C}}-(CH_2)_{16}-CH_3
\end{array}
$$

Glycerol   Ethyl esters used for biodiesel

CONCEPT CHECK 17.3

■ Hydrogenation, Hydrolysis, and Saponification

Identify each of the following as hydrogenation, hydrolysis, or saponification and identify the products:

a. the reaction of palm oil with KOH
b. the reaction of glyceryl trilinoleate from safflower oil with water and HCl
c. the reaction of corn oil and hydrogen (H_2) using a nickel catalyst

EXPLORE YOUR WORLD

Types of Fats

Read the labels on food products that contain fats, such as butter, margarine, vegetable oils, peanut butter, and potato chips. Look for terms such as saturated, monounsaturated, polyunsaturated, and partially or fully hydrogenated.

QUESTIONS

1. How many grams of saturated, monounsaturated, and polyunsaturated fat are in one serving of the product?
2. What type(s) of fats or oils are in the product?
3. What percent of the total fat is saturated fat? Unsaturated fat?
4. If the product is a vegetable oil, what information is given about how to store it? Why?
5. The label on a container of peanut butter states that the cottonseed and canola oils used to make the peanut butter have been fully hydrogenated. What are the typical products that would form when hydrogen is added?
6. For each packaged food, determine the following:
   a. How many grams of fat are in one serving of the food?
   b. Using the caloric value for fat (9 kcal/gram of fat), how many Calories (kilocalories) come from the fat in one serving?
   c. What is the percentage of fat in one serving?

ANSWER

a. The reaction of palm oil with KOH is saponification, and the products are glycerol and the potassium salts of the fatty acids, which are soaps.
b. In acid hydrolysis, glyceryl trilinoleate reacts with water, which splits the ester bonds to produce glycerol and three molecules of linoleic acid.
c. In hydrogenation, H_2 adds to double bonds in corn oil, which produces a more saturated and thus more solid fat.

SAMPLE PROBLEM 17.4

■ Reactions of Lipids

Write the equation for the reaction catalyzed by the enzyme lipase that hydrolyzes trilaurin (glyceryl trilaurate) during the digestion process.

SOLUTION

$$CH_2{-}O{-}\overset{\overset{\displaystyle O}{\|}}{C}{-}(CH_2)_{10}CH_3$$
$$CH{-}O{-}\overset{\overset{\displaystyle O}{\|}}{C}{-}(CH_2)_{10}CH_3 \;+\; 3H_2O \xrightarrow{\text{Lipase}}$$
$$CH_2{-}O{-}\overset{\overset{\displaystyle O}{\|}}{C}{-}(CH_2)_{10}CH_3$$

Glyceryl trilaurate
(trilaurin)

$$CH_2{-}OH$$
$$CH{-}OH \;+\; 3HO{-}\overset{\overset{\displaystyle O}{\|}}{C}{-}(CH_2)_{10}CH_3$$
$$CH_2{-}OH$$

Glycerol   3 Lauric acid
                    molecules

STUDY CHECK

What is the name of the product formed when a triacylglycerol containing oleic acid and linoleic acid is completely hydrogenated?

QUESTIONS AND PROBLEMS

Chemical Properties of Triacylglycerols

17.29 Write an equation for the hydrogenation of glyceryl trioleate, a fat formed from glycerol and three oleic acid units.

17.30 Write an equation for the hydrogenation of glyceryl trilinolenate, a fat formed from glycerol and three linolenic acid units.

17.31 A label on a container of margarine states that it contains partially hydrogenated corn oil.
   a. How has the liquid corn oil been changed?
   b. Why is the margarine product solid?

17.32 Why should a bottle of vegetable oil that has no preservatives be tightly covered and refrigerated?

17.33 a. Write an equation for the acid hydrolysis of glyceryl trimyristate (trimyristin).
    b. Write an equation for the NaOH saponification of glyceryl trimyristate (trimyristin).

17.34 a. Write an equation for the acid hydrolysis of glyceryl trioleate (triolein).
    b. Write an equation for the NaOH saponification of glyceryl trioleate (triolein).

17.35 Compare the structure of a triacylglycerol to the structure of olestra.

17.36 A vegetable oil is partially hydrogenated.
   a. Are all or just some of the double bonds converted to single bonds?
   b. What happens to some of the cis double bonds during hydrogenation?
   c. How can you reduce the amount of trans fatty acids in your diet?

17.37 Draw the product of the hydrogenation of the following triacylglycerol:

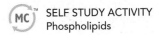

$$CH_2-O-\overset{\overset{\displaystyle O}{\|}}{C}-(CH_2)_{16}CH_3$$
$$CH-O-\overset{\overset{\displaystyle O}{\|}}{C}-(CH_2)_7CH=CH(CH_2)_7CH_3$$
$$CH_2-O-\overset{\overset{\displaystyle O}{\|}}{C}-(CH_2)_{16}CH_3$$

17.38 Draw all the products that would be obtained when the tri-acylglycerol in problem 17.37 undergoes complete hydrolysis.

17.5 Glycerophospholipids

The **glycerophospholipids** are a family of lipids similar to triacylglycerols except that one hydroxyl group of glycerol is replaced by the ester of phosphoric acid and an amino alcohol, bonded through a phosphodiester bond. We can compare the general structures of a triacylglycerol and a glycerophospholipid as follows:

LEARNING GOAL
Describe the characteristics of glycerophospholipids.

MC SELF STUDY ACTIVITY
Phospholipids

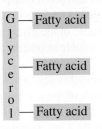 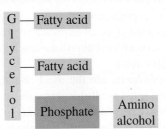

Triacylglycerol (triglyceride)   Glycerophospholipid

Phosphate Esters

In this group of compounds, ester bonds form between a hydroxyl group of an alcohol and phosphoric acid to give ester products similar to those formed with carboxylic acids:

$$HO-\overset{\overset{\displaystyle O}{\|}}{\underset{\underset{\displaystyle OH}{|}}{P}}-OH + HO-CH_3 \longrightarrow HO-\overset{\overset{\displaystyle O}{\|}}{\underset{\underset{\displaystyle OH}{|}}{P}}-O-CH_3 + H_2O$$

Phosphoric acid + Alcohol ⟶ Phosphate ester + Water

The phosphate ester forms a diester by reaction with a second alcohol:

$$HO-\overset{\overset{\displaystyle O}{\|}}{\underset{\underset{\displaystyle OH}{|}}{P}}-O-CH_3 + HO-CH_3 \longrightarrow CH_3-O-\overset{\overset{\displaystyle O}{\|}}{\underset{\underset{\displaystyle OH}{|}}{P}}-O-CH_3 + H_2O$$

Phosphate ester + Alcohol ⟶ Phosphate diester + Water

MC TUTORIAL
The Split Personality of Glycerophospholipids

Three amino alcohols found in glycerophospholipids are choline, serine, and ethanolamine. In the body, at a physiological pH of 7.4, these amino alcohols are ionized:

$$HO-CH_2-CH_2-\overset{\overset{\displaystyle CH_3}{|}}{\underset{\underset{\displaystyle CH_3}{|}}{\overset{+}{N}}}-CH_3 \qquad HO-CH_2-\overset{\overset{\displaystyle \overset{+}{N}H_3}{|}}{CH}-COO^- \qquad HO-CH_2-CH_2-\overset{+}{N}H_3$$

Choline   Serine   Ethanolamine

Lecithins and **cephalins** are two types of glycerophospholipids that are particularly abundant in brain and nerve tissues as well as in egg yolks, wheat germ, and yeast. Lecithins contain choline, and cephalins usually contain ethanolamine and sometimes serine. In the following structural formulas, palmitic acid is used as an example of a fatty acid:

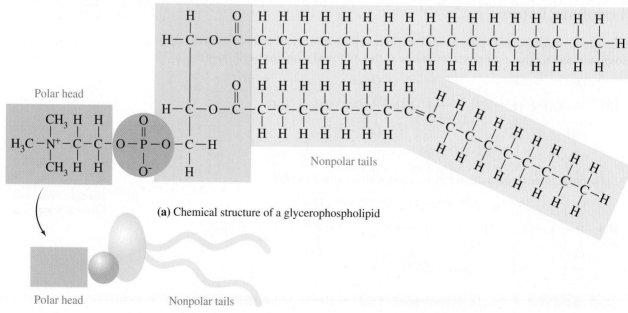

A lecithin

A cephalin

Glycerophospholipids contain both polar and nonpolar regions, which allow them to interact with both polar and nonpolar substances. The ionized amine and phosphate portion, called "the head," is polar and strongly attracted to water. (See Figure 17.6.) The two fatty acids connected to the glycerol molecule represent the nonpolar "tails" of the glycerophospholipid. The hydrocarbon chains that make up the "tails" are only soluble in other nonpolar substances, mostly lipids.

Glycerophospholipids are the most abundant lipids in cell membranes, where they play an important role in cellular permeability. They make up much of the myelin sheath that protects nerve cells. In the body fluids, glycerophospholipids combine with the less polar triglycerides and cholesterol to make them more soluble as they are transported in the body.

(a) Chemical structure of a glycerophospholipid

(b) Simplified way to draw a glycerophospholipid

FIGURE 17.6 **(a)** In a glycerophospholipid, a polar "head" contains the ionized amino alcohol and phosphoric acid groups, while the two fatty acids make up the nonpolar "tails." **(b)** A simplified drawing indicates the polar region and the nonpolar region.

Q Why are glycerophospholipids polar?

SAMPLE PROBLEM 17.5

■ Drawing Glycerophospholipid Structures

Draw the condensed structural formula of the cephalin that contains stearic acid and serine. Describe each component in the glycerophospholipid.

SOLUTION

In general, glycerophospholipids are composed of a glycerol molecule in which two carbon atoms are attached to fatty acids such as stearic acid. The third carbon atom is attached via an ester bond to phosphate linked to an amino alcohol. In this example, the amino alcohol is serine:

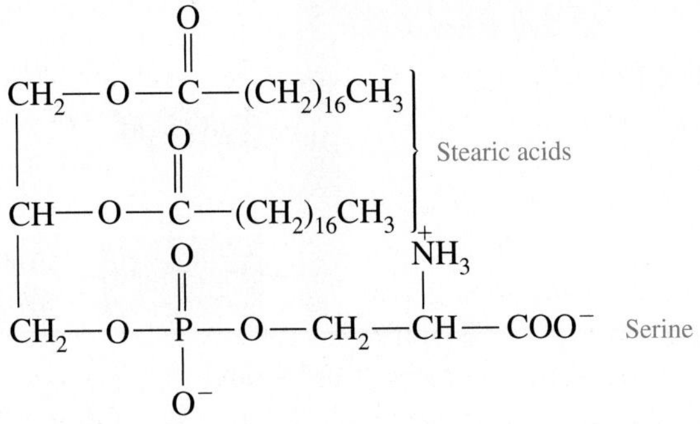

STUDY CHECK

What are the four components of glycerophospholipids?

QUESTIONS AND PROBLEMS

Glycerophospholipids

17.39 Describe the differences between triacylglycerols and glycerophospholipids.

17.40 Describe the differences between lecithins and cephalins.

17.41 Draw the structure of a glycerophospholipid containing two molecules of palmitic acid and ethanolamine. What is another name for this type of glycerophospholipid?

17.42 Draw the structure of a glycerophospholipid that contains choline and palmitic acids.

17.43 Identify the following glycerophospholipid and list its components:

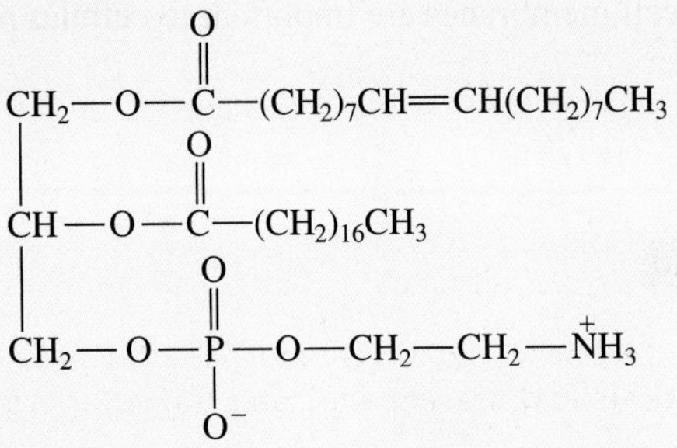

17.44 Identify the following glycerophospholipid and list its components:

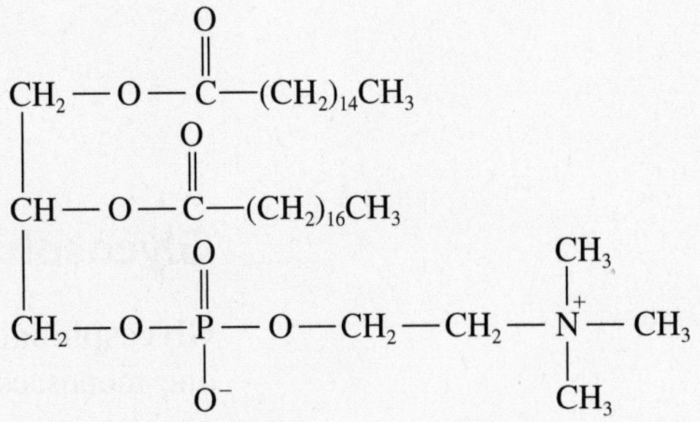

17.6 Sphingolipids

LEARNING GOAL

Describe the types of lipids that contain sphingosine.

SELF STUDY ACTIVITY
Phospholipids

Sphingolipids are lipids that contain a long-chain amino alcohol called *sphingosine*, rather than glycerol.

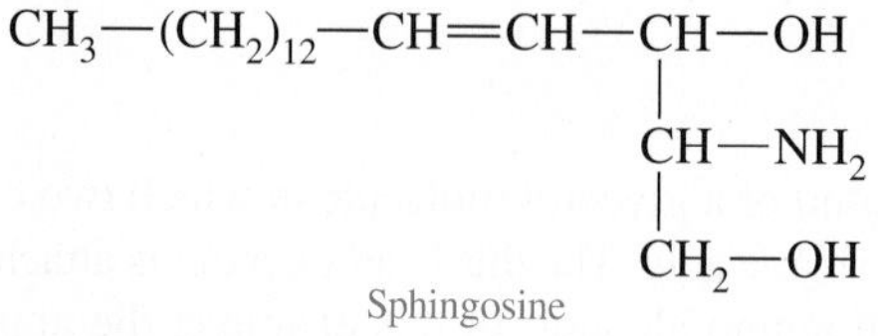

$$CH_3—(CH_2)_{12}—CH=CH—CH—OH$$
$$\underset{}{\overset{|}{CH}}—NH_2$$
$$\overset{|}{CH_2}—OH$$

Sphingosine

In **ceramides**, the —NH_2 group of sphingosine is attached by an *amide* link to a fatty acid:

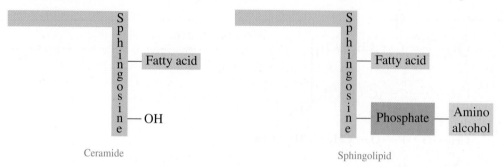

Ceramide   Sphingolipid

One of the most abundant groups of sphingolipids is the **sphingomyelins**, in which the —OH of a ceramide forms a phosphate ester of choline, an amino alcohol. The sphingomyelins are abundant in the white matter of the myelin sheath, a coating surrounding the nerve cells that increases the speed of nerve impulses and insulates and protects the nerve cells:

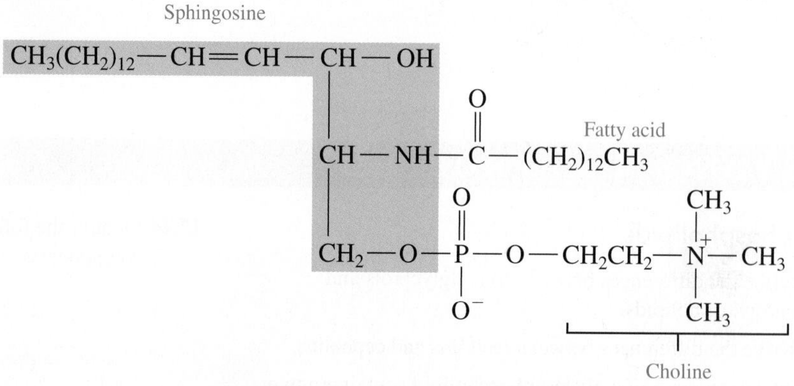

Sphingosine

$$CH_3(CH_2)_{12}—CH=CH—CH—OH$$

Fatty acid

$$CH—NH—\overset{\overset{O}{\|}}{C}—(CH_2)_{12}CH_3$$

$$CH_2—O—\overset{\overset{O}{\|}}{\underset{\underset{O^-}{|}}{P}}—O—CH_2CH_2—\overset{\overset{CH_3}{|}}{\underset{\underset{CH_3}{|}}{\overset{+}{N}}}—CH_3$$

Choline

Sphingomyelin (a sphingolipid)

Glycosphingolipids

Glycosphingolipids are sphingolipids that contain carbohydrates. In a **cerebroside**, one monosaccharide (galactose or glucose) forms a β-glycosidic bond with the —OH of the ceramide. Cerebrosides are present primarily in the brain and the myelin sheath. Glycosphingolipids on the surface of cell membranes are important to cellular recognition and tissue immunity.

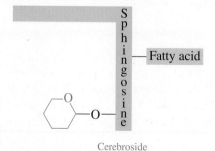

Cerebroside

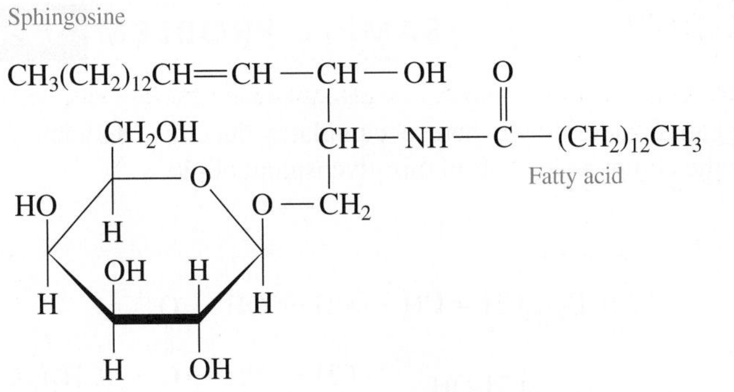

Sphingosine

Galactose   Galactocerebroside (a glycosphingolipid)

A **ganglioside** is similar to a cerebroside but contains chains of two to seven monosaccharides bonded to a ceramide. Gangliosides are found in the neurons of the brain and on the surface of cell membranes where they act as receptors for hormones, viruses, and certain drugs. In Tay–Sachs disease, the ganglioside known as GM_2 accumulates because of a genetic defect in hexosaminidase A, an enzyme needed for the removal of the N-acetyl-D-galactosamine.

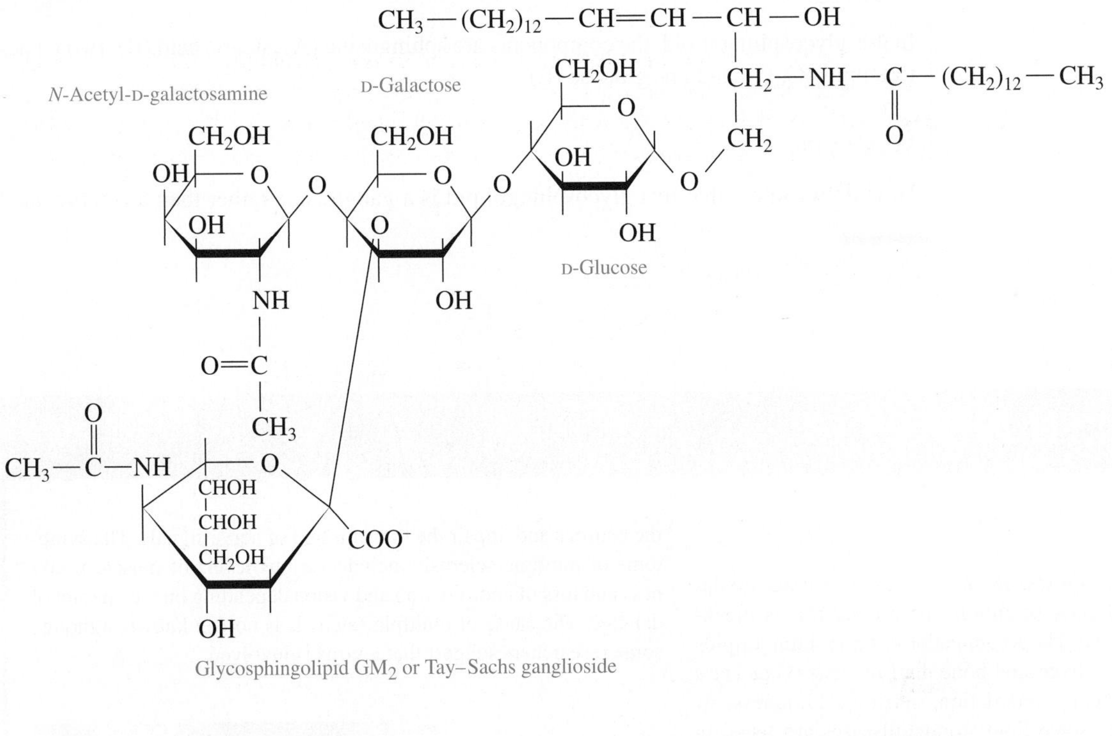

Glycosphingolipid GM_2 or Tay–Sachs ganglioside

CONCEPT CHECK 17.4

■ **Sphingolipids**

Describe the similarities and differences between the structures of sphingomyelin, cerebrosides, and gangliosides.

ANSWER

Sphingomyelin, cerebrosides, and gangliosides are all sphingolipids that contain the ceramide structure in which sphingosine is bonded to a fatty acid by an amide bond. In sphingomyelin, the —OH of a ceramide forms a phosphate ester with the amino alcohol choline. In cerebrosides, the —OH of a ceramide is bonded to one monosaccharide, galactose, or glucose. In gangliosides, the —OH of a ceramide is bonded to a chain of two to seven monosaccharides.

SAMPLE PROBLEM 17.6

■ Glycosphingolipid

In Fabry's disease, the ganglioside shown here accumulates due to a deficiency of α-galactosidase. Identify the components A–E in this glycosphingolipid:

$$
A
$$
$$
CH_3(CH_2)_{12}CH{=}CH{-}CH{-}OH \quad O
$$
$$
CH{-}NH{-}C{-}(CH_2)_{16}CH_3
$$
$$
B
$$

CH₂OH, HO, OH, OH — C

CH₂OH, OH — D

CH₂OH, O—CH₂, OH, OH — E

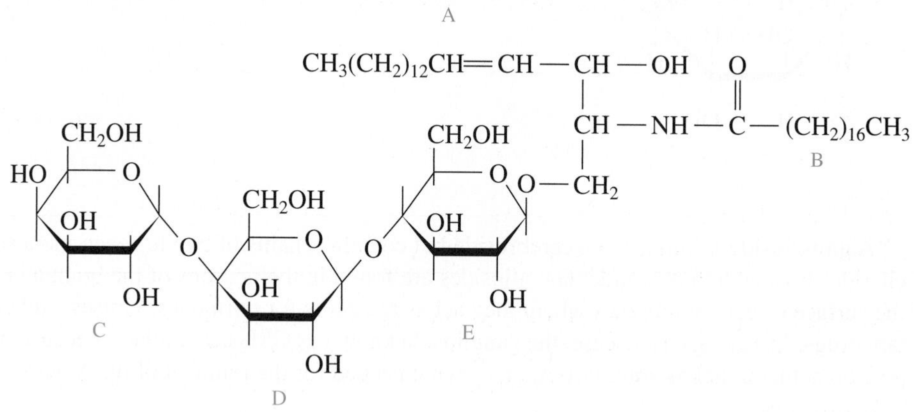

SOLUTION

In this glycosphingolipid, the components are sphingosine (A); stearic acid (B); two galactose units (C, D); and one glucose (E).

STUDY CHECK

How do we know that this glycosphingolipid is a ganglioside rather than a cerebroside?

HEALTH NOTE

Lipid Diseases

Many lipid diseases (*lipidoses*) involve the excessive accumulation of a sphingolipid because an enzyme needed for its breakdown is deficient or absent. The accumulation of these sphingolipids may enlarge the spleen, liver, and bone marrow cells (Gaucher's disease) and cause mental retardation, seizures, blindness, or death in early infancy. Some lipid storage diseases are listed in Table 17.3.

In multiple sclerosis, sphingomyelins are lost from the myelin sheath, which protects the neurons in the brain and spinal cord. As the disease progresses, the myelin sheath deteriorates. Scars form on the neurons and impair the transmission of nerve signals. The symptoms of multiple sclerosis include various levels of muscle weakness and loss of coordination and vision depending on the amount of damage. The cause of multiple sclerosis is not yet known, although some researchers suggest that a virus is involved.

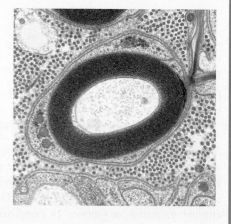

TABLE 17.3 Lipid Diseases

Name of Disease	Lipid Stored	Type	Enzyme Absent
Fabry's	Gal-gal-glucosylceramide	Ganglioside	α-Galactosidase
Gaucher's	Glucosylceramide	Cerebroside	β-Glucosidase
Niemann–Pick	Sphingomyelin	Sphingolipid	Sphingomyelinase
Tay–Sachs	GM₂ ganglioside	Ganglioside	Hexosaminidase A

QUESTIONS AND PROBLEMS

Sphingolipids

17.45 Describe the differences between glycerophospholipids and ceramides.

17.46 Describe the differences between a cerebroside and a ganglioside.

17.47 Draw the structure of a cerebroside containing palmitic acid and galactose.

17.48 What amino alcohol is found in sphingomyelin? Draw the structure of a sphingomyelin containing palmitic acid.

17.7 Steroids: Cholesterol, Bile Salts, and Steroid Hormones

Steroids are compounds containing the steroid nucleus, which consists of three cyclohexane rings and one cyclopentane ring fused together. Although they are large molecules, steroids do not hydrolyze to give fatty acids and alcohols. The four rings in the steroid nucleus are designated A, B, C, and D. The carbon atoms are numbered beginning with the carbons in ring A and ending with the two methyl groups:

LEARNING GOAL

Describe the structures of steroids.

TUTORIAL
Cholesterol

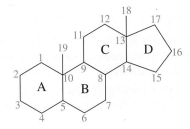

Steroid

Cholesterol

Attaching other atoms and groups of atoms to the steroid nucleus forms a wide variety of steroid compounds. **Cholesterol**, which is one of the most important and abundant steroids in the body, is a *sterol* because it contains an oxygen atom as a hydroxyl ($-$OH) group on carbon 3. Like many steroids, cholesterol has a double bond between carbon 5 and carbon 6, methyl groups at carbon 10 and carbon 13, and a carbon chain at carbon 17. In other steroids, the oxygen atom typically at carbon 3 forms a carbonyl (C$=$O) group:

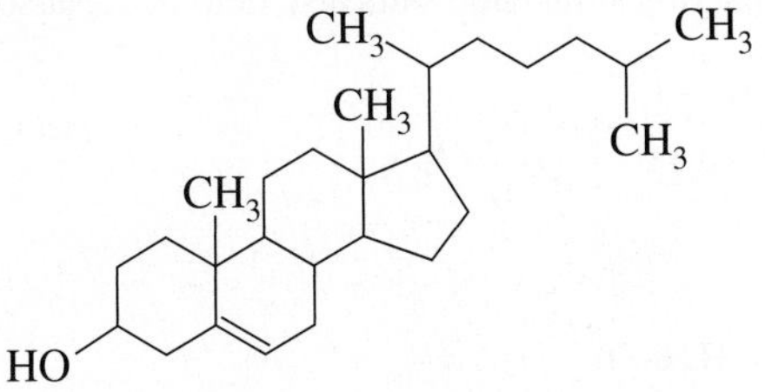

Cholesterol

Cholesterol in the Body

Cholesterol is a component of cellular membranes, myelin sheaths, and brain and nerve tissues. It is also found in the liver, bile salts, and skin, where it forms vitamin D. In the adrenal gland, cholesterol is used to synthesize steroid hormones. Cholesterol in the body is obtained from eating meats, milk, and eggs. The liver synthesizes cholesterol from fats, carbohydrates, and proteins. There is no cholesterol in vegetable and plant products.

TABLE 17.4 Cholesterol Content of Some Foods

Food	Serving Size	Cholesterol (mg)
Liver (beef)	3 oz	370
Large egg	1	200
Lobster	3 oz	175
Fried chicken	$3\frac{1}{2}$ oz	130
Hamburger	3 oz	85
Chicken (no skin)	3 oz	75
Fish (salmon)	3 oz	40
Butter	1 tablespoon	30
Whole milk	1 cup	35
Skim milk	1 cup	5
Margarine	1 tablespoon	0

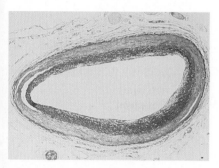

(a)

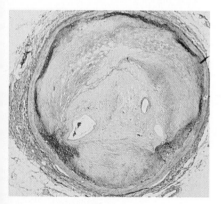

(b)

FIGURE 17.7 Excess cholesterol forms plaque that can block an artery, resulting in a heart attack. **(a)** A normal, open artery shows no buildup of plaque. **(b)** An artery that is almost completely clogged by atherosclerotic plaque.

Q What property of cholesterol would cause it to form deposits along the coronary arteries?

If a diet is high in cholesterol, the liver produces less. A typical daily American diet includes 400–500 mg of cholesterol, one of the highest in the world. The American Heart Association has recommended that we consume no more than 300 mg of cholesterol a day. The cholesterol contents of some typical foods are listed in Table 17.4.

High levels of cholesterol are associated with the accumulation of lipid deposits (plaque) that line and narrow the coronary arteries. (See Figure 17.7.) Clinically, cholesterol levels are considered elevated if the total plasma cholesterol level exceeds 200 mg/dL.

Saturated fats in the diet may stimulate the production of cholesterol by the liver. A diet that is low in foods containing cholesterol and saturated fats appears to be helpful in reducing the serum cholesterol level. Other factors that may also increase the risk of heart disease are family history, lack of exercise, smoking, obesity, diabetes, gender, and age.

SAMPLE PROBLEM 17.7

■ Cholesterol

Refer to the structure of cholesterol for the following questions:

a. What part of cholesterol is the steroid nucleus?
b. What features have been added to the steroid nucleus in cholesterol?
c. What classifies cholesterol as a sterol?

SOLUTION

a. The four fused rings form the steroid nucleus.
b. The cholesterol molecule contains an alcohol (—OH) group on the first ring, methyl groups on carbons 10 and 13, one double bond in the second ring, and a branched carbon chain on the fourth ring.
c. The alcohol group determines the sterol classification.

STUDY CHECK

Why is cholesterol in the lipid family?

Bile Salts

Bile salts are synthesized in the liver from cholesterol and stored in the gallbladder. When bile is secreted into the small intestine, the bile salts mix with the water-insoluble fats and oils in our diets. The bile salts with their nonpolar and polar regions act much like soaps, breaking apart and emulsifying large globules of fat. The emulsions that form have a larger surface area for the lipases, enzymes that digest fat. Bile salts also help in the absorption of cholesterol into the intestinal mucosa.

From cholic acid (a bile acid)   From glycine (an amino acid)

Sodium glycocholate (a bile salt)

When large amounts of cholesterol accumulate in the gallbladder, cholesterol can precipitate out and form gallstones. (See Figure 17.8.) Gallstones are composed of almost

100% cholesterol, with some calcium salts, fatty acids, and glycerophospholipids. If a gall-stone passes into the bile duct, the pain can be severe. If the gallstone obstructs the duct, bile cannot be excreted. Then bile pigments known as bilirubin enter the blood where they cause jaundice, which gives a yellow color to the skin and eyes.

Lipoproteins: Transporting Lipids

In the body, lipids must be transported through the bloodstream to tissues where they are stored, used for energy, or used to make hormones. However, most lipids are nonpolar and insoluble in the aqueous environment of blood. They are made more soluble by combining them with glycerophospholipids and proteins to form water-soluble complexes called **lipoproteins**. In general, lipoproteins are spherical particles with an outer surface of polar proteins and glycerophospholipids that surround hundreds of nonpolar molecules of tria-cylglycerols and cholesteryl esters. (See Figure 17.9.) Cholesteryl esters are the prevalent form of cholesterol in the blood. They are formed by the esterification of the hydroxyl group in cholesterol with a fatty acid:

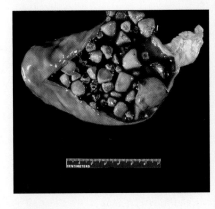

FIGURE 17.8 Gallstones form in the gallbladder when cholesterol levels are high.

Q What type of steroid is stored in the gallbladder?

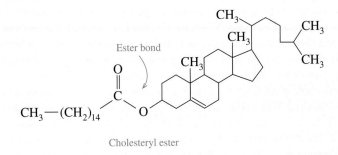

Cholesteryl ester

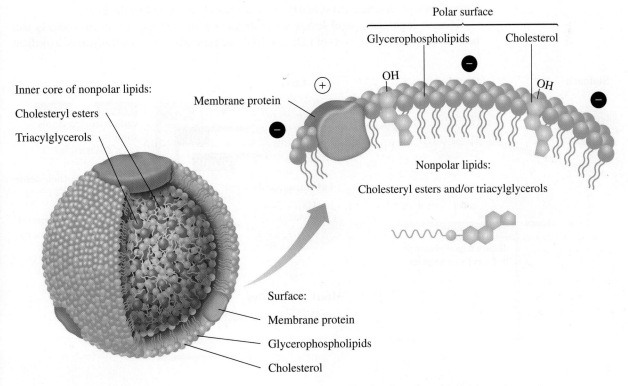

FIGURE 17.9 A spherical lipoprotein particle surrounds nonpolar lipids with polar lipids and protein for transport to body cells.

Q Why are the polar components on the surface of a lipoprotein particle and the nonpolar components at the center?

TABLE 17.5 Composition and Properties of Plasma Lipoproteins

	Chylomicron	VLDL	LDL	HDL
Density (g/mL)	0.940	0.950–1.006	1.006–1.063	1.063–1.210
	Composition (% by mass)			
Type of Lipid				
Triacylglycerol	86	55	6	4
Phospholipids	7	18	22	24
Cholesterol	2	7	8	2
Cholesteryl esters	3	12	42	15
Protein	2	8	22	55

Types of lipoproteins differ in density, lipid composition, and function. They include chylomicrons, very-low-density lipoprotein (VLDL), low-density lipoprotein (LDL), and high-density lipoprotein (HDL). The LDLs form when the triacylglycerol portion is removed from VLDLs. The density of the lipoproteins increases as the percentage of protein increases. (See Table 17.5.) The chylomicrons and the VLDLs transport triacylglycerols, glycerophospholipids, and cholesterol to the tissues for storage or to the muscles for energy. (See Figure 17.10.) The LDLs transport cholesterol to tissues to be used for the synthesis of cell membranes, steroid hormones, and bile salts. When the level of LDL exceeds the amount of cholesterol needed by the tissues, the LDLs deposit cholesterol in the arteries, which can restrict blood flow and increase the risk of developing heart disease and/or myocardial infarctions (heart attacks). This is why LDL cholesterol is called "bad" cholesterol.

The HDLs remove excess cholesterol from the tissues and carry it to the liver, where it is converted to bile salts and eliminated. When HDL levels are high, cholesterol that is not needed by the tissues is carried to the liver for elimination rather than deposited in the arteries, which gives the HDLs the name of "good" cholesterol. Most of the cholesterol in the body is synthesized in the liver, although some comes from the diet. However, a person on a high-fat diet reabsorbs cholesterol from the bile salts, causing less cholesterol to be eliminated. In addition, higher levels of saturated fats stimulate the synthesis of cholesterol by the liver.

Because high cholesterol levels are associated with the onset of atherosclerosis and heart disease, the serum levels of LDL and HDL are generally determined as part of a medical

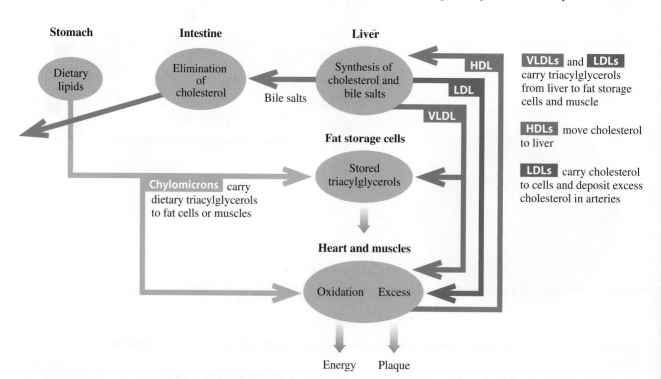

FIGURE 17.10 Lipoproteins such as HDLs and LDLs transport nonpolar lipids and cholesterol to cells and the liver.
Q What type of lipoprotein transports cholesterol to the liver?

examination. For adults, recommended levels for total cholesterol are less than 200 mg/dL with LDL less than 130 mg/dL and HDL higher than 40 mg/dL. A lower level of serum cholesterol decreases the risk of heart disease. Increased HDL levels are found in people who exercise regularly and eat less saturated fat.

Steroid Hormones

The word *hormone* comes from the Greek "to arouse" or "to excite." Hormones are chemical messengers that serve as a communication system from one part of the body to another. The *steroid* hormones, which include the sex hormones and the adrenocortical hormones, are closely related in structure to cholesterol and depend on cholesterol for their synthesis.

Two of the male sex hormones, *testosterone* and *androsterone*, promote the growth of muscle and of facial hair and the maturation of the male sex organs and of sperm.

The *estrogens*, a group of female sex hormones, direct the development of female sexual characteristics: the uterus increases in size, fat is deposited in the breasts, and the pelvis broadens. *Progesterone* prepares the uterus for the implantation of a fertilized egg. If an egg is not fertilized, the levels of progesterone and estrogen drop sharply, and menstruation follows. Synthetic forms of the female sex hormones are used in birth-control pills. As with other kinds of steroids, side effects include weight gain and a greater risk of forming blood clots. The structures of some steroid hormones follow:

Hormone	Biological Effects
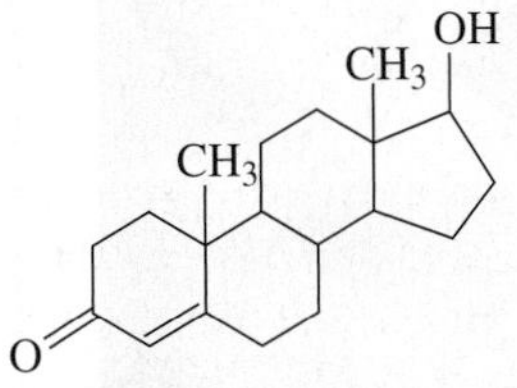 Testosterone (androgen) (produced in testes)	Development of male organs; male sexual characteristics including muscles and facial hair; sperm formation
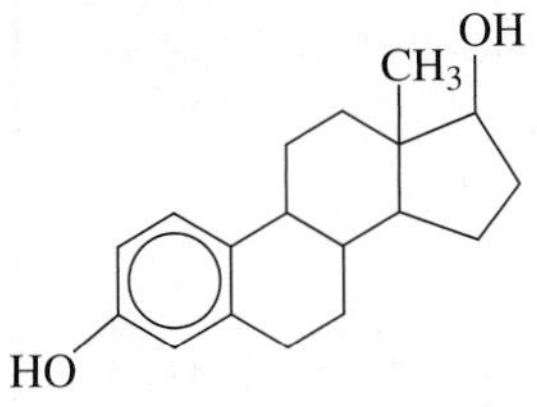 Estradiol (estrogen) (produced in ovaries)	Development of female sexual characteristics; ovulation
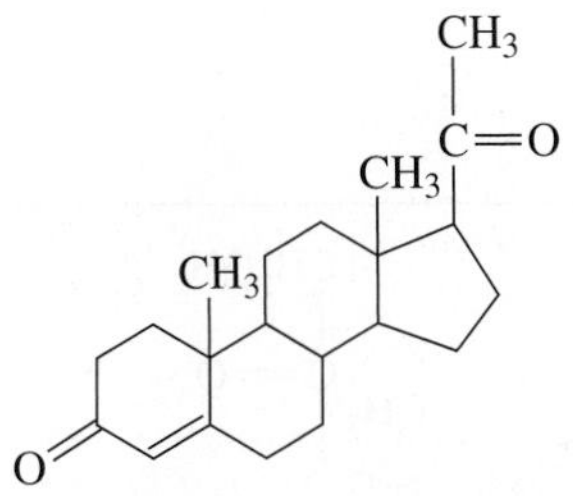 Progesterone (produced in ovaries)	Prepares uterus for fertilized egg
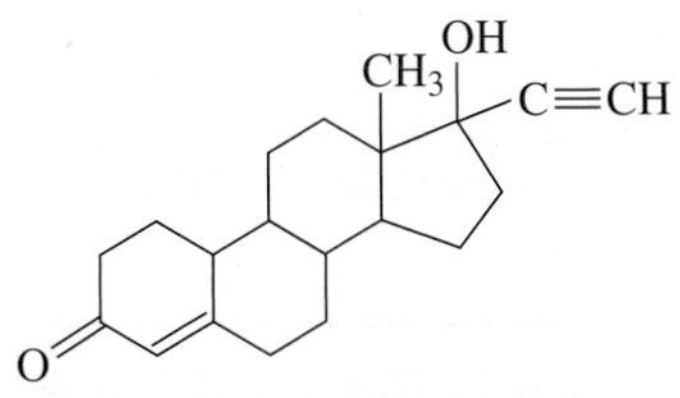 Norethindrone (synthetic progestin)	Contraceptive (birth-control) pill

Adrenal Corticosteroids

The adrenal glands, located on the top of each kidney, produce the corticosteroids. *Aldosterone*, a mineralocorticoid, is responsible for electrolyte and water balance by the kidneys. *Cortisone*, a glucocorticoid, increases the blood glucose level and stimulates the synthesis of glycogen in the liver from amino acids. Synthetic corticoids such as *prednisone* are derived from cortisone and used medically for reducing inflammation and treating asthma and rheumatoid arthritis, although health problems can result from long-term use.

HEALTH NOTE

Anabolic Steroids

Some of the physiological effects of testosterone are to increase muscle mass and decrease body fat. Derivatives of testosterone called *anabolic steroids* that enhance these effects have been synthesized. Although they have some medical uses, anabolic steroids have been used in rather high dosages by some athletes in an effort to increase muscle mass. Such use is banned by most sports organizations.

Use of anabolic steroids in attempting to improve athletic strength can cause side effects including hypertension, fluid retention, increased hair growth, sleep disturbances, and acne. Over a long period, their use may cause irreversible liver damage and decreased sperm production.

Some Anabolic Steroids

| Methandienone | Oxandrolone | Nandrolone | Stanozolol |

Corticosteroids

| Cortisone (produced in adrenal gland) | Aldosterone (mineralocorticoid) (produced in adrenal gland) | Prednisone (synthetic corticoid) |

Biological Effects

| Increases the blood glucose and glycogen levels from fatty acids and amino acids | Increases the reabsorption of Na^+ in kidneys; retention of water | Reduces inflammation; treatment of asthma and rheumatoid arthritis |

SAMPLE PROBLEM 17.8

■ Steroid Hormones

What are the groups on the steroid nucleus in the sex hormones estradiol and testosterone?

SOLUTION

Estradiol contains an aromatic ring, one methyl group, a hydroxyl group, and a phenol. Testosterone contains a ketone group, two methyl groups, an alkene, and a hydroxyl group.

STUDY CHECK

What are the similarities and differences in the structures of testosterone and the anabolic steroid nandrolone?

QUESTIONS AND PROBLEMS

Steroids: Cholesterol, Bile Salts, and Steroid Hormones

17.49 Draw the structure for the steroid nucleus.

17.50 Which of the following compounds are derived from cholesterol?
   a. glyceryl tristearate   **b.** cortisone
   c. bile salts   **d.** testosterone
   e. estradiol

17.51 What is the function of bile salts in digestion?

17.52 Why are gallstones composed of cholesterol?

17.53 What is the general structure of lipoproteins?

17.54 Why are lipoproteins needed to transport lipids in the bloodstream?

17.55 How do chylomicrons differ from very-low-density lipoproteins?

17.56 How do LDLs differ from HDLs?

17.57 Why are LDLs called "bad" cholesterol?

17.58 Why are HDLs called "good" cholesterol?

17.59 What are the similarities and differences between the sex hormones estradiol and testosterone?

17.60 What are the similarities and differences between the adrenal hormone cortisone and the synthetic corticoid prednisone?

17.61 Which of the following are male sex hormones?
   a. cholesterol   **b.** aldosterone
   c. estrogen   **d.** testosterone
   e. choline

17.62 Which of the following are adrenal corticosteroids?
   a. cholesterol   **b.** aldosterone
   c. estrogen   **d.** testosterone
   e. choline

17.8 Cell Membranes

The membrane of a cell separates the contents of the cell from the external fluids. It is semipermeable so that nutrients can enter the cell and waste products can leave. The main components of a cell membrane are glycerophospholipids and sphingolipids. Earlier in this chapter, we saw that glycerophospholipids consist of a nonpolar region or "tail" with long-chain fatty acids and a polar region or "head" from phosphoric acid and amino alcohols that ionize at physiological pH. The lipid composition of the membranes of human red blood cells and bacterial cells is given in Table 17.6.

LEARNING GOAL

Describe the composition and function of the lipid bilayer in cell membranes.

SELF STUDY ACTIVITIES

Membrane Structure
Diffusion
Osmosis
Active Transport

TABLE 17.6 Lipid Composition of Cell Membranes

Type of Lipid	Human Red Blood Cells (% m/m)	Bacterial Cells (% m/m)
Glycerophospholipids		
Choline	19	0
Ethanolamine	18	65
Serine	8	0
Triacylglycerol	0	18
Sphingomyelin	18	0
Glycosphingolipids	10	0
Cholesterol	25	0
Others	2	17

Data adapted from Mathews, C. K., Van Holde, K. K., and Ahem, K. G. *Biochemistry*; Addison Wesley/Longman/Benjamin Cummings: New York, 2000, p. 322.

FIGURE 17.11 In the fluid mosaic model of a cell membrane, proteins and cholesterol are embedded in a lipid bilayer of glycerophospholipids. The bilayer forms a membrane-type barrier with polar heads at the membrane surfaces and the nonpolar tails in the center away from the water.

Q What types of fatty acids are found in the glycerophospholipids of the lipid bilayer?

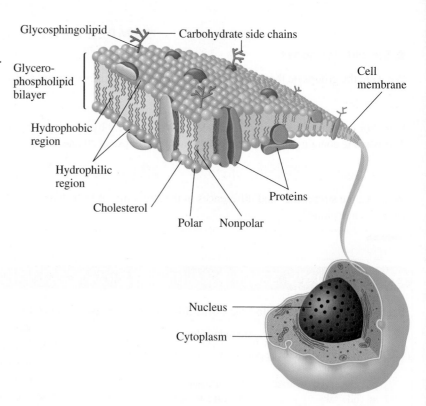

In a cell membrane, two rows of glycerophospholipids are arranged like a sandwich. Their nonpolar tails, which are hydrophobic ("water-fearing"), move to the center, while their polar heads, which are hydrophilic ("water-loving"), align on the outer edges of the membrane. This double row arrangement of glycerophospholipids is called a **lipid bilayer**. (See Figure 17.11.) One row of glycerophospholipids forms the outside surface of the membrane, which is in contact with the external fluids, and the other row forms the inside surface of the membrane, which is in contact with the internal contents of the cell.

Most of the glycerophospholipids in the lipid bilayer contain unsaturated fatty acids. Because of the kinks in the carbon chains at the cis double bonds, the glycerophospholipids do not fit closely together. As a result, the lipid bilayer is not a rigid, fixed structure, but one that is dynamic and fluid-like. This liquid-like bilayer also contains proteins, carbohydrates, and cholesterol molecules. For this reason, the model of biological membranes is referred to as the **fluid mosaic model** of membranes.

In the fluid mosaic model, peripheral proteins emerge on just one of the surfaces, outer or inner. The integral proteins extend through the entire lipid bilayer and appear on both surfaces of the membrane. Some proteins and lipids on the outer surface of the cell membrane are attached to carbohydrates to form glycoproteins and glycosphingolipids. These carbohydrate chains project into the surrounding fluid environment, where they are responsible for cell recognition and communication with chemical messengers such as hormones and neurotransmitters. In animals, cholesterol molecules embedded among the glycerophospholipids make up 20–25% of the lipid bilayer. Because cholesterol molecules are large and rigid, they reduce the flexibility of the lipid bilayer and add strength to the cell membrane.

Transport through Cell Membranes

Ions and molecules flow in and out of the cell in several ways. In the simplest transport mechanism called *diffusion* or *passive transport*, ions and small molecules migrate from a higher concentration to a lower concentration. For example, some ions as well as small molecules such as O_2, urea, and water diffuse through cell membranes. If their concentration

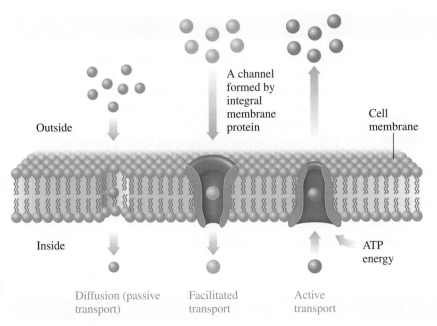

Outside

A channel
formed by
integral
membrane
protein

Cell
membrane

Inside

ATP
energy

Diffusion (passive
transport)

Facilitated
transport

Active
transport

FIGURE 17.12 Substances are transported across a cell membrane by either diffusion, facilitated transport, or by active transport.

Q What is the difference between diffusion and facilitated transport?

is greater outside the cell than inside, they diffuse into the cell. If water has a higher concentration in the cell, it diffuses out of the cell.

Another type of transport, called *facilitated transport*, increases the rate of diffusion for substances that diffuse too slowly by passive diffusion to meet cell needs. This process utilizes the integral proteins that extend from one edge of the cell membrane to the other. These protein channels allow transport of chloride ion (Cl^-), bicarbonate ion (HCO_3^-), and glucose molecules in and out of the cell.

Certain ions, such as K^+, Na^+, and Ca^{2+}, move across a cell membrane against a concentration gradient. For example, the K^+ concentration is greater inside a cell, and the Na^+ concentration is greater outside. However, in the conduction of nerve impulses and contraction of muscles, K^+ moves into the cell, and Na^+ moves out. To move an ion from a lower to a higher concentration requires energy, which is accomplished by a process known as *active transport*. In active transport, a protein complex called a Na^+/K^+ pump breaks down adenosine triphosphate (ATP) to adenosine diphosphate (ADP), which releases energy to move Na^+ and K^+ against their concentration gradients. (See Figure 17.12.)

SAMPLE PROBLEM 17.9

■ Lipid Bilayer in the Cell Membranes

Describe the role of glycerophospholipids in the lipid bilayer.

SOLUTION

Glycerophospholipids consist of polar and nonpolar parts. In a cell membrane, an alignment of the nonpolar sections toward the center with the polar sections on the outside produces a barrier that prevents the contents of a cell from mixing with the fluids on the outside of the cell.

STUDY CHECK

Why are protein channels needed in the lipid bilayer?

QUESTIONS AND PROBLEMS

Cell Membranes

17.63 What types of lipids are found in cell membranes?

17.64 Describe the structure of a lipid bilayer.

17.65 What is the function of the lipid bilayer in a cell membrane?

17.66 How do the unsaturated fatty acids in the glycerophospholipids affect the structure of cell membranes?

17.67 What is the difference between peripheral and integral proteins?

17.68 What components are attached to carbohydrates on the outer surface of a cell membrane?

17.69 What is the function of the carbohydrates on a cell membrane surface?

17.70 Describe how a cell membrane is semipermeable.

17.71 What are some ways that substances move in and out of cells?

17.72 Identify the type of transport described by each of the following:
  a. A molecule moves through a protein channel.
  b. O_2 moves into the cell from a higher concentration outside the cell.
  c. An ion moves from low to high concentration in the cell.

CONCEPT MAP

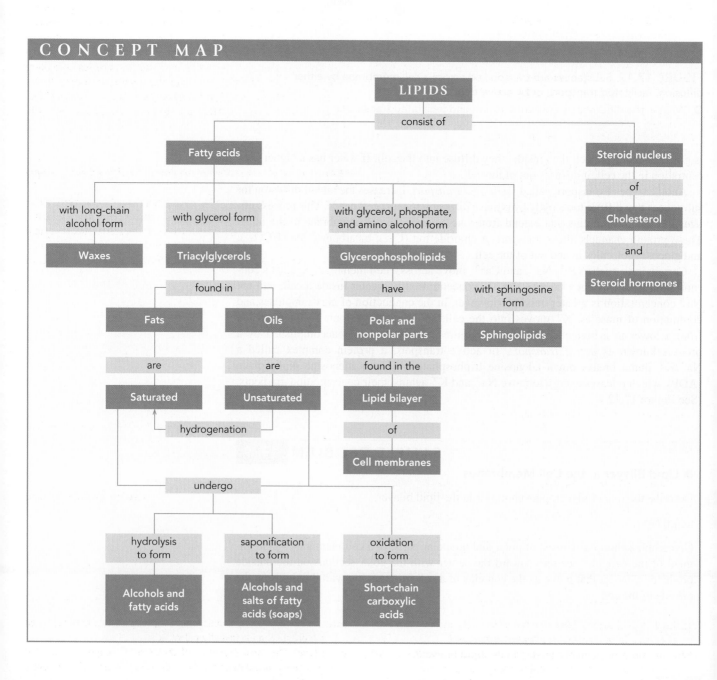

CHAPTER REVIEW

17.1 Lipids
LEARNING GOAL: *Describe the classes of lipids.*
Lipids are nonpolar compounds that are not soluble in water. Classes of lipids include waxes, fats and oils, glycerophospholipids, and steroids.

17.2 Fatty Acids
LEARNING GOAL: *Draw the condensed structural formula of a fatty acid and identify it as saturated or unsaturated.*
Fatty acids are unbranched carboxylic acids that typically contain an even number (12–18) of carbon atoms. Fatty acids may be saturated, monounsaturated with one double bond, or polyunsaturated with two or more double bonds. The double bonds in unsaturated fatty acids are almost always cis.

17.3 Waxes, Fats, and Oils
LEARNING GOAL: *Draw the condensed structural formula of a wax, fat, or oil produced by the reaction of a fatty acid and an alcohol or glycerol.*
A wax is an ester of a long-chain fatty acid and a long-chain alcohol. The triacylglycerols of fats and oils are esters of glycerol with three long-chain fatty acids. Fats contain more saturated fatty acids and have higher melting points than most vegetable oils.

17.4 Chemical Properties of Triacylglycerols
LEARNING GOAL: *Draw the structure of the product when a triacylglycerol is hydrogenated, hydrolyzed, or oxidized.*
The hydrogenation of unsaturated fatty acids converts double bonds to single bonds. The oxidation of unsaturated fatty acids produces short-chain fatty acids with disagreeable odors. The hydrolysis of the ester bonds in fats or oils produces glycerol and fatty acids. In saponification, a fat heated with a strong base produces glycerol and the salts of the fatty acids (soaps).

17.5 Glycerophospholipids
LEARNING GOAL: *Describe the characteristics of glycerophospholipids.*
Glycerophospholipids are esters of glycerol with two fatty acids and a phosphate group attached to an amino alcohol.

17.6 Sphingolipids
LEARNING GOAL: *Describe the types of lipids that contain sphingosine.*
In sphingolipids, the alcohol sphingosine forms a bond with a fatty acid and a phosphate–amino alcohol group. In glycosphingolipids, sphingosine is bonded to a fatty acid and one or more monosaccharides.

17.7 Steroids: Cholesterol, Bile Salts, and Steroid Hormones
LEARNING GOAL: *Describe the structures of steroids.*
Steroids are lipids containing the steroid nucleus, which is a fused structure of four rings. Steroids include cholesterol, bile salts, and vitamin D. Lipids, which are nonpolar, are transported through the aqueous environment of the blood by forming lipoproteins. Lipoproteins, such as chylomicrons and LDL, transport triacylglycerols from the intestines and the liver to fat cells for storage and muscles for energy. HDLs transport cholesterol from the tissues to the liver for elimination. The steroid hormones are closely related in structure to cholesterol and depend on cholesterol for their synthesis. The sex hormones, such as estrogen and testosterone, are responsible for sexual characteristics and reproduction. The adrenal corticosteroids, such as aldosterone and cortisone, regulate water balance and glucose levels in the cells.

17.8 Cell Membranes
LEARNING GOAL: *Describe the composition and function of the lipid bilayer in cell membranes.*
All animal cells are surrounded by a semipermeable membrane that separates the cellular contents from the external fluids. The membrane is composed of two rows of glycerophospholipids in a lipid bilayer. Nutrients and waste products move through the cell membrane using passive transport (diffusion), facilitated transport, or active transport.

SUMMARY OF REACTIONS

ESTERIFICATION

Glycerol + 3fatty acid molecules $\longrightarrow$ triacylglycerol + $3H_2O$

HYDROGENATION OF TRIACYLGLYCEROLS

Triacylglycerol (unsaturated) + H_2 $\xrightarrow{\text{Ni}}$ triacylglycerol (saturated)

OXIDATION OF UNSATURATED FATTY ACIDS

Fatty acids (unsaturated) $\longrightarrow$ (short-chain aldehydes) $\longrightarrow$ (short-chain carboxylic acids)

HYDROLYSIS OF TRIACYLGLYCEROLS

Triacylglycerol + $3H_2O$ $\xrightarrow{\text{HCl}}$ glycerol + 3 fatty acid molecules

SAPONIFICATION OF TRIACYLGLYCEROLS

Triacylglycerol + 3NaOH $\longrightarrow$ glycerol + 3 sodium salts of fatty acids

KEY TERMS

biodiesel A nonpetroleum fuel that can be used in place of diesel fuel; produced from renewable biological resources.

cephalin A glycerophospholipid found in brain and nerve tissues that incorporates the amino alcohol serine or ethanolamine.

ceramide A lipid in which sphingosine is attached to a fatty acid by an *amide* link.

cerebroside A glycolipid consisting of sphingosine, a fatty acid, and a monosaccharide (usually galactose).

cholesterol The most prevalent of the steroid compounds; needed for cellular membranes and the synthesis of vitamin D, hormones, and bile salts.

fat A triacylglycerol that is solid at room temperature and usually comes from animal sources.

fatty acid A long-chain carboxylic acid found in many lipids.

fluid mosaic model The concept that cell membranes are lipid bilayer structures that contain an assortment of polar lipids and proteins in a dynamic, fluid arrangement.

ganglioside A glycolipid consisting of sphingosine, a fatty acid, and two or more monosaccharides.

glycerophospholipid A polar lipid of glycerol attached to two fatty acids and a phosphate group connected to an amino alcohol such as choline, serine, or ethanolamine.

glycosphingolipid The phospholipid that combines sphingosine with a fatty acid bonded to the nitrogen group and one or more monosaccharides bonded by a glycosidic link, which replaces the —OH group of sphingosine.

hydrogenation The addition of hydrogen to unsaturated fats.

lecithins Glycerophospholipids containing choline as the amino alcohol.

lipid bilayer A model of a cell membrane in which glycerophospholipids are arranged in two rows.

lipids A family of compounds that is nonpolar in nature and not soluble in water; includes fats, waxes, glycerophospholipids, and steroids.

lipoprotein A combination of nonpolar lipids with glycerophospholipids and proteins to form a polar complex that can be transported through body fluids.

monounsaturated fatty acid A fatty acid with one double bond.

oil A triacylglycerol that is usually a liquid at room temperature and is obtained from a plant source.

polyunsaturated fatty acid A fatty acid that contains two or more double bonds.

prostaglandins (PGs) A number of compounds derived from arachidonic acid that regulate several physiological processes.

saturated fatty acids Fatty acids that have no double bonds; they have higher melting points than unsaturated fatty acids and are usually solid at room temperatures.

sphingolipids Types of lipids in which glycerol is replaced by sphingosine.

sphingomyelins Sphingolipids that consist of ceramide attached to a phosphate ester of choline, an amino alcohol.

steroids Types of lipid composed of a multicyclic ring system.

triacylglycerols A family of lipids composed of three fatty acids bonded through ester bonds to glycerol, a trihydroxy alcohol.

wax The ester of a long-chain alcohol and a long-chain saturated fatty acid.

■ UNDERSTANDING THE CONCEPTS

17.73 Palmitic acid is obtained from palm oil as glyceryl tripalmitate. Draw the condensed structural formula of glyceryl tripalmitate.

17.74 Jojoba wax in candles consists of stearic acid and a 22-carbon saturated alcohol. Draw the condensed structural formula of jojoba wax.

17.75 Sunflower oil can be used to make margarine. A triacylglycerol in sunflower oil consists of two linoleic acids and one oleic acid.

a. Draw the condensed structural formulas for two isomers of the triacylglycerol in sunflower oil.

b. Using one of the isomers, write the reaction that would be used when sunflower oil is used to make solid margarine.

17.76 Identify each of the following as saturated, monounsaturated, polyunsaturated, omega-3, or omega-6 fatty acid:

a.
$CH_3—(CH_2)_4—CH=CH—CH_2—CH=CH—(CH_2)_7—COOH$
b. linolenic acid
c. $CH_3—(CH_2)_{14}—COOH$
d. $CH_3—(CH_2)_7—CH=CH—(CH_2)_7—COOH$

ADDITIONAL QUESTIONS AND PROBLEMS

For instructor-assigned homework, go to www.masteringchemistry.com.

17.77 Among the ingredients in lipstick are beeswax, carnauba wax, hydrogenated vegetable oils, and glyceryl tricaprate (tricaprin). What types of lipids have been used? Draw the condensed structural formula of glyceryl tricaprate (tricaprin). Capric acid is the saturated 10-carbon fatty acid.

17.78 Because peanut oil floats on the top of peanut butter, many brands of peanut butter are hydrogenated. A solid product then forms that is mixed into the peanut butter and does not separate. If a triacylglycerol in peanut oil that contains one palmitic acid, one oleic acid, and one linoleic acid is completely hydrogenated, what is the product?

17.79 Trans fats are produced during the hydrogenation of polyunsaturated oils.
   a. What is the typical configuration of the double bond in a monounsaturated fatty acid?
   b. How does a trans fatty acid differ from a cis fatty acid?
   c. Draw the condensed structural formula of *trans*-oleic acid.

17.80 One mole of glyceryl trioleate (triolein) is completely hydrogenated. Draw the condensed structural formula of the product. How many moles of hydrogen are required? How many grams of hydrogen? How many liters of hydrogen are needed if the reaction is run at STP?

17.81 On the list of ingredients in a cosmetic product are glyceryl tristearate (tristearin) and a lecithin. Draw the condensed structural formula of glyceryl tristearate and a lecithin with palmitic acids and choline.

17.82 Some typical meals at fast-food restaurants are listed here. Calculate the number of kilocalories from fat and the percentage of total kilocalories due to fat (1 gram of fat = 9 kcal). Would you expect the fats to be mostly saturated or unsaturated? Why?

   a. a chicken dinner, 830 kcal, 46 g of fat
   b. a quarter-pound cheeseburger, 518 kcal, 29 g of fat
   c. pepperoni pizza (three slices), 560 kcal, 18 g of fat
   d. beef burrito, 470 kcal, 21 g of fat
   e. deep-fried fish (three pieces), 480 kcal, 28 g of fat

17.83 Identify each of the following as a fatty acid, soap, triacylglycerol, wax, glycerophospholipid, sphingolipid, or steroid:
   a. beeswax   **b.** cholesterol
   c. lecithin   **d.** glyceryl tripalmitate (tripalmitin)
   e. sodium stearate   **f.** safflower oil
   g. sphingomyelin   **h.** whale blubber
   i. adipose tissue   **j.** progesterone
   k. cortisone   **l.** stearic acid

17.84 Why would an animal that lives in a cold climate have more unsaturated triacylglycerols in its body fat than an animal that lives in a warm climate?

17.85 Identify the components (**1–6**) contained in each of the following lipids (**a–f**):
   1. glycerol   **2.** fatty acid
   3. phosphate   **4.** amino alcohol
   5. steroid nucleus   **6.** sphingosine

   a. estrogen   **b.** cephalin
   c. wax   **d.** triacylglycerol
   e. glycerophospholipid   **f.** sphingomyelin

17.86 Which of the following are found in cell membranes?
   a. cholesterol   **b.** triacylglycerols
   c. carbohydrates   **d.** proteins
   e. waxes   **f.** glycerophospholipids
   g. sphingolipids   **h.** prostaglandins

CHALLENGE QUESTIONS

17.87 Match each type of lipoprotein (**1–4**) with its description (**a–h**).
   1. chylomicron   **2.** VLDL   **3.** LDL   **4.** HDL
   a. "good" cholesterol
   b. transports most of the cholesterol to the cells
   c. carries triacylglycerols from the intestine to the fat cells
   d. transports cholesterol to the liver
   e. has the greatest abundance of protein
   f. "bad" cholesterol
   g. carries triacylglycerols synthesized in the liver to the muscles
   h. has the lowest density

17.88 **a.** Which of the following fatty acids has the lowest melting point? Explain.
   b. Which of the following fatty acids has the highest melting point? Explain.

   1. $CH_3-(CH_2)_{16}-COOH$ Stearic acid
   2.
   $CH_3-(CH_2)_4-CH=CH-CH_2-CH=CH-(CH_2)_7-COOH$
   Linoleic acid

   3. $CH_3-(CH_2)_7-CH=CH-(CH_2)_7-COOH$ Oleic acid

17.89 Draw the condensed structural formula of a glycerophospholipid that is made from stearic acid, palmitic acid, and a phosphate bonded to ethanolamine.

17.90 Olive oil consists of a high percentage of glyceryl trioleate (triolein).
   a. Draw the condensed structural formula for glyceryl trioleate (triolein).
   b. How many liters of H_2 gas at STP are needed to completely saturate 100. g of glyceryl trioleate (triolein)?
   c. How many mL of 0.250 M NaOH are needed to completely saponify 100. g of glyceryl trioleate (triolein)?

17.91 A sink drain can become clogged with solid fat such as glyceryl tristearate (tristearin).

    a. How would adding lye (NaOH) to the sink drain remove the blockage?

    b. Write an equation for the reaction that occurs.

ANSWERS

ANSWERS TO STUDY CHECKS

17.1 a glycosphingolipid

17.2 **a.** 16
    b. unsaturated
    c. liquid

17.3

$$CH_2-O-\overset{\displaystyle O}{\overset{\|}{C}}-(CH_2)_{12}-CH_3$$
$$CH-O-\overset{\displaystyle O}{\overset{\|}{C}}-(CH_2)_{12}-CH_3$$
$$CH_2-O-\overset{\displaystyle O}{\overset{\|}{C}}-(CH_2)_{12}-CH_3$$

17.4 glyceryl tristearate (tristearin)

17.5 Glycerophospholipids contain glycerol, fatty acids, a phosphate, and an amino alcohol.

17.6 Cerebrosides contain only one monosaccharide, and gangliosides contain two or more monosaccharide units.

17.7 Cholesterol is not soluble in water; it is classified with the lipid family.

17.8 Testosterone and nandrolone both contain a steroid nucleus with one double bond and a ketone group in the first ring, and a methyl and alcohol group on the five-carbon ring. Nandrolone does not have the second methyl group at the first and second ring fusion that is seen in the structure of testosterone.

17.9 Protein channels allow ions and polar molecules to flow in and out of the cell through the lipid bilayer.

ANSWERS TO SELECTED QUESTIONS AND PROBLEMS

17.1 Lipids provide energy, protection, and insulation for the organs in the body. Lipids are also an important part of cell membranes.

17.3 Because lipids are not soluble in water, a polar solvent, they are nonpolar molecules.

17.5 All fatty acids contain a long chain of carbon atoms with a carboxylic acid group. Saturated fatty acids contain only carbon–carbon single bonds; unsaturated fatty acids contain one or more double bonds.

17.7 **a.** palmitic acid

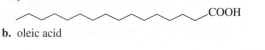

    b. oleic acid

17.9 **a.** saturated
    b. unsaturated
    c. unsaturated
    d. saturated

17.11 In a cis fatty acid, the hydrogen atoms are on the same side of the double bond, which produces a bend in the carbon chain. In a trans fatty acid, the hydrogen atoms are on opposite sides of the double bond, which gives a carbon chain without any bend.

17.13 In an omega-3 fatty acid, there is a double bond on carbon 3 counting from the methyl group, whereas in an omega-6 fatty acid, there is a double bond beginning at carbon 6 counting from the methyl group.

17.15 Arachidonic acid contains four double bonds and no side groups. In PGE_1, a part of the chain forms cyclopentane and there are hydroxyl and ketone functional groups.

17.17 Prostaglandins raise or lower blood pressure, stimulate contraction and relaxation of smooth muscle, and may cause inflammation and pain.

17.19 $CH_3-(CH_2)_{14}-\overset{\displaystyle O}{\overset{\|}{C}}-O-(CH_2)_{29}-CH_3$

17.21

$$CH_2-O-\overset{\displaystyle O}{\overset{\|}{C}}-(CH_2)_{16}-CH_3$$
$$CH-O-\overset{\displaystyle O}{\overset{\|}{C}}-(CH_2)_{16}-CH_3$$
$$CH_2-O-\overset{\displaystyle O}{\overset{\|}{C}}-(CH_2)_{16}-CH_3$$

17.23

$$CH_2-O-\overset{\displaystyle O}{\overset{\|}{C}}-(CH_2)_{14}-CH_3$$
$$CH-O-\overset{\displaystyle O}{\overset{\|}{C}}-(CH_2)_{14}-CH_3$$
$$CH_2-O-\overset{\displaystyle O}{\overset{\|}{C}}-(CH_2)_{14}-CH_3$$

17.25 Safflower oil contains fatty acids with two or more double bonds; olive oil contains a large amount of oleic acid, which has only one (monounsaturated) double bond.

17.27 Although coconut oil comes from a plant source, it has large amounts of saturated fatty acids and small amounts of unsaturated fatty acids.

17.29

$CH_2-O-\overset{\overset{\displaystyle O}{\|}}{C}-(CH_2)_7-CH=CH-(CH_2)_7-CH_3$

$CH-O-\overset{\overset{\displaystyle O}{\|}}{C}-(CH_2)_7-CH=CH-(CH_2)_7-CH_3 + 3H_2 \xrightarrow{\text{Ni}}$

$CH_2-O-\overset{\overset{\displaystyle O}{\|}}{C}-(CH_2)_7-CH=CH-(CH_2)_7-CH_3$

$CH_2-O-\overset{\overset{\displaystyle O}{\|}}{C}-(CH_2)_{16}-CH_3$

$CH-O-\overset{\overset{\displaystyle O}{\|}}{C}-(CH_2)_{16}-CH_3$

$CH_2-O-\overset{\overset{\displaystyle O}{\|}}{C}-(CH_2)_{16}-CH_3$

17.31 a. Some of the double bonds in the unsaturated fatty acids have been converted to single bonds.
   b. It now contains mostly saturated fatty acids.

17.33 a.

$CH_2-O-\overset{\overset{\displaystyle O}{\|}}{C}-(CH_2)_{12}-CH_3$

$CH-O-\overset{\overset{\displaystyle O}{\|}}{C}-(CH_2)_{12}-CH_3 + 3H_2O \xrightarrow{H^+}$

$CH_2-O-\overset{\overset{\displaystyle O}{\|}}{C}-(CH_2)_{12}-CH_3$

CH_2-OH

$CH-OH + 3HO-\overset{\overset{\displaystyle O}{\|}}{C}-(CH_2)_{12}-CH_3$

CH_2-OH

b.

$CH_2-O-\overset{\overset{\displaystyle O}{\|}}{C}-(CH_2)_{12}-CH_3$

$CH-O-\overset{\overset{\displaystyle O}{\|}}{C}-(CH_2)_{12}-CH_3 + 3NaOH \longrightarrow$

$CH_2-O-\overset{\overset{\displaystyle O}{\|}}{C}-(CH_2)_{12}-CH_3$

CH_2-OH

$CH-OH + 3Na^+ \ {}^-O-\overset{\overset{\displaystyle O}{\|}}{C}-(CH_2)_{12}-CH_3$

CH_2-OH

17.35 A triacylglycerol is composed of glycerol with three hydroxyl groups that form ester links with three long-chain fatty acids. In olestra, six to eight long-chain fatty acids form ester links with the hydroxyl groups on sucrose, a sugar. The olestra cannot be digested because our enzymes cannot break down the large olestra molecule.

17.37

$CH_2-O-\overset{\overset{\displaystyle O}{\|}}{C}-(CH_2)_{16}-CH_3$

$HC-O-\overset{\overset{\displaystyle O}{\|}}{C}-(CH_2)_{16}-CH_3$

$CH_2-O-\overset{\overset{\displaystyle O}{\|}}{C}-(CH_2)_{16}-CH_3$

17.39 A triacylglycerol consists of glycerol and three fatty acids. A glycerophospholipid consists of glycerol, two fatty acids, a phosphate group, and an amino alcohol.

17.41

$CH_2-O-\overset{\overset{\displaystyle O}{\|}}{C}-(CH_2)_{14}-CH_3$

$HC-O-\overset{\overset{\displaystyle O}{\|}}{C}-(CH_2)_{14}-CH_3$

$CH_2-O-\overset{\overset{\displaystyle O}{\|}}{\underset{\underset{\displaystyle O^-}{|}}{P}}-O-CH_2-CH_2-NH_3^+$

This is a cephalin

17.43 This glycerophospholipid is a cephalin. It contains glycerol, oleic acid, stearic acid, a phosphate, and ethanolamine.

17.45 A ceramide contains the amino alcohol sphingosine (instead of glycerol) and one fatty acid. A glycerophospholipid consists of glycerol, two fatty acids, a phosphate group, and an amino alcohol.

17.47 $CH_3-(CH_2)_{12}-CH=CH-OH$

$CH-NH-\overset{\overset{\displaystyle O}{\|}}{C}-(CH_2)_{14}-CH_3$

(sugar ring structure with HOCH$_2$, HO, OH, H substituents, O—CH$_2$)

17.49

(steroid nucleus structure)

17.51 Bile salts act to emulsify fat globules, allowing the fat to be more easily digested.

17.53 Lipoproteins are large, spherically shaped structures that transport lipids in the bloodstream. They consist of an outside layer of glycerophospholipids and proteins surrounding an inner core of hundreds of nonpolar lipids and cholesteryl esters.

17.55 Chylomicrons have a lower density than VLDLs. They pick up triacylglycerols from the intestine, whereas VLDLs transport triacylglycerols synthesized in the liver.

17.57 "Bad" cholesterol is the cholesterol carried by LDLs that can form deposits called plaque in the arteries, which narrow the arteries.

17.59 Both estradiol and testosterone contain the steroid nucleus and a hydroxyl group. Testosterone has a ketone group, a double bond, and two methyl groups. Estradiol has a benzene ring, a hydroxyl group in place of the ketone, and a methyl group.

17.61 d. Testosterone is a male sex hormone.

17.63 The lipids in a cell membrane are glycerophospholipids with smaller amounts of glycolipids and cholesterol.

17.65 The lipid bilayer in a cell membrane surrounds the cell and separates the contents of the cell from the external fluids.

17.67 The peripheral proteins in the membrane emerge on the inner or outer surface only, whereas the integral proteins extend through the membrane to both surfaces.

17.69 The carbohydrates (glycoproteins and glycosphingolipids) on the surface of cells act as receptors for cell recognition and chemical messengers such as neurotransmitters.

17.71 Substances move through cell membranes by passive transport, facilitated transport, and active transport.

17.73

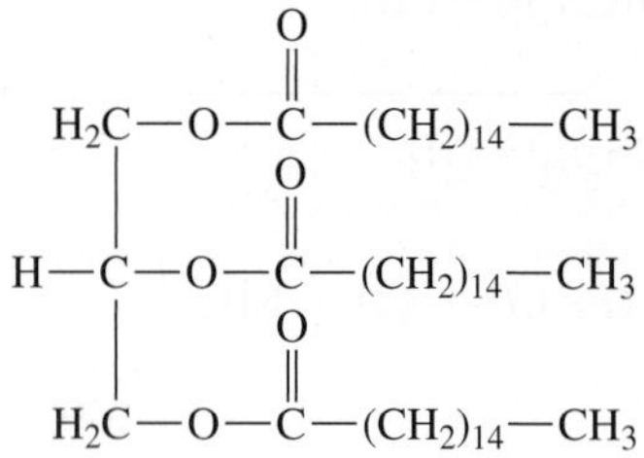

17.75 a.

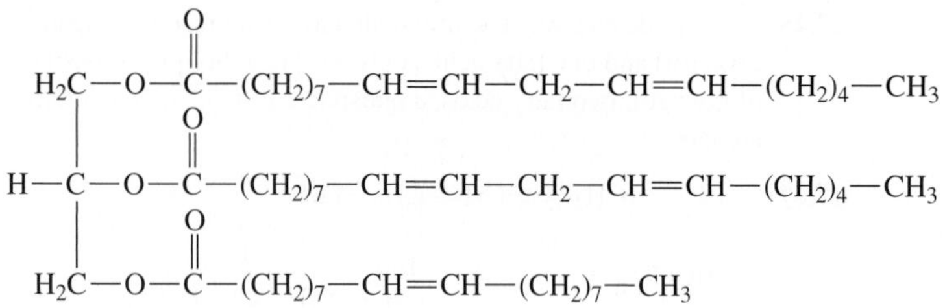

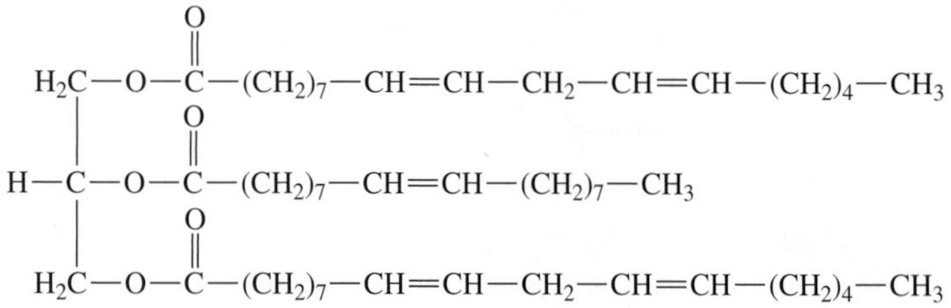

b.

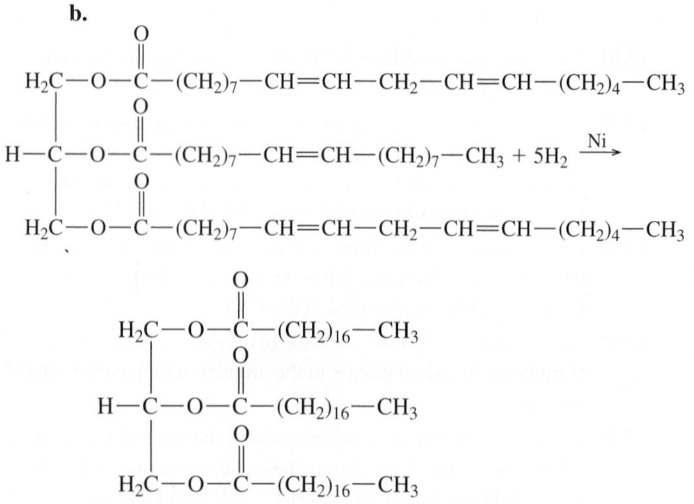

17.77 Beeswax and carnauba are waxes. Vegetable oil and glyceryl tricaprate (tricaprin) are triacylglycerols.

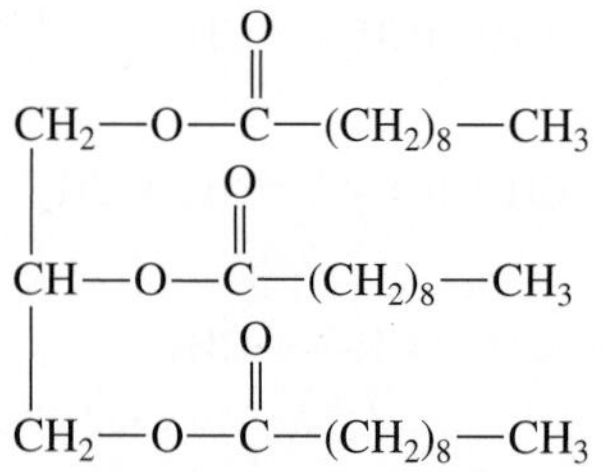

Glyceryl tricaprate (tricaprin)

17.79 a. A typical unsaturated fatty acid has a cis double bond.

b. A cis unsaturated fatty acid contains hydrogen atoms on the same side of each double bond. A trans unsaturated fatty acid has hydrogen atoms on opposite sides of the double bond that forms during hydrogenation:

c.

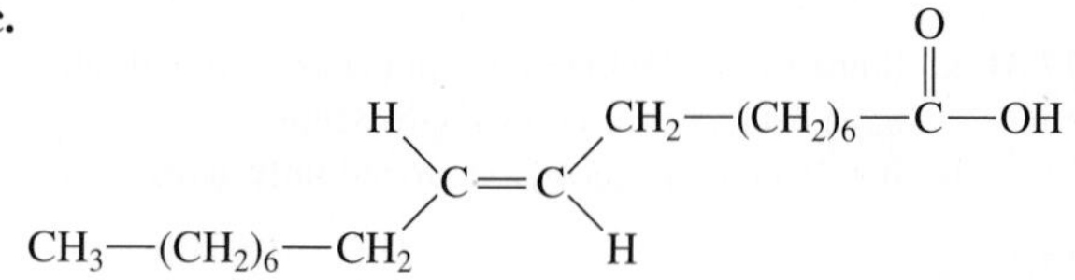

17.81

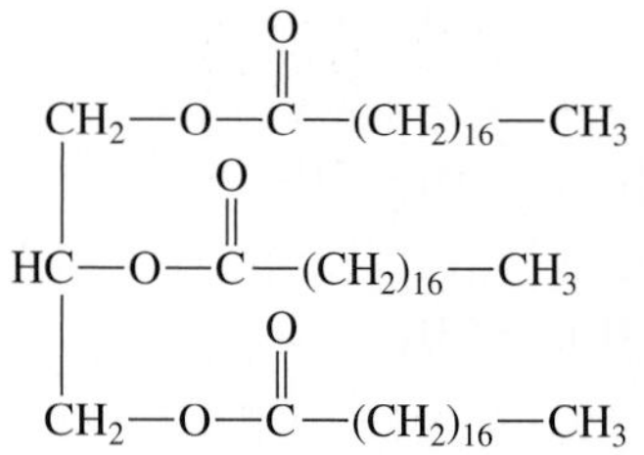

Glyceryl tristearate (tristearin)

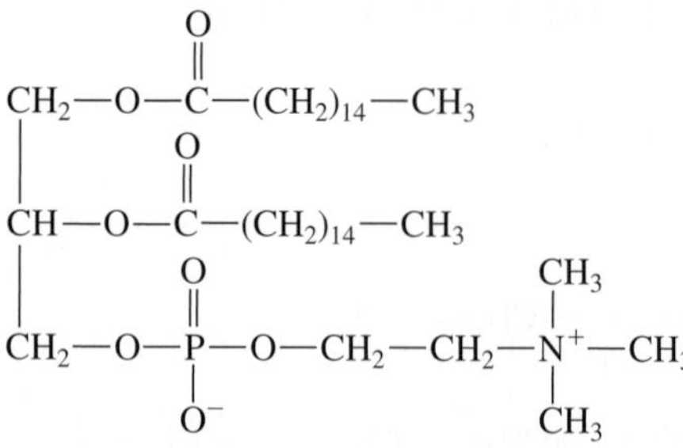

Lecithin

17.83 Stearic acid (**l**) is a fatty acid. Sodium stearate (**e**) is a soap. Glyceryl tripalmitate (**d**), safflower oil (**f**), whale blubber (**h**), and adipose tissue (**i**) are triacylglycerols. Beeswax (**a**) is a wax. Lecithin (**c**) is a glycerophospholipid. Sphingomyelin (**g**) is a sphingolipid. Cholesterol (**b**), progesterone (**j**), and cortisone (**k**) are steroids.

17.85 a. 5
b. 1, 2, 3, 4
c. 2
d. 1, 2
e. 1, 2, 3, 4
f. 2, 3, 4, 6

17.87 a. 4
b. 3
c. 1
d. 4
e. 4
f. 3
g. 2
h. 1

17.89

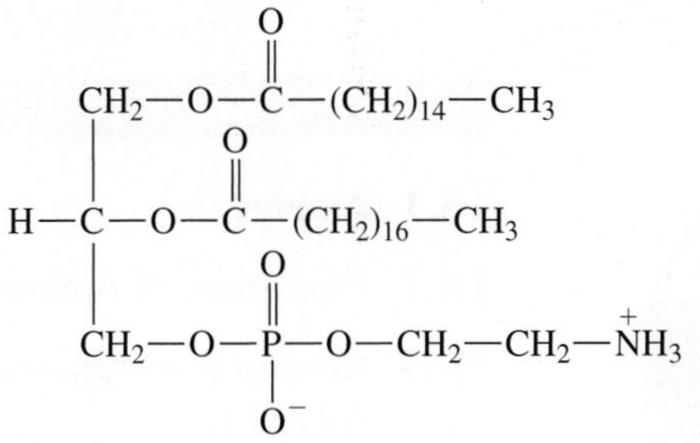

$$
\begin{array}{l}
\overset{\displaystyle O}{\overset{\|}{\text{CH}_2\!-\!\text{O}\!-\!\text{C}\!-\!(\text{CH}_2)_{14}\!-\!\text{CH}_3}} \\[4pt]
\overset{\displaystyle O}{\overset{\|}{\text{H}\!-\!\text{C}\!-\!\text{O}\!-\!\text{C}\!-\!(\text{CH}_2)_{16}\!-\!\text{CH}_3}} \\[4pt]
\overset{\displaystyle O}{\overset{\|}{\text{CH}_2\!-\!\text{O}\!-\!\text{P}\!-\!\text{O}\!-\!\text{CH}_2\!-\!\text{CH}_2\!-\!\overset{+}{\text{N}}\text{H}_3}} \\[4pt]
\underset{\displaystyle O^-}{}
\end{array}
$$

17.91 a. Adding NaOH would hydrolyze lipids such as glyceryl tristearate (tristearin), forming glycerol and salts of the fatty acids that are soluble in water and wash down the drain.

b.

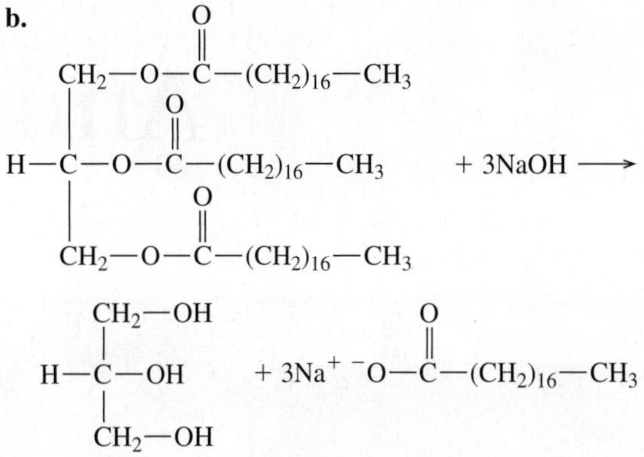

$$
\begin{array}{l}
\overset{\displaystyle O}{\overset{\|}{\text{CH}_2\!-\!\text{O}\!-\!\text{C}\!-\!(\text{CH}_2)_{16}\!-\!\text{CH}_3}} \\[4pt]
\overset{\displaystyle O}{\overset{\|}{\text{H}\!-\!\text{C}\!-\!\text{O}\!-\!\text{C}\!-\!(\text{CH}_2)_{16}\!-\!\text{CH}_3}} \qquad + \ 3\text{NaOH} \longrightarrow \\[4pt]
\overset{\displaystyle O}{\overset{\|}{\text{CH}_2\!-\!\text{O}\!-\!\text{C}\!-\!(\text{CH}_2)_{16}\!-\!\text{CH}_3}}
\end{array}
$$

$$
\begin{array}{l}
\text{CH}_2\!-\!\text{OH} \\
\text{H}\!-\!\text{C}\!-\!\text{OH} \qquad + \ 3\text{Na}^+\ ^-\text{O}\!-\!\overset{\displaystyle O}{\overset{\|}{\text{C}}}\!-\!(\text{CH}_2)_{16}\!-\!\text{CH}_3 \\
\text{CH}_2\!-\!\text{OH}
\end{array}
$$

Glycerol   Salts of stearic acid

18 Amines and Amides

"The pharmacy is one of the many factors in the final integration of chemistry and medicine in patient care," says Dorothea Lorimer, pharmacist, Kaiser Hospital. "If someone is allergic to a medication, I have to find out if a new medication has similar structural features. For instance, some people are allergic to sulfur. If there is sulfur in the new medication, there is a chance it will cause a reaction."

A prescription indicates a specific amount of a medication. At the pharmacy, the chemical name, formula, and quantity in milligrams or micrograms are checked. Then the prescribed number of capsules is prepared and placed in a container. If it is a liquid medication, a specific volume is measured and poured into a bottle.

Visit **www.masteringchemistry.com** for self-study materials and instructor-assigned homework.

A mines and amides are organic compounds that contain nitrogen. Many nitrogen-containing compounds are important to life as components of amino acids, proteins, and nucleic acids (DNA and RNA). Many amines that exhibit strong physiological activity are used in medicine as decongestants, anesthetics, and sedatives. Examples include dopamine, histamine, epinephrine, and amphetamine.

Alkaloids such as caffeine, nicotine, cocaine, and digitalis, which demonstrate powerful physiological activity, are naturally occurring amines obtained from plants. In amides, the functional group consists of a carboxyl group attached to an amine. In biochemistry, the amide bond that links amino acids in a protein is called a peptide bond. Some medically important amides include acetaminophen (Tylenol) used to reduce fever; phenobarbital, a sedative and anticonvulsant medication; and penicillin, an antibiotic.

18.1 Amines

Amines are derivatives of ammonia (NH_3) in which one or more hydrogen atoms is replaced with alkyl or aromatic groups. From Table 11.8, we know that a nitrogen atom has one lone pair along with three bonds. In methylamine, a methyl group replaces one hydrogen atom in ammonia. The bonding of two methyl groups to the nitrogen atom gives dimethylamine. In trimethylamine, methyl groups replace all three hydrogen atoms attached to the nitrogen atom.

LEARNING GOAL

Classify amines as primary (1°), secondary (2°), or tertiary (3°). Name amines using common and IUPAC names; draw the condensed structural formulas given the names.

Classification of Amines

Amines are classified by counting the number of carbon atoms directly bonded to a nitrogen atom. In a *primary (1°) amine*, a nitrogen atom is bonded to one carbon. In a *secondary (2°) amine*, a nitrogen atom is bonded to two carbons. In a *tertiary (3°) amine*, a nitrogen atom is bonded to three carbons.

In each of the following models of ammonia and amines, the atoms are arranged around the nitrogen atom in a trigonal pyramidal shape:

SELF STUDY ACTIVITY
Amine and Amide Functional Groups

Ammonia	Primary (1°) amine	Secondary (2°) amine	Tertiary (3°) amine
H—N̈—H | H	CH_3—N̈—H | H	CH_3—N̈—CH_3 | H	CH_3—N̈—CH_3 | CH_3

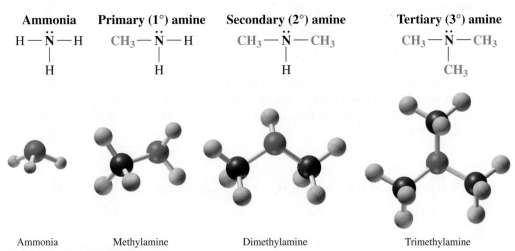

Ammonia   Methylamine   Dimethylamine   Trimethylamine

Line-Bond Formulas for Amines

We can draw line-bond formulas for amines just as we did for other organic compounds. For example, we can draw the following line-bond formulas and classify each of the amines:

TUTORIAL
Know What Amine?

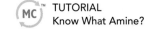

Primary amine (1°)   Secondary amine (2°)   Tertiary amine (3°)

SAMPLE PROBLEM 18.1

■ **Classifying Amines**

Classify the following amines as primary (1°), secondary (2°), or tertiary (3°):

a. 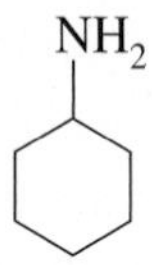 NH_2

b. CH_3
    $CH_3-N-CH_2-CH_3$

c. 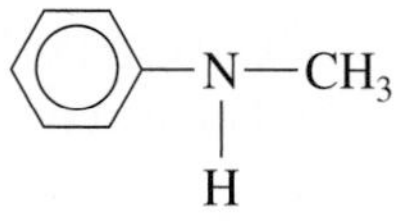 $-N-CH_3$
    H

d. 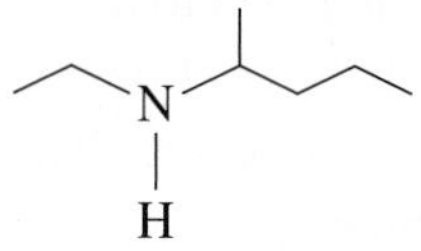 (line-bond structure) N
    H

SOLUTION

a. This is a primary (1°) amine because there is one alkyl group (cyclohexyl) attached to a nitrogen atom.
b. This is a tertiary (3°) amine. There are three alkyl groups (two methyls and one ethyl) attached to the nitrogen atom.
c. This is a secondary (2°) amine with two carbon groups, methyl and phenyl, bonded to the nitrogen atom.
d. The nitrogen atom in this line-bond formula is bonded to two carbon atoms, which makes it a secondary (2°) amine.

STUDY CHECK

Classify the following amine as primary (1°), secondary (2°), or tertiary (3°):

$CH_3-CH_2-N-CH_2-CH_3$
$\quad\quad\quad\quad|$
$\quad\quad\quad CH_3$

Naming Amines

Several systems are used for naming amines. For simple amines, the common names are often used. In the common name, the alkyl groups bonded to the nitrogen atom are listed in alphabetical order. The prefixes *di* and *tri* are used to indicate two and three identical substituents.

CH_3-NH_2 $CH_3-NH-CH_3$ $CH_3-CH_2-CH_2-N-CH_2-CH_3$
                                                                $\quad\quad\quad\quad\quad\quad\quad\quad\quad|$
                                                                $\quad\quad\quad\quad\quad\quad\quad\quad\quad CH_3$
Methylamine   Dimethylamine   Ethylmethylpropylamine

CONCEPT CHECK 18.1

■ **Common Names of Amines**

Give a common name for each of the following amines:

a. $CH_3-CH_2-NH_2$

b. CH_3
    CH_3-N-CH_3

ANSWER

a. This amine has one ethyl group attached to the nitrogen atom; its name is ethylamine.
b. The common name for an amine with three methyl groups attached to the nitrogen atom is trimethylamine.

HEALTH NOTE

Amines in Health and Medicine

In the body, the production of histamine increases the response to allergic reactions or injury. Histamine dilates blood vessels, increases the permeability of the cells, and causes redness and swelling. Using an antihistamine such as diphenylhydramine helps reduce the effects of histamine.

Histamine

Diphenylhydramine

In the body, hormones called *biogenic amines* carry messages between the central nervous system and nerve cells. Epinephrine (adrenaline) and norepinephrine (noradrenaline) are released by the adrenal medulla in "fight or flight" situations to raise the blood glucose level and move blood to the muscles. The prefix *nor* in a drug name means there is one less —CH_3 group on the nitrogen atom. Norepinephrine is used in remedies for colds, hay fever, and asthma because it contracts the capillaries in the mucous membranes of the respiratory passages. Parkinson's disease is a result of a deficiency in another biogenic amine called dopamine.

Epinephrine (adrenaline)

Norepinephrine (noradrenaline)

Dopamine

Produced synthetically, amphetamines (known as "uppers") are stimulants of the central nervous system much like epinephrine, but they also increase cardiovascular activity and depress the appetite. They are sometimes used to bring about weight loss, but they can cause chemical dependency. Benzedrine and Neo-Synephrine (phenylephrine) are used in medications to reduce respiratory congestion from colds, hay fever, and asthma. Sometimes, Benzedrine is used to combat the desire to sleep. Methedrine may be used to treat depression and in the illegal form is known as "speed" or "crank." The prefix *meth* means that there is one more methyl group on the nitrogen atom.

Benzedrine (amphetamine)

Neo-Synephrine (phenylephrine)

Methamphetamine (methedrine)

The IUPAC names for amines are similar to the names we used for alcohols, except that the *e* in the parent alkane name is replaced with *amine*:

CH_4 CH_3—**OH** CH_3—**NH_2**

Methane   Methan**ol**   Methan**amine**

STEP 1   **Name the longest carbon chain bonded to the N atom by replacing the *e* with *amine*:**

CH_3—NH_2 CH_3—CH_2—NH_2

Methan**amine**   Ethan**amine**

STEP 2   **Number the carbon chain to show the position of the amine group and other substituents:**

CH_3—CH_2—CH_2—NH_2

1-Propan**amine**

2-Propan**amine**

2-Butan**amine**

3-Methyl-1-butan**amine**

STEP 3 **In secondary and tertiary amines, use the prefix *N*- to name alkyl groups attached to the N atom.** Alkyl groups attached to the N atom are listed alphabetically:

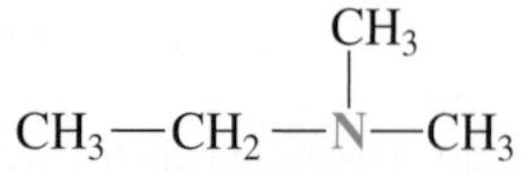

$$CH_3-CH_2-\overset{\overset{\displaystyle CH_3}{|}}{N}-CH_3$$
N,N-Dimethylethanamine

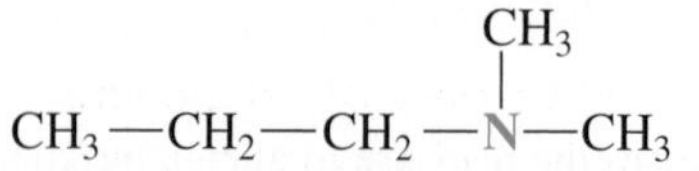

$$CH_3-CH_2-CH_2-\overset{\overset{\displaystyle CH_3}{|}}{N}-CH_3$$
N,N-Dimethyl-1-propanamine

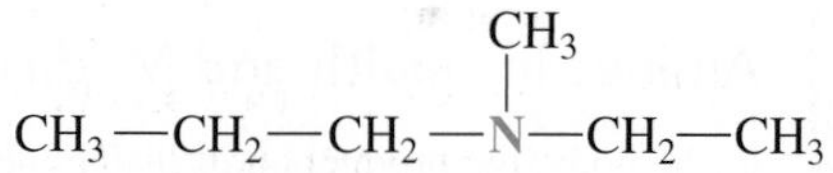

$$CH_3-CH_2-CH_2-\overset{\overset{\displaystyle CH_3}{|}}{N}-CH_2-CH_3$$
N-Ethyl-*N*-methyl-1-propanamine

An amine with two amine functional groups is named as a *diamine*. For example, the amines 1,4-butanediamine and 1,5-pentanediamine contribute to the odors of decaying flesh:

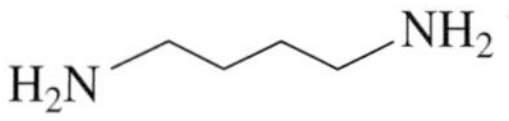

H_2N ⌇⌇⌇ NH_2
1,4-Butanediamine
(putrescine)

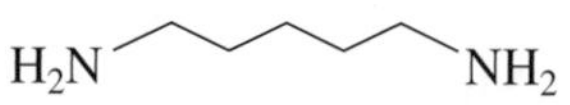

H_2N ⌇⌇⌇⌇ NH_2
1,5-Pentanediamine
(cadaverine)

In amines where another functional group takes priority, the $-NH_2$ group is named as a substituent *amino* group and numbered to show its location. For the major functional groups we have studied, the increasing priority follows the increase in oxidation:

Low priority $-NH_2 < -OH < -\overset{\overset{\displaystyle O}{||}}{C}- < -\overset{\overset{\displaystyle O}{||}}{C}-H < -\overset{\overset{\displaystyle O}{||}}{C}-OH$ High priority

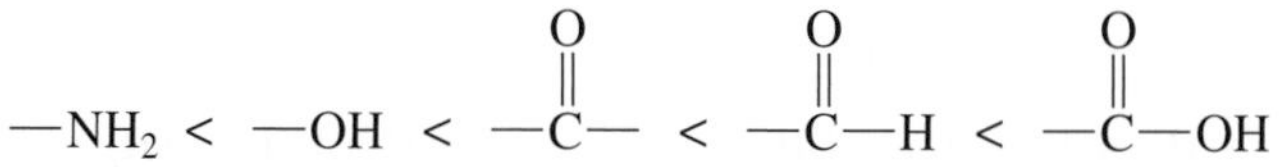

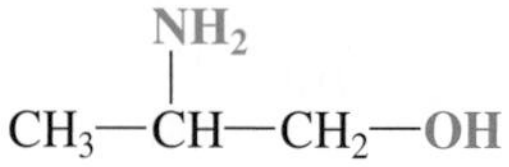

$$CH_3-\overset{\overset{\displaystyle NH_2}{|}}{CH}-CH_2-OH$$
2-Amino-1-propanol

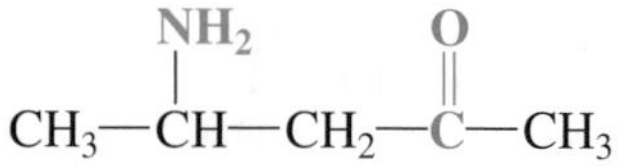

$$CH_3-\overset{\overset{\displaystyle NH_2}{|}}{CH}-CH_2-\overset{\overset{\displaystyle O}{||}}{C}-CH_3$$
4-Amino-2-pentanone

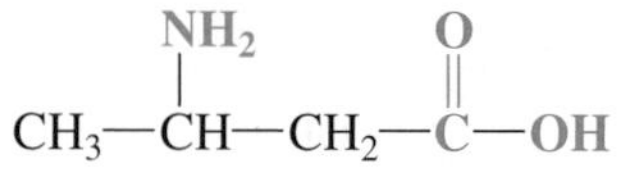

$$CH_3-\overset{\overset{\displaystyle NH_2}{|}}{CH}-CH_2-\overset{\overset{\displaystyle O}{||}}{C}-OH$$
3-Aminobutanoic acid

CONCEPT CHECK 18.2

■ IUPAC Names of Amines with Substituents

An amine has the name *N*-methyl-1-hexanamine.

a. How many carbon atoms are in the carbon chain attached to the N atom?
b. What is indicated by the "1" in the 1-hexanamine part of the name?
c. What is indicated by the "*N*-methyl" part of the name?
d. What is the condensed structural formula of the amine?
e. If the N atom were attached to the second carbon of the chain, how would the compound be named?

ANSWER
a. In a hexanamine, the carbon chain attached to the N atom has 6 carbon atoms.
b. The "1" in 1-hexanamine indicates that the N atom is attached to carbon 1 of the chain.
c. The "*N*-methyl" part of the name indicates that a methyl group ($-CH_3$) is attached to the N atom.
d. The condensed structural formula of *N*-methyl-1-hexanamine is as follows:

$$CH_3-CH_2-CH_2-CH_2-CH_2-CH_2-NH-CH_3$$

e. If the N atom were attached to the second carbon of the chain, the compound would be named *N*-methyl-2-hexanamine.

SAMPLE PROBLEM 18.2

■ IUPAC Names for Amines

Give the IUPAC name of the following amine:

$$CH_3-CH_2-CH_2-CH_2-NH-CH_2-CH_3$$

SOLUTION

STEP 1   **Name the longest carbon chain bonded to the *N* atom by replacing the *e* with *amine*.**   The four-carbon chain attached to a nitrogen atom is named by replacing the *e* in butane with *amine*: butanamine.

STEP 2   **Number the carbon chain to show the position of the amine group and other substituents.**   The N atom in the amine group is attached to carbon 1 of butanamine: 1-butanamine.

STEP 3   **In secondary and tertiary amines, use the prefix *N*- to name alkyl groups attached to the N atom.**   An ethyl group attached to the N atom is indicated as *N*-ethyl. The name of the amine is *N*-ethyl-1-butanamine.

STUDY CHECK

Draw the condensed structural formula of *N*-ethyl-1-propanamine.

Aromatic Amines

The aromatic amines use the name *aniline*, which is approved by IUPAC:

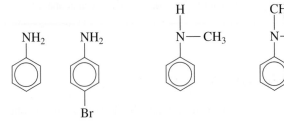

Aniline   4-Bromoaniline   *N*-Methylaniline   *N*,*N*-Dimethylaniline
             (*p*-bromoaniline)

QUESTIONS AND PROBLEMS

Amines

18.1 What is a primary amine?

18.2 What is a tertiary amine?

18.3 Classify each of the following amines as primary (1°), secondary (2°), or tertiary (3°):

a. $CH_3-CH_2-CH_2-NH_2$

b. $CH_3-\overset{\overset{\displaystyle H}{|}}{N}-CH_2-CH_3$

c. 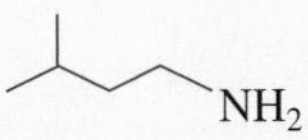   ![structure] NH_2

d. 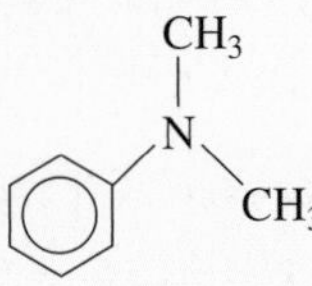   ![benzene ring with] $\overset{\overset{\displaystyle N}{|}}{}$ CH$_3$, CH$_3$

e. $CH_3-\overset{\overset{\displaystyle CH_3}{|}}{\underset{\underset{\displaystyle CH_3}{|}}{CH}}-N-CH_2-CH_3$

c. ![structure] $\overset{\overset{\displaystyle H}{|}}{N}$ (with propyl and ethyl groups)

d. ![benzene ring] $\overset{\overset{\displaystyle CH_3}{|}}{CH}-NH_2$

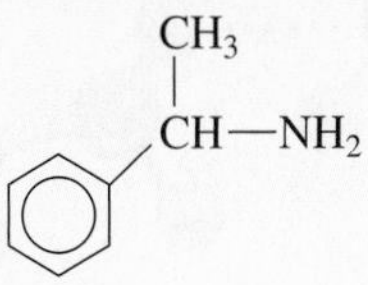

e. $CH_3-\overset{\overset{\displaystyle H}{|}}{N}-\overset{\overset{\displaystyle CH_3}{|}}{\underset{\underset{\displaystyle CH_3}{|}}{C}}-CH_3$

18.5 Write the common and IUPAC names for each of the following:

a. $CH_3-CH_2-NH_2$

b. $CH_3-NH-CH_2-CH_2-CH_3$

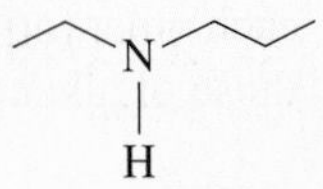

c. $CH_3-CH_2-\overset{\overset{\displaystyle CH_3}{|}}{N}-CH_2-CH_3$

d. $CH_3-\overset{\overset{\displaystyle NH_2}{|}}{CH}-CH_3$

18.4 Classify each of the following amines as primary (1°), secondary (2°), or tertiary (3°):

a. $CH_3-CH_2-\overset{\overset{\displaystyle NH_2}{|}}{CH}-CH_3$

b. $CH_3-CH_2-\overset{\overset{\displaystyle CH_3}{|}}{N}-CH_2-CH_3$

18.6 Write the common and IUPAC names for each of the following:

a. $CH_3-CH_2-CH_2-NH_2$

b. $CH_3-NH-CH_2-CH_3$

c. $CH_3-CH_2-CH_2-CH_2-NH_2$

d. $CH_3-CH_2-\overset{\displaystyle CH_2-CH_3}{\underset{|}{N}}-CH_2-CH_3$

18.7 Write the IUPAC names for each of the following:

a. $CH_3-\overset{\displaystyle NH_2}{\underset{|}{CH}}-CH_2-CH_3$

b. 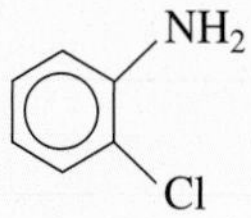 [benzene ring with NH_2 and Cl substituents]

c. $H_2N-CH_2-CH_2-\overset{\displaystyle O}{\overset{||}{C}}-H$

d. 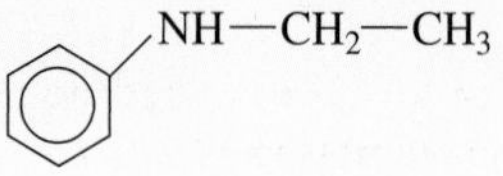 [benzene ring with $NH-CH_2-CH_3$ substituent]

18.8 Write the IUPAC names for each of the following:

a. $CH_3-\overset{\displaystyle O}{\overset{||}{C}}-\overset{\displaystyle NH_2}{\underset{|}{CH}}-CH_3$

b. $CH_3-\overset{\displaystyle NH_2}{\underset{|}{CH}}-CH_2-CH_2-CH_2-NH_2$

c. 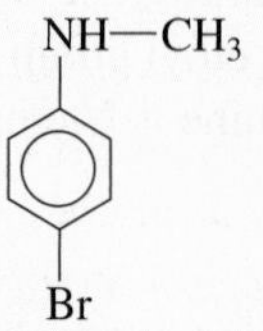 [benzene ring with $NH-CH_3$ and Br substituents]

d. 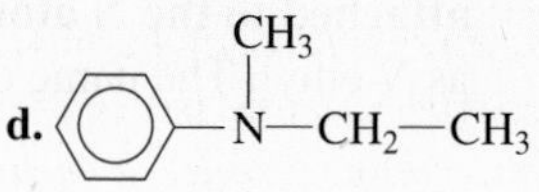 [benzene ring with $\overset{\displaystyle CH_3}{\underset{|}{N}}-CH_2-CH_3$ substituent]

18.9 Draw the condensed structural formula for each of the following amines:

a. ethylamine
b. N-methylaniline
c. butylpropylamine
d. 2-pentanamine

18.10 Draw the condensed structural formula for each of the following amines:

a. dimethylamine
b. p-chloroaniline
c. N,N-diethylaniline
d. 1-amino-3-pentanone

18.2 Properties of Amines

LEARNING GOAL

Describe the boiling points and solubility of amines; write equations for the ionization and neutralization of amines.

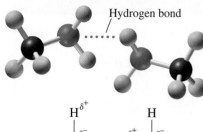

Hydrogen bond

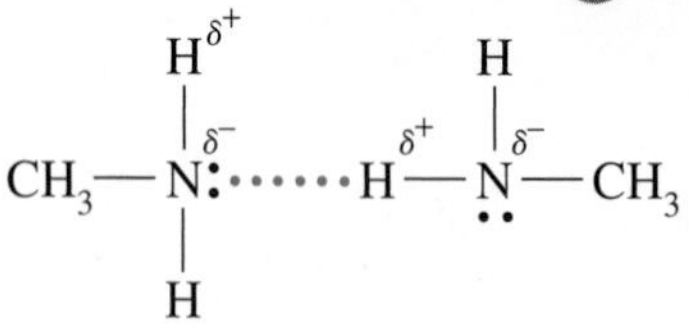

$CH_3-\overset{H}{\underset{|}{\overset{\delta^+}{N}:}} \cdots \cdots \overset{\delta^+}{H}-\overset{H}{\underset{|}{\overset{\delta^-}{N}}}-CH_3$

Amines have boiling points higher than alkanes of similar mass but lower than the alcohols:

CH_3-CH_3 CH_3-NH_2 CH_3-OH
Ethane   Methanamine   Methanol
bp −84 °C   bp −7 °C   bp 65 °C

Because amines contain a polar N—H bond, they form hydrogen bonds. However, nitrogen is not as electronegative as oxygen, which makes the hydrogen bonds in amines weaker. The —NH_2 in primary (1°) amines, which have two N—H bonds, can form more hydrogen bonds, which gives them higher boiling points than the secondary (2°) amines of the same mass. It is not possible for tertiary (3°) amines to hydrogen bond with each other (no N—H bonds), which makes their boiling points much lower and similar to those of alkanes:

$CH_3-CH_2-CH_2-NH_2$ $CH_3-CH_2-NH-CH_3$ $CH_3-\overset{\displaystyle CH_3}{\underset{|}{N}}-CH_3$
Propylamine (1°)   Ethylmethylamine (2°)   Trimethylamine (3°)
bp 48 °C   bp 36 °C   bp 3 °C

Solubility in Water

Like alcohols, the smaller amines, including tertiary ones, are soluble because they form hydrogen bonds with water. (See Figure 18.1.) However, in amines with more than six carbon atoms, the effect of hydrogen bonding is diminished. As with alcohols, the nonpolar alkyl part of the molecules decreases the solubility of an amine in water.

CONCEPT CHECK 18.3

■ Boiling Points and Solubility of Amines

a. If the compounds trimethylamine and ethylmethylamine have the same molar mass, why is the boiling point of trimethylamine (3 °C) lower than that of ethylmethylamine (37 °C)?

b. Why is $CH_3—CH_2—NH—CH_2—CH_3$ more soluble in water than

$$CH_3—CH_2—CH_2—CH_2—\overset{\overset{\displaystyle H}{|}}{N}—CH_2—CH_2—CH_3?$$

ANSWER
a. With polar N—H bonds, ethylmethylamine molecules form hydrogen bonds. Thus, a higher temperature is required to break the hydrogen bonds and form a gas. However, trimethylamine, which is a tertiary amine, does not have N—H bonds and cannot hydrogen bond with other trimethylamine molecules.
b. Hydrogen bonding is sufficient to make amines with six or fewer carbon atoms soluble in water. Amines with seven or more carbon atoms are not soluble because the effect of hydrogen bonding is not sufficient to overcome the effect of the large hydrocarbon groups that are nonpolar and not soluble in water.

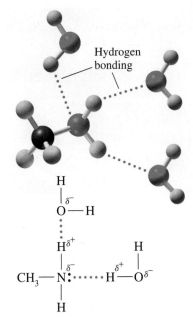

FIGURE 18.1 Hydrogen bonding occurs between amines and water molecules.

Q Why are tertiary (3°) amines soluble in water?

Ionization of an Amine in Water

In Chapter 10, we saw that ammonia (NH_3) acts as a Brønsted–Lowry base because it accepts a proton (H^+) from water to produce an ammonium ion (NH_4^+) and a hydroxide ion (OH^-):

$$\ddot{N}H_3 + H_2O \rightleftharpoons NH_4^+ + OH^-$$

Ammonia   Ammonium ion   Hydroxide ion

In water, amines also act as Brønsted–Lowry bases because the lone electron pair on the nitrogen atom accepts a proton from water. The products are an alkyl ammonium ion and hydroxide ion. The name of the alkyl ammonium ion is similar to the common amine name, but *amine* is replaced by *ammonium ion*:

$$CH_3—\ddot{N}H_2 + H_2O \rightleftharpoons CH_3—\overset{+}{N}H_3 + OH^-$$

Methylamine   Methylammonium ion   Hydroxide ion

Secondary and tertiary amines also accept a proton to form ammonium ions:

$$CH_3—\underset{\underset{\displaystyle CH_3}{|}}{\ddot{N}H} + H_2O \rightleftharpoons CH_3—\underset{\underset{\displaystyle CH_3}{|}}{\overset{+}{N}H_2} + OH^-$$

Dimethylamine   Dimethylammonium ion   Hydroxide ion

TUTORIAL
Reactions of Amines

Basicity of Amines

Because amines act as weak bases by accepting protons from water and producing hydroxide ions, their aqueous solutions are basic. We can write the equilibrium constant K for methylamine as follows:

$$K = \frac{[CH_3—NH_3^+][OH^-]}{[CH_3—NH_2]} = 4.4 \times 10^{-4}$$

Most of the K values for amines are less than 10^{-3} at 25 °C, which means that the equilibrium favors the amine molecules. Aqueous solutions of amines have basic pH values and turn red litmus paper blue. We can compare the strengths of some amines by looking at their K values:

SELF STUDY ACTIVITY
Amines as Bases

Ammonia	1° Amine		2° Amine	3° Amine
NH_3	$CH_3—NH_2$	$CH_3—CH_2—NH_2$	$CH_3—NH—CH_3$	$CH_3—\overset{\overset{\displaystyle CH_3}{|}}{N}—CH_3$
K 1.8×10^{-5}	4.4×10^{-4}	5.6×10^{-4}	5.1×10^{-4}	5.3×10^{-5}

Amine Salts

When you squeeze lemon juice on fish, the "fishy odor" of the amines is removed by converting them to amine salts. In a *neutralization reaction*, an amine acts as a base and reacts with an acid to form an **amine salt**. The lone pair of electrons on the nitrogen atom accepts a proton H^+ from an acid to give an amine salt; no water is formed. An amine salt is named by replacing the *amine* part of the name with *ammonium* followed by the name of the negative ion.

Neutralization of an Amine

Amine   Acid   Amine salt

$CH_3-\overset{\cdot\cdot}{N}H_2 + HCl \longrightarrow CH_3-\overset{+}{N}H_3\,Cl^-$

Methyl**amine**   Methyl**ammonium chloride**

$CH_3-\overset{\cdot\cdot}{N}H + HCl \longrightarrow CH_3-\overset{+}{N}H_2\,Cl^-$
      | |
      CH_3 CH_3

Dimethyl**amine**   Dimethyl**ammonium chloride**

The ammonium ions are classified as primary (1°), secondary (2°), and tertiary (3°) depending on the number of alkyl groups bonded to the N atom:

H CH_3 CH_3

$CH_3-\overset{+}{N}-H$ $CH_3-\overset{+}{N}-H$ $CH_3-\overset{+}{N}-H$

H   H CH_3

Primary (1°)   Secondary (2°)   Tertiary (3°)

In a **quaternary ammonium ion**, a nitrogen atom bonds to four carbon groups. In the quaternary ion, the nitrogen atom has a positive charge just as it does in other amine salts. Choline, an amino alcohol present in glycerophospholipids, is a quaternary ammonium ion:

CH_3 CH_3

$CH_3-\overset{+}{N}-CH_3\,Cl^-$ $HO-CH_2-CH_2-\overset{+}{N}-CH_3$

CH_3 CH_3

Tetramethylammonium chloride   Choline

The quaternary salts differ from other amine salts because the nitrogen atom is not bonded to an H atom. Thus, quaternary salts do not react with bases.

Properties of Amine Salts

Amine salts are ionic compounds with strong attractions between the positively charged ammonium ion and an anion, usually chloride. Like most salts, amine salts are solid at room temperature, odorless, and soluble in water and body fluids. For this reason, amines used as drugs are converted to their amine salts. The amine salt of ephedrine is used as a bronchodilator and in decongestant products such as Sudafed. The amine salt of diphenhydramine is used in products such as Benadryl for relief of itching and pain from skin irritations and rashes. (See Figure 18.2.) In pharmaceuticals, the naming of the amine salt follows an older method of giving the amine name followed by the name of the acid:

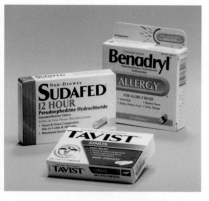

FIGURE 18.2 Decongestants and products that relieve itch and skin irritations can contain ammonium salts.

Q Why are ammonium salts used in drugs rather than the biologically active amines?

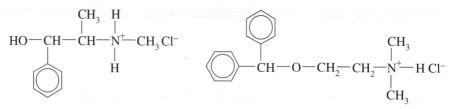

Ephedrine hydrochloride   Diphenhydramine hydrochloride
ephedrine HCl   diphenylhydramine HCl
Sudafed®   Benadryl®

When an amine salt reacts with a strong base such as NaOH, it is converted back to the amine, which is also called the free amine or free base:

$$CH_3-NH_3^+Cl^- + NaOH \longrightarrow CH_3-NH_2 + NaCl + H_2O$$

The narcotic cocaine is typically extracted from coca leaves using an acidic solution to give a white, solid amine salt, which is cocaine hydrochloride. It is the salt of cocaine (cocaine hydrochloride) that is smuggled and used illegally on the street. "Crack cocaine" is the free amine or free base of the amine obtained by treating the cocaine hydrochloride with NaOH and ether, a process known as "free-basing." The solid product is known as "crack cocaine" because it makes a cracking noise when heated. The free amine is rapidly absorbed when smoked and gives stronger highs than the cocaine hydrochloride, which makes crack cocaine more addictive:

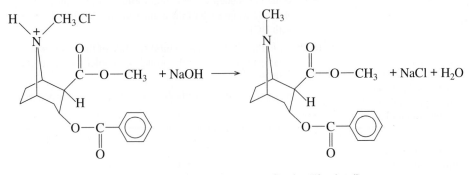

Cocaine hydrochloride   Cocaine ("free base")

MC   CASE STUDY
      Death by Chocolate?

CONCEPT CHECK 18.4

■ Reacting an Amine with HCl

Consider the reaction of dimethylamine with HCl.

a. What type of reaction takes place?
b. What type of product forms?
c. What is the name of the product that forms?

ANSWER
a. The reaction of an amine acting as a base and an acid is neutralization.
b. The product that forms is an amine salt.
c. The product is dimethylammonium chloride.

SAMPLE PROBLEM 18.3

■ Reactions of Amines

Write an equation that shows ethylamine

a. ionizing as a weak base in water.
b. neutralized by HCl.

SOLUTION

a. In water, ethylamine acts as a weak base by accepting a proton from water to produce ethylammonium hydroxide:

$$CH_3-CH_2-NH_2 + H-OH \rightleftharpoons CH_3-CH_2-NH_3^+ + OH^-$$

b. $CH_3-CH_2-NH_2 + HCl \longrightarrow CH_3-CH_2-NH_3^+Cl^-$

STUDY CHECK

What is the condensed structural formula of the salt formed by the reaction of trimethylamine and HCl?

QUESTIONS AND PROBLEMS

Properties of Amines

18.11 Identify the compound in each pair that has the higher boiling point. Explain.
   a. $CH_3-CH_2-NH_2$ or CH_3-CH_2-OH
   b. CH_3-NH_2 or $CH_3-CH_2-CH_2-NH_2$

   c. $CH_3-\overset{\overset{\displaystyle CH_3}{|}}{N}-CH_3$ or $CH_3-CH_2-CH_2-NH_2$

18.12 Identify the compound in each pair that has the higher boiling point. Explain.
   a. $CH_3-CH_2-CH_2-CH_3$ or $CH_3-CH_2-CH_2-NH_2$
   b. CH_3-NH_2 or $CH_3-CH_2-NH_2$

   c. $CH_3-CH_2-CH_2-OH$ or $CH_3-\overset{\overset{\displaystyle NH_2}{|}}{CH}-CH_3$

18.13 Propylamine (59 g/mole) has a boiling point of 48 °C, and ethylmethylamine (59 g/mole) has a boiling point of 37 °C. Butane (58 g/mole) has a much lower boiling point of –1 °C. Explain.

18.14 Assign the boiling point of 3 °C, 48 °C, or 97 °C to the appropriate compound: 1-propanol, propylamine, and trimethylamine.

18.15 Indicate if each of the following is soluble in water. Explain.
   a. $CH_3-CH_2-NH_2$ **b.** $CH_3-NH-CH_3$

   c. $CH_3-CH_2-CH_2-\overset{\overset{\displaystyle CH_2-CH_2-CH_3}{|}}{N}-CH_2-CH_2-CH_3$

   d. $CH_3-\overset{\overset{\displaystyle NH_2}{|}}{CH}-CH_2-CH_3$

18.16 Indicate if each of the following is soluble in water. Explain.

   a. $CH_3-CH_2-CH_2-NH_2$

   b. $CH_3-CH_2-CH_2-NH-CH_2-CH_3$

   c. $CH_3-\overset{\overset{\displaystyle CH_3}{|}}{N}-CH_3$ **d.**

18.17 Write an equation for the ionization of each of the following amines in water:
   a. methylamine
   b. dimethylamine
   c. aniline

18.18 Write an equation for the ionization of each of the following amines in water:
   a. ethylamine
   b. propylamine
   c. N-methylaniline

18.19 Write the condensed structural formula of the amine salt obtained when each of the amines in problem 18.17 reacts with HCl.

18.20 Write the condensed structural formula of the amine salt obtained when each of the amines in problem 18.18 reacts with HCl.

18.21 Novocain, a local anesthetic, is the amine salt of procaine:

Procaine

   a. What is the condensed structural formula of the amine salt (procaine hydrochloride) formed when procaine reacts with HCl? (Hint: The tertiary amine reacts with HCl.)
   b. Why is procaine hydrochloride used rather than procaine?

18.22 Lidocaine (Xylocaine) is used as a local anesthetic and cardiac depressant:

Lidocaine (Xylocaine®)

   a. What is the condensed structural formula of the amine salt formed when lidocaine reacts with HCl?
   b. Why is the amine salt of lidocaine used rather than the amine?

18.3   Heterocyclic Amines and Alkaloids

LEARNING GOAL

Identify heterocyclic amines; distinguish between the types of heterocyclic amines.

A **heterocyclic amine** is a cyclic organic compound that contains one or more nitrogen atoms in the ring. The heterocyclic amine rings typically consist of five or six atoms and one or more nitrogen atoms. Of the five-atom rings, the simplest one is pyrrolidine, which is a ring of four carbon atoms and a nitrogen atom, all with single bonds. Pyrrole is a five-atom ring with one nitrogen atom and two double bonds. Imidazole is a five-atom ring that contains two nitrogen atoms.

Pyrrolidine   Pyrrole   Imidazole

Some of the pungent aroma and taste we associate with black pepper is due to a compound called *piperidine*, which is a six-atom heterocyclic ring with a nitrogen atom. The fruit from the black pepper plant is dried and ground to give the black pepper we use to season our foods.

Many of the other six-atom heterocyclic amines are aromatic. Pyridine is similar to benzene, except it has a nitrogen atom in place of a carbon atom. Pyrimidine, which is found in nucleic acids, is also similar to benzene, except it has two nitrogen atoms. In purine, another component of nucleic acids, a pyrimidine ring is fused with imidazole.

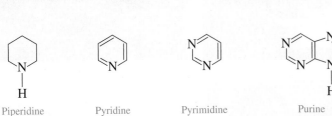

Piperidine   Pyridine   Pyrimidine   Purine

CONCEPT CHECK 18.5

■ **Heterocyclic Amines**

Identify each of the following heterocyclic amines:

a. 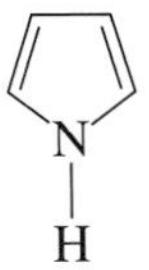   b. 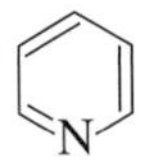   c.

ANSWER
a. Pyrrole has a five-atom ring with one nitrogen atom.
b. Pyridine has a six-atom ring similar to benzene with one nitrogen atom.
c. Pyrimidine has a six-atom ring similar to benzene with two nitrogen atoms.

TUTORIAL
MC™ Identifying Types of Heterocyclic Amines

Alkaloids: Amines in Plants

Alkaloids are physiologically active nitrogen-containing compounds produced by plants. The term *alkaloid* refers to the "alkali-like" or basic characteristics we have seen for amines. Certain alkaloids are used in anesthetics, in antidepressants, and as stimulants, although many are habit forming.

As a stimulant, nicotine increases the level of adrenaline in the blood, which increases the heart rate and blood pressure. Nicotine is responsible for the addiction of smoking. Nicotine has a simple alkaloid structure that includes a pyrrolidine ring. Coniine, which is obtained from hemlock, is an extremely toxic alkaloid that contains a piperidine ring.

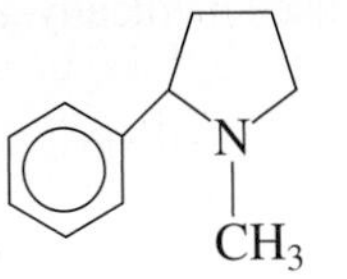

Nicotine 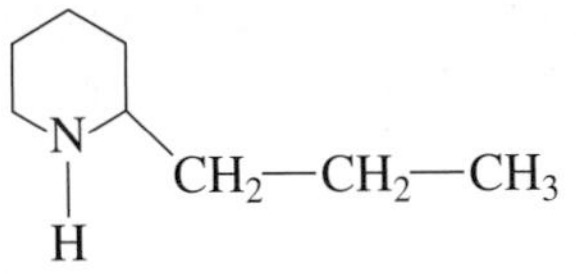   Coniine

Caffeine contains an imidazole ring and is a central nervous system stimulant. Present in coffee, tea, soft drinks, chocolate, and cocoa, caffeine increases alertness, but it may cause nervousness and insomnia. Caffeine is also used in certain pain relievers to counteract the drowsiness caused by an antihistamine. (See Figure 18.3.)

FIGURE 18.3 Coffee beans contain caffeine, which is an alkaloid that is a stimulant of the central nervous system.

Q Why is caffeine considered an alkaloid?

Caffeine

Several alkaloids are used in medicine. Quinine, obtained from the bark of the cinchona tree, has been used in the treatment of malaria since the 1600s. Atropine from belladonna is used in low concentrations to accelerate slow heart rates and as an anesthetic for eye examinations.

Quinine

Atropine

For many centuries, morphine and codeine, alkaloids found in the opium poppy plant, have been used as effective painkillers. (See Figure 18.4.) Codeine, which is structurally similar to morphine, is used in some prescription painkillers and cough syrups. Heroin, obtained by a chemical modification of morphine, is strongly addictive and is not used medically.

Heroin

FIGURE 18.4 The green, unripe poppy seed capsule contains a milky sap (opium) that is the source of the alkaloids morphine and codeine.

Q Where is the piperidine ring in the structures of morphine and codeine?

HEALTH NOTE

Synthesizing Drugs

One area of research in pharmacology is the synthesis of compounds that retain the anesthetic characteristic of naturally occurring alkaloids such as cocaine and morphine without the addictive side effects. For example, cocaine is an effective anesthetic, but it is addictive. Research chemists modified the structure of cocaine but kept the benzene group and nitrogen atom. The synthetic products procaine and lidocaine retain the anesthetic qualities of the natural alkaloid without the addictive side effects:

The structure of morphine was also modified to make a synthetic alkaloid, meperidine, or Demerol, which acts as an effective painkiller:

Meperidine
(Demerol®)

Cocaine

Procaine (Novocaine®)

Lidocaine (Xylocaine®)

SAMPLE PROBLEM 18.4

■ Heterocyclic Amines

Identify the heterocyclic amines in the alkaloids nicotine and caffeine.

SOLUTION

In nicotine, the heterocyclic amine is the five-atom ring of pyrrolidine. Caffeine contains a purine, which is pyrimidine and imidazole fused together.

STUDY CHECK

What is the heterocyclic amine in meperidine (Demerol)?

QUESTIONS AND PROBLEMS

Heterocyclic Amines and Alkaloids

18.23 Identify the following as amines or heterocyclic amines:

a. 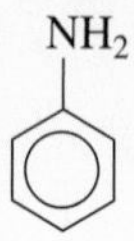 NH$_2$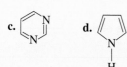

b. CH$_3$—CH$_2$—N—CH$_3$ with CH$_3$ above the N

c. (pyrimidine structure)

d. (pyrrole structure with N—H)

18.24 Identify the following as amines or heterocyclic amines:

a. 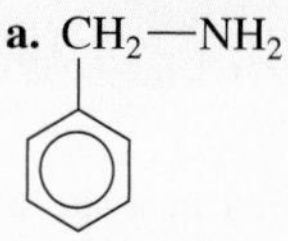 CH$_2$—NH$_2$ (attached to benzene ring)

b. 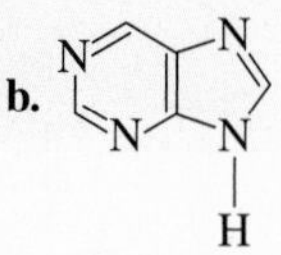 (purine structure)

c. 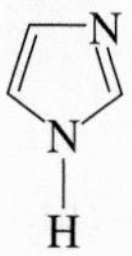 (imidazole structure with N—H)

d. 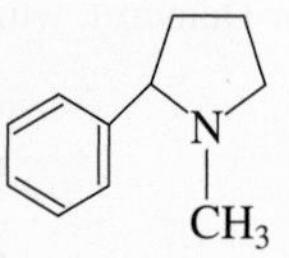 (structure with benzene, pyrrolidine ring, and N—CH$_3$)

18.25 Identify the types of heterocyclic amines in problem 18.23.

18.26 Identify the types of heterocyclic amines in problem 18.24.

18.27 Low levels of serotonin in the brain appear to be associated with depressed states. What type of heterocyclic amine is serotonin?

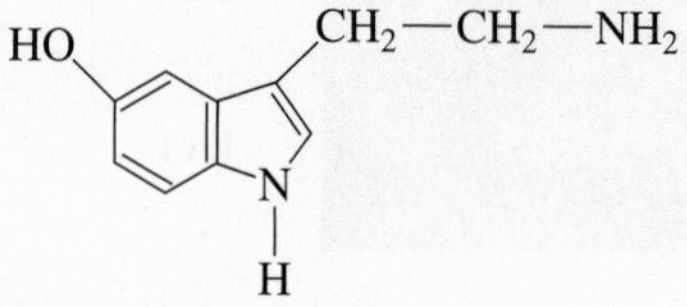

HO—(indole ring)—CH$_2$—CH$_2$—NH$_2$, with N—H

Serotonin

18.28 LSD is made from lysergic acid, which is produced by a fungus that grows on rye. What types of heterocyclic amines are in lysergic acid?

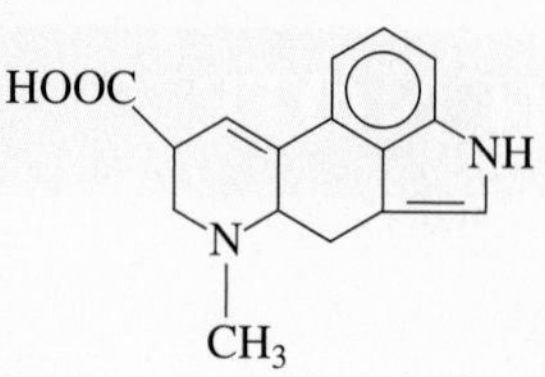

HOOC—(ring system)—NH, N—CH$_3$

Lysergic acid

18.4 Amides

LEARNING GOAL

Write the amide products of amidation, and give their common and IUPAC names.

The **amides** are derivatives of carboxylic acids in which an amino group replaces the hydroxyl group:

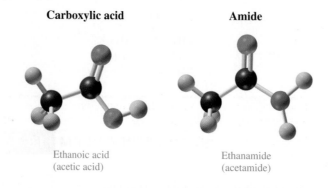

Carboxylic acid   **Amide**

Ethanoic acid
(acetic acid)

Ethanamide
(acetamide)

Preparation of Amides

MC TUTORIAL
Amidation Reactions

An amide is produced in a reaction called **amidation**, in which a carboxylic acid reacts with ammonia or a primary or secondary amine. A molecule of water is eliminated, and the fragments of the carboxylic acid and amine molecules join to form the amide, much like the formation of an ester. Because a hydrogen atom must be lost from the amines, only primary and secondary amines undergo amidation:

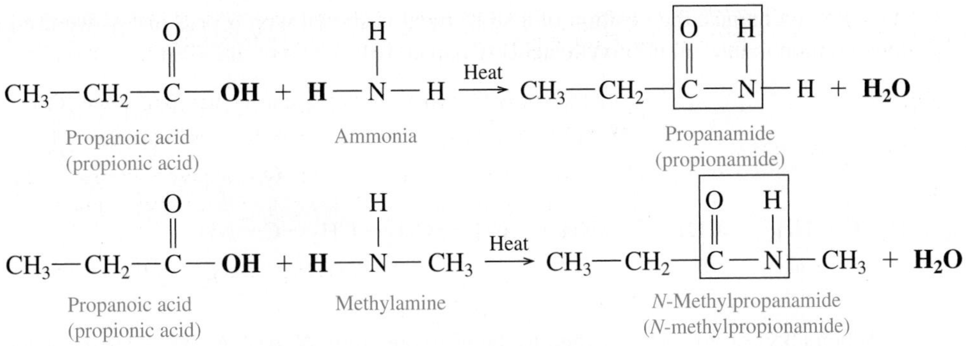

$$CH_3-CH_2-\overset{\overset{\displaystyle O}{\|}}{C}-OH \;+\; H-\overset{\overset{\displaystyle H}{|}}{N}-H \;\xrightarrow{\text{Heat}}\; CH_3-CH_2-\boxed{\overset{\overset{\displaystyle O}{\|}}{C}-\overset{\overset{\displaystyle H}{|}}{N}}-H \;+\; H_2O$$

Propanoic acid · Ammonia · Propanamide
(propionic acid) · · (propionamide)

$$CH_3-CH_2-\overset{\overset{\displaystyle O}{\|}}{C}-OH \;+\; H-\overset{\overset{\displaystyle H}{|}}{N}-CH_3 \;\xrightarrow{\text{Heat}}\; CH_3-CH_2-\boxed{\overset{\overset{\displaystyle O}{\|}}{C}-\overset{\overset{\displaystyle H}{|}}{N}}-CH_3 \;+\; H_2O$$

Propanoic acid · Methylamine · N-Methylpropanamide
(propionic acid) · · (N-methylpropionamide)

SAMPLE PROBLEM 18.5

■ Amidation

Give the condensed structural formula of the amide product in each of the following reactions:

a.

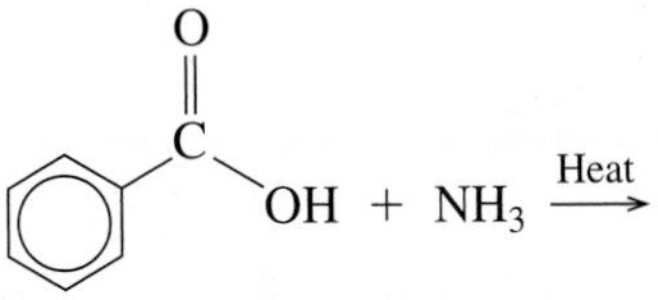

$\text{OH} + NH_3 \xrightarrow{\text{Heat}}$

b.

$$CH_3-\overset{\overset{\displaystyle O}{\|}}{C}-OH + NH_2-CH_2-CH_3 \xrightarrow{\text{Heat}}$$

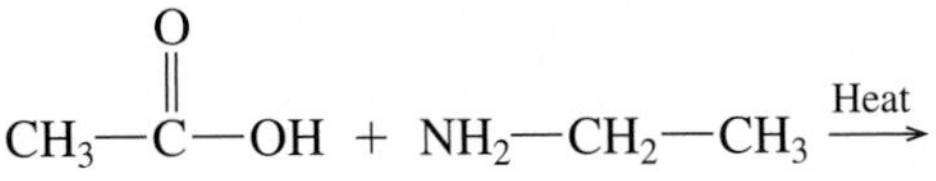

SOLUTION

a. The condensed structural formula of the amide product can be written by attaching the carbonyl group from the acid to the nitrogen atom of the amine. —OH is removed from the acid and —H from the amine to form water:

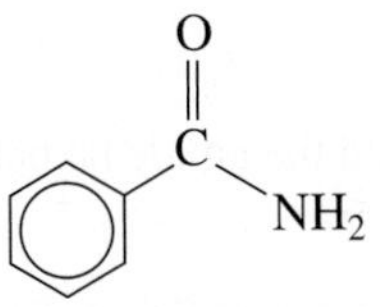

NH_2

b.

$$CH_3-\overset{\overset{\displaystyle O}{\|}}{C}-\overset{\overset{\displaystyle H}{|}}{N}-CH_2-CH_3$$

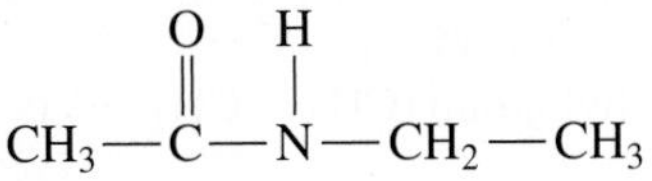

STUDY CHECK

What are the condensed structural formulas of the carboxylic acid and amine needed to prepare the following amide? (Hint: Separate the N and C=O of the amide group, and add —H and —OH to give the original amine and carboxylic acid.)

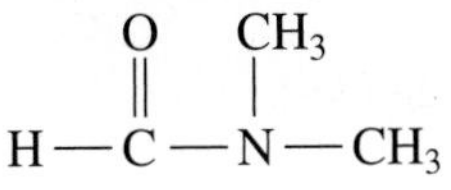

$$H-\overset{\overset{\displaystyle O}{\|}}{C}-\overset{\overset{\displaystyle CH_3}{|}}{N}-CH_3$$

Naming Amides

In both the common and IUPAC names, amides are named by dropping the *ic acid* or *oic acid* from the carboxylic acid names (IUPAC or common) and adding the suffix *amide*. In the common names, the position of a substituent is shown with α or β just as we used for the common names of carboxylic acids (Chapter 16):

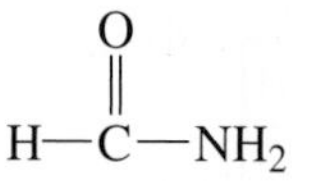

Methanamide (formamide) 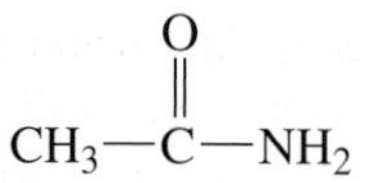 Ethanamide (acetamide) 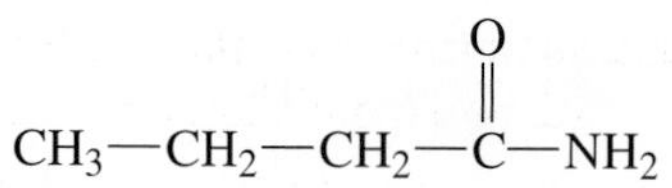 Butanamide (butyramide) 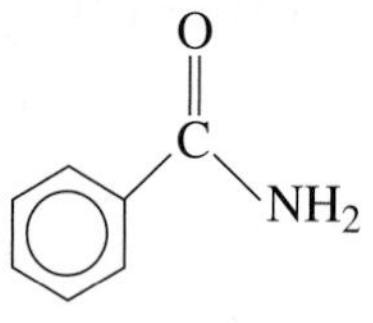 Benzamide

When alkyl groups are attached to the nitrogen atom, *N-* or *N,N-* precedes the name of the amide depending on whether there are one or two groups:

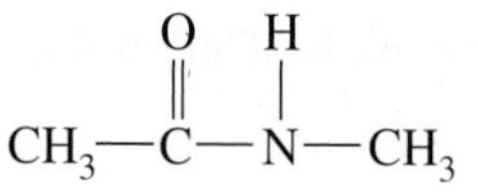

N-Methylethanamide (*N*-methylacetamide) 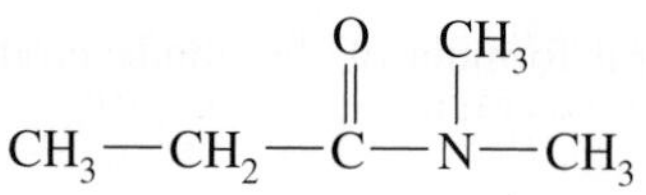 *N,N*-Dimethylpropanamide (*N,N*-dimethylpropionamide) 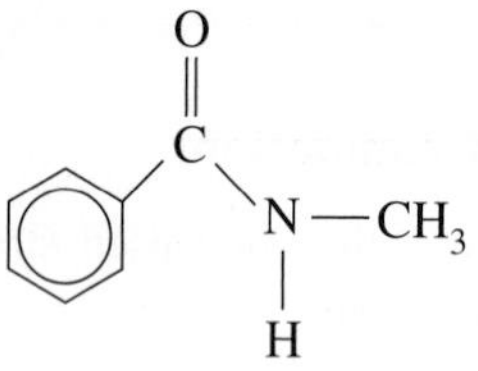 *N*-Methylbenzamide

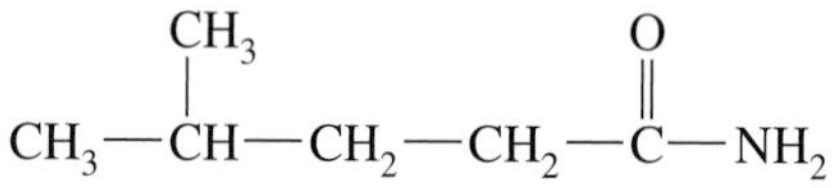

4-Methylpentanamide 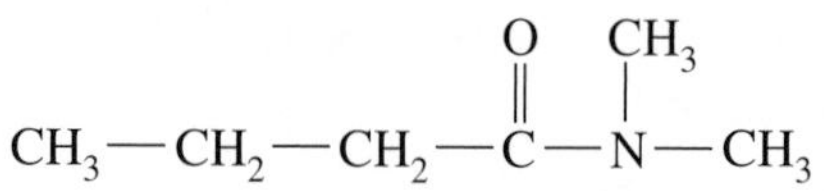 *N,N*-Dimethylbutanamide (*N,N*-dimethylbutyramide)

CONCEPT CHECK 18.6

■ IUPAC Names of Amides

An amide has the name *N*-ethylpentanamide.

a. What is the IUPAC name of the carboxylic acid used in the amidation reaction to form this amide?
b. What is indicated by the "*N*-ethyl" part of the name?
c. If a methyl group were also attached to the N atom, how would the amide be named?

ANSWER
a. Pentanamide indicates that there are 5 carbon atoms. The corresponding carboxylic acid used in the amidation reaction would be pentanoic acid.
b. The "*N*-ethyl" part of the name indicates that an ethyl group (CH_3—CH_2—) is attached to the N atom.
c. If the N atom were attached to an ethyl group and a methyl group, the amide would be named *N*-ethyl-*N*-methylpentanamide.

Guide to Naming Amides

STEP 1
Identify the corresponding carboxylic acid of the amide.

STEP 2
Name the amide by replacing the *oic* or *ic* acid in the name of the corresponding carboxylic acid by *amide*.

STEP 3
Name a substituent on the N atom using the prefix *N*– and the alkyl name.

SAMPLE PROBLEM 18.6

■ Naming Amides

Give the IUPAC and common names for each of the following amides:

a. 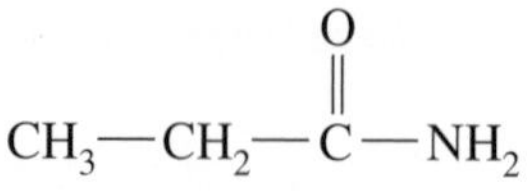 CH_3—CH_2—C(=O)—NH_2 b. 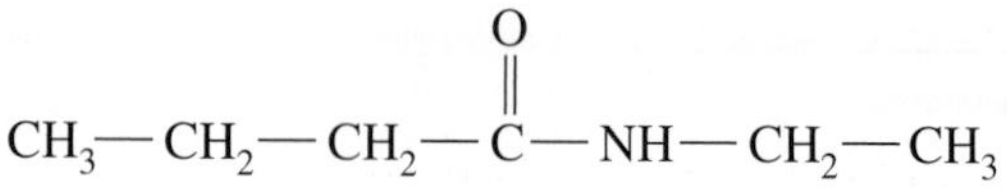 CH_3—CH_2—CH_2—C(=O)—NH—CH_2—CH_3

SOLUTION

a. STEP 1 **Identify the corresponding carboxylic acid of the amide.** The IUPAC name of the corresponding carboxylic acid is propanoic acid. The common name of the corresponding carboxylic acid is propionic acid.

STEP 2 **Name the amide by replacing the *oic* or *ic acid* in the name of the corresponding carboxylic acid by *amide*.** The *oic acid* ending of propanoic acid is replaced with *amide* to give the IUPAC name of propanamide. Replacing the *ic acid* ending of propionic acid with *amide* gives the common name of propionamide.

STEP 3 **Name a substituent on the N atom using the prefix *N*- and the alkyl name.** This compound has no substituent on the N atom.

b. STEP 1 **Identify the corresponding carboxylic acid of the amide.** The IUPAC name of the corresponding carboxylic acid is butanoic acid. The common name of the corresponding carboxylic acid is butyric acid.

STEP 2 **Name the amide by replacing the *oic* or *ic acid* in the name of the corresponding carboxylic acid by *amide*.** The *oic acid* ending of butanoic acid is replaced by *amide* to give the IUPAC name butanamide. Replacing the *ic acid* ending of butryic acid with *amide* gives the common name butyramide.

STEP 3 **Name a substituent on the N atom using the prefix *N*- and the alkyl name.** The ethyl group attached to the nitrogen atom is named *N-ethyl*. The IUPAC name is *N*-ethylbutanamide, and the common name is *N*-ethylbutyramide.

STUDY CHECK

Draw the condensed structural formula of *N,N*-dimethylbenzamide.

Physical Properties of Amides

The amides do not have the properties of bases that we saw for the amines. Only formamide is a liquid at room temperature, while the other amides are solids. For primary amides, the $-NH_2$ group can form hydrogen bonds, which gives primary amides high melting points. The melting points of the secondary amides are lower because there is only one N—H bond, and the number of hydrogen bonds decreases. Tertiary amides have even lower melting points because they have no N—H bonds and thus cannot form hydrogen bonds with other tertiary amides.

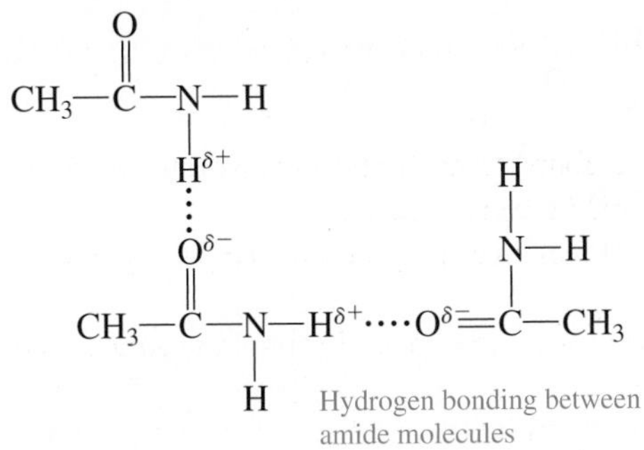

Hydrogen bonding between amide molecules

The amides with one to five carbon atoms are soluble in water because they can hydrogen bond with water molecules:

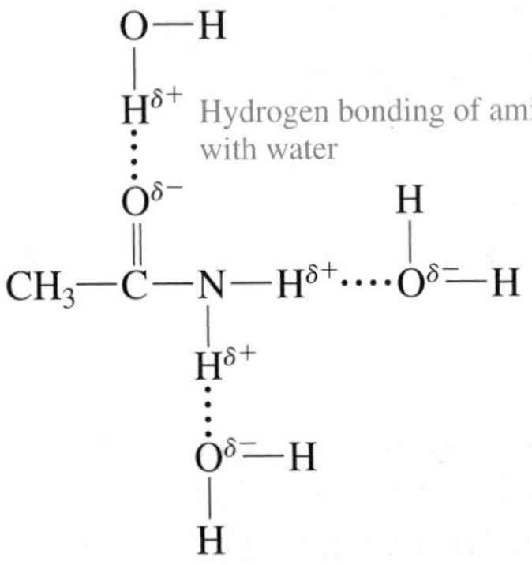

Hydrogen bonding of amides with water

HEALTH NOTE

Amides in Health and Medicine

The simplest natural amide is urea, an end product of protein metabolism in the body. The kidneys remove urea from the blood and provide for its excretion in urine. If the kidneys malfunction, urea is not removed and builds to a toxic level, a condition called uremia. Urea is also used as a component of fertilizer to increase nitrogen in the soil.

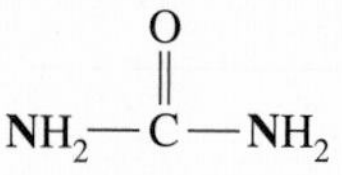

$$NH_2-\overset{\overset{\displaystyle O}{\|}}{C}-NH_2 \quad \text{Urea}$$

Synthetic amides are used as substitutes for sugar and aspirin. Saccharin is a very powerful sweetener and is used as a sugar substitute. The sweetener aspartame is made from two amino acids: aspartic acid and phenylalanine.

Aspirin substitutes contain phenacetin or acetaminophen, which is used in Tylenol. Like aspirin, acetaminophen reduces fever and pain, but it has little anti-inflammatory effect.

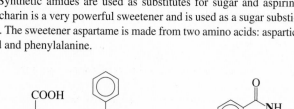

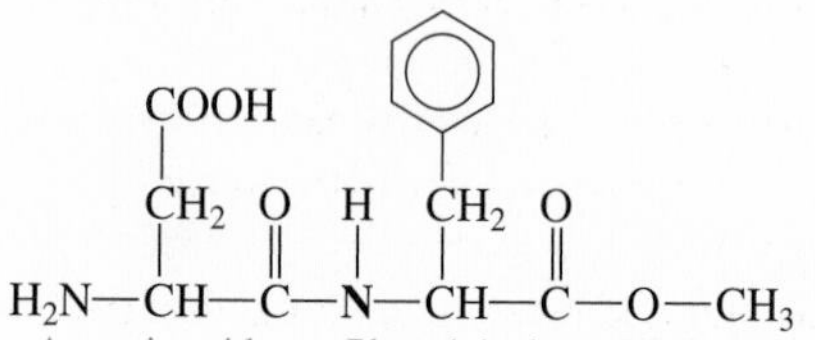

Aspartic acid   Phenylalanine   Methyl ester
Aspartame

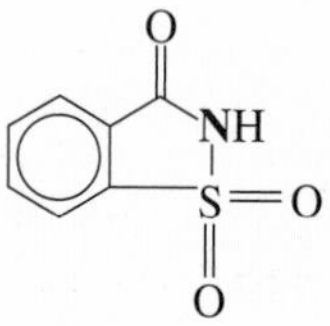

Saccharin

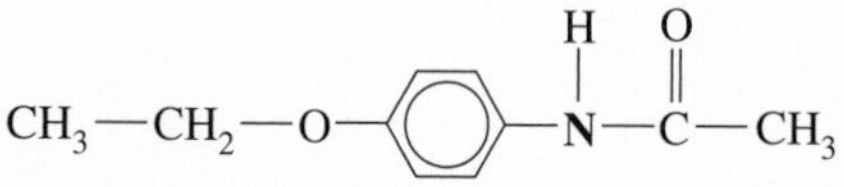

Phenacetin

Acetaminophen

Many barbiturates are cyclic amides of barbituric acid that act as sedatives in small dosages or sleep inducers in larger dosages. They are often habit forming. Barbiturate drugs include phenobarbital (Luminal), pentobarbital (Nembutal), and secobarbital (Seconal).

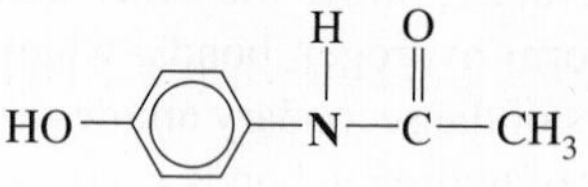

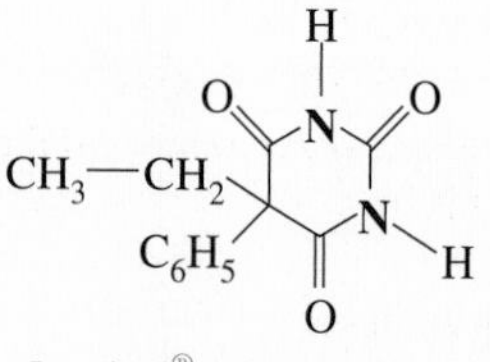

Luminal® (phenobarbital)

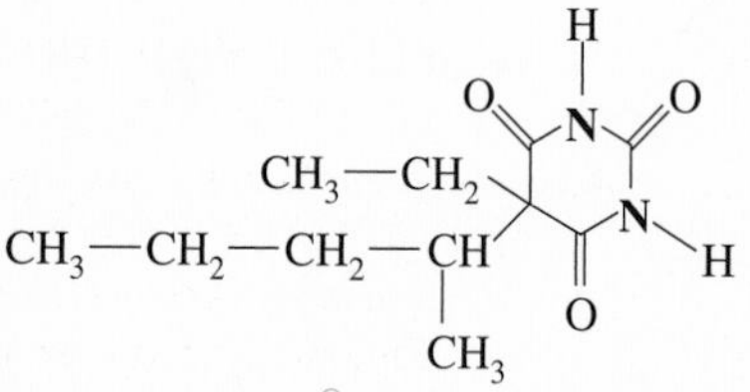

Nembutal® (pentobarbital)

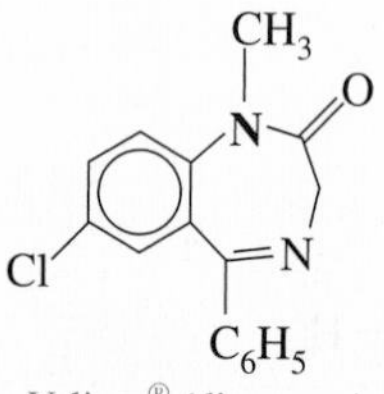

Valium® (diazepam)

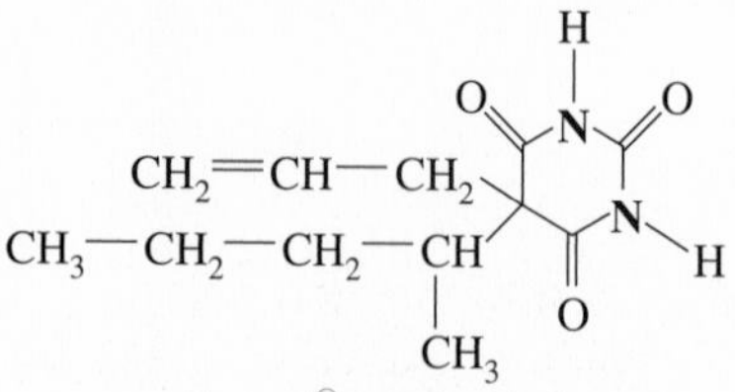

Seconal® (secobarbital)

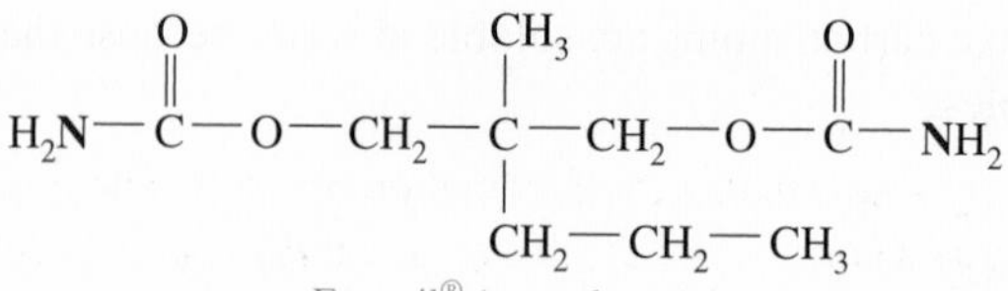

Equanil® (meprobamate)

QUESTIONS AND PROBLEMS

Amides

18.29 Draw the condensed structural formula of the amide formed in each of the following reactions:

a. $CH_3-\overset{\overset{\displaystyle O}{\|}}{C}-OH + NH_3 \xrightarrow{\text{Heat}}$

b. $CH_3-\overset{\overset{\displaystyle O}{\|}}{C}-OH + NH_2-CH_2-CH_3 \xrightarrow{\text{Heat}}$

c. 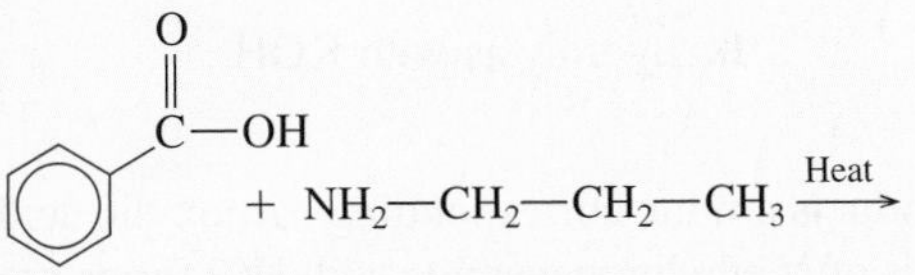 benzene ring—$\overset{\overset{\displaystyle O}{\|}}{C}-OH + NH_2-CH_2-CH_2-CH_3 \xrightarrow{\text{Heat}}$

18.30 Draw the condensed structural formula of the amide formed in each of the following reactions:

a. $CH_3-CH_2-CH_2-CH_2-\overset{\overset{\displaystyle O}{\|}}{C}-OH + NH_3 \xrightarrow{\text{Heat}}$

b. $CH_3-\overset{\overset{\displaystyle CH_3}{|}}{CH}-CH_2-\overset{\overset{\displaystyle O}{\|}}{C}-OH + NH_2-CH_2-CH_2-CH_3 \xrightarrow{\text{Heat}}$

c. 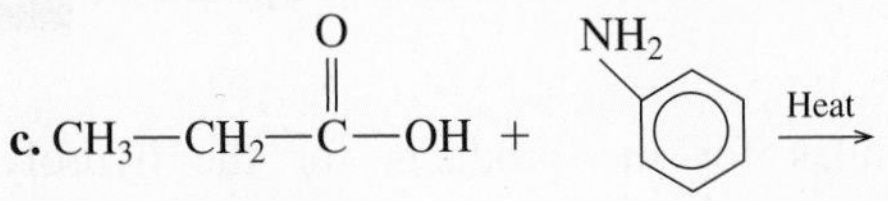 $CH_3-CH_2-\overset{\overset{\displaystyle O}{\|}}{C}-OH +$ benzene ring with $NH_2 \xrightarrow{\text{Heat}}$

18.31 Give the IUPAC and common name (if any) for each of the following amides:

a. $CH_3-\overset{\overset{\displaystyle O}{\|}}{C}-NH-CH_3$

b. $CH_3-CH_2-CH_2-\overset{\overset{\displaystyle O}{\|}}{C}-NH_2$

c. $H-\overset{\overset{\displaystyle O}{\|}}{C}-NH_2$ **d.** 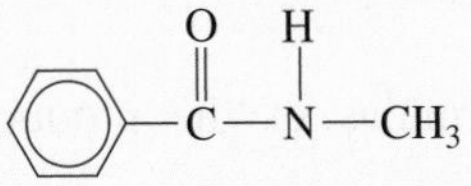 benzene ring—$\overset{\overset{\displaystyle O}{\|}}{C}-\overset{\overset{\displaystyle H}{|}}{N}-CH_3$

18.32 Give the IUPAC and common name (if any) for each of the following amides:

a. $CH_3-CH_2-\overset{\overset{\displaystyle O}{\|}}{C}-\overset{\overset{\displaystyle H}{|}}{N}-CH_2-CH_3$

b. $CH_3-CH_2-CH_2-CH_2-CH_2-\overset{\overset{\displaystyle O}{\|}}{C}-NH_2$

c. $CH_3-\overset{\overset{\displaystyle O}{\|}}{C}-\overset{\overset{\displaystyle CH_3}{|}}{N}-CH_2-CH_2-CH_3$

d. 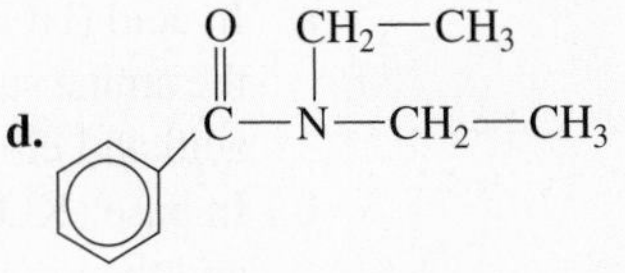 benzene ring—$\overset{\overset{\displaystyle O}{\|}}{C}-\overset{\overset{\displaystyle CH_2-CH_3}{|}}{N}-CH_2-CH_3$

18.33 Draw the condensed structural formula for each of the following amides:
  a. propionamide   **b.** pentanamide
  c. methanamide   **d.** N-ethylbenzamide
  e. N-ethylbutyramide

18.34 Draw the condensed structural formula for each of the following amides:
  a. formamide
  b. N,N-dimethylbenzamide
  c. 3-methylbutyramide
  d. hexanamide
  e. N-propylpentanamide

18.35 For each of the following pairs, identify the compound that has the higher melting point. Explain.
  a. acetamide or N-methylacetamide
  b. butane or propionamide
  c. N,N-dimethylpropanamide or N-methylpropanamide

18.36 For each of the following pairs, identify the compound that has the higher melting point. Explain.
  a. propane or acetamide
  b. N-methylacetamide or propanamide
  c. N,N-dimethylpropanamide or N-methylpropanamide

18.5 Hydrolysis of Amides

As we have seen, amide bonds are formed by the elimination of water. The reverse reaction, called **hydrolysis**, occurs when water is added back to the amide bond to split the molecule. When an acid is used, the hydrolysis products of an amide are the carboxylic acid and the ammonium salt. In base hydrolysis, the amide produces the salt of the carboxylic acid and ammonia or the amine.

Acid Hydrolysis of Amides

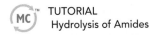

$$CH_3-\overset{\overset{\displaystyle O}{\|}}{C}-NH_2 + HOH + HCl \longrightarrow CH_3-\overset{\overset{\displaystyle O}{\|}}{C}-OH + NH_4^+Cl^-$$

Ethanamide   Ethanoic acid   Ammonium
(acetamide)   (acetic acid)   chloride

LEARNING GOAL

Write equations for the hydrolysis of amides.

(MC) **TUTORIAL**
Hydrolysis of Amides

Base Hydrolysis of Amides

$$CH_3-CH_2-\overset{\overset{\displaystyle O}{\|}}{C}-NH-CH_3 \; + \; NaOH \longrightarrow CH_3-CH_2-\overset{\overset{\displaystyle O}{\|}}{C}-O^-Na^+ \; + \; NH_2-CH_3$$

N-Methylpropanamide   Sodium propanoate, a salt   Methanamine
(N-methylpropionamide)   (sodium propionate)   (methylamine)

CONCEPT CHECK 18.7

■ **Acid and Base Hydrolysis of Amides**

Give the names of the products when N-ethylpropanamide undergoes each of the following:

a. hydrolysis with HCl   **b.** hydrolysis with KOH

ANSWER

a. In acid (HCl) hydrolysis, the products are the corresponding carboxylic acid and the amine salt. The acid hydrolysis of N-ethylpropanamide with HCl forms propanoic acid and ethylammonium chloride.

b. In base (KOH) hydrolysis, the products are the corresponding carboxylic acid salt and the amine. The base hydrolysis of N-ethylpropanamide with KOH forms potassium propanoate and ethylamine.

SAMPLE PROBLEM 18.7

■ **Hydrolysis of Amides**

Write the condensed structural formulas for the products for the hydrolysis of N-methylpentanamide with NaOH.

SOLUTION

Hydrolysis of the amide with a base produces a carboxylate salt (sodium pentanoate) and the corresponding amine (methylamine):

$$CH_3-CH_2-CH_2-CH_2-\overset{\overset{\displaystyle O}{\|}}{C}-O^-Na^+ \; + \; NH_2-CH_3$$

STUDY CHECK

Draw the condensed structural formulas of the products from the hydrolysis of N-methylbutyramide with HBr.

QUESTIONS AND PROBLEMS

Hydrolysis of Amides

18.37 Draw the condensed structural formulas for the products of the acid hydrolysis of each of the following amides with HCl:

a. $CH_3-\overset{\overset{\displaystyle O}{\|}}{C}-NH_2$

b. $CH_3-CH_2-\overset{\overset{\displaystyle O}{\|}}{C}-NH_2$

c. $CH_3-CH_2-CH_2-\overset{\overset{\displaystyle O}{\|}}{C}-NH-CH_3$

d. $\overset{\overset{\displaystyle O}{\|}}{C}-NH_2$

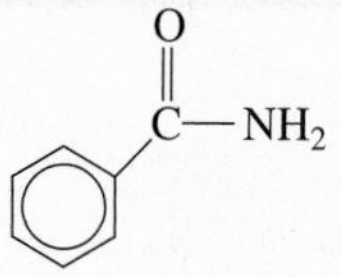

e. N-ethylpentanamide

18.38 Draw the condensed structural formulas for the products of the base hydrolysis of each of the following amides with NaOH:

a. $CH_3-CH_2-\overset{\overset{\displaystyle CH_3}{|}}{CH}-\overset{\overset{\displaystyle O}{\|}}{C}-NH_2$

b. $CH_3-CH_2-CH_2-\overset{\overset{\displaystyle O}{\|}}{C}-\overset{\overset{\displaystyle CH_2-CH_3}{|}}{N}-CH_2-CH_3$

c. $\underset{\text{(benzene ring)}}{C_6H_5}-\overset{\overset{\displaystyle O}{\|}}{C}-\overset{\overset{\displaystyle CH_3}{|}}{N}-CH_2-CH_2-CH_2-CH_3$

d. $CH_3-\overset{\overset{\displaystyle Cl}{|}}{CH}-\overset{\overset{\displaystyle O}{\|}}{C}-\overset{\overset{\displaystyle CH_3}{|}}{N}-CH_2-CH_3$

e. *N*-propylbenzamide

CONCEPT MAP

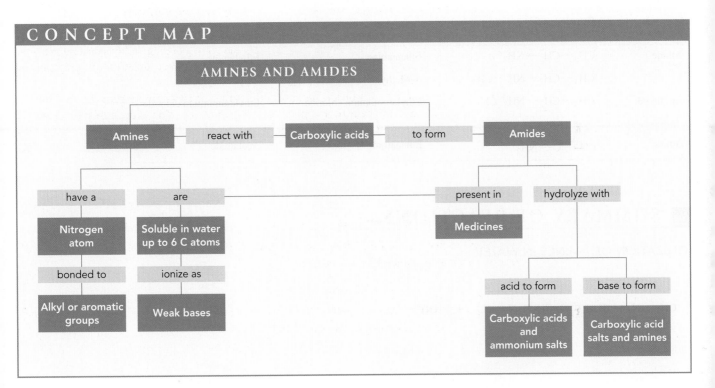

CHAPTER REVIEW

18.1 Amines

LEARNING GOAL: *Classify amines as primary (1°), secondary (2°), or tertiary (3°). Name amines using common and IUPAC names; draw the condensed structural formulas given the names.*

A nitrogen atom attached to one, two, or three alkyl or aromatic groups forms a primary (1°), secondary (2°), or tertiary (3°) amine. In the IUPAC system, the *amine* suffix is added to the alkane name (after dropping the *e*) of the longer carbon chain. Groups attached to the nitrogen atom use a *N*- prefix. When other functional groups are present, the —NH₂ is named as an amino group. In the common names of simple amines, the alkyl groups are listed alphabetically followed by the suffix *amine*.

18.2 Properties of Amines

LEARNING GOAL: *Describe the boiling points and solubility of amines; write equations for the ionization and neutralization of amines.*
Primary and secondary amines form hydrogen bonds, which make their boiling points higher than alkanes of similar mass but lower than those of alcohols. Amines with up to six carbon atoms are soluble in water. In water, amines act as weak bases because the nitrogen atom accepts a proton from water to produce ammonium and hydroxide ions. When amines react with acids, they form amine salts, which are named as ammonium salts. As ionic compounds, amine salts are solids, soluble in water, and odorless compared to the amines. Quaternary ammonium salts contain four carbon groups bonded to the nitrogen atom.

18.3 Heterocyclic Amines and Alkaloids

LEARNING GOAL: *Identify heterocyclic amines; distinguish between the types of heterocyclic amines.*
Heterocyclic amines are cyclic organic compounds that contain one or more nitrogen atoms in the ring. The amine rings typically consist of five or six atoms and one or more nitrogen atoms. Alkaloids such as caffeine and nicotine are naturally occurring amines derived from plants. Many are known for their physiological activity.

18.4 Amides

LEARNING GOAL: *Write the amide products of amidation, and give their common and IUPAC names.*

Amides are derivatives of carboxylic acids in which the hydroxyl group is replaced by —NH_2 or a primary or secondary amine group. Amides are formed when carboxylic acids react with ammonia or primary or secondary amines in the presence of heat. Amides are named by replacing the *ic acid* or *oic acid* with *amide*. Any carbon group attached to the nitrogen atom is named using the *N-* prefix.

18.5 Hydrolysis of Amides

LEARNING GOAL: *Write equations for the hydrolysis of amides.*

Hydrolysis of an amide by an acid produces a carboxylic acid and an amine salt. Hydrolysis by a base produces the salt of the carboxylic acid and an amine.

SUMMARY OF NAMING

Family	Condensed Structural Formula	IUPAC Name	Common Name
Amine	$CH_3—CH_2—NH_2$	Ethanamine	Ethylamine
	$CH_3—CH_2—NH—CH_3$	N-Methylethanamine	Ethylmethylamine
Amine salt	$CH_3—CH_2—NH_3^+Cl^-$	Ethylammonium chloride	Ethylammonium chloride
Amide	$CH_3—\overset{\overset{O}{\|\|}}{C}—NH_2$	Ethanamide	Acetamide

SUMMARY OF REACTIONS

IONIZATION OF AMINES IN WATER

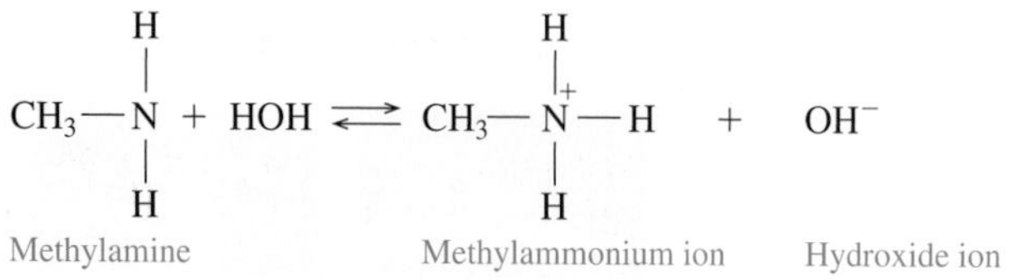

$$CH_3—\underset{\underset{H}{\|}}{\overset{\overset{H}{\|}}{N}} + HOH \rightleftharpoons CH_3—\underset{\underset{H}{\|}}{\overset{\overset{H}{\|}}{\overset{+}{N}}}—H + OH^-$$

Methylamine   Methylammonium ion   Hydroxide ion

FORMATION OF AMINE SALTS

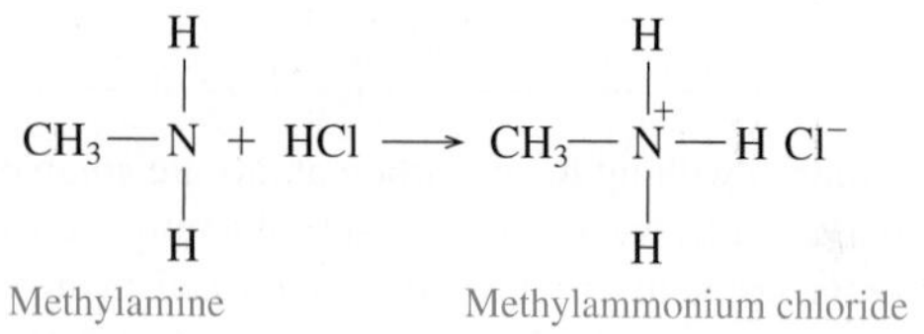

$$CH_3—\underset{\underset{H}{\|}}{\overset{\overset{H}{\|}}{N}} + HCl \longrightarrow CH_3—\underset{\underset{H}{\|}}{\overset{\overset{H}{\|}}{\overset{+}{N}}}—H\ Cl^-$$

Methylamine   Methylammonium chloride

FORMATION OF AMIDES

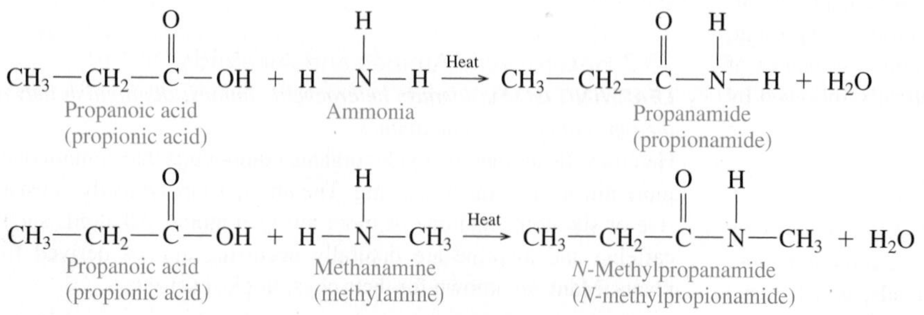

$$CH_3—CH_2—\overset{\overset{O}{\|\|}}{C}—OH + H—\overset{\overset{H}{\|}}{N}—H \xrightarrow{Heat} CH_3—CH_2—\overset{\overset{O}{\|\|}}{C}—\overset{\overset{H}{\|}}{N}—H + H_2O$$

Propanoic acid   Ammonia   Propanamide
(propionic acid)   (propionamide)

$$CH_3—CH_2—\overset{\overset{O}{\|\|}}{C}—OH + H—\overset{\overset{H}{\|}}{N}—CH_3 \xrightarrow{Heat} CH_3—CH_2—\overset{\overset{O}{\|\|}}{C}—\overset{\overset{H}{\|}}{N}—CH_3 + H_2O$$

Propanoic acid   Methanamine   N-Methylpropanamide
(propionic acid)   (methylamine)   (N-methylpropionamide)

ACID HYDROLYSIS OF AMIDES

$$CH_3 - \overset{\overset{\displaystyle O}{\|}}{C} - NH_2 \ + \ HOH \ + \ HCl \longrightarrow CH_3 - \overset{\overset{\displaystyle O}{\|}}{C} - OH \ + \ NH_4^+Cl^-$$

Ethanamide   Ethanoic acid   Ammonium
(acetamide)   (acetic acid)   chloride

BASE HYDROLYSIS OF AMIDES

$$CH_3 - CH_2 - \overset{\overset{\displaystyle O}{\|}}{C} - NH - CH_3 \ + \ NaOH \longrightarrow CH_3 - CH_2 - \overset{\overset{\displaystyle O}{\|}}{C} - O^-Na^+ \ + \ NH_2 - CH_3$$

N-Methylpropanamide   Sodium propanoate   Methanamine
(*N*-methylpropionamide)   (sodium propionate)   (methylamine)

■ KEY TERMS

alkaloids Amines having physiological activity that are produced in plants.

amidation The formation of an amide from a carboxylic acid and ammonia or an amine.

amides Organic compounds containing the carbonyl group attached to an amino group or a substituted nitrogen atom.

amines Organic compounds containing a nitrogen atom attached to one, two, or three hydrocarbon groups.

amine salt An ionic compound produced from an amine and an acid.

heterocyclic amine A cyclic organic compound that contains one or more nitrogen atoms in the ring.

hydrolysis The splitting of a molecule by the addition of water. Amides yield the corresponding carboxylic acid and amine or their salts.

quaternary ammonium ion An amine ion in which the nitrogen atom is bonded to four carbon groups.

■ UNDERSTANDING THE CONCEPTS

18.39 The sweetener aspartame is made from two amino acids: aspartic acid and phenylalanine. Identify the functional groups in aspartame.

18.40 Some aspirin substitutes contain phenacetin to reduce fever. Identify the functional groups in phenacetin.

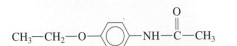

ADDITIONAL QUESTIONS AND PROBLEMS

For instructor-assigned homework, go to www.masteringchemistry.com.

18.41 The insect repellent DEET can be made from 3-methylbenzoic acid and *N,N*-diethylamine. What is the condensed structural formula of DEET?

18.42 Nylon 66 is a polymer used to make shirts and jackets. The condensed structural formula of one unit of Nylon 66 is shown below. Draw the condensed structural formulas of the carboxylic acid and amine that are polymerized to make Nylon 66.

18.43 There are four amine isomers with the molecular formula C_3H_9N. Draw their condensed structural formulas. Give the common name and classify each as a primary (1°), secondary (2°), or tertiary (3°) amine.

18.44 There are four amide isomers with the molecular formula C_3H_7NO. Draw their condensed structural formulas.

18.45 Name and classify each of the following compounds as a primary (1°), secondary (2°), or tertiary (3°) amine or as a quaternary ammonium salt:

$$\begin{array}{c} CH_2{-}CH_3 \\ | \end{array}$$
a. 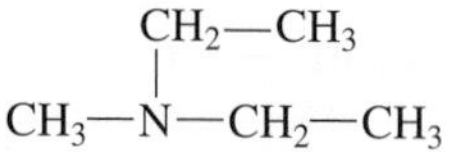 $CH_3{-}N{-}CH_2{-}CH_3$
b. $CH_3{-}CH_2{-}CH_2{-}CH_2{-}NH_2$
c. $CH_3{-}CH_2{-}CH_2{-}NH{-}CH_2{-}CH_3$

18.46 Name and classify each of the following compounds as a primary (1°), secondary (2°), or tertiary (3°) amine or as a quaternary ammonium salt:

a. 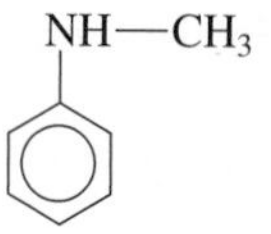 $NH{-}CH_3$ (attached to benzene ring)

b. 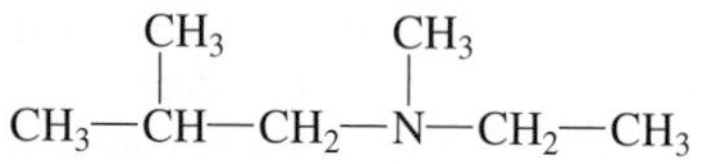 $CH_3{-}CH{-}CH_2{-}N{-}CH_2{-}CH_3$ with CH_3 groups

c. 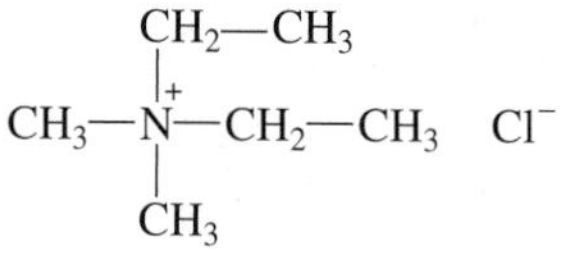 $CH_3{-}N^+{-}CH_2{-}CH_3 \quad Cl^-$ with $CH_2{-}CH_3$ and CH_3 groups

18.47 Draw the condensed structural formula of each of the following compounds:
a. 3-pentanamine   **b.** cyclohexylamine
c. dimethylammonium chloride   **d.** triethylamine

18.48 Draw the condensed structural formula of each of the following compounds:
a. 3-amino-2-hexanol
b. tetramethylammonium bromide
c. *N,N*-dimethylaniline
d. butylethylmethylamine

18.49 In each of the following pairs, indicate the compound that has the higher boiling point. Explain.
a. 1-butanol or butanamine
b. trimethylamine or propylamine

18.50 In each of the following pairs, indicate the compound that has the higher boiling point. Explain.
a. butylamine or diethylamine
b. butane or propylamine

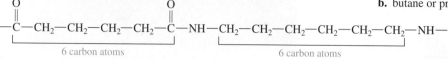

6 carbon atoms   6 carbon atoms

Nylon 66

18.51 In each of the following pairs, indicate the compound that is more soluble in water. Explain.
  a. ethylamine or dibutylamine
  b. trimethylamine or *N*-ethylcyclohexylamine

18.52 In each of the following pairs, indicate the compound that is more soluble in water. Explain.
  a. butylamine or pentane
  b. butyramide or hexane

18.53 Give the IUPAC name for each of the following amides:

  a. H—$\overset{\overset{\displaystyle O}{\|}}{C}$—NH$_2$ **b.** CH$_3$—CH$_2$—$\overset{\overset{\displaystyle O}{\|}}{C}$—NH$_2$

  c. CH$_3$—$\overset{\overset{\displaystyle O}{\|}}{C}$—$\overset{\overset{\displaystyle H}{|}}{N}$—CH$_3$

18.54 Give the IUPAC name for each of the following amides:

  a. CH$_3$—CH$_2$—CH$_2$—$\overset{\overset{\displaystyle O}{\|}}{C}$—NH—CH$_2$—CH$_3$

  b. CH$_3$—$\overset{\overset{\displaystyle O}{\|}}{C}$—$\overset{\overset{\displaystyle CH_3}{|}}{N}$—CH$_2$—CH$_2$—CH$_2$—CH$_3$

  c. CH$_3$—$\overset{\overset{\displaystyle O}{\|}}{C}$—$\overset{\overset{\displaystyle CH_3}{|}}{N}$—CH$_3$

18.55 Give the name of the alkaloid described in each of the following:
  a. from the bark of the cinchona tree used in malaria treatment
  b. found in tobacco
  c. found in coffee and tea
  d. a painkiller found in the opium poppy plant

18.56 Identify the heterocyclic amine in each of the following:
  a. caffeine   **b.** Demerol
  c. nicotine   **d.** quinine

18.57 Write the condensed structural formulas of the products of the following reactions:
  a. CH$_3$—CH$_2$—NH$_2$ + H$_2$O $\rightleftharpoons$
  b. CH$_3$—CH$_2$—NH$_2$ + HCl $\longrightarrow$
  c. CH$_3$—CH$_2$—NH—CH$_3$ + H$_2$O $\rightleftharpoons$

18.58 Write the condensed structural formulas of the products of the following reactions:
  a. CH$_3$—CH$_2$—NH—CH$_3$ + HCl $\longrightarrow$
  b. CH$_3$—CH$_2$—CH$_2$—NH$_3^+$Cl$^-$ + NaOH $\longrightarrow$
  c. CH$_3$—CH$_2$—$\overset{\overset{\displaystyle CH_3}{|}}{N}H_2^+Cl^-$ + NaOH $\longrightarrow$

18.59 Voltaren is indicated for acute and chronic treatment of the symptoms of rheumatoid arthritis. Name the functional groups in this molecule.

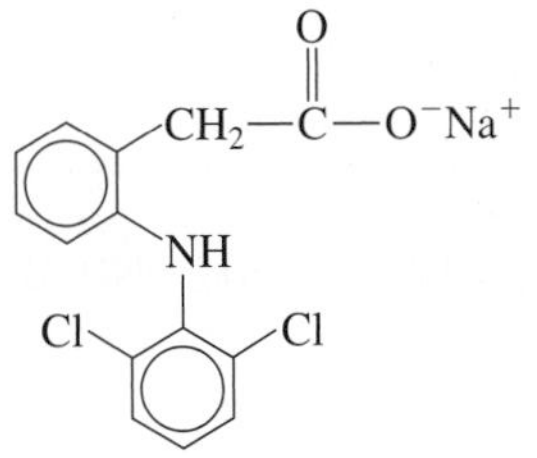

18.60 Toradol is used in dentistry to relieve pain. Name the functional groups in this molecule.

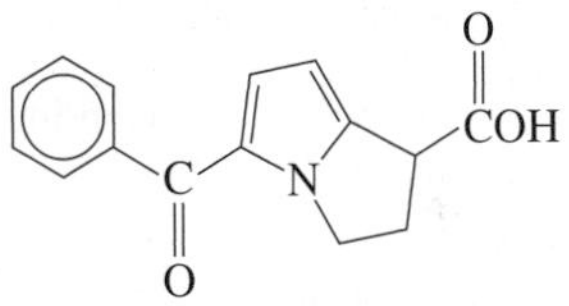

CHALLENGE QUESTIONS

18.61 Use the Internet or a reference book such as the *Merck Index* or *Physicians' Desk Reference* to look up the structural formula of the following medicinal drugs. List the functional groups in each compound.
  a. Keflex, an antibiotic
  b. Inderal, a β-channel blocker used to treat heart irregularities
  c. ibuprofen, an anti-inflammatory agent
  d. Aldomet (methyldopa)
  e. Percodan, a narcotic pain reliever
  f. triamterene, a diuretic

18.62 Many amine-containing drugs are given to patients in their salt form, such as hydrochloride or sulfate. What might be the reason?

18.63 Use the K of methylamine to calculate the pH of a 1.0 M solution of methylamine.

18.64 Kevlar is a lightweight polymer used in tires and bulletproof vests. Part of the strength of Kevlar is due to hydrogen bonds between polymer chains. The polymer chain is shown below:

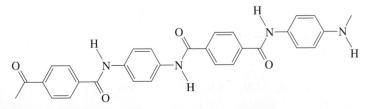

  a. Draw the condensed structural formulas of the carboxylic acid and amine that are polymerized to make Kevlar.
  b. What feature of Kevlar will give the hydrogen bonds between the polymer chains?

ANSWERS

ANSWERS TO STUDY CHECKS

18.1 tertiary (3°)

18.2 $CH_3-CH_2-\overset{\overset{H}{|}}{N}-CH_2-CH_2-CH_3$

18.3 $CH_3-\overset{\overset{CH_3}{|}}{\underset{\underset{CH_3}{|}}{\overset{+}{N}}}-H \ Cl^-$

18.4 piperidine

18.5 $H-\overset{\overset{O}{||}}{C}-OH$ and $H-\overset{\overset{CH_3}{|}}{N}-CH_3$

18.6 [benzene ring]$-\overset{\overset{O}{||}}{C}-\overset{\overset{CH_3}{|}}{N}-CH_3$

18.7 $CH_3-CH_2-CH_2-\overset{\overset{O}{||}}{C}-OH$ and $CH_3-\overset{+}{N}H_3 \ Br^-$

ANSWERS TO SELECTED QUESTIONS AND PROBLEMS

18.1 In a primary amine, there is one alkyl group (and two hydrogens) attached to a nitrogen atom.

18.3 **a.** primary (1°) **b.** secondary (2°) **c.** primary (1°)
d. tertiary (3°) **e.** tertiary (3°)

18.5 **a.** ethylamine, ethanamine
b. methylpropylamine, N-methyl-1-propanamine
c. diethylmethylamine, N-ethyl-N-methylethanamine
d. isopropylamine, 2-propanamine

18.7 **a.** 2-butanamine **b.** 2-chloroaniline
c. 3-aminopropanal **d.** N-ethylaniline

18.9 **a.** $CH_3-CH_2-NH_2$ **b.** [benzene ring]$-NH-CH_3$

c. $CH_3-CH_2-CH_2-CH_2-\overset{\overset{H}{|}}{N}-CH_2-CH_2-CH_3$

d. $CH_3-\overset{\overset{NH_2}{|}}{CH}-CH_2-CH_2-CH_3$

18.11 **a.** CH_3-CH_2-OH has a higher boiling point because the $-OH$ forms stronger hydrogen bonds than the $-NH_2$.
b. $CH_3-CH_2-CH_2-NH_2$ has the higher boiling point because it has a greater molar mass.
c. $CH_3-CH_2-CH_2-NH_2$ has the higher boiling point because it is a primary amine that forms hydrogen bonds. A tertiary amine cannot form hydrogen bonds with other tertiary amines.

18.13 As a primary amine, propylamine can form two hydrogen bonds, which gives it the highest boiling point. Ethylmethylamine, a secondary amine, can form one hydrogen bond, and butane cannot form hydrogen bonds. Thus, butane has the lowest boiling point of the three compounds.

18.15 **a.** Yes, amines with fewer than six carbon atoms are soluble in water.
b. Yes, amines with fewer than six carbon atoms are soluble in water.
c. No, an amine with nine carbon atoms is not soluble in water.
d. Yes, amines with fewer than six carbon atoms are soluble in water.

18.17 **a.** $CH_3-NH_2 + H_2O \rightleftharpoons CH_3-NH_3^+ + OH^-$

b. $CH_3-NH-CH_3 + H_2O \rightleftharpoons$
$CH_3-\overset{+}{N}H_2-CH_3 + OH^-$

c. [benzene ring with NH_2] $+ H_2O \rightleftharpoons$ [benzene ring with NH_3^+] $+ OH^-$

18.19 **a.** $CH_3-\overset{+}{N}H_3 \ Cl^-$

b. $CH_3-\overset{+}{N}H_2-CH_3 \ Cl^-$ **c.** [benzene ring with $\overset{+}{N}H_3 \ Cl^-$]

18.21 **a.** H_2N-[benzene ring]$-\overset{\overset{O}{||}}{C}-O-CH_2-CH_2-\overset{\overset{CH_2-CH_3}{|}}{\underset{\underset{CH_2-CH_3}{|}}{\overset{+}{N}}}-H \ Cl^-$

b. The amine salt (Novocain) is more soluble in aqueous body fluids than procaine.

18.23 **a.** amine **b.** amine
c. heterocyclic amine **d.** heterocyclic amine

18.25 **c.** pyrimidine **d.** pyrrole

18.27 pyrrole

18.29 **a.** $CH_3-\overset{\overset{O}{||}}{C}-NH_2$

b. $CH_3-\overset{\overset{O}{||}}{C}-\overset{\overset{H}{|}}{N}-CH_2-CH_3$

c. [benzene ring]$-\overset{\overset{O}{||}}{C}-\overset{\overset{H}{|}}{N}-CH_2-CH_2-CH_3$

18.31 **a.** N-methylethanamide (N-methylacetamide)
b. butanamide (butyramide)
c. methanamide (formamide)
d. N-methylbenzamide

18.33 **a.** $CH_3-CH_2-\overset{\overset{O}{||}}{C}-NH_2$

b. $CH_3-CH_2-CH_2-CH_2-\overset{\overset{O}{||}}{C}-NH_2$

c. $H-\overset{\overset{O}{||}}{C}-NH_2$ **d.** [benzene ring]$-\overset{\overset{O}{||}}{C}-\overset{\overset{H}{|}}{N}-CH_2-CH_3$

e. $CH_3-CH_2-CH_2-\overset{\overset{O}{||}}{C}-\overset{\overset{H}{|}}{N}-CH_2-CH_3$

18.35 a. Acetamide has the higher melting point because it forms more hydrogen bonds as a primary amide than *N*-methylpropanamide, which is a secondary amide.
b. Propionamide has the higher melting point because it forms hydrogen bonds, but butane does not.
c. *N*-methylpropanamide has the higher melting point because it forms hydrogen bonds as a secondary amide, but *N,N*-dimethylpropanamide cannot form hydrogen bonds as a tertiary amide.

18.37 a. $CH_3-\overset{\overset{O}{\|}}{C}-OH \ + \ NH_4^+Cl^-$

b. $CH_3-CH_2-\overset{\overset{O}{\|}}{C}-OH \ + \ NH_4^+Cl^-$

c. $CH_3-CH_2-CH_2-\overset{\overset{O}{\|}}{C}-OH \ + \ CH_3-NH_3^+Cl^-$

d. $\text{(phenyl)}-\overset{\overset{O}{\|}}{C}-OH \ + \ NH_4^+Cl^-$

e. $CH_3-CH_2-CH_2-CH_2-\overset{\overset{O}{\|}}{C}-OH \ +$

$CH_3-CH_2-NH_3^+Cl^-$

18.39 amine, carboxylic acid, amide, aromatic, ester

18.41

$\text{(aromatic ring with } CH_3 \text{ substituent)}-\overset{\overset{O}{\|}}{C}-N\begin{smallmatrix}CH_2-CH_3\\CH_2-CH_3\end{smallmatrix}$

18.43 $CH_3-CH_2-CH_2-NH_2$
  Propylamine (1°)

$CH_3-CH_2-NH-CH_3$
  Ethylmethylamine (2°)

$CH_3-\overset{\overset{CH_3}{|}}{N}-CH_3$
  Trimethylamine (3°)

$CH_3-\overset{\overset{CH_3}{|}}{CH}-NH_2$
  Isopropylamine (1°)

18.45 a. diethylmethylamine (common), *N*-ethyl-*N*-methylethanamine; tertiary (3°)
b. butylamine (common), 1-butanamine; primary (1°)
c. ethylpropylamine (common), *N*-ethyl-1-propanamine; secondary (2°)

18.47 a. $CH_3-CH_2-\overset{\overset{NH_2}{|}}{CH}-CH_2-CH_3$ **b.** $\text{(cyclohexyl)}-NH_2$

c. $CH_3-\overset{\overset{CH_3}{|}}{NH_2^+} \ Cl^-$

d. $CH_3-CH_2-\overset{\overset{CH_2-CH_3}{|}}{N}-CH_2-CH_3$

18.49 a. An alcohol with an —OH group such as 1-butanol forms stronger hydrogen bonds than an amine and has a higher boiling point than an amine.
b. Propylamine, a primary amine, forms hydrogen bonds and has a higher boiling point than trimethylamine, a tertiary amine that does not form hydrogen bonds.

18.51 a. Ethylamine is a small amine that is soluble because it forms hydrogen bonds with water. Dibutylamine has two large nonpolar alkyl groups that decrease the solubility in water.
b. Trimethylamine is a small tertiary amine that is soluble because it hydrogen bonds with water.

18.53 a. methanamide
b. propanamide
c. *N*-methylethanamide

18.55 a. quinine
b. nicotine
c. caffeine
d. morphine, codeine

18.57 a. $CH_3-CH_2-NH_3^+ + OH^-$
b. $CH_3-CH_2-NH_3^+ Cl^-$
c. $CH_3-CH_2-\overset{+}{NH_2}-CH_3 + OH^-$

18.59 carboxylate salt, aromatic, amine, haloaromatic

18.61 a. aromatic, amine, amide, carboxylic acid, cycloalkene
b. aromatic, ether, alcohol, amine
c. aromatic, carboxylic acid
d. phenol, amine, carboxylic acid
e. aromatic, ether, alcohol, amine, ketone
f. aromatic, amine

18.63 The pH is 12.32.

19 Amino Acids and Proteins

"This lamb is fed with Lamb Lac, which is a chemically formulated replacement for ewe's milk," says part-time farmer Dennis Samuelson. "Its mother had triplets and didn't have enough milk to feed them all, so they weren't thriving the way the other lambs were. The Lamb Lac includes dried skim milk, dried whey, milk proteins, egg albumin, the amino acids methionine and lysine, vitamins, and minerals."

A veterinary technician diagnoses and treats diseases of animals, takes blood and tissue samples, and administers drugs and vaccines. Agricultural technologists assist in the study of farm crops to increase productivity and ensure a safe food supply. They look for ways to improve crop yields, develop safer methods of weed and pest control, and design methods to conserve soil and water.

Mastering**CHEMISTRY**™

Visit **www.masteringchemistry.com** for self-study materials and instructor-assigned homework.

The word "protein" is derived from the Greek word *proteios*, meaning "first." Made of amino acids, proteins provide structure in membranes, build cartilage and connective tissue, transport oxygen in blood and muscle, direct biological reactions as enzymes, defend the body against infection, and control metabolic processes as hormones. Proteins can even be a source of energy.

Protein molecules, compared with many of the compounds we have studied, can be gigantic. Insulin has a molar mass of 5800 g/mole, and hemoglobin has a molar mass of about 67 000 g/mole. Some virus proteins are even larger, having molar masses of more than 40 million g/mole. Yet all proteins in humans are polymers made up of only 20 different amino acids. Each kind of protein is composed of amino acids arranged in a specific sequence that determines the characteristics of the protein and its biological action.

Proteins perform many functions in the body: making up skin and hair, moving muscles, carrying oxygen, and regulating metabolism. All of these different functions depend on the structures and chemical behavior of amino acids, the building blocks. We will see how peptide bonds link amino acids and how the sequence of the amino acids in these protein polymers directs the formation of unique three-dimensional structures.

19.1 Proteins and Amino Acids

The many kinds of proteins perform different functions in the body. Some proteins form structural components such as cartilage, muscles, hair, and nails. Wool, silk, feathers, and horns in animals are made of proteins. Proteins that function as enzymes regulate biological reactions such as digestion and cellular metabolism. Other proteins, such as hemoglobin and myoglobin, transport oxygen in the blood and muscle. (See Figure 19.1.) Table 19.1 gives examples of proteins that are classified by their functions in biological systems.

LEARNING GOAL

Classify proteins by their functions in the body. Give the name and abbreviation of an amino acid and draw its ionized structure.

TABLE 19.1 Classification of Some Proteins and Their Functions

Class of Protein	Function in the Body	Examples
Structural	Provide structural components	*Collagen* is in tendons and cartilage. *Keratin* is in hair, skin, wool, and nails.
Contractile	Move muscles	*Myosin* and *actin* contract muscle fibers.
Transport	Carry essential substances throughout the body	*Hemoglobin* transports oxygen. *Lipoproteins* transport lipids.
Storage	Store nutrients	*Casein* stores protein in milk. *Ferritin* stores iron in the spleen and liver.
Hormone	Regulate body metabolism and nervous system	*Insulin* regulates blood glucose level. *Growth hormone* regulates body growth.
Enzyme	Catalyze biochemical reactions in the cells	*Sucrase* catalyzes the hydrolysis of sucrose. *Trypsin* catalyzes the hydrolysis of proteins.
Protection	Recognize and destroy foreign substances	*Immunoglobulins* stimulate immune responses.

FIGURE 19.1 The horns, feathers, and wool of animals are made of proteins.

Q What class of protein would be in horns?

Amino Acids

Proteins are composed of building blocks called amino acids. Every **amino acid** has a central carbon atom (α carbon) bonded to an ammonium group ($-NH_3^+$), a carboxylate group ($-COO^-$), a hydrogen atom ($-H$), and a side chain called an *R group*. The differences in the 20 α-amino acids present in human proteins are due to the unique characteristics of the R groups.

At the pH of most body fluids, amino acids are ionized. Under physiological conditions, the carboxylic acid groups ($-COOH$) lose H^+ to give carboxylate groups ($-COO^-$), and the amino groups ($-NH_2$) accept H^+ to give ammonium groups ($-NH_3^+$).

 TUTORIAL
Protein Building Blocks

 TUTORIAL
Proteins "R" Us

 SELF STUDY ACTIVITY
Functions of Proteins

General Structure of an α-Amino Acid

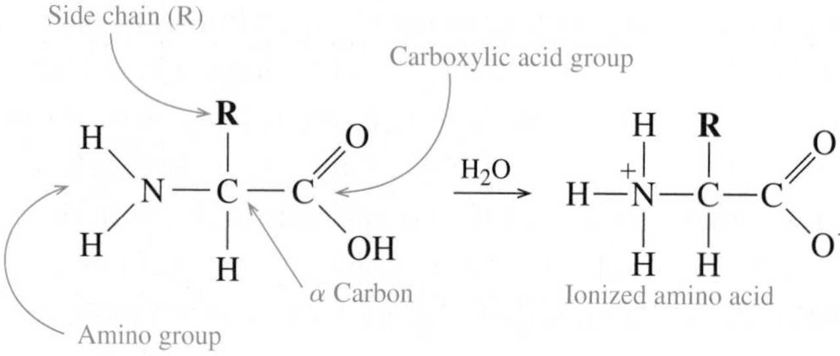

Classification of Amino Acids

Nonpolar amino acids contain alkyl or aromatic R groups, which make them *hydrophobic* ("water fearing"). **Polar amino acids (neutral)** contain polar R groups such as hydroxyl ($-OH$), thiol ($-SH$), and amide ($-CONH_2$) that interact with water; they are *hydrophilic* ("water attracting"). **Acidic amino acids** contain R groups that have carboxylate ($-COO^-$), and **basic amino acids** contain R groups that have ammonium ($-NH_3^+$). The R groups of acidic and basic amino acids interact with water, which makes them hydrophilic.

The ionized structures of the 20 α-amino acids found in proteins at physiological pH with their R groups highlighted in yellow, common names, and three-letter abbreviations are listed in Table 19.2. The isoelectric points, known as pI values, are discussed in Section 19.2.

SAMPLE PROBLEM 19.1

■ Structural Formulas of Amino Acids

Draw the condensed structural formula of the given ionized amino acid, and write the abbreviation for each of the following:

a. serine
b. aspartic acid

SOLUTION

a. The ionized form of serine is written by attaching $-NH_3^+$, $-COO^-$, $-H$, and the R group ($-CH_2-OH$) to the α carbon atom:

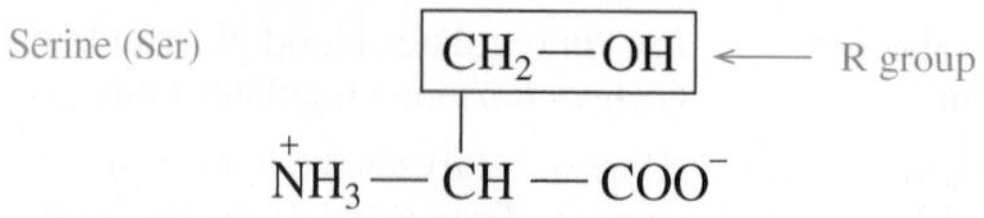

Serine (Ser)

$$CH_2-OH \quad \longleftarrow \text{ R group}$$
$$\overset{+}{N}H_3-CH-COO^-$$

b. The ionized form of aspartic acid is written by attaching $-NH_3^+$, $-COO^-$, $-H$, and the R group ($-CH_2-COO^-$) to the alpha carbon atom.

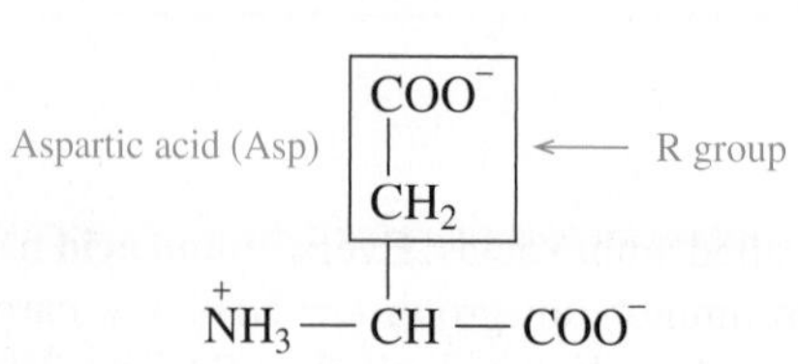

Aspartic acid (Asp)

$$COO^-$$
$$| $$
$$CH_2 \quad \longleftarrow \text{ R group}$$
$$| $$
$$\overset{+}{N}H_3-CH-COO^-$$

STUDY CHECK

Classify the amino acids in the sample problem as polar or nonpolar.

TABLE 19.2 The 20 Amino Acids (Ionized) in Proteins

Nonpolar Amino Acids

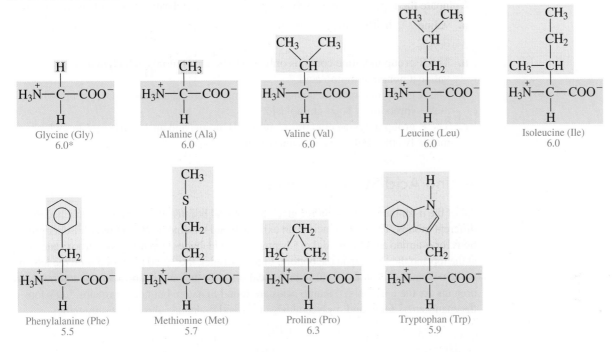

Glycine (Gly)
6.0*

Alanine (Ala)
6.0

Valine (Val)
6.0

Leucine (Leu)
6.0

Isoleucine (Ile)
6.0

Phenylalanine (Phe)
5.5

Methionine (Met)
5.7

Proline (Pro)
6.3

Tryptophan (Trp)
5.9

Polar Amino Acids (Neutral)

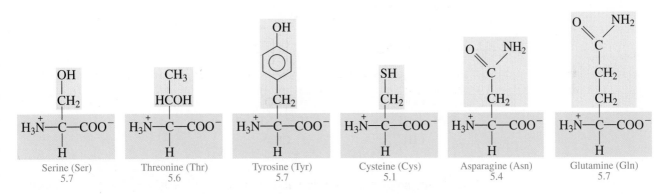

Serine (Ser)
5.7

Threonine (Thr)
5.6

Tyrosine (Tyr)
5.7

Cysteine (Cys)
5.1

Asparagine (Asn)
5.4

Glutamine (Gln)
5.7

Polar Amino Acids (Acidic)   ### Polar Amino Acids (Basic)

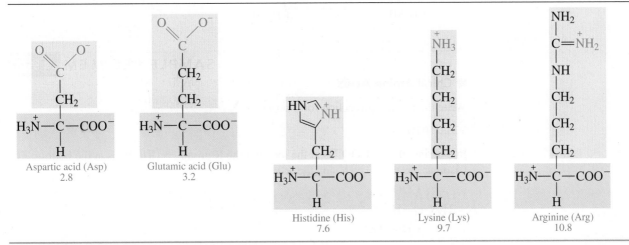

Aspartic acid (Asp)
2.8

Glutamic acid (Glu)
3.2

Histidine (His)
7.6

Lysine (Lys)
9.7

Arginine (Arg)
10.8

*Isoelectric points (pI)

■ R Groups and Polarity of Amino Acids

Compare the types of atoms in the R groups and the polarity of each of the following:

a. valine   **b.** threonine   **c.** lysine

ANSWER

a. The R group in valine contains only C atoms and H atoms, which makes valine a nonpolar amino acid.

b. The R group in threonine contains C atoms, H atoms, and an —OH group, which makes threonine a polar amino acid.

c. The R group in lysine contains C atoms, H atoms, and an —NH_3^+ group, which makes lysine a polar (basic) amino acid.

Amino Acid Stereoisomers

All of the α-amino acids except for glycine are chiral because the α carbon is attached to four different groups. Thus amino acids can exist as D and L isomers. We can write Fischer projections for α-amino acids as we did in Chapter 14 for aldehydes by placing the carboxylate group at the top and the R group at the bottom. In the L isomer, the —NH_3^+ group is on the left, and in the D isomer, it is on the right. In biological systems, the only amino acids incorporated into proteins are the L isomers; D amino acids are found in nature but not in proteins. Let's look at the enantiomers for L- and D-glyceraldehyde, L- and D-alanine, and L- and D-cysteine:

L-Glyceraldehyde

D-Glyceraldehyde

L-Alanine

D-Alanine

L-Cysteine

D-Cysteine

■ Chiral Amino Acids

Write the Fischer projection for L-serine.

SOLUTION

In L-serine, the —COO^- is at the top, and the R group —CH_2OH is at the bottom. The L isomer has the —NH_3^+ on the left:

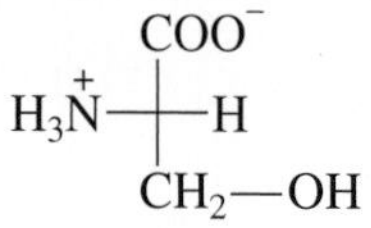

L-Serine

STUDY CHECK

How does the Fischer projection for D-serine differ from L-serine?

QUESTIONS AND PROBLEMS

Proteins and Amino Acids

19.1 Classify each of the following proteins according to its function:
  a. hemoglobin, carries oxygen in the blood
  b. collagen, a major component of tendons and cartilage
  c. keratin, a protein found in hair
  d. amylases, catalyze hydrolysis of starch

19.2 Classify each of the following proteins according to its function:
  a. insulin, a hormone needed for glucose utilization
  b. antibodies, disable foreign proteins
  c. casein, milk protein
  d. lipases, catalyze the hydrolysis of lipids

19.3 Describe the functional groups found in all α-amino acids.

19.4 How does the polarity of the R group in leucine compare to the R group in serine?

19.5 Draw the ionized form of each of the following amino acids:
  a. alanine   **b.** threonine
  c. glutamic acid   **d.** phenylalanine

19.6 Draw the ionized form of each of the following amino acids:
  a. lysine   **b.** aspartic acid
  c. leucine   **d.** tyrosine

19.7 Classify the amino acids in problem 19.5 as hydrophobic (nonpolar) or hydrophilic (polar neutral, acidic, or basic).

19.8 Classify the amino acids in problem 19.6 as hydrophobic (nonpolar) or hydrophilic (polar neutral, acidic, or basic).

19.9 Give the name of the amino acid represented by each of the following three-letter abbreviations:
  a. Ala   **b.** Val   **c.** Lys   **d.** Cys

19.10 Give the name of the amino acid represented by each of the following three-letter abbreviations:
  a. Trp   **b.** Met   **c.** Pro   **d.** Gly

19.11 Draw the Fischer projection for each of the following amino acids:
  a. L-valine   **b.** D-cysteine

19.12 Draw the Fischer projection for each of the following amino acids:
  a. L-threonine   **b.** D-valine

19.2 Amino Acids as Zwitterions

At a specific pH known as the **isoelectric point (pI)**, the positive and negative charges of an ionized amino acid are equal. This ionized structure is called a **zwitterion**, which has an overall charge of zero:

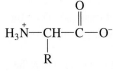

Zwitterion

The pI values for the zwitterions are included in the list of the amino acids in Table 19.2.

As zwitterions, amino acids have very high melting points because they are salts. The ionic charges of the zwitterions make amino acids soluble in water, but not in organic solvents.

Zwitterions of Nonpolar and Polar Amino Acids (Neutral)

The zwitterions of the nonpolar and polar (neutral) amino acids exist at pH values from 5.1 to 6.3. Let's look at the how the zwitterion of glycine reacts in acid and base. In a solution that is more acidic (lower pH) than its pI of 6.0, the $-COO^-$ group of glycine accepts an H^+ to form $-COOH$. Because of the remaining $-NH_3{}^+$, glycine has an overall positive charge ($1+$):

$$H_3\overset{+}{N}-\underset{\overset{|}{H}}{\overset{|}{C}H}-\boxed{\overset{\overset{O}{\parallel}}{C}-O^-} + H_3O^+ \rightleftarrows H_3\overset{+}{N}-\underset{\overset{|}{H}}{\overset{|}{C}H}-\boxed{\overset{\overset{O}{\parallel}}{C}-OH} + H_2O$$

Zwitterion ion accepts H^+ Positively charged ion

When glycine is placed in a solution that is more basic (higher pH) than its pI of 6.0, the $-NH_3{}^+$ group donates H^+ to form $-NH_2$. Because of the remaining carboxylate group $-COO^-$, glycine has an overall negative charge ($1-$):

Condition	pH < pI	pH = pI	pH > pI
Change in H⁺	$[H^+]$ ⇑	None	$[H^+]$ ⇓
Change in ionized groups	—COOH	—COO⁻	—COO⁻
	—NH₃⁺	—NH₃⁺	—NH₂
Overall charge	1+	0	1−

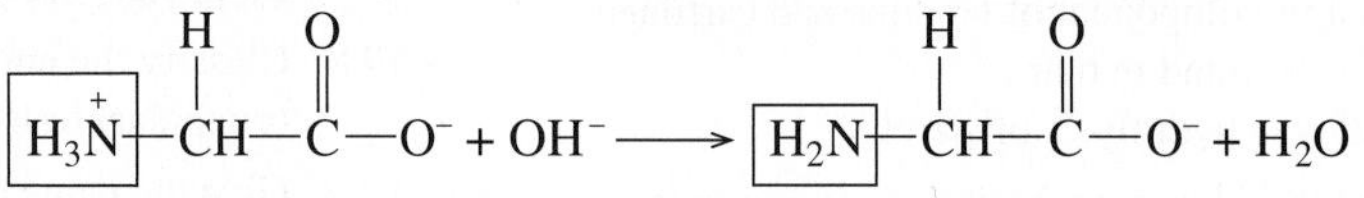

Zwitterion donates H⁺   Negatively charged ion

In another example, we look at the changes in the zwitterion of alanine with a pI of 6.0 when it is placed in a more acidic solution and in a more basic solution:

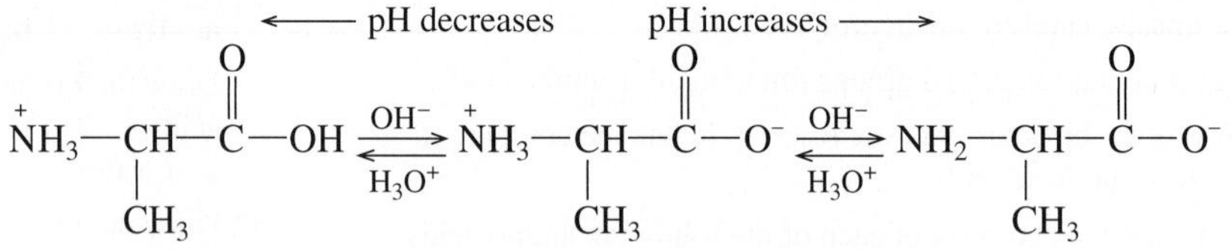

Alanine at
pH < 6
(charge = 1+)

Zwitterion of alanine
pH = 6.0
(charge = 0)

Alanine at
pH > 6
(charge = 1−)

CONCEPT CHECK 19.2

■ **Zwitterions of Amino Acids**

Consider the amino acid cysteine.

a. What is the pI of cysteine, and what does it mean?
b. At a pH of 2.0, how does the zwitterion change?
c. At a pH of 8.0, how does the zwitterion change?

ANSWER

a. From Table 5.2, the pI of cysteine is 5.1. This means that at pH of 5.1 cysteine exists as a zwitterion with a net charge of zero.
b. From Table 5.2, a pH of 2.0 is more acidic and below the pI of cysteine. Then the —COO⁻ accepts H⁺ to give —COOH. The remaining —NH₃⁺ group gives cysteine a positive charge (1+).
c. From Table 5.2, a pH of 8.0 is more basic and above the pI of cysteine. Then the —NH₃⁺ donates H⁺ to give —NH₂. The remaining —COO⁻ gives cysteine a negative charge (1−).

Zwitterions of Acidic and Basic Amino Acids

In physiological solutions, all of the R groups of the acidic and basic amino acids are ionized. The zwitterions of acidic amino acids exist only at lower pH values from 2.8 to 3.2, when a carboxylate group accepts H⁺ to give an overall charge of zero. The zwitterions of basic amino acids exist only at higher pH values from 7.6 to 10.8, when an amino group donates H⁺ to give an overall charge of zero.

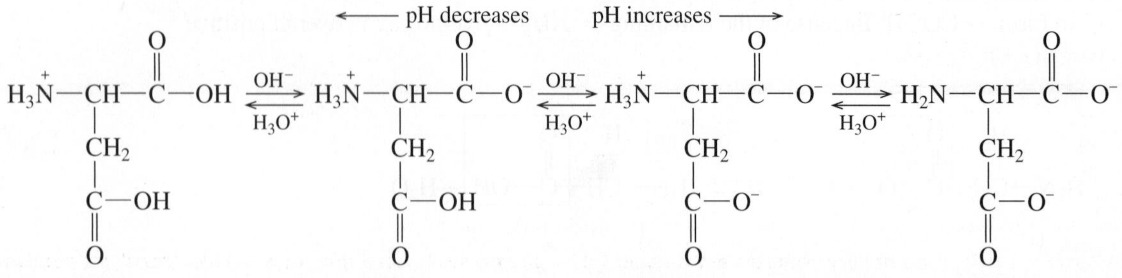

Aspartic acid
pH < 2
(charge = 1+)

Zwitterion
pH = 2.8
(charge = 0)

Aspartic acid
at pH 7
(charge = 1−)

Aspartic acid
pH > 10
(charge = 2−)

SAMPLE PROBLEM 19.3

■ Amino Acids as Zwitterions

Draw the zwitterion of serine at pH 5.7, which is the pI of serine.

SOLUTION

At the pI of 5.7, serine exists as a zwitterion with both a carboxylate and an ammonium group:

$$\overset{+}{NH_3} - CH - \overset{\displaystyle \overset{O}{\|}}{C} - O^-$$

OH
|
CH₂

Zwitterion of serine

STUDY CHECK

Draw the ionized structure of serine at a pH of 3.

Electrophoresis

It is possible to separate a mixture of amino acids using a laboratory method called **electrophoresis**. A buffered amino acid mixture is applied to a gel on a thin plate or piece of filter paper that is connected to two electrodes. A voltage applied to the electrodes causes the positively charged amino acids to move toward the negative electrode, and the negatively charged amino acids to move toward the positive electrode. Any amino acid at its isoelectric point with a zero net charge would not move. After several hours, the sample is removed. It can be sprayed with a dye such as ninhydrin to make the amino acids visible, which are identified by their direction and rate of migration toward the electrodes. The amino acids are recovered separately by cutting the filter paper or removing the amino acids from the gel. Electrophoresis is a method used in medicine to screen for the sickle-cell trait in newborn infants.

Suppose we have a mixture of valine (pI 6.0), aspartic acid (pI 2.8), and lysine (pI 9.7) in a buffer of pH 6.0. When the mixture is placed between two electrodes at a high voltage, the aspartic acid, which has a negative charge at pH 6.0, moves to the positive electrode (anode). (See Figure 19.2.) The lysine, which has a positive charge at a pH of 6.0, moves toward the negative electrode (cathode). Valine, which is neutral at pH 6.0, does not move in the presence of an electric field.

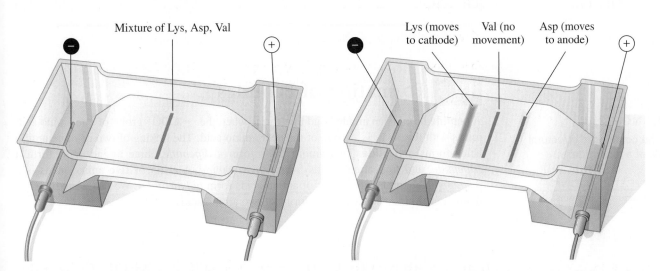

FIGURE 19.2 A positively charged amino acid (pH < pI) moves toward the negative electrode; a negatively charged amino acid (pH > pI) moves toward the positive electrode; an amino acid with no net charge (pH = pI) does not migrate.
Q How would the three amino acids migrate if the mixture were buffered to pH 9.7, the pI of lysine?

CONCEPT CHECK 19.3

■ **Ionized Forms of Amino Acids**

Explain each of the following:

a. Glutamic acid moves toward the positive electrode during electrophoresis at a pH of 7.0.

b. The pI of lysine is much higher than the pI of phenylalanine.

ANSWER

a. A pH of 7.0 is higher (more basic) than the pI of 3.2 for glutamic acid. At a pH of 7.0, glutamic acid would have two negatively charged $-COO^-$ groups and one $-NH_3^+$, which gives an overall negative charge of $1-$.

b. At a pH of 5.5, the nonpolar phenylalanine forms a zwitterion with a zero net charge. However, lysine is a basic amino acid with two $-NH_3^+$ groups and one $-COO^-$. To form the zwitterion of lysine, a more basic environment is needed so that an $-NH_3^+$ group donates H^+ to give $-NH_2$ and a zwitterion with a net charge of zero. Thus, lysine has a higher pI because it requires a higher pH to form the zwitterion.

QUESTIONS AND PROBLEMS

Amino Acids as Zwitterions

19.13 Draw the zwitterion of each of the following amino acids:
 a. glycine   b. cysteine   c. threonine   d. alanine

19.14 Draw the zwitterion of each of the following amino acids:
 a. phenylalanine   b. methionine
 c. leucine   d. valine

19.15 Draw the positive ion (acidic ion) of each of the amino acids in problem 19.13 at a pH below 1.0.

19.16 Draw the negative ion (basic ion) of each of the amino acids in problem 19.13 at a pH above 12.0.

19.17 Would each of the following ions of valine exist at a pH above, below, or at pI?

 a. $H_2N-CH-COO^-$
       |
       CH
      / \
   CH_3 CH_3

 b. $\overset{+}{H_3N}-CH-COOH$
        |
        CH
       / \
    CH_3 CH_3

 c. $\overset{+}{H_3N}-CH-COO^-$
         |
         CH
        / \
     CH_3 CH_3

19.18 Would each of the following ions of serine exist at a pH above, below, or at pI?

 a. $\overset{+}{H_3N}-CH-COO^-$
          |
        CH_2OH

 b. $\overset{+}{H_3N}-CH-COOH$
          |
        CH_2OH

 c. $H_2N-CH-COO^-$
         |
       CH_2OH

19.3 Formation of Peptides

LEARNING GOAL

Draw the condensed structural formula of a dipeptide.

 SELF STUDY ACTIVITY
Structure of Proteins

A **peptide bond** is an amide bond that forms when the $-COO^-$ group of one amino acid reacts with the $-NH_3^+$ group of the next amino acid. The linking of two or more amino acids forms a **peptide**. Two amino acids form a *dipeptide*, three amino acids form a *tripeptide*, and four amino acids form a *tetrapeptide*. A chain of five amino acids is a *pentapeptide*, and longer chains of amino acids form *polypeptides*. We can write the amidation reaction for the zwitterion forms of two amino acids as follows:

$$\overset{+}{H_3N}-CH-\boxed{\overset{\overset{O}{\|}}{C}-O^-} + \boxed{\overset{+}{H_3N}}-CH-\overset{\overset{O}{\|}}{C}-O^- \longrightarrow \overset{+}{H_3N}-CH-\boxed{\overset{\overset{O}{\|}}{C}-\overset{H}{N}}-CH-\overset{\overset{O}{\|}}{C}-O^- + H_2O$$

| R | R | R | R |

   Amino acid 1   Amino acid 2   Dipeptide

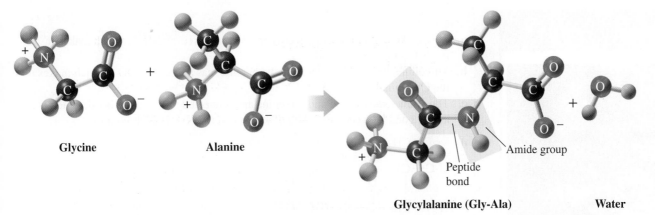

Glycine   **Alanine**   **Glycylalanine (Gly-Ala)**   **Water**

FIGURE 19.3 A peptide bond between glycine and alanine as zwitterions forms the dipeptide glycylalanine.

Q What functional groups in glycine and alanine form the peptide bond?

We can write the formation of the dipeptide glycylalanine (Gly-Ala) between glycine and alanine as follows. (See Figure 19.3.) In this peptide, glycine is written on the left. Because the glycine has a free —NH_3^+, it is the **N terminal** amino acid. The amino acid alanine written on the right has a free —COO^- and is called the **C terminal** amino acid.

$$\underset{\text{Glycine}}{H_3\overset{+}{N}-CH_2-\overset{O}{\overset{||}{C}}-O^-} + \underset{\text{Alanine}}{H_3\overset{+}{N}-\underset{\underset{CH_3}{|}}{CH}-\overset{O}{\overset{||}{C}}-O^-} \longrightarrow \underset{\text{Glycylalanine (Gly-Ala)}}{H_3\overset{+}{N}-CH_2-\overset{\overset{\text{N terminal}}{}}{\underset{}{\boxed{\overset{O}{\overset{||}{C}}-\overset{H}{\overset{|}{N}}}}}\underset{\underset{CH_3}{|}}{CH}-\overset{\overset{\text{C terminal}}{}}{\overset{O}{\overset{||}{C}}}-O^- + H_2O$$

Naming Peptides

In the name of a peptide, each amino acid beginning from the N terminal end has the *ine* (or *ic acid*) replaced by *yl*. The last amino acid at the C terminal end of the peptide has its full name. For example, a tripeptide consisting of alanine, glycine, and serine is named as ala**nyl**gly**cyl**serine. For convenience, the order of amino acids in the peptide is often written as the sequence of three-letter abbreviations:

$$\boxed{H_3\overset{+}{N}-\underset{\underset{CH_3}{|}}{CH}-\overset{O}{\overset{||}{C}}} \boxed{NH-CH_2-\overset{O}{\overset{||}{C}}} \boxed{NH-\underset{\underset{CH_2OH}{|}}{CH}-\overset{O}{\overset{||}{C}}-O^-}$$

From alanine   From glycine   From serine
alanyl   glycyl   serine

Alanylglycylserine
(Ala-Gly-Ser)

CONCEPT CHECK 19.4

■ Structure and Names of Peptides

Consider the dipeptide Val-Thr:

a. What amino acid is the N terminal amino acid?
b. What amino acid is the C terminal amino acid?
c. How are the amino acids connected?
d. Draw the condensed structural formula of Val-Thr.
e. Give the name of the dipeptide.

CAREER FOCUS

Rehabilitation Specialist

"I am interested in the biomechanical part of rehabilitation, which involves strengthening activities that help people return to the activities of daily living," says Minna Robles, rehabilitation specialist. "Here I am fitting a patient with a wrist extension splint that allows her to lift her hand. This exercise will also help the muscles and soft tissues in that wrist area to heal. An understanding of the chemicals of the body, how they interact, and how we can affect the body on a chemical level is important in understanding our work. One technique we use is called myofacial release. We apply pressure to a part of the body, which helps to increase circulation. By increasing circulation, we can move the soft tissues better, which improves movement and range of motion."

ANSWER

a. Valine, the first amino acid in the peptide, has a free $-NH_3^+$, which makes it the N terminal amino acid.

b. Threonine, the last amino acid in the peptide, has a free $-COO^-$, which makes it the C terminal amino acid.

c. The amino acids valine and threonine are connected by a peptide bond, which is an amide bond between the C=O of valine and the N—H of threonine.

d.

$$H_3C-\overset{\overset{\displaystyle CH_3}{|}}{CH} \qquad \overset{\overset{\displaystyle CH_3}{|}}{CH}-OH$$

$$\overset{+}{H_3N}-CH-\overset{O}{\overset{||}{C}}-\overset{H}{\overset{|}{N}}-CH-\overset{O}{\overset{||}{C}}-O^-$$

e. In the name of a peptide, the ending *ine* (or *ic acid*) of each amino acid preceding the C terminal amino acid is changed to *yl*. The C terminal amino acid does not change its name. The dipeptide is named valylthreonine.

SAMPLE PROBLEM 19.4

■ Identifying a Tripeptide

Consider the following tripeptide:

$$\overset{+}{H_3N}-CH-\overset{O}{\overset{||}{C}}-NH-CH-\overset{O}{\overset{||}{C}}-NH-CH-\overset{O}{\overset{||}{C}}-O^-$$

with side chains: HC—OH / CH$_3$; CH$_2$ / HC—CH$_3$ / CH$_3$; CH$_2$ / (benzene ring)

a. What amino acid is the N terminal? What amino acid is the C terminal?
b. What is the three-letter abbreviation for the tripeptide?
c. What is the name of the tripeptide?

SOLUTION

a. Threonine is the N terminal; phenylalanine is the C terminal.
b. Thr-Leu-Phe
c. Beginning at the N terminal, the amino acids in the tripeptide are threonine, leucine, and phenylalanine. Changing the *ine* endings of the amino acids preceding the C terminal amino acid (name does not change) gives the name threonylleucylphenylalanine.

STUDY CHECK

What is the name of the pentapeptide called *enkephalin*, a natural painkiller produced in the body, if it has the abbreviation Tyr-Gly-Gly-Phe-Met?

QUESTIONS AND PROBLEMS

Formation of Peptides

19.19 Draw the condensed structural formula of each of the following peptides, and give the abbreviation for their names:
  a. alanylcysteine   **b.** serylphenylalanine
  c. glycylalanylvaline   **d.** valylisoleucyltryptophan

19.20 Draw the condensed structural formula of each of the following peptides, and give the abbreviation for their names:
  a. methionylaspartic acid
  b. alanyltryptophan
  c. methionylglutaminyllysine
  d. histidylglycylglutamylalanine

19.4 Protein Structure: Primary and Secondary Levels

When there are more than 50 amino acids in a chain, the polypeptide is usually called a **protein**. Each protein in our cells has a unique sequence of amino acids that determines its biological function.

Primary Structure

The **primary structure** of a protein is the particular sequence of amino acids held together by peptide bonds. For example, a hormone that stimulates the thyroid to release thyroxine is a tripeptide with the amino acid sequence Glu-His-Pro:

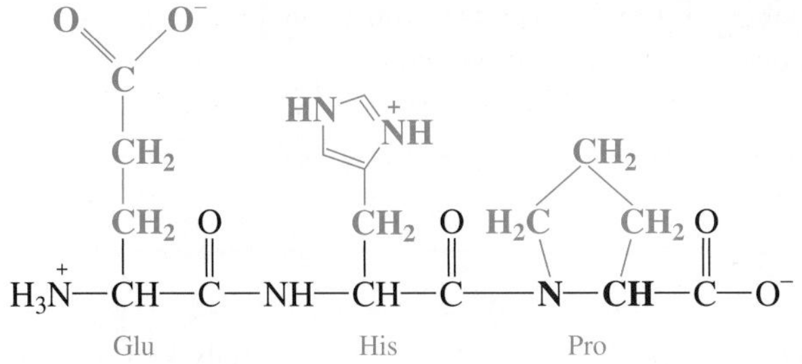

Although other amino acid sequences are possible, such as His-Pro-Glu or Pro-His-Glu, they do not produce hormonal activity. Only the tripeptide with the Glu-His-Pro sequence of amino acids has hormonal activity. Thus, the biological function of peptides and proteins depends on the specific sequence of the amino acids.

The first protein to have its primary structure determined was insulin, which is a hormone that regulates the glucose level in the blood. The primary structure of human insulin has two polypeptide chains. Chain A has 21 amino acids, and chain B has 30 amino acids. The polypeptide chains are held together by disulfide bonds formed by the R groups of the cysteine amino acids in each of the chains. (See Figure 19.4.)

The primary structure of insulin in humans is very similar to the primary structure of insulin in cows (bovine). Only the three amino acids at positions 8, 9, and 10 in chain A and position 30 in chain B vary from one species to another. For many years, bovine insulin obtained from the pancreas of cows was used to treat diabetics who lacked insulin. Today, human insulin produced through genetic engineering is used in the treatment of diabetes.

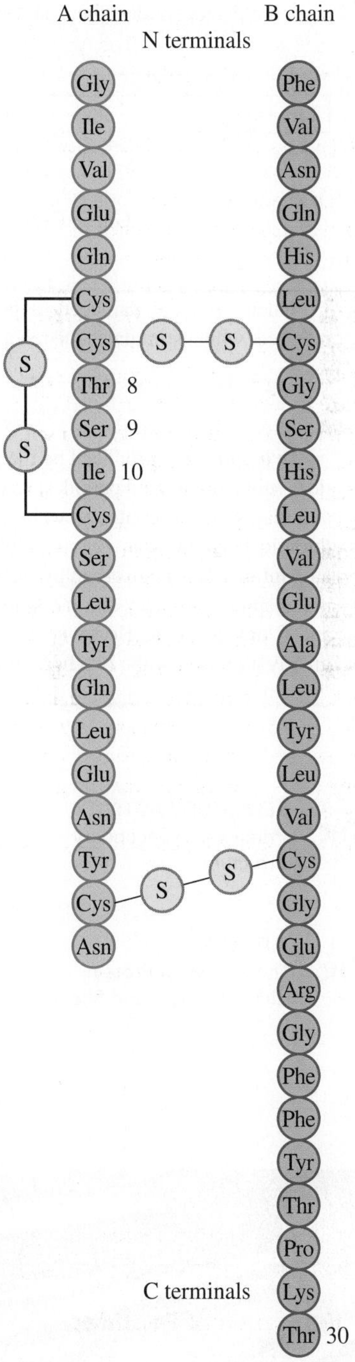

CONCEPT CHECK 19.5

■ Primary Structure

What are the abbreviations of the possible tetrapeptides containing two valines, one proline, and one histidine if the C terminal is proline?

ANSWER
The C terminal of proline in the possible tetrapeptides would be preceded by three different sequences of two valines and one histidine: Val-Val-His-Pro, Val-His-Val-Pro, and His-Val-Val-Pro.

Secondary Structure

The **secondary structure** of a protein describes the type of structure that forms when amino acids form hydrogen bonds within a polypeptide or between polypeptides. The three most common types of secondary structure are the *alpha helix*, the *beta-pleated sheet*, and the *triple helix*.

LEARNING GOAL

Describe the primary and secondary structures of a protein.

TUTORIAL
MC Peptides Are Chains of Amino Acids

FIGURE 19.4 The sequence of amino acids in human insulin is its primary structure.

Q What kinds of bonds occur in the primary structure of a protein?

HEALTH NOTE

Polypeptides in the Body

Enkephalins and endorphins are natural painkillers produced in the body. They are polypeptides that bind to receptors in the brain to give relief from pain. This effect appears to be responsible for the runner's high and the temporary loss of pain when severe injury occurs.

The *enkephalins*, which are found in the thalamus and the spinal cord, are pentapeptides, the smallest molecules with opiate activity.

The amino acid sequence of an enkephalin is found in the longer amino acid sequence of the endorphins.

Four groups of *endorphins* have been identified: α-endorphin contains 16 amino acids, β-endorphin contains 31 amino acids, γ-endorphin has 17 amino acids, and δ-endorphin has 27 amino acids. Endorphins may produce their sedating effects by preventing the release of substance P, a polypeptide with 11 amino acids, which has been found to transmit pain impulses to the brain.

α-Endorphin

Tyr — Gly — Gly — Phe — Met — Thr — Ser — Glu — Lys — Ser — Glu — Thr — Pro — Leu — Val — Thr

Enkephalin

Leu

Glu — Gly — Lys — Lys — Tyr — Ala — Asn — Lys — Ile — Ile — Ala — Asn — Lys — Phe

β-Endorphin

When cells are damaged, a polypeptide called bradykinin is released, which stimulates the release of prostaglandins:

Arg — Pro — Pro — Gly — Phe — Ser — Pro — Phe — Arg

Bradykinin

Two hormones produced by the pituitary gland are the nonapeptides (nine-amino-acid peptides) oxytocin and vasopressin. Oxytocin stimulates uterine contractions in labor, and vasopressin is an antidiuretic hormone that regulates blood pressure by adjusting the amount of water reabsorbed by the kidneys. The structures of these nonapeptides are very similar. Only the amino acids in positions 3 and 8 are different. However, the difference of two amino acids greatly affects how the two hormones function in the body.

1 Cys — S — S — 6 Cys — 7 Pro — 8 Leu/Arg — 9 Gly — C(=O) — NH₂

2 Tyr   5 Asn

3 Ile/Phe — 4 Gln

Oxytocin
Vasopressin

SELF STUDY ACTIVITY
Primary and Secondary Structure

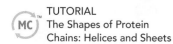

TUTORIAL
The Shapes of Protein Chains: Helices and Sheets

In an **alpha helix (α helix)**, hydrogen bonds form between each N—H group and the oxygen of a C=O group of an amino acid in the next turn of the α helix. (See Figure 19.5.) Because there are many hydrogen bonds along the polypeptide, it has the helical shape of a coiled telephone cord. All the R groups of the different amino acids in the polypeptide extend to the outside of the helix.

Another type of secondary structure is known as the **beta-pleated sheet (β-pleated sheet)**. In a β-pleated sheet, polypeptide chains are held together side by side by hydrogen bonds between the peptide chains. In a β-pleated sheet of silk fibroin, the small R groups of the prevalent amino acids, glycine, alanine, and serine, extend above and below the sheet. This arrangement of amino acids results in a series of β-pleated sheets that are stacked close together. The hydrogen bonds holding the β-pleated sheets tightly in place account for the strength and durability of fibrous proteins such as silk. (See Figure 19.6.)

In some proteins, the polypeptide chain consists of mostly the α helix secondary structure, whereas other proteins consist of mostly the β-pleated sheet structure. Another group of proteins have a mixture with some sections of the polypeptide chain in α helices and other sections in the β-pleated sheet structure. The tendency to form a certain type of secondary structure depends on the amino acids in a particular segment of the polypeptide chain. Amino acids such as valine, proline, serine, and aspartic acid are found in β-pleated sheet regions. The α helix region has large amounts of amino acids such as alanine, histidine, leucine, and methionine.

Collagen, which is the most abundant protein in the body, makes up 25–35% of all protein in vertebrates. It is found in connective tissue, blood vessels, skin, tendons, ligaments,

The secondary structure in silk is a beta-pleated sheet.

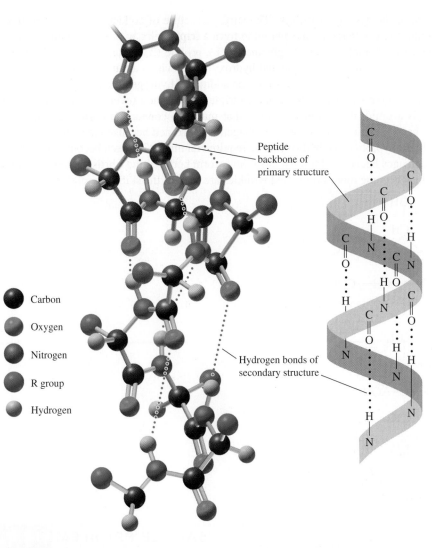

FIGURE 19.5 The α (alpha) helix acquires a coiled shape from hydrogen bonds between the N—H of the peptide bond in one loop and the C═O of the peptide bond in the next loop.

Q What are the partial charges of the H in N—H and the O in C═O that permits hydrogen bonds to form?

Carbon
Oxygen
Nitrogen
R group
Hydrogen

Peptide backbone of primary structure

Hydrogen bonds of secondary structure

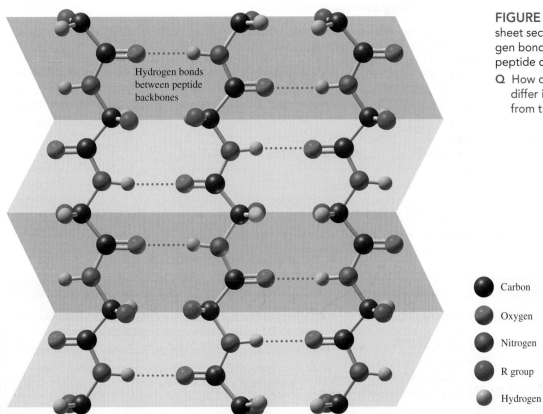

Hydrogen bonds between peptide backbones

FIGURE 19.6 In a β-pleated sheet secondary structure, hydrogen bonds form between the peptide chains.

Q How do the hydrogen bonds differ in a β-pleated sheet from the α helix?

Carbon
Oxygen
Nitrogen
R group
Hydrogen

Triple helix   3 α-helix peptide chains

FIGURE 19.7 Hydrogen bonds between polar R groups in three polypeptide chains form the triple helices that combine to make fibers of collagen.

Q What are some of the amino acids in collagen that form hydrogen bonds between the polypeptide chains?

the cornea of the eye, and cartilage. The strong structure of collagen is a result of three polypeptides woven together like a braid to form a **triple helix**, as seen in Figure 19.7.

Collagen has a high content of glycine (33%), proline (22%), and alanine (12%), and smaller amounts of hydroxyproline and hydroxylysine, which are modified forms of proline and lysine. These —OH groups provide additional hydrogen bonds between the peptide chains to give strength to the collagen triple helix. When several triple helices wrap together as a braid, they form the fibrils that make up connective tissues and tendons. When a diet is deficient in vitamin C, collagen is weakened because the enzymes needed to form hydroxyproline and hydroxylysine require vitamin C. Collagen becomes less elastic as a person ages because additional cross-links form between the fibrils. Bones, cartilage, and tendons become more brittle, and wrinkles are seen as the skin loses elasticity.

Hydroxyproline

Hydroxylysine

SAMPLE PROBLEM 19.5

■ **Identifying Secondary Structures**

Indicate the secondary structure (α helix, β-pleated sheet, or triple helix) described in each of the following statements:

a. a coiled peptide chain held in place by hydrogen bonding between peptide bonds in the same chain

b. a structure that has hydrogen bonds between polypeptide chains arranged side by side

SOLUTION

a. α helix   **b.** β-pleated sheet

STUDY CHECK

What is the secondary structure in collagen?

QUESTIONS AND PROBLEMS

Protein Structure: Primary and Secondary Levels

19.21 What type of bonding occurs in the primary structure of a protein?

19.22 How can two proteins with exactly the same number and type of amino acids have different primary structures?

19.23 Two peptides each contain one molecule of valine and two molecules of serine. What are their possible primary structures?

19.24 What are three different types of secondary protein structure?

19.25 What happens to the primary structure of a protein when a protein forms a secondary structure?

19.26 In an α helix, how does bonding occur between the amino acids in the polypeptide chain?

19.27 What is the difference in bonding between an α helix and a β-pleated sheet?

19.28 How is the secondary structure of a β-pleated sheet different from that of a triple helix?

HEALTH NOTE

Essential Amino Acids

Of the 20 amino acids used to build the proteins in the body, only 10 can be synthesized in the body. The other 10 amino acids, listed in Table 19.3, are **essential amino acids** that cannot be synthesized and must be obtained from the proteins in the diet.

TABLE 19.3 Essential Amino Acids

Arginine (Arg)*	Methionine (Met)
Histidine (His)*	Phenylalanine (Phe)
Isoleucine (Ile)	Threonine (Thr)
Leucine (Leu)	Tryptophan (Trp)
Lysine (Lys)	Valine (Val)

*Required in diets of children, not adults

Complete proteins, which contain all of the essential amino acids, are found in most animal products, such as eggs, milk, meat, fish, and poultry. However, gelatin and plant proteins such as grains, beans, and nuts are *incomplete proteins* because they are deficient in one or more of the essential amino acids. Diets that rely on plant foods for protein must contain a variety of protein sources to obtain all the essential amino acids. For example, a diet of rice and beans contains all the essential amino acids because rice and beans have complementary proteins. Rice contains the methionine and tryptophan deficient in beans, while beans contain the lysine that is lacking in rice. (See Table 19.4.)

TABLE 19.4 Amino Acid Deficiency in Selected Vegetables and Grains

Food Source	Amino Acids Missing
Eggs, milk, meat, fish, poultry	None
Wheat, rice, oats	Lysine
Corn	Lysine, tryptophan
Beans	Methionine, tryptophan
Peas	Methionine
Almonds, walnuts	Lysine, tryptophan
Soy	Low in methionine

19.5 Protein Structure: Tertiary and Quaternary Levels

The **tertiary structure** of a protein involves attractions and repulsions between the R groups of the amino acids in the polypeptide chain. As interactions occur between different parts of the peptide chain, segments of the chain twist and bend until the protein acquires a specific three-dimensional shape.

Cross-Links in Tertiary Structures

Many proteins are **globular proteins** because they acquire compact, spherical shapes when the secondary structures of their polypeptide chains fold over on top of each other. Globular proteins carry out cell functions such as synthesis, transport, and metabolism. The tertiary structure of a globular protein is stabilized by interactions between the R groups of the amino acids in one region of the polypeptide chain with the R groups of amino acids in other regions of the protein. (See Figure 19.8.) Table 19.5 lists the stabilizing interactions of tertiary structures, which are detailed as follows:

LEARNING GOAL

Describe the tertiary and quaternary structures of a protein.

 SELF STUDY ACTIVITY
Tertiary and Quaternary Structure

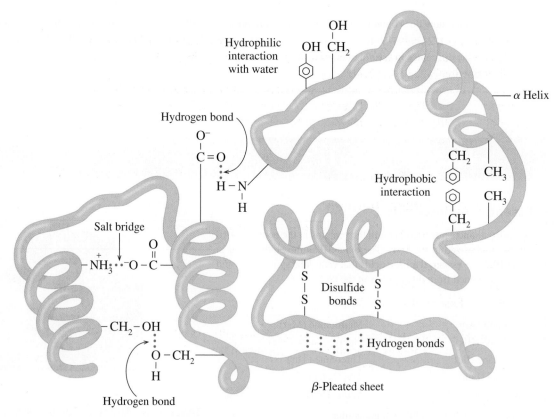

FIGURE 19.8 Interactions between amino acid R groups fold a protein into a specific three-dimensional shape called its tertiary structure.

Q Why would one section of the protein chain move to the center while another section remains on the surface of the tertiary structure?

TABLE 19.5 Some Cross-Links in Tertiary Structures

	Nature of Bonding
Hydrophobic interactions	Interactions between nonpolar groups
Hydrophilic interactions	Attractions between polar or ionized groups and water on the surface of the tertiary structure
Salt bridges	Ionic interactions between ionized acidic and basic amino acids
Hydrogen bonds	Occur between H and O or N
Disulfide bonds	Strong covalent links between sulfur atoms of two cysteine amino acids

1. **Hydrophobic interactions** are interactions between two nonpolar R groups. Within a protein, the amino acids with nonpolar R groups push as far away from the aqueous environment as possible, which forms a hydrophobic center at the interior of the protein molecule.

2. **Hydrophilic interactions** are attractions between the external aqueous environment and amino acids that have polar or ionized R groups. The polar R groups move to the outer surface where they hydrogen bond with water.

3. **Salt bridges** are ionic bonds between the ionized R groups of basic and acidic amino acids. For example, at physiological pH, the R group of lysine ($-NH_3^+$) attracts the R group of glutamic acid ($-COO^-$) to form an ionic bond called a salt bridge. If the pH changes, the basic and acidic R groups lose their ionic charges and cannot form salt bridges, which causes a change in the shape of the protein.

4. **Hydrogen bonds** form between the H of one R group and the O or N of another polar amino acid. For example, a hydrogen bond can occur between the $-OH$ groups of two serines or between the $-OH$ of serine and the $-NH_2$ in the R group of glutamine.

5. **Disulfide bonds** ($-S-S-$) are covalent bonds that form between the $-SH$ groups of cysteines in the polypeptide chain. In some proteins, there are several disulfide bonds between the R groups of cysteines in the polypeptide chain.

(MC)™ TUTORIAL
Levels of Structure in Proteins

CONCEPT CHECK 19.6

■ **Structural Levels in Proteins**

In a tertiary structure of a globular protein, the R groups of lysine and aspartic acid interact.

a. What type of interaction occurs?

b. What happens to this interaction when acid is added to the protein?

ANSWER
a. The R group of lysine contains $-NH_3^+$, and the R group of aspartic acid contains $-COO^-$. The interaction between positively and negatively charged R groups is an ionic attraction called a salt bridge.
b. If acid is added to the protein until the pH equals the pI of the aspartic acid, the zwitterion forms. The $-COO^-$ accepts H^+ to form $-COOH$, which causes a loss of ionic attraction, and breaks down the salt bridge.

SAMPLE PROBLEM 19.6

■ Cross-Links in Tertiary Structures

What type of interaction would you expect between the R groups of the following amino acids in a tertiary structure?

a. cysteine and cysteine
b. glutamic acid and lysine

SOLUTION

a. Because cysteine has an R group containing $-SH$, a disulfide bond will form.
b. An ionic bond (salt bridge) can form by the interaction of the $-COO^-$ of glutamic acid and the $-NH_3^+$ of lysine.

STUDY CHECK

Would you expect to find valine and leucine in a globular protein on the outside or the inside of the tertiary structure? Why?

Examples of Globular and Fibrous Proteins

Myoglobin is a globular protein that stores oxygen in skeletal muscle. High concentrations of myoglobin have been found in the muscles of sea mammals, such as seals and whales, that stay under the water for long periods. Myoglobin contains 153 amino acids in a single polypeptide chain with about three-fourths of the chain in the α helix secondary structure. The polypeptide chain, including its helical regions, forms a compact tertiary structure by folding upon itself. (See Figure 19.9.) Within the tertiary structure, a pocket of amino acids and a heme group binds and stores oxygen (O_2).

The **fibrous proteins** are proteins that consist of long, thin, fiber-like shapes. They are typically involved in the structure of cells and tissues. Two types of fibrous protein are the α- and β-keratins. The **α-keratins** are the proteins that make up hair, wool, skin, and nails. In hair, three α helices coil together like a braid to form a fibril. Within the fibril, the α helices are held together by disulfide ($-S-S-$) linkages between the R groups of the many cysteine amino acids in hair. Several fibrils bind together to form a strand of hair. (See Figure 19.10.)

The β-keratins are the type of proteins found in the feathers of birds and scales of reptiles. In β-keratins, the proteins consist of large amounts of twisted β-pleated sheet structure.

Quaternary Structure: Hemoglobin

When a biologically active protein consists of two or more polypeptide chains or subunits, the structural level is referred to as a **quaternary structure**. Hemoglobin, a globular protein that transports oxygen in blood, consists of four polypeptide chains, two α chains and two β chains.

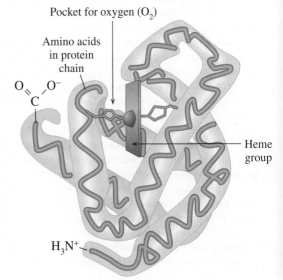

FIGURE 19.9 Myoglobin is a globular protein with a heme pocket in its tertiary structure that binds oxygen to be carried to the tissues.

Q Would hydrophilic amino acids be found on the outside or inside of the myoglobin structure?

α helix

Alpha keratin

FIGURE 19.10 The fibrous proteins of α-keratin wrap together to form fibrils that make up hair and wool. The proteins called β-keratins are found in the feathers of birds and scales of reptiles.

Q Why does hair have a large amount of cysteine amino acids?

HEALTH NOTE

Prions and Mad Cow Disease

Until recently, researchers thought that only viruses or bacteria were responsible for transmitting diseases. Now a group of diseases has been found in which the infectious agents are proteins called *prions*. Bovine spongiform encephalopathy (BSE), or "mad cow disease," is a fatal brain disease of cattle in which the brain fills with cavities, resembling a sponge. In the noninfectious form of the prion PrP^c, the N-terminal portion is a random coil. (See structure at right.) Although the noninfectious form may be ingested from meat products, its structure can change to what is known as PrP^s, or *prion-related protein scrapie*. In this infectious form, which has disastrous effects on the brain and spinal cord, the end of the peptide chain folds into a beta-pleated sheet. The conditions that cause this structural change are not yet known.

BSE was diagnosed in Great Britain in 1986. The protein is present in nerve tissue of animals, but it is not found in their meat. Control measures that exclude brain and spinal cord from animal feed are now in place to reduce the incidence of BSE.

The human variant of this disease is called Creutzfeldt-Jakob disease (CJD). Around 1955, Dr. Carleton Gajdusek was studying the Fore people of Papua, New Guinea, where many tribe members were dying of the neurological disease known as "kuru." Among the Fore, it was a custom to cannibalize members of the tribe upon their death. Gajdusek eventually determined that this practice was responsible for transmitting the infectious agent from one tribe member to another.

After Gajdusek identified the infectious agent in kuru as similar to the prions that cause BSE, he received the Nobel Prize in Physiology or Medicine in 1976.

In the quaternary structure, the subunits are held together by the same interactions that stabilize their tertiary structures, such as hydrogen bonds and salt bridges between R groups, disulfide bonds, and hydrophobic interactions. (See Figure 19.11.) Each subunit of the hemoglobin contains a heme group that binds oxygen. In the adult hemoglobin molecule, all four subunits ($\alpha_2\beta_2$) must be combined for the hemoglobin to properly function as an oxygen carrier. Therefore, the complete quaternary structure of hemoglobin can bind and transport four molecules of oxygen.

Hemoglobin and myoglobin have similar biological functions. Hemoglobin carries oxygen in the blood, whereas myoglobin carries oxygen in muscle. Myoglobin, a single polypeptide chain with a molar mass of 17 000 g/mole, has about one-fourth the molar mass of hemoglobin (67 000 g/mole). The tertiary structure of the single polypeptide myoglobin is almost identical to the tertiary structure of each of the subunits of hemoglobin. Myoglobin stores just one molecule of oxygen, just as each subunit of hemoglobin carries one oxygen molecule. The similarity in tertiary structures allows each protein to bind and release oxygen in a similar manner. Table 19.6 and Figure 19.12 summarize the structural levels of proteins.

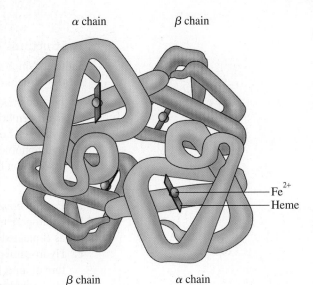

FIGURE 19.11 The quaternary structure of hemoglobin consists of four polypeptide subunits, each containing a heme group that binds an oxygen molecule.

Q What is the difference between a tertiary structure and a quaternary structure?

TABLE 19.6 Summary of Structural Levels in Proteins

Structural Level	Characteristics
Primary	The sequence of amino acids
Secondary	The α helix, β-pleated sheet, or a triple helix forms by hydrogen bonding between peptide bonds along the chain
Tertiary	A protein folds into a compact, three-dimensional shape stabilized by interactions between R groups of amino acids
Quaternary	Two or more protein subunits combine to form a biologically active protein

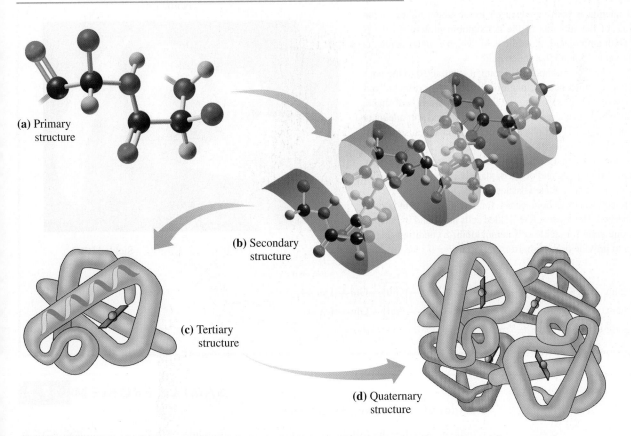

(a) Primary structure

(b) Secondary structure

(c) Tertiary structure

(d) Quaternary structure

FIGURE 19.12 Proteins consist of (a) primary, (b) secondary, (c) tertiary, and sometimes (d) quaternary structural levels.

Q What is the difference between a primary structure and a tertiary structure?

■ **Structures of Proteins**

Indicate which of the following are present in the primary, secondary, tertiary, and quaternary structures of proteins:

a. peptide bonds
b. hydrogen bonds between adjacent peptides
c. hydrogen bonds within a single peptide
d. hydrophobic interactions
e. association of four polypeptide chains

ANSWER

a. Peptide bonds are present at all levels of protein structures.
b. Hydrogen bonds between adjacent peptides occur in the secondary structures such as β-pleated sheets and triple helices.
c. Hydrogen bonds within a single peptide is a characteristic of the secondary structure of an α helix.
d. Hydrophobic interactions between two nonpolar R groups occur in the tertiary and quaternary structures of proteins.
e. The association of four polypeptide chains occurs in the quaternary structures of proteins.

HEALTH NOTE

Sickle-Cell Anemia

Sickle-cell anemia is a disease caused by an abnormality in the shape of one of the subunits of the hemoglobin protein. In the β chain, the sixth amino acid, glutamic acid, which is polar acidic, is replaced by valine, a nonpolar amino acid.

Because valine has a nonpolar R group, it is attracted to the nonpolar regions of other beta hemoglobin chains. The affected red blood cells (RBC) change from a rounded shape to a crescent shape, like a sickle, which interferes with their ability to transport adequate quantities of oxygen. Hydrophobic interactions also cause sickle-cell hemoglobin molecules to stick together. They form insoluble fibers of sickle-cell hemoglobin that clog capillaries, where they cause inflammation, pain, and organ damage. Critically low oxygen levels may occur in the affected tissues.

In sickle-cell anemia, both genes for the altered hemoglobin must be inherited. However, a few sickled cells are found in persons who carry one gene for sickle-cell hemoglobin, a condition that is also known to provide protection from malaria.

RBC beginning to sickle   Normal RBC

Sickled RBC

Normal β chain: Val — His — Leu — Thr — Pro — | Glu | — Glu — Lys —
Sickled β chain: Val — His — Leu — Thr — Pro — | Val | — Glu — Lys —

↗ Polar amino acid
↘ Nonpolar amino acid

■ **Identifying Protein Structure**

Indicate whether the following conditions are responsible for primary, secondary, tertiary, or quaternary protein structures:

a. Disulfide bonds form between portions of a protein chain.
b. Peptide bonds form a chain of amino acids.

SOLUTION

a. Disulfide bonds help to stabilize the tertiary structure of a protein.
b. The sequence of amino acids in a polypeptide is a primary structure.

STUDY CHECK

What structural level is represented by the interaction of the two subunits in insulin?

QUESTIONS AND PROBLEMS

Protein Structure: Tertiary and Quaternary Levels

19.29 What type of interaction would you expect between the following groups in a tertiary structure?
   a. two cysteines   b. glutamic acid and lysine
   c. serine and aspartic acid   d. two leucines

19.30 What type of interaction would you expect between the following groups in a tertiary structure?
   a. phenylalanine and leucine
   b. aspartic acid and histidine
   c. asparagine and tyrosine
   d. alanine and proline

19.31 A portion of a polypeptide chain contains the following sequence of amino acids:

   -Leu-Val-Cys-Asp-

   a. Which amino acid can form a disulfide cross-link?
   b. Which amino acids are likely to be found on the inside of the protein structure? Why?
   c. Which amino acids would be found on the outside of the protein? Why?
   d. How does the primary structure of a protein affect its tertiary structure?

19.32 In myoglobin, about one-half of the 153 amino acids have nonpolar R groups.
   a. Where would you expect those amino acids to be located in the tertiary structure?
   b. Where would you expect the polar R groups to be?
   c. Why is myoglobin more soluble in water than silk or wool?

19.33 State whether the following statements describe the primary, secondary, tertiary, or quaternary protein structure:
   a. R groups interact to form disulfide bonds or ionic bonds.
   b. Peptide bonds join amino acids in a polypeptide chain.
   c. Several polypeptides in a β-pleated sheet are held together by hydrogen bonds between adjacent chains.
   d. Hydrogen bonding between amino acids in the same polypeptide gives a coiled shape to the protein.

19.34 State whether the following statements describe the primary, secondary, tertiary, or quaternary protein structure:
   a. Hydrophobic R groups seeking a nonpolar environment move toward the inside of the folded protein.
   b. Protein chains of collagen form a triple helix.
   c. An active protein contains four tertiary subunits.
   d. In sickle-cell anemia, valine replaces glutamic acid in the β chain.

19.6 Protein Hydrolysis and Denaturation

Peptide bonds can be hydrolyzed to give individual amino acids. This process occurs in the stomach when enzymes such as pepsin or trypsin catalyze the hydrolysis of proteins to give amino acids. This hydrolysis disrupts the primary structure by breaking the covalent amide bonds that link the amino acids. In the digestion of proteins, the amino acids are absorbed through the intestinal walls and carried to the cells where they can be used to synthesize new proteins:

LEARNING GOAL

Describe the hydrolysis and denaturation of proteins.

TUTORIAL
Protein Demolition

$$\overset{+}{H_3N}-\underset{\underset{CH_3}{|}}{CH}-\overset{\overset{O}{\|}}{C}-NH-CH_2-\overset{\overset{O}{\|}}{C}-NH-\underset{\underset{CH_2OH}{|}}{CH}-\overset{\overset{O}{\|}}{C}-O^-$$

Alanylglycylserine (Ala-Gly-Ser)

H_2O | Enzyme
↓

$$\overset{+}{H_3N}-\underset{\underset{CH_3}{|}}{CH}-\overset{\overset{O}{\|}}{C}-O^- + \overset{+}{H_3N}-CH_2-\overset{\overset{O}{\|}}{C}-O^- + \overset{+}{H_3N}-\underset{\underset{CH_2OH}{|}}{CH}-\overset{\overset{O}{\|}}{C}-O^-$$

Alanine (Ala)   Glycine (Gly)   Serine (Ser)

Denaturation of Milk Protein

Place some milk in each of five glasses. Add the following to the milk samples in glasses 1–4. The fifth glass of milk is a reference sample.

1. Vinegar, drop by drop. Stir.
2. One-half teaspoon of meat tenderizer. Stir.
3. One teaspoon of fresh pineapple juice. (Canned juice has been heated and cannot be used.)
4. One teaspoon of fresh pineapple juice after the juice is heated to boiling.

QUESTIONS

1. How did the appearance of the milk change in each of the samples?
2. What enzyme is listed on the package label of the tenderizer?
3. How does the effect of the heated pineapple juice compare with that of the fresh juice? Explain.
4. Why is cooked pineapple used when making gelatin (a protein) desserts?

Denaturation of Proteins

Denaturation of a protein occurs when there is a disruption of any of the bonds that stabilize the secondary, tertiary, or quaternary structure. However, the covalent amide bonds of the primary structure are not affected.

The loss of secondary and tertiary structures occurs when conditions change, such as increasing the temperature or making the pH very acidic or basic. If the pH changes, the basic and acidic R groups lose their ionic charges and cannot form salt bridges, which causes a change in the shape of the protein. Denaturation can also occur with the addition of certain organic compounds or heavy metal ions, or through mechanical agitation.

When there is a disruption of the interactions between the R groups, a globular protein unfolds like a loose piece of cooked spaghetti. With the loss of its overall shape (tertiary structure), the protein is no longer biologically active. (See Figure 19.13.)

Heat

Heat denatures proteins by breaking apart hydrogen bonds and the hydrophobic interactions between nonpolar R groups. Few proteins can remain biologically active above 50 °C. Whenever you cook food, you are using heat to denature protein. The nutritional value of the proteins in food is not changed, but they are made more digestible. High temperatures are also used to disinfect surgical instruments and gowns by denaturing the proteins of any bacteria present.

Acids and Bases

When an acid or a base is added to a protein, the change in pH breaks down hydrogen bonds and disrupts the ionic bonds (salt bridges). In the preparation of yogurt and cheese, bacteria that produce lactic acid are added to denature the milk protein and produce solid casein. Tannic acid, a weak acid used in burn ointments, is used to coagulate proteins at the site of the burn, forming a protective cover and preventing further loss of fluid from the burn.

FIGURE 19.13 Denaturation of a protein occurs when the bonds of the tertiary structure are disrupted, which destroys the shape and renders the protein biologically inactive.

Q What are some ways in which proteins are denatured?

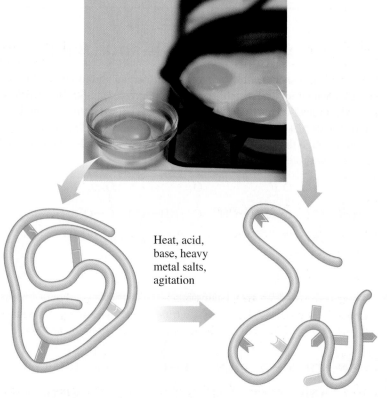

Heat, acid, base, heavy metal salts, agitation

Active protein   Denatured protein

Organic Compounds

Ethanol and isopropyl alcohol act as disinfectants by forming their own hydrogen bonds with a protein and disrupting the hydrophobic interactions. An alcohol swab is used to clean wounds or to prepare the skin for an injection because the alcohol passes through the cell walls and coagulates the proteins inside the bacteria.

Heavy Metal Ions

Heavy metal ions such as Ag^+, Pb^{2+}, and Hg^{2+} denature protein by forming bonds with ionic R groups or reacting with disulfide ($-S-S-$) bonds. In hospitals, a dilute (1%) solution of $AgNO_3$ is placed in the eyes of newborn babies to destroy the bacteria that cause gonorrhea. If heavy metals are ingested, they act as poisons by severely denaturing body proteins and disrupting metabolic reactions. An antidote is a high-protein food such as milk, eggs, or cheese that combines with the heavy metal ions until the stomach can be pumped.

Agitation

The whipping of cream and the beating of egg whites are examples of using mechanical agitation to denature protein. The whipping action stretches the polypeptide chains until the stabilizing interactions are disrupted.

CONCEPT CHECK 19.8

▓ Denaturation of Proteins

Describe the denaturation process in each of the following:

a. An appetizer known as ceviche is prepared without heat by placing slices of raw fish in a solution of lemon or lime juice. After 3 or 4 hours, the fish appears to be "cooked."

b. In baking sliced potatoes and milk to prepare scalloped potatoes, the milk curdles (forms solids).

ANSWER

a. The acids in lemon or lime juice break down the hydrogen bonds between polar R groups and disrupt salt bridges, which denature the proteins of the fish.

b. The heat during baking breaks apart hydrogen bonds and hydrophobic interactions between nonpolar R groups. When the milk denatures, the proteins become insoluble and form solids called curds.

SAMPLE PROBLEM 19.8

▓ Effects of Denaturation

What happens to the tertiary structure of a globular protein when it is placed in an acidic solution?

SOLUTION

An acid causes denaturation by disrupting the hydrogen bonds and the ionic bonds between the R groups. A loss in interactions causes the tertiary structure to lose stability. As the protein unfolds, both the shape and biological function are lost.

STUDY CHECK

Why is a dilute solution of $AgNO_3$ used to disinfect the eyes of newborn infants?

QUESTIONS AND PROBLEMS

Protein Hydrolysis and Denaturation

19.35 What products would result from the complete hydrolysis of Gly-Ala-Ser?

19.36 Would the hydrolysis products of the tripeptide Ala-Ser-Gly be the same or different from the products in problem 19.35? Explain.

19.37 What dipeptides could be produced from the partial hydrolysis of His-Met-Gly-Val?

19.38 What tripeptides could be produced from the partial hydrolysis of Ser-Leu-Gly-Gly-Ala?

19.39 What structural level of a protein is affected by hydrolysis?

19.40 What structural level of a protein is affected by denaturation?

19.41 Indicate the changes in the secondary and tertiary structural levels of proteins for each of the following:

a. An egg placed in water at 100 °C is soft boiled in about 3 minutes.

b. Prior to giving an injection, the skin is wiped with an alcohol swab.

c. Surgical instruments are placed in a 120 °C autoclave.

d. During surgery, a wound is closed by cauterization (heat).

19.42 Indicate the changes in the secondary and tertiary structural levels of proteins for each of the following:

a. Tannic acid is placed on a burn.

b. Milk is heated to 60 °C to make yogurt.

c. To avoid spoilage, seeds are treated with a solution of $HgCl_2$.

d. Hamburger is cooked at high temperatures to destroy *E. coli* bacteria that may cause intestinal illness.

CONCEPT MAP

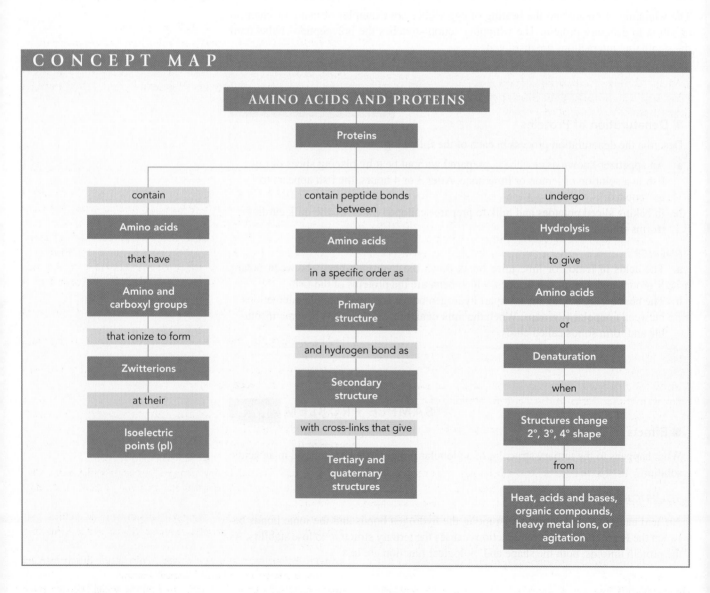

CHAPTER REVIEW

19.1 Proteins and Amino Acids
LEARNING GOAL: *Classify proteins by their functions in the body. Give the name and abbreviation of an amino acid and draw its ionized structure.*

Some proteins are enzymes or hormones, whereas others are important in structure, transport, protection, storage, and muscle contraction. A group of 20 amino acids provides the molecular building blocks of proteins. Attached to the central α (alpha) carbon of each amino acid are an ammonium group, a carboxylate group, and a unique R group. The R group gives an amino acid the property of being nonpolar, polar, acidic, or basic.

19.2 Amino Acids as Zwitterions
LEARNING GOAL: *Draw the zwitterion of an amino acid at its isoelectric point and its ionized structure at pH values above or below its isoelectric point.*

Amino acids exist as dipolar ions called zwitterions, as positive ions at low pH, and as negative ions at high pH levels. At the isoelectric point, zwitterions have a net charge of zero.

19.3 Formation of Peptides
LEARNING GOAL: *Draw the condensed structural formula of a dipeptide.*

Peptides form when an amide bond links the carboxylate group of one amino acid and the ammonium group of a second amino acid. Long chains of amino acids are called proteins.

19.4 Protein Structure: Primary and Secondary Levels
LEARNING GOAL: *Describe the primary and secondary structures of a protein.*

The primary structure of a protein is its sequence of amino acids. In the secondary structure, hydrogen bonds between peptide groups produce a characteristic shape such as an α helix, β-pleated sheet, or a triple helix.

19.5 Protein Structure: Tertiary and Quaternary Levels
LEARNING GOAL: *Describe the tertiary and quaternary structures of a protein.*

In globular proteins, the polypeptide chain, including α-helical and β-pleated sheet regions, folds upon itself to form a tertiary structure. A tertiary structure is stabilized by interactions that move hydrophobic R groups to the inside and hydrophilic R groups to the outside surface, and by attractions between R groups that form hydrogen bonds, disulfide bonds, and salt bridges. In a quaternary structure, two or more tertiary subunits must combine for biological activity. They are held together by the same interactions found in tertiary structures.

19.6 Protein Hydrolysis and Denaturation
LEARNING GOAL: *Describe the hydrolysis and denaturation of proteins.*

Denaturation of a protein occurs when heat or other denaturing agents destroy the structure of the protein (but not the primary structure) until biological activity is lost.

KEY TERMS

acidic amino acid An amino acid that has an R group with a carboxylate ($-COO^-$) ion.

α (alpha) helix A secondary level of protein structure, in which hydrogen bonds connect the N—H of one peptide bond with the C=O of a peptide bond farther down the chain to form a coiled or corkscrew structure.

α-keratins Fibrous proteins containing mostly α helices found in hair, nails, and skin.

amino acid The building block of proteins, consisting of an ammonium group, a carboxylate group, and a unique R group attached to the α carbon.

basic amino acid An amino acid that contains an R group with an ammonium ($-NH_3^+$) ion.

β (beta)-pleated sheet A secondary level of protein structure that consists of hydrogen bonds between peptide links in parallel polypeptide chains.

C terminal The end amino acid in a peptide chain with a free carboxylate ($-COO^-$) group.

collagen The most abundant form of protein in the body, which is composed of fibrils of triple helices with hydrogen bonding between —OH groups of hydroxyproline and hydroxylysine.

denaturation The loss of secondary and tertiary protein structure caused by heat, acids, bases, organic compounds, heavy metals, and/or agitation.

disulfide bonds Covalent —S—S— bonds that form between the —SH groups of two cysteines in a protein to stabilize the tertiary structure.

electrophoresis The use of electrical current to separate proteins or other charged molecules with different isoelectric points.

essential amino acids Amino acids that must be supplied by the diet because they are not synthesized by the body.

fibrous proteins Proteins that are insoluble in water; consisting of polypeptide chains with α helices or β-pleated sheets, and comprising the fibers of hair, wool, skin, nails, and silk.

globular proteins Proteins that acquire a compact shape from attractions between the R groups of the amino acids in the protein.

hydrogen bonds The interactions between water and the polar R groups such as —OH, —NH₂, and —COOH on the outside surface of a polypeptide chain.

hydrophilic interactions The attractions between polar R groups on the protein surface and water.

hydrophobic interactions The attractions between nonpolar R groups on the inside of a globular protein.

isoelectric point (pI) The pH at which an amino acid exists as a zwitterion with a net charge of zero.

N terminal The end amino acid in a peptide with a free —NH₃⁺ group.

nonpolar amino acids Amino acids with nonpolar R groups containing only C and H atoms.

peptide The combination of two or more amino acids joined by peptide bonds; dipeptide, tripeptide, and so on.

peptide bond The amide bond in peptides that joins the carboxylate group of one amino acid with the ammonium group in the next amino acid.

polar amino acids (neutral) Amino acids with polar R groups.

primary structure The specific sequence of the amino acids in a protein.

protein Polypeptides containing many amino acids linked together by peptide bonds that are biologically active.

quaternary structure A protein structure in which two or more protein subunits form an active protein.

salt bridge The attraction between the ionized R groups of basic and acidic amino acids in the tertiary structure of a protein.

secondary structure The formation of an α helix, β-pleated sheet, or triple helix.

tertiary structure The folding of the secondary structure of a protein into a compact structure that is stabilized by the interactions of R groups such as ionic and disulfide bonds.

triple helix The protein structure found in collagen consisting of three polypeptide chains woven together like a braid.

zwitterion The dipolar form of an amino acid consisting of two oppositely charged ionic regions, $-NH_3^+$ and $-COO^-$.

UNDERSTANDING THE CONCEPTS

19.43 Seeds and vegetables are often deficient in one or more essential amino acids. Using the following table, state whether the given combinations would provide the essential amino acids lysine, tryptophan, and methionine.

Source	Lysine	Tryptophan	Methionine
Oatmeal	No	Yes	Yes
Rice	No	Yes	Yes
Garbanzo beans	Yes	No	Yes
Lima beans	Yes	No	No
Cornmeal	No	No	Yes

    a. rice and garbanzo beans
    b. lima beans and cornmeal
    c. a salad of garbanzo beans and lima beans

19.44 Seeds and vegetables are often deficient in one or more essential amino acids. Using the table in question 19.43, state whether the following combinations would provide the essential amino acids lysine, tryptophan, and methionine:
    a. rice and lima beans
    b. rice and oatmeal
    c. oatmeal and lima beans

Consider the following structures of cysteine to answer questions 19.45 and 19.46:

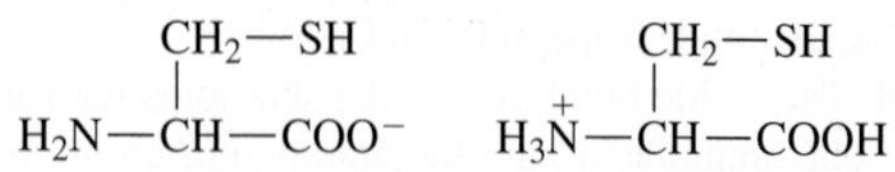

$$\begin{array}{cc} \text{CH}_2-\text{SH} & \text{CH}_2-\text{SH} \\ | & | \\ \text{H}_2\text{N}-\text{CH}-\text{COO}^- & \text{H}_3\overset{+}{\text{N}}-\text{CH}-\text{COOH} \\ (1) & (2) \end{array}$$

$$\begin{array}{cc} \text{CH}_2-\text{SH} & \text{CH}_2-\text{SH} \\ | & | \\ \text{H}_3\overset{+}{\text{N}}-\text{CH}-\text{COO}^- & \text{H}_2\text{N}-\text{CH}-\text{COOH} \\ (3) & (4) \end{array}$$

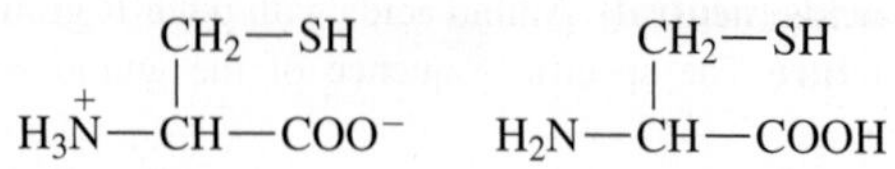

19.45 If cysteine, an amino acid prevalent in hair, has a pI of 5.1, which structure would it have in solutions with the following pH values?
    a. pH = 10.5   **b.** pH = 5.1   **c.** pH = 1.8

19.46 If cysteine, an amino acid prevalent in hair, has a pI of 5.1, which structure would it have in solutions with the following pH values?
    a. pH = 2.0   **b.** pH = 3.5   **c.** pH = 9.1

19.47 For each of the following pairs of R groups, identify the amino acids and the type of cross-link that forms between them:

$$\text{a. } -\text{CH}_2-\overset{\displaystyle O}{\overset{\|}{\text{C}}}-\text{NH}_2 \text{ and } \text{HO}-\text{CH}_2-$$

$$\text{b. } -\text{CH}_2-\overset{\displaystyle O}{\overset{\|}{\text{C}}}-\text{O}^- \text{ and } \text{H}_3\overset{+}{\text{N}}-(\text{CH}_2)_4-$$

$$\text{c. } -\text{CH}_2-\text{SH} \text{ and } \text{HS}-\text{CH}_2-$$

$$\text{d. } -\text{CH}_2-\overset{\displaystyle \text{CH}_3}{\overset{|}{\text{CH}}}-\text{CH}_3 \text{ and } \text{CH}_3-$$

19.48 Consider a mixture of the amino acids lysine, valine, and aspartic acid at pH 6.0 that is subjected to an electric voltage.
    a. Indicate which amino acid would migrate toward the positive electrode (+), the negative electrode (−), or remain stationary.

 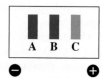

Mixture of amino acids

    b. If the mixture is the result of hydrolyzing a tripeptide, what are the possible sequences if one unit of each amino acid is present?
    c. If present in an enzyme, which of these amino acids would
        1. be found in hydrophobic regions?
        2. be found in hydrophilic regions?
        3. form hydrogen bonds?
        4. form salt bridges?
        5. form disulfide bonds?

ADDITIONAL QUESTIONS AND PROBLEMS

*For instructor-assigned homework, go to **www.masteringchemistry.com**.*

19.49 a. What are some functions of α-keratins?
 b. What amino acids give strength to the α-keratins?

19.50 a. Where is collagen found?
 b. What type of secondary structure is used to form collagen?

19.51 a. Draw the condensed structural formula of Ser-Lys-Asp.
 b. Would you expect to find this segment at the center or at the surface of a globular protein? Why?

19.52 a. Draw the condensed structural formula of Val-Ala-Leu.
 b. Would you expect to find this segment at the center or at the surface of a globular protein? Why?

19.53 Would you expect the following segments in a polypeptide to have an α helix or β-pleated sheet secondary structure?
 a. a segment with a high content of Val, Pro, and Ser
 b. a segment with a high content of His, Met, and Leu

19.54 What type of interaction would you expect between the following R groups in a tertiary structure?
 a. threonine and asparagine
 b. valine and alanine
 c. arginine and aspartic acid

19.55 If serine were replaced by valine in a protein, how would the tertiary structure be affected?

19.56 If you eat rice, what other vegetable protein source(s) could you eat to ingest all essential amino acids?

19.57 Draw the condensed structural formula of each of the following amino acids at pH 4:
 a. serine   **b.** alanine   **c.** lysine

19.58 Draw the condensed structural formula of each of the following amino acids at pH 11:
 a. cysteine   **b.** aspartic acid   **c.** valine

CHALLENGE QUESTIONS

19.59 Indicate the overall net charge (1−, 0, or 1+) for each of the following amino acids at the following pH values:
 a. serine at pH 5.7
 b. lysine at pH 7.7
 c. methionine at pH 7.6
 d. isoleucine at pH 3.0
 e. leucine at pH 9.0

19.60 Indicate the overall net charge (1−, 0, or 1+) for each of the following amino acids at the given pH values:
 a. serine at pH 3.0
 b. lysine at pH 9.7
 c. methionine at pH 10.0
 d. isoleucine at pH 8.5
 e. leucine at pH 3.5

19.61 A mixture of cysteine, aspartic acid, and histidine are placed on a gel for electrophoresis. A buffer of pH 5.1 is placed on the gel.
 a. Which amino acid will migrate toward the positive electrode?
 b. Which amino acid will migrate toward the negative electrode?
 c. Which amino acid will remain at the same place it was originally placed?

19.62 The proteins placed on a gel for electrophoresis have the following isoelectric points: albumin, 4.9; hemoglobin, 6.8; and lysozyme, 11.0. A buffer of pH 6.8 is placed on the gel.
 a. Which protein will migrate toward the positive electrode?
 b. Which protein will migrate toward the negative electrode?
 c. Which protein will remain at the same place it was originally placed?

19.63 What are some differences between each of the following?
 a. secondary and tertiary protein structures
 b. essential and nonessential amino acids
 c. polar and nonpolar amino acids
 d. dipeptides and tripeptides

19.64 What are some differences between each of the following?
 a. an ionic bond (salt bridge) and a disulfide bond
 b. fibrous and globular proteins
 c. α helix and β-pleated sheet
 d. tertiary and quaternary structures of proteins

19.65 In the preparation of meringue for a pie, tartaric acid is added and the egg whites are whipped. What causes the meringue to form?

19.66 How does denaturation of a protein differ from its hydrolysis?

ANSWERS

ANSWERS TO STUDY CHECKS

19.1 a. polar   **b.** polar

19.2 In the Fischer projection of D-serine, the $-NH_3^+$ group is on the right side.

19.3

$$\begin{array}{c} OH \\ | \\ CH_2 \quad O \\ | \quad\quad || \\ \overset{+}{N}H_3-CH-C-OH \end{array}$$

19.4 tyrosylglycylglycylphenylalanylmethionine

19.5 a triple helix

19.6 Both are nonpolar and would be found on the inside of the tertiary structure.

19.7 quaternary

19.8 The heavy metal Ag^+ denatures the proteins in bacteria that cause gonorrhea.

ANSWERS TO SELECTED QUESTIONS AND PROBLEMS

19.1 a. transport   **b.** structural
 c. structural   **d.** enzyme

19.3 All amino acids contain a carboxylate group and an ammonium group on the α carbon.

19.5

a.
$$H_3\overset{+}{N}-CH-\overset{O}{\overset{\|}{C}}-O^-$$
with CH_3 on the CH

b.
$$H_3\overset{+}{N}-CH-\overset{O}{\overset{\|}{C}}-O^-$$
with $HO-CH$ and CH_3 above

c.
$$H_3\overset{+}{N}-CH-\overset{O}{\overset{\|}{C}}-O^-$$
with $CH_2-CH_2-\overset{O}{\overset{\|}{C}}-O^-$

d.
$$H_3\overset{+}{N}-CH-\overset{O}{\overset{\|}{C}}-O^-$$
with CH_2—(benzene ring)

c.
$$H_3\overset{+}{N}-CH-\overset{O}{\overset{\|}{C}}-NH-CH-\overset{O}{\overset{\|}{C}}-NH-CH-\overset{O}{\overset{\|}{C}}-O^-$$
(H, CH_3, CH with H_3C CH_3)
Gly-Ala-Val

d.
$$H_3\overset{+}{N}-CH-\overset{O}{\overset{\|}{C}}-NH-CH-\overset{O}{\overset{\|}{C}}-NH-CH-\overset{O}{\overset{\|}{C}}-O^-$$
Val-Ile-Trp

19.7
a. hydrophobic (nonpolar)
b. hydrophilic (polar, neutral)
c. hydrophilic (acidic)
d. hydrophobic (nonpolar)

19.9
a. alanine   b. valine
c. lysine   d. cysteine

19.11

a.
$$COO^-$$
$$H_3\overset{+}{N}-\!\!\!-H$$
$$CH$$
$$H_3C\quad CH_3$$

b.
$$COO^-$$
$$H-\!\!\!-\overset{+}{NH_3}$$
$$CH_2SH$$

19.13
a. $H_3\overset{+}{N}-CH-\overset{O}{\overset{\|}{C}}-O^-$ (H)
b. $H_3\overset{+}{N}-CH-\overset{O}{\overset{\|}{C}}-O^-$ (CH_2, SH)
c. $H_3\overset{+}{N}-CH-\overset{O}{\overset{\|}{C}}-O^-$ (HO—CH, CH_3)
d. $H_3\overset{+}{N}-CH-\overset{O}{\overset{\|}{C}}-O^-$ (CH_3)

19.15
a. $H_3\overset{+}{N}-CH-\overset{O}{\overset{\|}{C}}-OH$ (H)
b. $H_3\overset{+}{N}-CH-\overset{O}{\overset{\|}{C}}-OH$ (CH_2, SH)
c. $H_3\overset{+}{N}-CH-\overset{O}{\overset{\|}{C}}-OH$ (HO—CH, CH_3)
d. $H_3\overset{+}{N}-CH-\overset{O}{\overset{\|}{C}}-OH$ (CH_3)

19.17 a. above pI   b. below pI   c. at pI

19.19
a. $H_3\overset{+}{N}-CH-\overset{O}{\overset{\|}{C}}-NH-CH-\overset{O}{\overset{\|}{C}}-O^-$ (CH_3; CH_2, SH)
Ala-Cys

b. $H_3\overset{+}{N}-CH-\overset{O}{\overset{\|}{C}}-NH-CH-\overset{O}{\overset{\|}{C}}-O^-$ (CH_2, OH; CH_2, benzene)
Ser-Phe

19.21 Amide bonds form to connect the amino acids that make up the protein.

19.23 Val-Ser-Ser, Ser-Val-Ser, or Ser-Ser-Val

19.25 The primary structure remains unchanged and intact as hydrogen bonds form between carbonyl oxygen atoms and amino hydrogen atoms in the secondary structure.

19.27 In the α helix, hydrogen bonds form between the carbonyl oxygen atom and the amino hydrogen atom in the next turn of the helix. In the β-pleated sheet, hydrogen bonds occur between parallel peptides or across sections of a long polypeptide chain.

19.29 a. disulfide bond   b. salt bridge
c. hydrogen bond   d. hydrophobic interaction

19.31 a. cysteine
b. Leucine and valine will be found on the inside of the protein because they are hydrophobic.
c. The cysteine and aspartic acid would be on the outside of the protein because they are polar.
d. The order of the amino acids (the primary structure) provides the R groups whose interactions determine the tertiary structure of the protein.

19.33 a. tertiary and quaternary
b. primary   c. secondary   d. secondary

19.35 The products would be the amino acids glycine, alanine, and serine.

19.37 His-Met, Met-Gly, Gly-Val

19.39 Hydrolysis splits the amide linkages in the primary structure.

19.41 a. Placing an egg in boiling water coagulates the proteins of the egg by disrupting hydrogen bonds and hydrophobic interactions.
b. Using an alcohol swab coagulates the proteins of any bacteria present by forming hydrogen bonds and disrupting hydrophobic interactions.
c. The heat from an autoclave will coagulate the proteins of any bacteria on the surgical instruments by disrupting hydrogen bonds and hydrophobic interactions.
d. Heat will coagulate the surrounding proteins to close the wound by disrupting hydrogen bonds and hydrophobic interactions.

19.43 a. yes   b. no   c. no

19.45 a. (1)   b. (3)   c. (2)

19.47 a. asparagine and serine, hydrogen bond
b. aspartic acid and lysine, salt bridge
c. cysteine and cysteine, disulfide bond
d. leucine and alanine, hydrophobic interaction

19.49 a. α-Keratins are fibrous proteins that provide structure to hair, wool, skin, and nails.

b. α-Keratins have a high content of cysteine.

19.51 a.

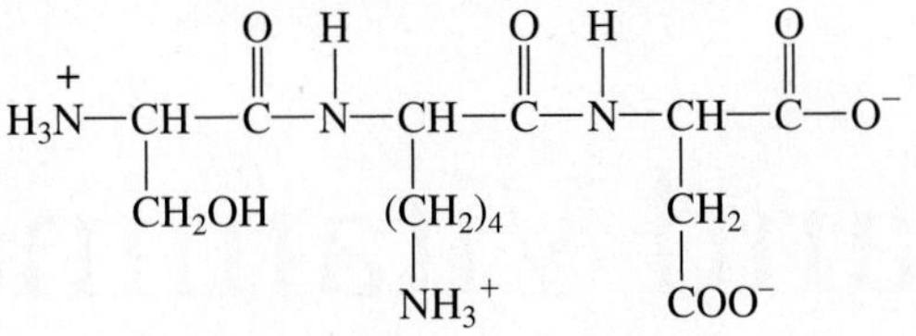

$$\overset{+}{H_3N}-CH-\overset{\overset{\displaystyle O}{\|}}{C}-\overset{\overset{\displaystyle H}{|}}{N}-CH-\overset{\overset{\displaystyle O}{\|}}{C}-\overset{\overset{\displaystyle H}{|}}{N}-CH-\overset{\overset{\displaystyle O}{\|}}{C}-O^-$$

with side groups CH_2OH, $(CH_2)_4$ / NH_3^+, and CH_2 / COO^-

b. This segment contains polar R groups, which would be found on the surface of a globular protein where they hydrogen bond with water.

19.53 a. β-pleated sheet   **b.** α helix

19.55 Serine is a polar amino acid, whereas valine is nonpolar. Serine would form hydrogen bonds with water on the outside surface of the protein. However, valine would pull that part of the peptide chain to the center of the tertiary structure where it forms hydrophobic interactions.

19.57 a.

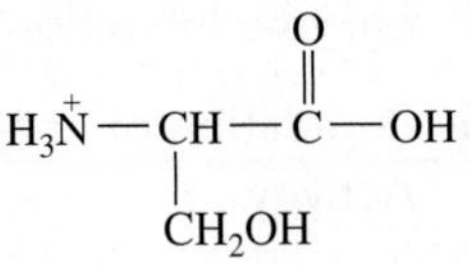

$$\overset{+}{H_3N}-CH-\overset{\overset{\displaystyle O}{\|}}{C}-OH$$

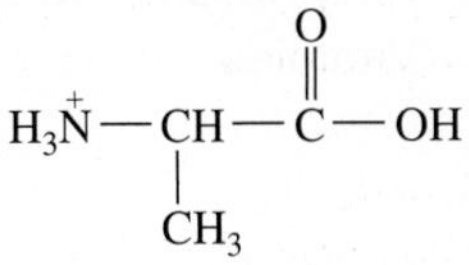

with side group CH_2OH

b.

$$\overset{+}{H_3N}-CH-\overset{\overset{\displaystyle O}{\|}}{C}-OH$$

with side group CH_3

c.

$$\overset{+}{H_3N}-CH-\overset{\overset{\displaystyle O}{\|}}{C}-OH$$

with side group $(CH_2)_4$ / $\overset{+}{NH_3}$

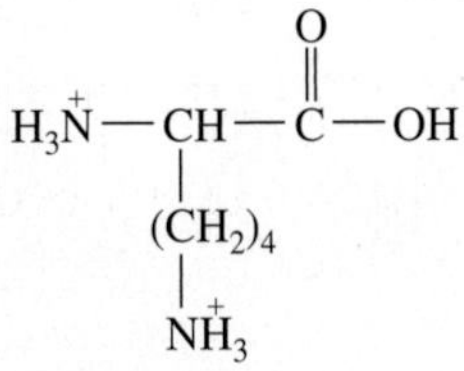

19.59 a. 0   **b.** 1+   **c.** 1−   **d.** 1+   **e.** 1−

19.61 a. Aspartic acid (1−) will migrate to the positive electrode.

b. Histidine (1+) will migrate to the negative electrode.

c. Cysteine (0) will not move from where it is placed.

19.63 a. In the secondary structure of proteins, hydrogen bonds form a helix or a pleated sheet; the tertiary structure is determined by hydrogen bonds as well as by disulfide bonds and salt bridges.

b. Nonessential amino acids can be synthesized by the body; essential amino acids must be supplied by the diet.

c. Polar amino acids have hydrophilic R groups, whereas nonpolar amino acids have hydrophobic R groups.

d. A dipeptide contains two amino acids, but a tripeptide contains three amino acids.

19.65 The tartaric acid and the mechanical whipping (agitation) of the egg white denatures the proteins, which turn into solids as meringue.

20 Enzymes and Vitamins

"At a time when we have a shortage of health care professionals, I think of myself as a physician extender," says Pushpinder Beasley, orthopedic physician assistant, Kaiser Hospital. "We can put a significant amount of time into our patient care. Just today, I examined a child's knee. One of the most common injuries to children is disruption of either knee ligaments or the soft tissue around the knees. In this child's case, we were checking her anterior ligaments, also known as ACL. I think an important role of the health care professional is to earn the trust of young people."

As part of a health care team, physician assistants examine patients, order laboratory tests, make diagnoses, report patient progress, order therapeutic procedures, and, in most states, prescribe medications.

Every second, thousands of chemical reactions occur in the cells of the human body. For example, many reactions occur to digest the food we eat, convert the products to chemical energy, and synthesize proteins and other macromolecules in our cells. In the laboratory, we can carry out reactions that hydrolyze polysaccharides, fats, or proteins, but we must use a strong acid or base, high temperatures, and long reaction times. In the cells of our body, these reactions must take place at rates that meet our physiological and metabolic needs. To make this happen, enzymes catalyze the chemical reactions in our cells, with a different enzyme for every reaction. Digestive enzymes in the mouth, stomach, and small intestine catalyze the hydrolysis of carbohydrate, fats, and proteins. Enzymes in the mitochondria extract energy from biomolecules to give us energy.

Every enzyme responds to what comes into the cells and to what the cells need. Enzymes keep reactions going when our cells need certain products and turn off reactions when they don't need those products.

Many enzymes require cofactors to function properly. Cofactors are inorganic metal ions (minerals) or organic compounds such as vitamins. We obtain minerals such as zinc (Zn^{2+}) and iron (Fe^{3+}) and vitamins from our diets. A lack of minerals and vitamins can lead to certain nutritional diseases. For example, rickets is a deficiency of vitamin D, and scurvy occurs when a diet is low in vitamin C.

20.1 Enzymes

Biological catalysts known as **enzymes** catalyze nearly all the chemical reactions that take place in the body. As we discussed in Chapter 9, a *catalyst* increases the rate of a reaction by changing the way a reaction takes place; the enzyme itself is not changed. An uncatalyzed reaction in a cell may take place eventually, but not at a rate fast enough for survival. For example, the hydrolysis of proteins in our diet would eventually occur without a catalyst, but the reactions would not occur fast enough to meet the body's requirements for amino acids. The chemical reactions in our cells must occur at incredibly fast rates under mild conditions of pH 7.4 and a body temperature of 37 °C. Enzymes permit cells to use energy and materials efficiently while responding to cellular needs.

As catalysts, enzymes lower the activation energy for a chemical reaction. (See Figure 20.1.) Less energy is required to convert reactant molecules to products, which increases the rate of a biochemical reaction compared to the rate of the uncatalyzed reaction. The rates of enzyme-catalyzed reactions are much faster than the rates of the uncatalyzed reactions. Some enzymes can increase the rate of a biological reaction by a factor of a billion, a trillion, or even a hundred million trillion compared to the rate of the uncatalyzed reaction. For example, an enzyme in the blood called carbonic anhydrase converts carbon dioxide and water to carbonic acid. In 1 minute, 1 molecule of carbonic anhydrase can catalyze the reaction of about 1 million molecules of carbon dioxide. An enzyme does not affect the equilibrium position, because the rates of both the forward and reverse directions increase.

$$CO_2 + H_2O \underset{\text{anhydrase}}{\overset{\text{Carbonic}}{\rightleftharpoons}} H_2CO_3$$

LEARNING GOAL

Describe how enzymes function as catalysts; name and classify them.

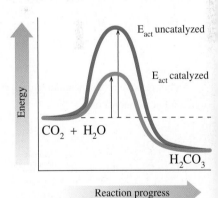

FIGURE 20.1 The enzyme carbonic anhydrase lowers the activation energy needed for the reaction of CO_2 and H_2O.

Q Why are enzymes needed in biological reactions?

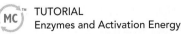
TUTORIAL
Enzymes and Activation Energy

Names and Classification of Enzymes

The name of an enzyme describes the compound or the reaction that is catalyzed. The actual names of enzymes are derived by replacing the end of the name of the reaction or reacting compound with the suffix *ase*. For example, an *oxidase* is an enzyme that catalyzes an oxidation reaction, and a *dehydrogenase* is an enzyme that removes hydrogen atoms.

The enzyme named *sucrase* hydrolyzes the compound sucrose, and an enzyme named *lipase* hydrolyzes a lipid. Some enzymes use names that end in the suffix *in*, such as *papain* found in papaya; *rennin* found in milk; and *pepsin* and *trypsin*, enzymes that catalyze the hydrolysis of proteins.

The International Commission on Enzymes has classified enzymes according to the six general types of reactions they catalyze. (See Table 20.1.)

TABLE 20.1 Classification of Enzymes

Class	Typical Subclass/Function
1. Oxidoreductases Catalyze oxidation–reduction reactions	*Oxidases* oxidize a substance. *Reductases* reduce a substance. *Dehydrogenases* remove two H atoms to form a double bond.

$$CH_3-CH_2-OH + NAD^+ \xrightarrow{\text{Alcohol dehydrogenase}} CH_3-\overset{O}{\overset{\|}{C}}-H + NADH + H^+$$

Ethanol   Coenzyme   Acetaldehyde   Coenzyme

| **2. Transferases**
Transfer groups between two compounds | *Transaminases* move amino groups between molecules.
Kinases move phosphate groups. |

$$CH_3-\overset{NH_3^+}{\underset{}{CH}}-COO^- + {}^-OOC-\overset{O}{\overset{\|}{C}}-CH_2CH_2-COO^- \underset{\text{Alanine transaminase}}{\rightleftharpoons} CH_3-\overset{O}{\overset{\|}{C}}-COO^- + {}^-OOC-\overset{NH_3^+}{\underset{}{CH}}-CH_2CH_2-COO^-$$

Alanine   α-Ketoglutarate   Pyruvate   Glutamate

| **3. Hydrolases**
Add water to break bonds | *Peptidases* hydrolyze peptide bonds.
Lipases hydrolyze ester bonds in lipids.
Amylases hydrolyze 1,4-glycosidic bonds in amylose. |

$$-\overset{R}{\underset{H}{N}}-CH-\overset{O}{\overset{\|}{C}}-\overset{R}{\underset{H}{N}}-CH-COO^- + H_2O \xrightarrow{\text{Peptidase}} -\overset{}{\underset{H}{N}}-CH-\overset{O}{\overset{\|}{C}}-O^- + H_3\overset{+}{N}-\overset{R}{\underset{}{CH}}-COO^-$$

Polypeptide C terminal   Shorter polypeptide   Amino acid from C terminal

| **4. Lyases**
Add or remove groups without hydrolysis or oxidation that may result in a double bond | *Decarboxylases* remove CO_2.
Hydrases add H_2O.
Dehydrases remove H_2O.
Deaminases remove NH_3. |

$$CH_3-\overset{O}{\overset{\|}{C}}-COO^- + H^+ \xrightarrow{\text{Pyruvate decarboxylase}} CH_3-\overset{O}{\overset{\|}{C}}-H + CO_2$$

Pyruvate   Acetaldehyde   Carbon dioxide

| **5. Isomerases**
Rearrange atoms to form isomers | *Isomerases* convert cis and trans bonds.
Epimerases convert D and L isomers. |

Maleate ⇌ (Maleate isomerase) Fumarate

| **6. Ligases**
Join molecules using ATP energy
(See Section 22.2) | *Synthetases* combine molecules.
Carboxylases add CO_2. |

$${}^-OOC-\overset{O}{\overset{\|}{C}}-CH_3 + CO_2 + ATP \xrightarrow{\text{Pyruvate carboxylase}} {}^-OOC-\overset{O}{\overset{\|}{C}}-CH_2-COO^- + ADP + P_i + H^+$$

Pyruvate   Oxaloacetate

P_i (inorganic phosphate HPO_4^{2-})

CONCEPT CHECK 20.1

■ **Classes of Enzymes**

Identify the general class of enzyme that catalyzes each of the following reactions:

a. a kinase that moves a phosphate group from one reactant to another
b. a peptidase that hydrolyzes a peptide bond in a protein
c. a decarboxylase that removes a carbon as CO_2 from a reactant

ANSWER

a. A kinase that moves a phosphate group from one reactant to another is part of the *transferase* class of enzymes.
b. A peptidase that hydrolyzes a peptide bond in a protein is part of the *hydrolase* class of enzymes.
c. A decarboxylase that removes a carbon as CO_2 from a reactant is part of the *lyase* class of enzymes.

SAMPLE PROBLEM 20.1

■ **Naming Enzymes**

What class of enzymes catalyzes each of the following?

a. the transfer of an amino group
b. the removal of hydrogen from lactate

SOLUTION

a. The class of enzymes called *transferases* includes enzymes that move functional groups, such as an amino group from one reactant to another.
b. The class of enzymes called *oxidoreductases* includes enzymes, such as lactate dehydrogenase, that remove two H atoms from lactate.

STUDY CHECK

What is the class of the enzyme lipase that catalyzes the hydrolysis of ester bonds in triglycerides?

QUESTIONS AND PROBLEMS

Enzymes

20.1 Why do chemical reactions in the body require enzymes?

20.2 How do enzymes make chemical reactions in the body proceed at faster rates?

20.3 What type of reaction is catalyzed by each of the following classes of enzymes?
a. oxidoreductases   **b.** transferases   **c.** hydrolases

20.4 What type of reaction is catalyzed by each of the following classes of enzymes?
a. lyases   **b.** isomerases   **c.** ligases

20.5 What is the name of the class of enzymes that catalyzes each of the following reactions?
a. hydrolysis of sucrose
b. addition of oxygen
c. converting glucose ($C_6H_{12}O_6$) to fructose ($C_6H_{12}O_6$)
d. moving an amino group from one molecule to another

20.6 What is the name of the class of enzymes that catalyzes each of the following reactions?
a. addition of water to a double bond
b. removing hydrogen atoms
c. splitting peptide bonds in proteins
d. removing CO_2 from pyruvate

20.7 Identify the class of enzyme that catalyzes each of the following reactions:

a. $CH_3-\overset{\displaystyle O}{\overset{\|}{C}}-COO^- + H^+ \longrightarrow CH_3-\overset{\displaystyle O}{\overset{\|}{C}}-H + CO_2$

b. $CH_3-\overset{\displaystyle NH_3^+}{\underset{|}{C}H}-COO^- + {}^-OOC-\overset{\displaystyle O}{\overset{\|}{C}}-CH_2-CH_3 \rightleftharpoons$

$CH_3-\overset{\displaystyle O}{\overset{\|}{C}}-COO^- + {}^-OOC-\overset{\displaystyle NH_3^+}{\underset{|}{C}H}-CH_2-CH_3$

20.8 Identify the class of enzyme that catalyzes each of the following reactions:

a.

$$CH_3-\overset{\overset{\displaystyle O}{\|}}{C}-COO^- + CO_2 + ATP \longrightarrow$$

$$^-OOC-CH_2-\overset{\overset{\displaystyle O}{\|}}{C}-COO^- + ADP + P_i$$

b.

$$CH_3-CH_2-OH + NAD^+ \longrightarrow$$

$$CH_3-\overset{\overset{\displaystyle O}{\|}}{C}-H + NADH + H^+$$

20.9 Name the enzyme that catalyzes each of the following reactions:
   a. oxidizes succinate
   b. adds water to fumarate
   c. removes 2H from an alcohol

20.10 Name the enzyme that catalyzes each of the following reactions:
   a. hydrolyzes sucrose
   b. transfers an amino group from aspartate
   c. removes a carboxylate group from pyruvate

20.2 Enzyme Action

LEARNING GOAL

Describe the role of an enzyme in an enzyme-catalyzed reaction.

Nearly all enzymes are globular proteins. Each has a unique three-dimensional shape that recognizes and binds a small group of reacting molecules, which are called **substrates**. The tertiary structure of an enzyme plays an important role in how that enzyme catalyzes reactions.

Active Site

In a catalyzed reaction, an enzyme must first bind to a substrate in a way that favors catalysis. A typical enzyme is much larger than its substrate. However, within the enzyme's large tertiary structure is a region called the **active site**, where the enzyme binds a substrate or substrates and catalyzes the reaction. (See Figure 20.2.) This active site is often a small pocket that closely fits the structure of the substrate. Within the active site, R groups from specific amino acids interact with the R groups on the substrate to form hydrogen bonds, salt bridges, and hydrophobic interactions. The active site of a particular enzyme fits the shape of only a few types of substrates, which makes the enzyme very specific about the type of substrate it binds.

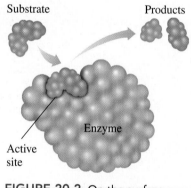

MC   SELF STUDY ACTIVITY
     How Enzymes Work

FIGURE 20.2 On the surface of an enzyme, a small region called an active site binds a substrate and catalyzes a reaction of that substrate.

Q Why does an enzyme catalyze a reaction of only certain substrates?

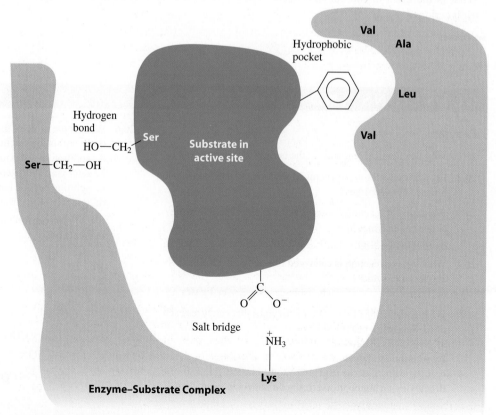

Enzyme–Substrate Complex

TABLE 20.2 Types of Enzyme Specificity

Type	Reaction Type	Example
Absolute	Catalyze one type of reaction for a single substrate	Urease catalyzes only the hydrolysis of urea.
Group	Catalyze one type of reaction for similar substrates	Hexokinase adds a phosphate group to hexoses.
Linkage	Catalyze one type of reaction for a specific type of bond	Chymotrypsin catalyzes the hydrolysis of peptide bonds.

Some enzymes show absolute specificity by catalyzing only one reaction of one specific substrate. Other enzymes catalyze a reaction for a group of substrates. Still other enzymes catalyze a reaction for a specific type of bond in a substrate. Types of enzyme specificity are listed in Table 20.2.

Enzyme-Catalyzed Reaction

The proper alignment of a substrate within the active site forms an **enzyme–substrate (ES) complex**. This combination of an enzyme and a substrate provides an alternative pathway for the reaction with a lower activation energy. Within the active site, amino acid side chains take part in catalyzing the chemical reaction. For example, acidic and basic side chains remove protons from or provide protons for the substrate. As soon as the catalyzed reaction is complete, the products are released from the enzyme so it can bind to a new substrate molecule.

We can write the catalyzed reaction of an enzyme (E) with a substrate (S) to form product (P) as follows:

Step 1   E + S   ⇌   ES

Step 2   ES ⟶ E + P
_____

     E + S   ⇌   ES ⟶ E + P

   Enzyme + substrate   ES complex   Enzyme + product

Let's consider the hydrolysis of sucrose by sucrase. When a molecule of sucrose binds to the active site of sucrase, its glycosidic bond is in a position favorable for reaction. The amino acid side chains catalyze the hydrolysis of sucrose with water to give the products glucose and fructose.

    E + S   ES complex   E + P_1 + P_2

  Sucrase + sucrose ⇌ sucrase–sucrose complex ⟶ sucrase + glucose + fructose

Because the structures of the products are no longer attracted to the active site, they are released, and the sucrase binds another sucrose substrate. (See Figure 20.3.)

Lock-and-Key and Induced-Fit Models

An early theory of enzyme action, called the **lock-and-key model**, described the active site as having a rigid, nonflexible shape. Thus, only those substrates with shapes that fit exactly into the active site are able to bind with that enzyme. The shape of the active site is analogous to a lock, and the proper substrate is the key that fits into the lock. (See Figure 20.4a.)

While the lock-and-key model explains the binding of substrates for many enzymes, certain enzymes have a broader range of specificity than the lock-and-key model allows. In the **induced-fit model**, there is an interaction between both the enzyme and substrate. (See Figure 20.4b.) The active site adjusts to fit the shape of the substrate more closely. At the same time, the substrate adjusts its shape to better adapt to the geometry of the active site. As a result, the reacting section of the substrate becomes aligned exactly with the groups in the active site that catalyze the reaction.

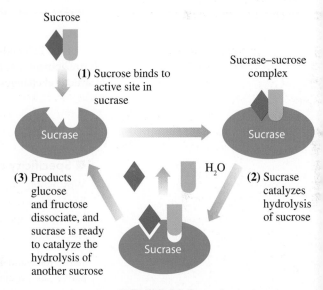

Sucrose

(1) Sucrose binds to active site in sucrose

Sucrase

Sucrase–sucrose complex

Sucrase

(3) Products glucose and fructose dissociate, and sucrase is ready to catalyze the hydrolysis of another sucrose

H_2O

Sucrase

(2) Sucrase catalyzes hydrolysis of sucrose

FIGURE 20.3 At the active site, sucrose is aligned for the hydrolysis reaction. The monosaccharides produced dissociate from the active site, and the enzyme is ready to bind to another sucrose molecule.

Q Why does the enzyme-catalyzed hydrolysis of sucrose go faster than the hydrolysis of sucrose in the chemistry laboratory?

FIGURE 20.4 **(a)** In the lock-and-key model, a substrate fits the shape of the active site and forms an enzyme–substrate complex. **(b)** In the induced-fit model, a flexible active site and substrate adjust shape to provide the best fit for the reaction. **(c)** A substrate that does not fit or induce a fit in the active site cannot undergo catalysis by the enzyme.

Q How does the induced-fit model differ from the lock-and-key model?

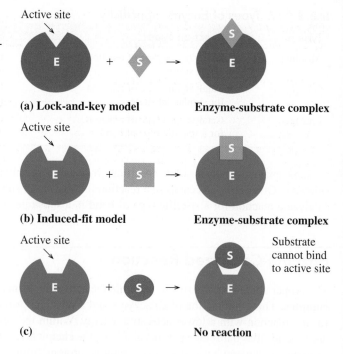

(a) Lock-and-key model   **Enzyme-substrate complex**

(b) Induced-fit model   **Enzyme-substrate complex**

(c)   **No reaction**

In the induced-fit model, substrate and enzyme work together to acquire a geometrical arrangement that lowers the activation energy. A different substrate would not induce these structural changes, and no catalysis would occur. (See Figure 20.4c.)

CONCEPT CHECK 20.2

■ **Specificity of Enzymes**

Why would the lock-and-key model of enzyme action explain why certain enzymes have absolute specificity, but the induced-fit model would explain why other enzymes have group specificity?

ANSWER

In the lock-and-key model of enzyme action, the shape of the substrate must fit the active site precisely. Therefore, an enzyme that has absolute specificity reacts with only a single substrate. In the induced-fit model, the shapes of an active site and substrate adjust to give the best fit to catalyze a reaction. An enzyme with group specificity can catalyze substrates that have similar shapes.

SAMPLE PROBLEM 20.2

■ **The Enzyme Active Site**

What is the function of the active site in an enzyme?

SOLUTION

The R groups of the active site bind the substrate by forming hydrogen bonds, salt bridges, and hydrophobic interactions with the substrate and catalyze the reaction.

STUDY CHECK

How do the lock-and-key and the induced-fit models differ in their description of the active site in an enzyme?

HEALTH NOTE

Isoenzymes as Diagnostic Tools

Isoenzymes are different forms of an enzyme that catalyze the same reaction in different cells or tissues of the body. Isoenzymes consist of quaternary structures with slight variations in the amino acids in the polypeptide subunits. For example, five isoenzymes of *lactate dehydrogenase (LDH)* catalyze the conversion between lactate and pyruvate.

$$CH_3-\overset{\overset{OH}{|}}{CH}-COO^- \quad \underset{\rightleftharpoons}{\overset{\text{Lactate dehydrogenase}}{}} \quad CH_3-\overset{\overset{O}{||}}{C}-COO^- + 2H$$

Lactate   Pyruvate

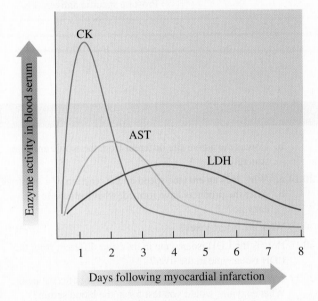

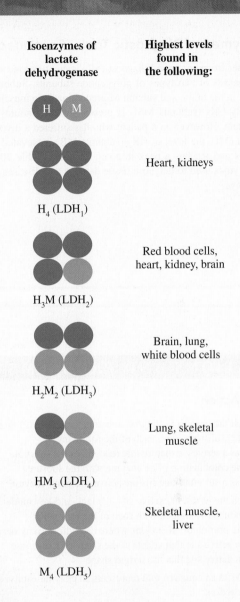

Isoenzymes of lactate dehydrogenase	Highest levels found in the following:
H$_4$ (LDH$_1$)	Heart, kidneys
H$_3$M (LDH$_2$)	Red blood cells, heart, kidney, brain
H$_2$M$_2$ (LDH$_3$)	Brain, lung, white blood cells
HM$_3$ (LDH$_4$)	Lung, skeletal muscle
M$_4$ (LDH$_5$)	Skeletal muscle, liver

Each LDH isoenzyme contains a mix of polypeptide subunits, M and H. In the liver and muscle, lactate is converted to pyruvate by the LDH$_5$ isoenzyme with four M subunits, designated M$_4$. In the heart, the same reaction is catalyzed by the LDH$_1$ isoenzyme (H$_4$) containing four H subunits. Different combinations of the M and H subunits are found in the LDH isoenzymes of the brain, red blood cells, kidney, and white blood cells.

The different forms of an enzyme allow a medical diagnosis of damage or disease to a particular organ or tissue. In healthy tissues, isoenzymes function within the cells. However, when a disease damages a particular organ, cells die, which releases cell contents including the isoenzymes into the blood. Measurements of the elevated levels of specific isoenzymes in the blood serum help to identify the disease and its location in the body. For example, an elevation in the serum LDH$_5$, which is the M$_4$ isoenzyme of lactate dehydrogenase, indicates liver damage or disease. When a myocardial infarction (MI), or heart attack, damages the cells in heart muscle, an increase in the level of LDH$_1$ (H$_4$) isoenzyme is detected in the blood serum. (See Table 20.3.)

TABLE 20.3 Isoenzymes of Lactate Dehydrogenase and Creatine Kinase

Isoenzyme	Abundant in	Subunits
Lactate Dehydrogenase (LDH)		
LDH$_1$	Heart, kidneys	H$_4$
LDH$_2$	Red blood cells, heart, kidney, brain	H$_3$M
LDH$_3$	Brain, lung, white blood cells	H$_2$M$_2$
LDH$_4$	Lung, skeletal muscle	HM$_3$
LDH$_5$	Skeletal muscle, liver	M$_4$
Creatine Kinase (CK)		
CK$_1$	Brain, lung	BB
CK$_2$	Heart	MB
CK$_3$	Skeletal muscle, red blood cells	MM

HEALTH NOTE (CONTINUED)

Isoenzymes as Diagnostic Tools (Continued)

Another isoenzyme used diagnostically is creatine kinase (CK), which consists of two types of polypeptide subunits. Subunit B is prevalent in the brain, and subunit M predominates in muscle. Normally only CK_3 (subunits MM) is present in low amounts in the blood serum. However, in a patient who has suffered a myocardial infarction (MI), the level of CK_2 (subunits MB) is elevated within 4–6 hours and reaches a peak in about 24 hours. Table 20.4 lists some enzymes used to diagnose tissue damage and diseases of certain organs.

TABLE 20.4 Serum Enzymes Used in Diagnosis of Tissue Damage

Condition	Diagnostic Enzymes Elevated
Heart attack or liver disease (cirrhosis, hepatitis)	Lactate dehydrogenase (LDH) Aspartate transaminase (AST)
Heart attack	Creatine kinase (CK)
Hepatitis	Alanine transaminase (ALT)
Liver (carcinoma) or bone disease (rickets)	Alkaline phosphatase (ALP)
Pancreatic disease	Amylase, cholinesterase, lipase (LPS)
Prostate carcinoma	Acid phosphatase (ACP) Prostate specific antigen (PSA)

QUESTIONS AND PROBLEMS

Enzyme Action

20.11 Match the terms, (1) enzyme–substrate complex, (2) enzyme, and (3) substrate, with each of the following:
   a. has a tertiary structure that recognizes the substrate
   b. the combination of an enzyme with the substrate
   c. has a structure that fits the active site of an enzyme

20.12 Match the terms, (1) active site, (2) lock-and-key model, and (3) induced-fit model, with each of the following:
   a. the portion of an enzyme where catalytic activity occurs
   b. an active site that adapts to the shape of a substrate
   c. an active site that has a rigid shape

20.13 a. Write an equation that represents an enzyme-catalyzed reaction.

   b. How is the active site different from the whole enzyme structure?

20.14 a. Why does an enzyme speed up the reaction of a substrate?
   b. After the products have formed, what happens to the enzyme?

20.15 What are isoenzymes?

20.16 How is the LDH isoenzyme in the heart different from the LDH isoenzyme in the liver?

20.17 A patient arrives in emergency complaining of chest pains. What enzymes would you test for in the blood serum?

20.18 A patient who is an alcoholic has elevated levels of LDH and AST. What condition might be indicated?

20.3 Factors Affecting Enzyme Activity

LEARNING GOAL

Describe the effect of temperature, pH, concentration of enzyme, and concentration of substrate on enzyme activity.

The **activity** of an enzyme describes how fast an enzyme catalyzes the reaction that converts a substrate to product. This activity is strongly affected by reaction conditions, which include the temperature, pH, concentration of the substrate, and concentration of the enzyme. (See Section 19.6 to review the conditions that denature proteins.)

Temperature

Enzymes are very sensitive to temperature. At low temperatures, most enzymes show little activity because there is not a sufficient amount of energy for the catalyzed reaction to take place. At higher temperatures, enzyme activity increases as reacting molecules move faster to cause more collisions with enzymes. Enzymes are most active at **optimum temperature**, which is 37 °C, or body temperature, for most enzymes. (See Figure 20.5.) At temperatures above 50 °C, the tertiary structure, and thus the shape of most proteins, is

TUTORIAL
Denaturation and Enzyme Activity

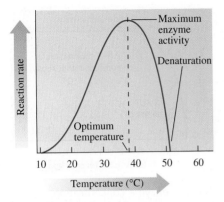

FIGURE 20.5 An enzyme attains maximum activity at its optimum temperature, usually 37 °C. Lower temperatures slow the rate of reaction, and temperatures above 50 °C denature an enzyme, resulting in a loss of catalytic activity.

Q Why is 37 °C the optimum temperature for many enzymes?

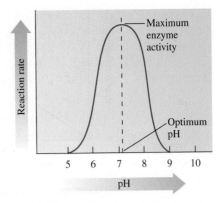

FIGURE 20.6 Enzymes are most active at their optimum pH. At a higher or lower pH, denaturation of the enzyme causes a loss of catalytic activity.

Q Why does the digestive enzyme pepsin have an optimum pH of 2?

destroyed, which causes a loss in enzyme activity. For this reason, equipment in hospitals and laboratories is sterilized in autoclaves where the high temperatures denature the enzymes in harmful bacteria. A high fever in the body may be helpful in denaturing enzymes in bacteria that cause infection.

pH

Enzymes are most active at their **optimum pH**, the pH that maintains the proper tertiary structure of the protein. (See Figure 20.6.) If a pH value is above or below the optimum pH, the R group interactions are disrupted, which destroys the tertiary structure and the active site. As a result, the enzyme no longer binds substrate properly, and no reaction occurs. Small changes in pH can be reversed that permit an enzyme to regain its structure and activity. However, large variations from optimum pH permanently destroy the structure of the enzyme.

Enzymes in most cells have optimum pH values at physiological pH around 7.4. However, enzymes in the stomach have a low optimum pH because they hydrolyze proteins at the acidic pH in the stomach. For example, pepsin, a digestive enzyme in the stomach, has an optimum pH of 1.5–2. Between meals, the pH in the stomach is 4 or 5, and pepsin shows little or no digestive activity. When food enters the stomach, the secretion of HCl lowers the pH to about 2, which activates pepsin. Table 20.5 lists the optimum pH values for selected enzymes.

TABLE 20.5 Optimum pH for Selected Enzymes

Enzyme	Location	Substrate	Optimum pH
Pepsin	Stomach	Peptide bonds	1.5–2.0
Sucrase	Small intestine	Sucrose	6.2
Amylase	Pancreas	Amylose	6.7–7.0
Urease	Liver	Urea	7.0
Trypsin	Small intestine	Peptide bonds	7.7–8.0
Lipase	Pancreas	Lipid (ester bonds)	8.0
Arginase	Liver	Arginine	9.7

Enzyme and Substrate Concentration

In any catalyzed reaction, the substrate must first bind with the enzyme to form the enzyme–substrate complex. For a particular substrate concentration, an increase in enzyme concentration increases the rate of the catalyzed reaction. At higher enzyme concentrations,

EXPLORE YOUR WORLD

Enzyme Activity

The enzymes on the surface of a freshly cut apple, avocado, or banana react with oxygen in the air to turn the surface brown. An antioxidant, such as vitamin C in lemon juice, prevents the oxidation reaction. Cut an apple, an avocado, or a banana into several slices. Place one slice in a plastic zipper bag, squeeze out all the air, and close the zipper lock. Dip another slice in lemon juice and place it on a plate. Sprinkle another slice with a crushed vitamin C tablet. Leave another slice alone as a control. Observe the surface of each of your samples. Record your observations immediately, then every hour for 6 hours or longer.

QUESTIONS

1. Which slice(s) shows the most oxidation (turns brown)?
2. Which slice(s) shows little or no oxidation?
3. How was the oxidation reaction on each slice affected by treatment with an antioxidant?

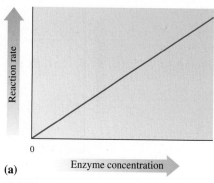
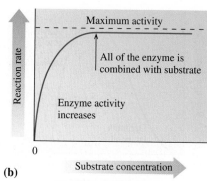

FIGURE 20.7 (a) The rate of reaction increases when the enzyme concentration increases with substrate. **(b)** Increasing the substrate concentration increases the rate of reaction until the enzyme molecules are saturated with substrate.

Q What happens to the rate of reaction when substrate saturates the enzyme?

MC TUTORIAL
Enzyme and Substrate
Concentrations

more molecules are available to bind and catalyze the reaction. As long as the substrate concentration is greater than the enzyme concentration, there is a direct relationship between the enzyme concentration and enzyme activity. (See Figure 20.7a.)

For a particular enzyme concentration, an increase in substrate increases the rate of the reaction until all the enzymes molecules are involved in catalyzing the reaction continuously. When the substrate concentration is high enough to bind with all the enzyme molecules, the rate of the catalyzed reaction reaches a maximum. After that, the addition of more substrate does not increase the rate. (See Figure 20.7b.)

CONCEPT CHECK 20.3

■ **Enzyme Activity**

Describe how each of the following affects the activity of an enzyme:

a. decreasing the pH from the optimum pH
b. increasing the temperature from the optimum temperature
c. increasing the substrate concentration at constant temperature and pH

ANSWER

a. A more acidic environment disrupts the hydrogen bonds and salt bridges of the tertiary structure, which causes a loss of enzyme activity.
b. When the temperature is increased above the optimum temperature, the tertiary structure breaks down (denaturation), the shape of the active site deteriorates, and enzyme activity is lost.
c. An increase in a substrate concentration increases the rate of reaction until all the enzyme is combining with substrate continuously. Then the reaction rate is constant.

SAMPLE PROBLEM 20.3

■ **Factors Affecting Enzymatic Activity**

Describe what effect the following changes would have on the rate of the reaction catalyzed by urease:

$$H_2N-\overset{\overset{\displaystyle O}{\|}}{C}-NH_2 + H_2O \xrightarrow{\text{Urease}} 2NH_3 + CO_2$$
Urea

a. increasing the urea concentration
b. lowering the temperature to 10 °C

SOLUTION

a. An increase in urea concentration will increase the rate of reaction until all the enzyme molecules bind to urea. Then no further increase in rate occurs.

b. Because 10 °C is lower than the optimum temperature of 37 °C, there is a decrease in the rate of the reaction.

STUDY CHECK

If urease has an optimum pH of 7.0, what is the effect of lowering the pH to 3.0?

QUESTIONS AND PROBLEMS

Factors Affecting Enzyme Action

20.19 Trypsin, a peptidase that hydrolyzes polypeptides, functions in the small intestine at an optimum pH of 7.7–8.0. How is the rate of a trypsin-catalyzed reaction affected by each of the following conditions?
   a. lowering the concentration of polypeptides
   b. changing the pH to 3.0
   c. running the reaction at 75 °C
   d. adding more trypsin

20.20 Pepsin, a peptidase that hydrolyzes proteins, functions in the stomach at an optimum pH of 1.5–2.0. How is the rate of a pepsin-catalyzed reaction affected by each of the following conditions?
   a. increasing the concentration of proteins
   b. changing the pH to 5.0
   c. running the reaction at 0 °C
   d. using less pepsin

20.21 The following graph shows the curves for pepsin, sucrase, and trypsin. Estimate the optimum pH for each.

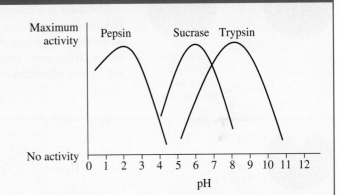

20.22 Refer to the graph in problem 20.21 to determine if the reaction rate in each condition will be at the optimum rate or not.
   a. trypsin, pH 5.0
   b. sucrase, pH 5.0
   c. pepsin, pH 4.0
   d. trypsin, pH 8.0
   e. pepsin, pH 2.0

20.4 Enzyme Inhibition

Many kinds of molecules called **inhibitors** cause enzymes to lose catalytic activity. Although inhibitors act differently, they all prevent the active site from binding with a substrate. An enzyme with a reversible inhibitor can regain enzymatic activity, but an enzyme attached to an irreversible inhibitor loses enzymatic activity permanently.

Reversible Inhibition

In **reversible inhibition**, an inhibitor causes a loss of enzymatic activity that can be reversed. A reversible inhibitor can act in different ways but does not form covalent bonds with the enzyme. Reversible inhibition can be competitive or noncompetitive. In competitive inhibition, an inhibitor competes for the active site, whereas in noncompetitive inhibition, the inhibitor acts on a site that is not the active site.

A **competitive inhibitor** has a structure that is so similar to the substrate it can bond to the enzyme just like the substrate. Thus, the competitive inhibitor competes with the substrate for the active site on the enzyme. As long as the inhibitor occupies the active site, the substrate cannot bind to the enzyme, and no reaction takes place. (See Figure 20.8.)

LEARNING GOAL

Describe competitive and noncompetitive inhibition and reversible and irreversible inhibition.

TUTORIAL
Enzyme Inhibition

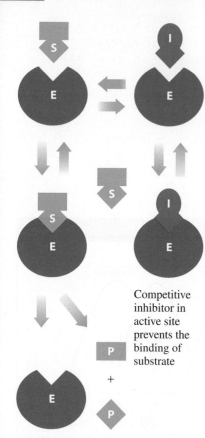

Competitive inhibitor in active site prevents the binding of substrate

FIGURE 20.8 With a structure similar to the substrate for an enzyme, a competitive inhibitor also fits the active site and competes with the substrate when both are present.

Q Does an increase in substrate concentration reverse the inhibition by a competitive inhibitor?

 **SELF STUDY ACTIVITY**
    Enzyme Inhibition

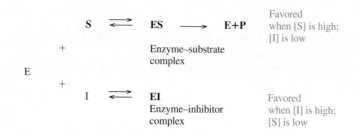

$$S \rightleftharpoons ES \longrightarrow E+P$$

Enzyme–substrate complex

Favored when [S] is high; [I] is low

$$E$$

$$I \rightleftharpoons EI$$

Enzyme–inhibitor complex

Favored when [I] is high; [S] is low

As long as the concentration of the inhibitor is substantial, there is a loss of enzymatic activity. However, adding more substrate displaces the competitive inhibitor, which increases the rate of the reaction. As more enzyme molecules bind to substrate (ES), enzymatic activity is regained.

Malonate is a competitive inhibitor of the enzyme succinate dehydrogenase. Because malonate has a structure similar to succinate, the two substances compete for the active site on the dehydrogenase. As long as malonate (inhibitor) occupies the active site, no reaction occurs. When more succinate is added, more active sites will fill with substrate, and there will be less inhibition.

Succinate   Malonate

Some bacterial infections are treated with competitive inhibitors called antimetabolites. Sulfanilamide, one of the first sulfa drugs, competes with PABA (*p*-aminobenzoic acid), which is an essential substance (metabolite) in the growth cycle of bacteria:

Substrate needed for bacterial growth   Inhibitor

PABA (*p*-aminobenzoic acid)   Sulfanilamide

The structure of a **noncompetitive inhibitor** does not resemble the substrate and does not compete for the active site. Instead, a noncompetitive inhibitor binds to a site on the enzyme that is not the active site. When the noncompetitive inhibitor is bonded to the enzyme, the shape of the enzyme is distorted. Inhibition occurs because the substrate cannot fit in the active site or because it does not fit properly. Without the proper alignment of substrate with the amino acid side groups, no catalysis can take place. (See Figure 20.9.)

Because a noncompetitive inhibitor is not competing for the active site, the addition of more substrate does not reverse this type of inhibition. However, enzyme activity can be regained by lowering the concentration of the noncompetitive inhibitor and thus making more enzyme molecules available. Examples of noncompetitive inhibitors are the heavy metal ions Pb^{2+}, Ag^{+}, and Hg^{2+} that bond with amino acid side groups such as $—COO^{-}$ or with $—OH$. Catalytic activity is restored when chemical reagents remove the inhibitors.

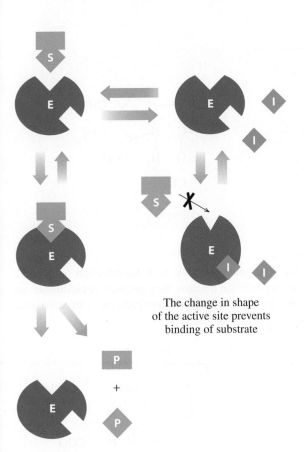

FIGURE 20.9 A noncompetitive inhibitor (I) binds to an enzyme at a site other than the active site, which distorts the enzyme and prevents the proper binding and catalysis of the substrate at the active site.

Q Does an increase in the substrate concentration reverse the inhibition by a noncompetitive inhibitor?

The change in shape
of the active site prevents
binding of substrate

Irreversible Inhibition

In **irreversible inhibition**, a toxic substance causes an enzyme to permanently lose enzymatic activity. These inhibitors form a covalent bond with an amino acid side group within the active site, which prevents the substrate from entering the active site or prevents catalytic activity.

Insecticides and nerve gases act as irreversible inhibitors of acetylcholinesterase, an enzyme needed for nerve conduction. The compound DFP (diisopropyl fluorophosphate) forms a covalent bond with the side chain $-CH_2-OH$ of serine in the active site. When acetylcholinesterase is inhibited, the transmission of nerve impulses is blocked, and paralysis occurs.

$$\boxed{E}-CH_2-OH \;+\; F-\underset{\underset{(CH_3)_2}{\underset{\mid}{CH}}}{\overset{\overset{(CH_3)_2}{\overset{\mid}{CH}}}{\overset{\mid}{\underset{\mid}{O}}}}{\overset{\mid}{P}}{=}O \;\longrightarrow\; \boxed{E}-CH_2-O-\underset{\underset{(CH_3)_2}{\underset{\mid}{CH}}}{\overset{\overset{(CH_3)_2}{\overset{\mid}{CH}}}{\overset{\mid}{\underset{\mid}{O}}}}{\overset{\mid}{P}}{=}O \;+\; HF$$

Enzyme—Serine

DFP (diisopropyl fluorophosphate)   Serine covalently bonded to DFP

Antibiotics produced by bacteria, mold, or yeast are irreversible inhibitors used to inhibit bacterial growth. For example, penicillin inhibits a transpeptidase enzyme needed to catalyze a step in the formation of cell walls in bacteria but not human cell membranes. Penicillin, an irreversible inhibitor, forms a covalent bond with the R group ($-CH_2-OH$) of a serine in the polypeptide of transpeptidase that is stable and cannot be hydrolyzed. The resulting enzyme is inactive.

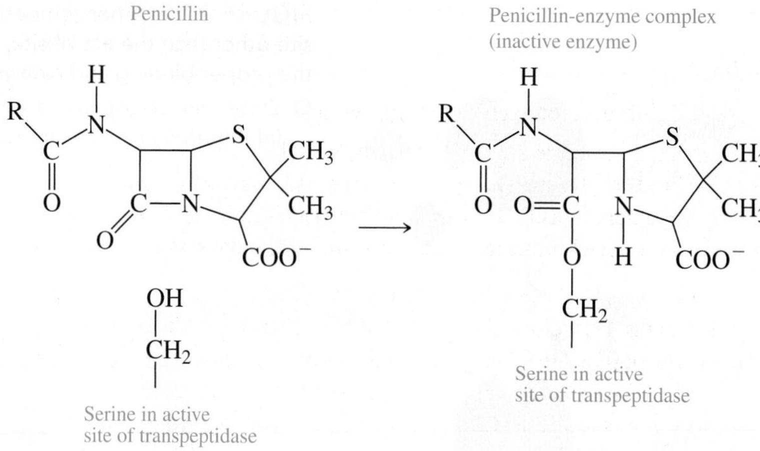

Penicillin

Penicillin-enzyme complex
(inactive enzyme)

Serine in active
site of transpeptidase

Serine in active
site of transpeptidase

Without a complete cell wall, bacteria cannot survive, and the infection is stopped. However, some bacteria are resistant to penicillin because they produce penicillinase, an enzyme that breaks down penicillin. The penicillinase hydrolyzes the four-atom ring converting penicillin to penicillinoic acid, which is inactive:

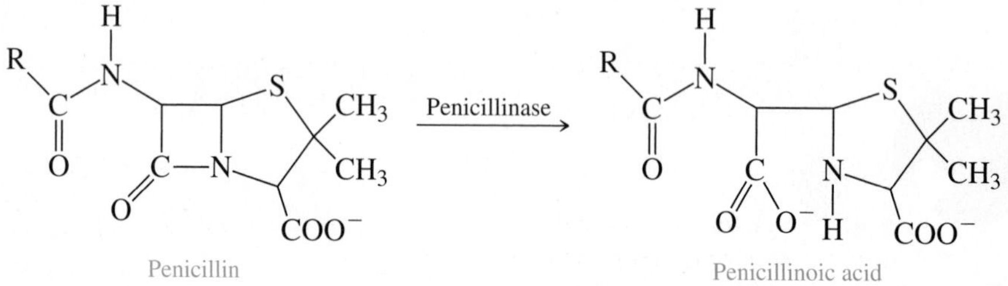

Penicillin

Penicillinase

Penicillinoic acid

Over the years, derivatives of penicillin to which bacteria have not yet become resistant have been produced. Examples of some irreversible enzyme inhibitors are listed in Table 20.6.

TABLE 20.6 Examples of Irreversible Enzyme Inhibitors

Name	Structure	Source	Inhibitory Action
Cyanide	CN^-	Bitter almonds	Bonds to metal ions in enzymes in electron transport
Sarin	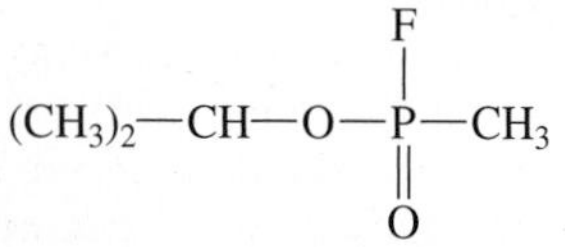	Nerve gas	Similar to DFP
Parathion	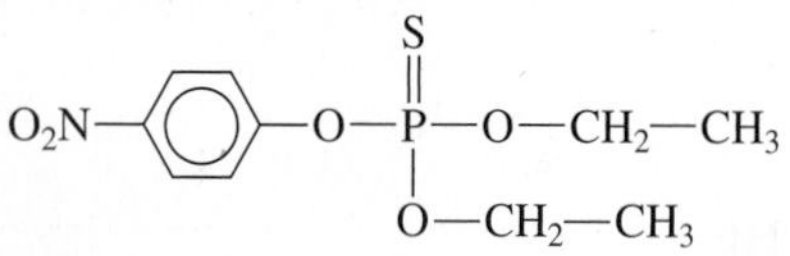	Insecticide	Similar to DFP
Penicillin	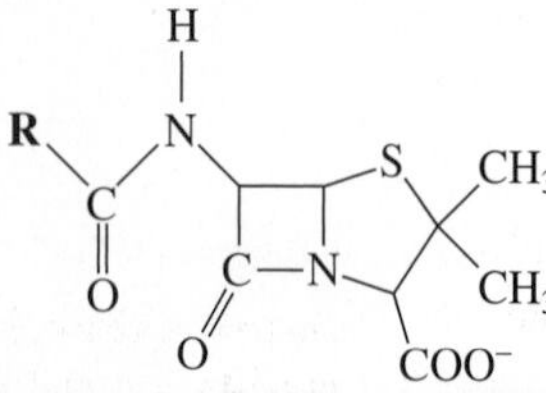	*Penicillium* fungus	Inhibits enzymes that build cell walls in bacteria

R Groups for Penicillin Derivatives

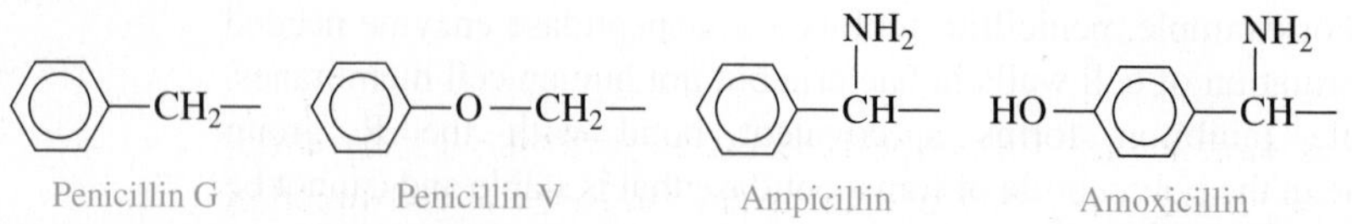

Penicillin G   Penicillin V   Ampicillin   Amoxicillin

CONCEPT CHECK 20.4

■ Enzyme Inhibition

Describe the type of inhibition for each of the following:

a. an inhibitor that has a structure similar to that of the substrate
b. an inhibitor that binds to the surface of the enzyme and changes its shape
c. the inhibitor Sarin, a nerve gas that forms covalent bonds with the R group of serine in the active site of acetylcholinesterase, an enzyme involved in nerve impulses

ANSWER

a. When an inhibitor has a structure similar to that of the substrate, it competes with the substrate for the active site. This type of inhibition is competitive inhibition, which is reversed by increasing the concentration of the substrate.
b. When an inhibitor binds to the surface of the enzyme, it changes the shape of the enzyme and the active site. This type of inhibition is noncompetitive inhibition because the inhibitor does not have a similar shape to the substrate and does not compete with the substrate for the active site.
c. Sarin is a noncompetitive inhibitor. Because it forms a stable, covalent bond with an R group in the active site of the enzyme, the inhibition of Sarin is irreversible.

QUESTIONS AND PROBLEMS

Enzyme Inhibition

20.23 Indicate whether the following describe (1) a competitive or a noncompetitive enzyme inhibitor and if they are (2) reversible or irreversible:
   a. The inhibitor has a structure similar to the substrate.
   b. The effect of the inhibitor cannot be reversed by adding more substrate.
   c. The inhibitor competes with the substrate for the active site.
   d. The structure of the inhibitor is not similar to the substrate.
   e. The addition of more substrate reverses the inhibition.

20.24 Oxaloacetate is an inhibitor of succinate dehydrogenase:

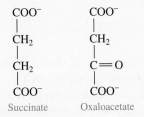
Succinate   Oxaloacetate

   a. Would you expect oxaloacetate to be a competitive or a noncompetitive inhibitor? Why?
   b. Would oxaloacetate bind to the active site or elsewhere on the enzyme?
   c. How would you reverse the effect of the inhibitor?

20.25 Methanol and ethanol are oxidized by alcohol dehydrogenase. In methanol poisoning, ethanol is given intravenously to prevent the formation of formaldehyde that has toxic effects.
   a. Draw the structures of methanol and ethanol.
   b. Would ethanol compete for the active site or bind to a different site?
   c. Would ethanol be a competitive or noncompetitive inhibitor of methanol oxidation?

20.26 In humans, the antibiotic amoxicillin (a type of penicillin) is used to treat certain bacterial infections.
   a. Does the antibiotic inhibit enzymes in humans?
   b. Why does the antibiotic kill bacteria but not humans?
   c. Is amoxicillin a reversible or irreversible inhibitor?

20.5 Regulation of Enzyme Activity

In an enzyme-catalyzed reaction, compounds are produced in the amounts and at the times they are needed. This means that the rate of a catalyzed reaction must be controlled so it can speed up when more molecules of a compound are needed and slow down when that compound is no longer needed.

LEARNING GOAL

Describe the role of zymogens, feedback control, and allosteric enzymes in regulating enzyme activity.

TUTORIAL
Regulating Enzyme Action

Zymogens

Many enzymes are active as soon as they are synthesized and acquire their tertiary structure. However, **zymogens**, or *proenzymes*, are produced as an inactive form and stored in an organ such as the pancreas. Many zymogens are inactive forms of enzymes that hydrolyze protein such as the digestive enzymes. Zymogens are transported to the parts of the body where their active form is needed. A zymogen is converted to the active form by the removal of a polypeptide section with up to 40 amino acids, which uncovers the active site of the enzyme. If zymogen activation occurs in the storage organ such as pancreas, the tissue within the pancreas is digested, which can result in a painful condition called *pancreatitis.*

Most protein hormones, such as insulin, as well as digestive enzymes and the enzymes needed for blood clotting, are initially synthesized as zymogens. (See Table 20.7.) For example, the hormone *insulin* is synthesized in an inactive form called *proinsulin.* To form insulin (Chapter 19), a polypeptide containing 33 amino acids is removed.

TABLE 20.7 Example of Zymogens and Their Active Forms

Zymogen (Inactive Enzyme)	Produced in	Activated in	Enzyme (Active)
Proinsulin	Pancreas	Pancreas	Insulin
Chymotrypsinogen	Pancreas	Small intestine	Chymotrypsin
Pepsinogen	Gastric mucosa	Stomach	Pepsin
Trypsinogen	Pancreas	Small intestine	Trypsin
Fibrinogen	Blood	Damaged tissues	Fibrin
Prothrombin	Blood	Damaged tissues	Thrombin

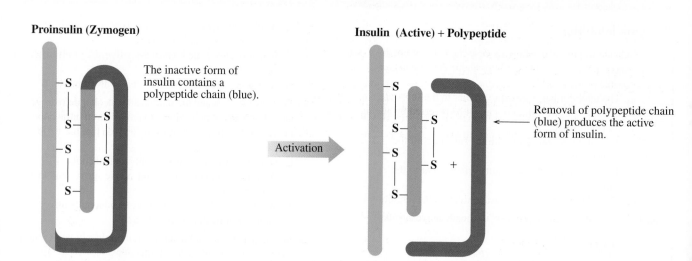

Proinsulin (Zymogen)

The inactive form of insulin contains a polypeptide chain (blue).

Activation

Insulin (Active) + Polypeptide

Removal of polypeptide chain (blue) produces the active form of insulin.

The zymogen of a digestive enzyme called pepsinogen is produced in the gastric mucosal cells that line the stomach. As food enters the stomach, HCl is secreted. Under these acidic conditions (about pH 2), a polypeptide of 42 amino acids is hydrolyzed from pepsinogen to form pepsin, which is the active enzyme that digests proteins in our foods:

$$\text{Pepsinogen} \xrightarrow{\text{H}^+} \text{pepsin + peptides + amino acids}$$

Several digestive enzymes, such as *trypsinogen, chymotrypsinogen,* and *procarboxypeptidase,* are produced as inactive enzymes and stored in the pancreas. After food is ingested and reaches the small intestine, hormones trigger the release of the zymogens of the digestive enzymes from the pancreas. When the zymogens enter the small intestine, they are converted into active enzymes by proteases that remove peptide sections from their protein chains. The result is the active form of the enzyme. For example, an enzyme called enteropeptidase removes a hexapeptide from trypsinogen to give active trypsin. Trypsin in turn removes peptide sections from the zymogens chymotrypsinogen and procarboxypeptidase to give the active forms chymotrypsin and carboxypeptidase.

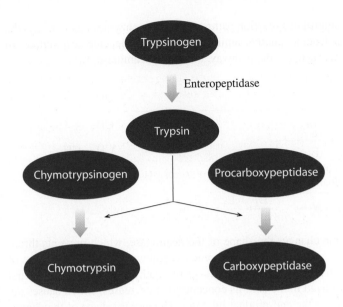

Feedback Control

Certain enzymes known as **allosteric enzymes** are capable of binding a regulator molecule that is different from the substrate. The binding of a regulator causes a change in the shape of the enzyme and therefore a change in the active site. There are both positive and negative regulators. A *positive regulator* speeds up a reaction by causing a change in the shape of the active site that permits the substrate to bind more effectively. A *negative regulator* slows down the rate of catalysis by preventing the proper binding of the substrate. In **feedback control**, the end product acts as a negative regulator. (See Figure 20.10.) When the end product is present in sufficient amounts for the cell, some end product molecules bind to the first enzyme in the reaction pathway (E_1), which is an allosteric enzyme. The inhibition of the reaction of the initial substrate stops the production of any intermediate compounds in the reaction pathway. The entire enzyme-catalyzed reaction sequence shuts down.

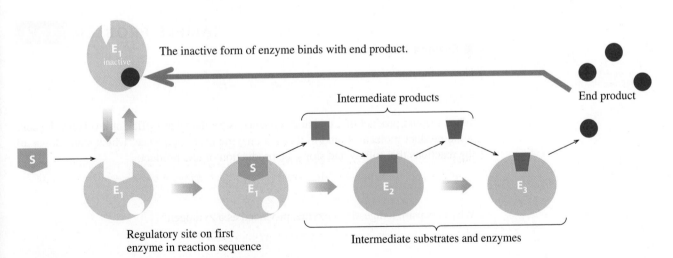

FIGURE 20.10 In feedback control, the end product binds to a regulatory site on the first enzyme in the reaction pathway, which prevents the formation of all intermediate compounds needed in the synthesis of the end product.
Q Do the intermediate enzymes in a reaction sequence have regulatory sites?

When the level of end product is too low, the regulator dissociates from the allosteric enzyme (E_1), which unblocks the active site. The enzyme becomes active and binds to the initial substrate once again. Thus, feedback control allows the reaction only when the end product is needed by the cell. This control prevents the accumulation of unneeded end product, thereby conserving the materials in the cell.

Let's look at feedback control in a reaction pathway with five enzymes that converts the amino acid threonine to isoleucine, another amino acid. When isoleucine accumulates in the cell, it binds to the first enzyme in the pathway, threonine deaminase, E_1:

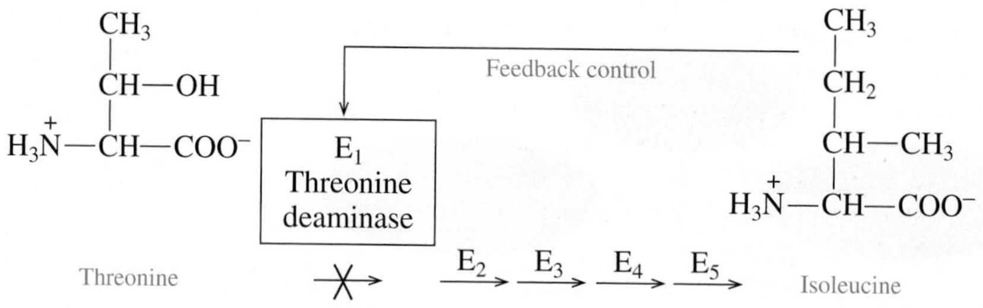

The binding of isoleucine changes the shape of the deaminase, which prevents threonine from binding with the active site. The entire reaction pathway is turned off. None of the intermediate products from the other enzymes in the pathway can inhibit the first enzyme. As isoleucine is utilized in the cell, its concentration decreases, which causes the threonine deaminase to release the end-product inhibitor. The tertiary shape of the deaminase returns to its active form and the reaction sequence once again converts threonine to isoleucine.

CONCEPT CHECK 20.5

■ **Regulation of Enzyme Activity**

Why are the enzymes trypsin and chymotrypsin produced as zymogens in the pancreas rather than as active enzymes?

ANSWER

Trypsin and chymotrypsin are digestive enzymes that break down proteins. If they were produced as active enzymes in the pancreas, they would digest the proteins of the pancreas. They are produced as zymogens that are activated when digestive activity is needed.

SAMPLE PROBLEM 20.4

■ **Enzyme Regulation**

How is the rate of a reaction sequence regulated in feedback control?

SOLUTION

When the end product of a reaction sequence is produced at sufficient levels for the cell, some product molecules bind to the first enzyme in the sequence, which shuts down all the reactions that follow and stops the production of end product.

STUDY CHECK

Why is pepsin, a digestive enzyme, produced as a zymogen?

QUESTIONS AND PROBLEMS

Regulation of Enzyme Activity

20.27 Why are many of the enzymes that act on proteins synthesized as zymogens?

20.28 The zymogen trypsinogen produced in the pancreas is activated in the small intestine, where it catalyzes the digestion and

hydrolysis of proteins. Explain how the activation of the zymogen while still in the pancreas can lead to an inflammation of the pancreas called pancreatitis.

20.29 In feedback control, how does the end product of a reaction sequence regulate enzyme activity?

20.30 Why are the second or third enzymes in a reaction sequence function not used as regulatory enzymes?

20.31 How does an allosteric enzyme function as a regulatory enzyme?

20.32 What is the difference between a negative regulator and a positive regulator?

20.33 Indicate if the following statements describe (1) a zymogen, (2) a positive regulator, (3) a negative regulator, or (4) an allosteric enzyme:
a. It slows down a reaction, but its shape is different from that of the substrate.

b. An enzyme that binds a regulator molecules that differs from the substrate.
c. It is produced as an inactive enzyme.

20.34 Indicate if the following statements describe (1) a zymogen, (2) a positive regulator, (3) a negative regulator, or (4) an allosteric enzyme:
a. It is activated when a peptide section is removed from its protein chain.
b. It speeds up a reaction, but it is not the substrate.
c. When it binds to end product, it stops the formation of more end product.

20.6 Enzyme Cofactors and Vitamins

Enzymes known as **simple enzymes** consist only of proteins. However, many enzymes require small molecules such as vitamins or metal ions called **cofactors** to catalyze reactions properly. When the cofactor is a small organic molecule, it is known as a **coenzyme**. If an enzyme requires a cofactor, neither the protein structure nor the cofactor alone has catalytic activity.

LEARNING GOAL
Describe the types of cofactors found in enzymes.

TUTORIAL
Enzyme Cofactors and Vitamins

Forms of Active Enzymes

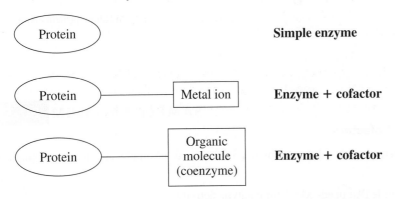

Metal Ions

Many enzymes must contain a metal ion to carry out their catalytic activity. The metal ions are bonded to one or more of the amino acid side chains. The metal ions from the minerals that we obtain from foods in our diet have various functions in catalysis. Ions such as Fe^{2+} and Cu^{2+} are used by oxidases, losing or gaining electrons in oxidation and reduction reactions. Other metal ions such as Zn^{2+} stabilize the amino acid side chains during hydrolysis reactions. Some metal cofactors required by enzymes are listed in Table 20.8.

TABLE 20.8 Enzymes and the Metal Ions Required as Cofactors

Enzyme	Metal Ion Cofactor	Function
Cytochrome oxidase	Cu^{2+}	Oxidation–reduction
Catalase	Fe^{2+}/Fe^{3+}	Oxidation–reduction
Cytochrome oxidase		
Alcohol dehydrogenase	Zn^{2+}	Used with NAD^+
Carbonic anhydrase		
Carboxypeptidase A		
Glucose-6-phosphatase	Mg^{2+}	Hydrolyzes phosphate esters
Arginase	Mn^{2+}	Removes electrons
Urease	Ni^{2+}	Hydrolyzes amides

Let's look at an example of a metal ion in an enzyme-catalyzed reaction. The enzyme carboxypeptidase A cleaves the C terminal amino acid of a protein when that amino acid has a bulky hydrophobic or aromatic side chain. (See Figure 20.11.) With the substrate in the active site, the Zn^{2+} helps to stabilize the negative charge on the oxygen atom of the carbonyl group and promotes the hydrolysis of the peptide bond.

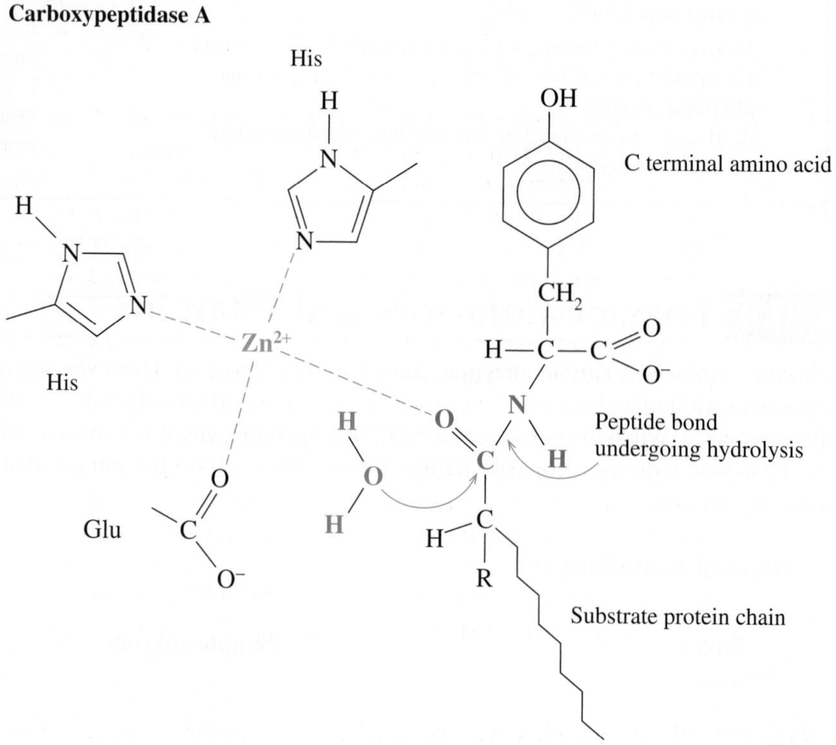

FIGURE 20.11 A Zn^{2+} cofactor aids in the hydrolysis of the peptide bond of a bulky C terminal amino acid by helping to stabilize the carbonyl oxygen.

Q When would the Zn^{2+} be utilized as a cofactor by other enzymes?

Carboxypeptidase A

SAMPLE PROBLEM 20.5

■ Enzyme Cofactors

Indicate whether each of the following is active as a simple enzyme or requires a cofactor:

a. a polypeptide that needs Mg^{2+} for catalytic activity
b. an active enzyme composed only of a polypeptide chain
c. an enzyme that consists of a quaternary structure attached to vitamin B_6

SOLUTION

a. The enzyme requires a cofactor.
b. An active enzyme that consists of only a polypeptide chain is a simple enzyme.
c. The enzyme requires a cofactor.

STUDY CHECK

Which of the nonprotein portions of the enzymes in Sample Problem 20.5 is a coenzyme?

Vitamins and Coenzymes

Vitamins are organic molecules that are essential for normal health and growth. They are required in trace amounts and are obtained from the diet because sufficient amounts are not synthesized in the body. Before vitamins were discovered, it was known that lime juice prevented the disease scurvy in sailors and that cod liver oil could prevent rickets. In 1912, scientists found that in addition to carbohydrates, fats, and proteins, certain other factors called vitamins must be obtained from the diet.

Vitamins are classified into two groups by solubility: water-soluble and fat-soluble. **Water-soluble vitamins** have polar groups such as —OH and —COOH, which make them soluble in the aqueous environment of the cells. The **fat-soluble vitamins** are nonpolar compounds, which are soluble in the fat (lipid) components of the body such as fat deposits and cell membranes.

Water-Soluble Vitamins

Most water-soluble vitamins are not stored in the body, because excess amounts are eliminated in the urine each day. Therefore, the water-soluble vitamins must be in the foods of our daily diets. Because many water-soluble vitamins are easily destroyed by heat, oxygen, and ultraviolet light, care must be taken in food preparation, processing, and storage. Because refining grains such as wheat causes a loss of vitamins, during the 1940s the Committee on Food and Nutrition of the National Research Council began to recommend dietary enrichment of cereal grains. Thiamine (B_1), riboflavin (B_2), niacin, and iron were in the first group of added nutrients recommended. We now see the Recommended Daily Allowance (RDA) for many vitamins and minerals on food product labels such as cereals and bread.

The water-soluble vitamins are required by many enzymes as cofactors to carry out certain aspects of catalytic action. (See Table 20.9.) The coenzymes do not remain bonded to a particular enzyme, but are used repeatedly by different enzymes to facilitate an enzyme-catalyzed reaction. (See Figure 20.12.) Thus, only small amounts of coenzymes are required in the cells.

Thiamine (vitamin B_1) was the first B vitamin to be identified, thus the abbreviation B_1. The coenzyme thiamine pyrophosphate (TPP) is obtained when a synthetase adds two

TABLE 20.9 Function, RDA, Sources, and Deficiency Symptoms of Water-Soluble Vitamins

Vitamin	Function	RDA (Adults)	Sources	Deficiency Symptoms
Thiamine (vitamin B_1)	Decarboxylation	1.2 mg	Liver, yeast, whole grain bread, cereals, milk	Beriberi: fatigue, poor appetite, weight loss, nerve degeneration, heart failure
Riboflavin (vitamin B_2)	Electron transfer	1.2–1.8 mg	Beef liver, chicken, eggs, green leafy vegetables, dairy foods, peanuts, whole grains	Dermatitis, dry skin, tongue inflammation, cataracts
Niacin (vitamin B_3)	Oxidation–reduction	14–18 mg	Brewer's yeast, chicken, beef, fish, liver, brown rice, whole grains	Pellagra: dermatitis, muscle fatigue, loss of appetite, diarrhea, mouth sores, mental disorders
Pantothenic acid (vitamin B_5)	Acetyl group transfer	5 mg	Salmon, beef, liver, eggs, brewer's yeast, whole grains, fresh vegetables	Fatigue, retarded growth, muscle cramps, anemia
Pyridoxine (vitamin B_6)	Transamination	1.3–2.0 mg	Meat, liver, fish, nuts, whole grains, spinach	Dermatitis, fatigue, anemia, retarded growth
Cobalamin (vitamin B_{12})	Methyl group transfer	2.0–2.6 μg	Liver, beef, kidney, chicken, fish, milk products	Pernicious anemia, malformed red blood cells, nerve damage
Ascorbic acid (vitamin C)	Collagen synthesis, healing of wounds	60–95 mg	Blueberries, oranges, strawberries, cantaloupe, tomatoes, peppers, broccoli, cabbage, spinach	Scurvy: bleeding gums, weakened connective tissues, slow-healing wounds, anemia
Biotin	Carboxylation	30 μg	Liver, yeast, nuts, eggs	Dermatitis, loss of hair, fatigue, anemia, nausea, depression
Folic acid (folate)	Methyl group transfer	400 μg	Green leafy vegetables, beans, meat, seafood, yeast, asparagus, whole grains enriched with folic acid	Abnormal red blood cells, anemia, intestinal-tract disturbances, loss of hair, growth impairment, depression, spina bifida

FIGURE 20.12 The active forms of many enzymes require the combination of the protein with a coenzyme.

Q What is the function of water-soluble vitamins in enzymes?

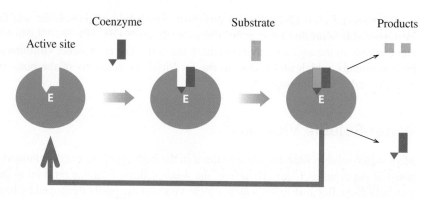

phosphate groups from ATP to the alcohol group of thiamine. (ATP and AMP are discussed in Section 22.2.)

Thiamine (vitamin B_1)   +   ATP $\xrightarrow{\text{TPP synthetase}}$ Thiamine pyrophosphate (TPP)   +   AMP

The TPP coenzyme is involved in the decarboxylation reactions of α-keto carboxylic acids and reactions that cleave bonds to carbonyl carbons of α-hydroxy ketones.

Riboflavin (vitamin B_2) is used to make the coenzymes flavin adenine dinucleotide (FAD) and flavin mononucleotide (FMN). The *ribo* part of the name comes from the sugar alcohol ribitol in the *riboflavin* molecule. Enzymes called *flavoenzymes* use the coenzymes FAD and FMN to catalyze oxidation–reduction reactions of carbohydrates, fats, and proteins.

Riboflavin (vitamin B_2)

Niacin (vitamin B_3) is a component of coenzymes nicotinamide adenine dinucleotide (NAD^+) and $NADP^+$, the phosphate form of NAD^+. The name *niacin* was assigned to the vitamin because its actual name, *nicotinic acid*, might be confused with nicotine. These coenzymes participate in oxidation–reduction, energy-production reactions in carbohydrate, fat, and protein metabolism.

Niacin (vitamin B_3)

Pantothenic acid (vitamin B_5) is part of a complex coenzyme known as coenzyme A. Coenzyme A transfers a two-carbon acetyl group from pyruvate to the citric acid cycle for the production of energy. Coenzyme A is also involved in the conversion of amino acids and lipids to glucose as well as in the synthesis of cholesterol and steroid hormones.

$$HO-CH_2-\underset{\underset{CH_3}{|}}{\overset{\overset{CH_3}{|}}{C}}-\underset{\underset{}{|}}{\overset{\overset{OH}{|}}{CH}}-\overset{\overset{O}{\|}}{C}-\underset{\underset{H}{|}}{N}-CH_2-CH_2-\overset{\overset{O}{\|}}{C}-OH$$

Pantothenic acid (vitamin B_5)

Pyridoxine (vitamin B_6) and *pyridoxal* (an aldehyde) are converted to the coenzyme pyridoxal phosphate (PLP). The PLP coenzyme participates in enzyme-catalyzed reactions such as transamination of amino acids and decarboxylation.

Pyridoxine (vitamin B_6)   Pyridoxal (vitamin B_6)   Pyridoxal phosphate (PLP)

Vitamin B_{12} (cobalamin)

Cobalamin (vitamin B_{12}) is a coenzyme consisting of four pyrrole rings with a cobalt ion (Co^{2+}) in the center. In its coenzyme form, cobalamin participates in the transfer of methyl groups, molecular rearrangements, the formation of red blood cells, and the synthesis of acetylcholine for nerve cells. Because vitamin B_{12} is not present in plants, strict vegetarians can experience symptoms of pernicious anemia.

Ascorbic acid (vitamin C) has a simple chemical structure compared to most of the other vitamins. Its major function in the cells is its role in the synthesis of hydroxyproline and hydroxylysine, which are needed to form collagen. Collagen is the protein found in tendons, connective tissue, bone structure, and skin. (See Figure 20.13.)

FIGURE 20.13 Oranges, lemons, peppers, and tomatoes contain vitamin C, or ascorbic acid.

Q What happens to any excess vitamin C that is consumed over the course of a day?

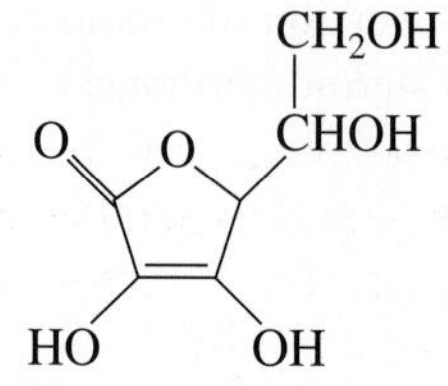

Ascorbic acid (vitamin C)

Biotin is a coenzyme for enzymes that transfer a carboxyl group in the reaction of pyruvate to oxaloacetate or acetyl CoA to malonyl CoA, which occurs in the synthesis of fatty acids.

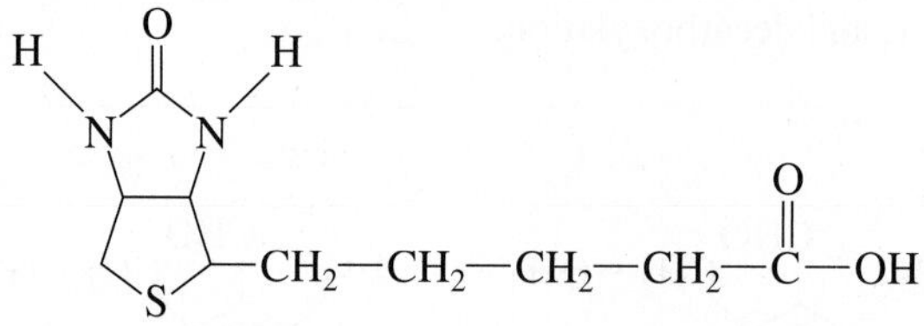

Biotin

Folic acid (folate) is composed of a pyrimidine ring, *p*-aminobenzoic acid (PABA), and glutamate. The vitamin was discovered during the 1930s when people with a form of anemia were cured with extracts from liver or yeast. Folic acid is also found in spinach leaves, hence the name *folium*, Latin for *leaf*. In the cells, an enzyme called dihydrofolate reductase adds hydrogen atoms to the atoms in the heterocyclic ring of folate to yield the coenzyme tetrahydrofolate (THF). This coenzyme is used in reactions that transfer single-carbon groups and synthesize purines and pyrimidines to make DNA and RNA. It also plays a role with cobalamin in the production of red blood cells.

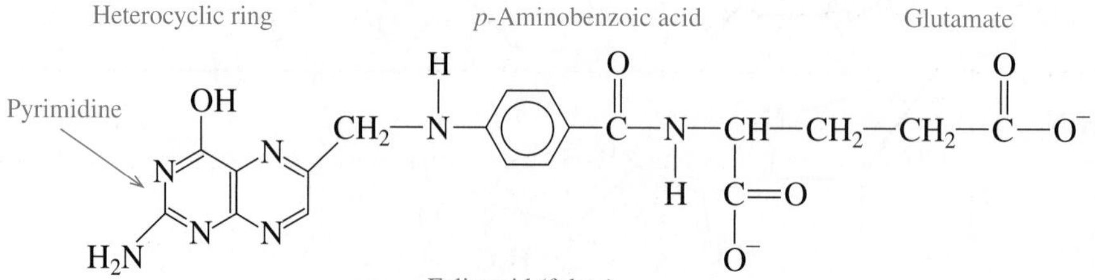

Folic acid (folate)

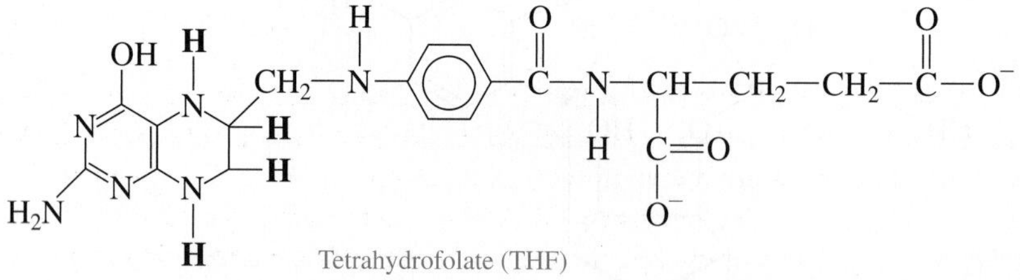

Tetrahydrofolate (THF)

Some compounds related to folate bring about remissions in people with leukemia. For example, 4-aminofolate, referred to medically as *methotrexate*, acts as a competitive inhibitor of the dihydrofolate reductase that forms THF. The growth of cells, including tumor cells, depends on THF to build purines and thymine. By inhibiting the reductase enzyme with methotrexate, THF cannot be produced, and the rapid growth of tumor cells is blocked.

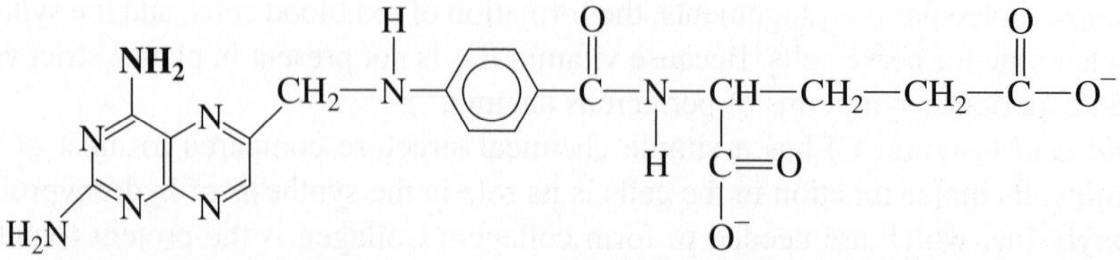

4- Aminofolate (methotrexate)

Fat-Soluble Vitamins

The fat-soluble vitamins—A, D, E, and K—are not involved as coenzymes, but they are important in processes such as vision, formation of bone, protection from oxidation, and proper blood clotting. (See Table 20.10.) Because the fat-soluble vitamins are stored in the body and not eliminated, it is possible to take too much, which could be toxic.

TABLE 20.10 Function, RDA, Sources, and Deficiency Symptoms of Fat-Soluble Vitamins

Vitamin	Function	RDA (Adults)	Sources	Deficiency Symptoms
Retinol (vitamin A)	Vision, synthesis of RNA	800 μg	Yellow and green fruits and vegetables	Night blindness, immune system repression, slowed growth rickets
Cholecalciferol (vitamin D_3)	Regulation of absorption of P and Ca	5–10 μg	Sunlight, cod liver oil, enriched milk, eggs	Rickets, weak bone structure, osteomalacia
Tocopherol (vitamin E)	Antioxidant, cell protection	15 mg	Meats, whole grains, vegetables	Hemolysis, anemia
Menaquinone (vitamin K_2)	Blood clotting	90–120 μg	Liver, spinach, cauliflower	Prolonged bleeding time, bruising

Vitamin A consists of three different forms depending on the oxidation of the functional group: *retinol* (alcohol), *retinal* (aldehyde), and *retinoic acid* (carboxylic acid). Vitamin A is obtained from animal sources in the diet or the β-carotenes of plants, which are converted to vitamin A in the liver. The retinol in the retinas of the eyes accumulates in the rod and cone cells, where it plays a role in vision. Vitamin A is also involved in the synthesis of RNA and glycoproteins. (See Figure 20.14.)

FIGURE 20.14 Yellow and green fruits and vegetables contain vitamin A.

Q Why is vitamin A called a fat-soluble vitamin?

β-Carotene

Liver enzymes

Retinol (vitamin A)

The most prevalent form of vitamin D is vitamin D_3, or *cholecalciferol*. Technically, this is not a vitamin, because it is not required in the diet. In skin, vitamin D_3 is synthesized from 7-dehydrocholesterol by the ultraviolet rays from sunlight. In regions of limited sunlight, vitamin D_3 is added to milk products to avoid a vitamin D_3 deficiency. Its function in the body is to regulate the absorption of phosphorus and calcium during bone growth.

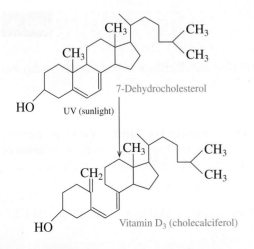

7-Dehydrocholesterol

UV (sunlight)

Vitamin D_3 (cholecalciferol)

Vitamin E, or *tocopherol*, has a major role in cells as an antioxidant, but not much is known about the mechanism of its activity. It appears to protect the cells in the body by removing damaging chemicals and by preventing the oxidation of unsaturated fatty acids. Vitamin E has been used to reduce the damage to the retinas that can be caused by the high oxygen levels needed for respiration by premature infants.

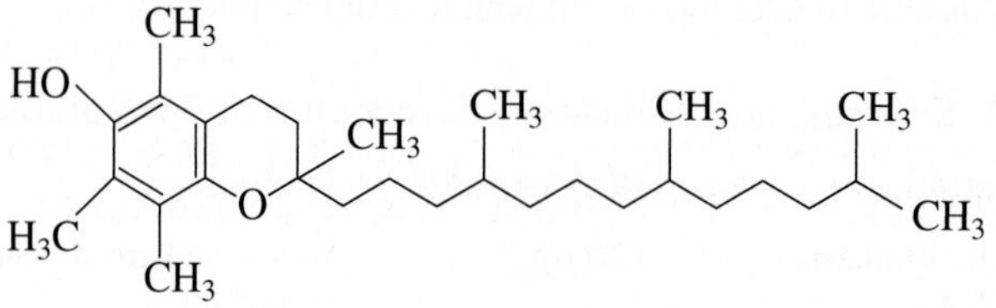

Vitamin E (tocopherol)

Vitamin K_1, or *phylloquinone*, a substance found in plants, has a large saturated side chain. Vitamin K_2, or *menaquinone*, found in animals, has a very long unsaturated side chain. Vitamin K_2 takes part in the synthesis of zymogens needed for blood clotting.

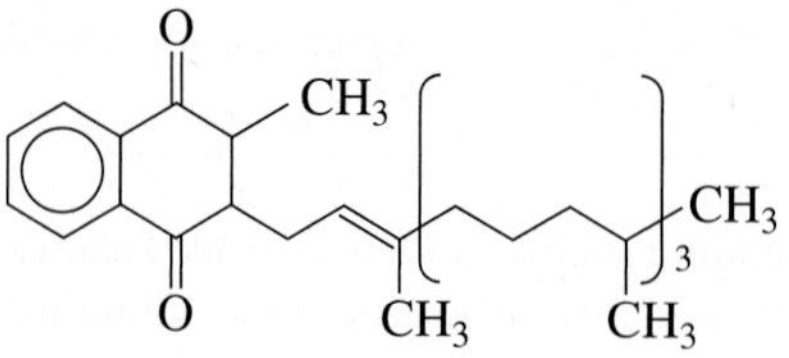

Vitamin K_1 (phylloquinone)

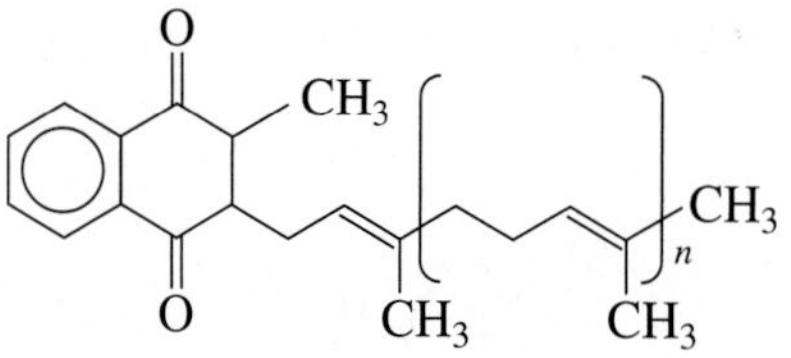

Vitamin K_2 (menaquinone)

CONCEPT CHECK 20.6

■ Vitamins

Identify the vitamin(s) described by each of the following:

a. is synthesized in the skin by sunlight
b. contains a Co^{2+} ion
c. is fat soluble
d. can lead to scurvy and slow-healing wounds if deficient in the diet

ANSWER

a. Vitamin D_3 (cholecalciferol) is synthesized in the skin by sunlight.
b. Vitamin B_{12} (cobalamin) contains a Co^{2+} ion.
c. Vitamins A (retinol), D, E (tocopherol), and K (menaquinone) are fat soluble.
d. Vitamin C (ascorbic acid) deficiency can lead to scurvy and slow-healing wounds.

SAMPLE PROBLEM 20.6

■ Vitamins

Why do you need a certain amount of thiamine and riboflavin in your diet every day but not vitamin A or D?

SOLUTION

Water-soluble vitamins like thiamine and riboflavin are not stored in the body, whereas fat-soluble vitamins such as A and D are stored in the liver. Any excess of thiamine or riboflavin are eliminated in the urine and must be replenished each day from the diet.

STUDY CHECK

Why are fresh fruits rather than cooked fruits recommended as a source of vitamin C?

QUESTIONS AND PROBLEMS

Enzyme Cofactors and Vitamins

20.35 Is the enzyme described in each of the following statements a simple enzyme or one that requires a cofactor?
  a. requires vitamin B_1 (thiamine)
  b. needs Zn^{2+} for catalytic activity
  c. its active form consists of two polypeptide chains

20.36 Is the enzyme described in each of the following statements a simple enzyme or one that requires a cofactor?
  a. requires vitamin B_2 (riboflavin)
  b. its active form composed of 155 amino acids
  c. uses Cu^{2+} during catalysis

20.37 Give the abbreviation for each of the following coenzymes:
  a. tetrahydrofolate
  b. nicotinamide adenine dinucleotide

20.38 Give the abbreviation for each of the following coenzymes:
  a. flavin adenine dinucleotide
  b. thiamine pyrophosphate

20.39 Identify a vitamin that is a component of each of the following coenzymes:
  a. coenzyme A   **b.** tetrahydrofolate (THF)
  c. NAD^+

20.40 Identify a vitamin that is a component of each of the following coenzymes:
  a. thiamine pyrophosphate
  b. FAD
  c. pyridoxal phosphate

20.41 What vitamin may be deficient in the following conditions?
  a. rickets   **b.** scurvy   **c.** pellagra

20.42 What vitamin may be deficient in the following conditions?
  a. poor night vision
  b. pernicious anemia
  c. beriberi

20.43 The RDA for pyridoxine (vitamin B_6) is 2 mg daily. Why will it not improve your nutrition to take 100 mg of pyridoxine daily?

20.44 The RDA for vitamin A is 3 mg daily. What would happen if you took 25 mg of vitamin A every day?

20.45 What is the change in the structure of pyridoxine (B_6) that yields the coenzyme PLP?

20.46 What is the change in the structure of folate that yields the coenzyme THF?

CONCEPT MAP

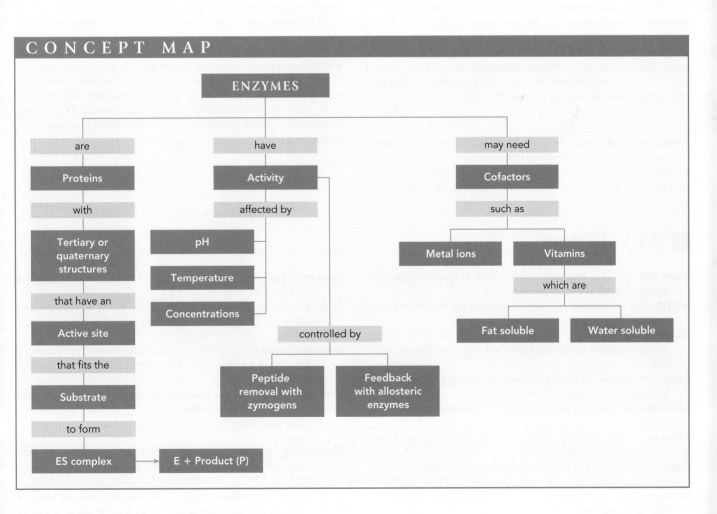

CHAPTER REVIEW

20.1 Enzymes

LEARNING GOAL: *Describe how enzymes function as catalysts; name and classify them.*

Enzymes are globular proteins that act as biological catalysts by lowering activation energy and accelerating the rate of cellular reactions. The names of most enzymes ending in *ase* describe the compound or reaction catalyzed by the enzyme. Enzymes are classified by the main type of reaction they catalyze, such as oxidoreductase, transferase, or isomerase.

20.2 Enzyme Action

LEARNING GOAL: *Describe the role of an enzyme in an enzyme-catalyzed reaction.*

Within the tertiary structure of an enzyme, a small pocket called the active site binds the substrates. In the lock-and-key model, a substrate precisely fits the shape of the active site. In the induced-fit model, substrates induce the active site to change structure to give an optimal fit by the substrate. In the enzyme–substrate complex, catalysis takes place when amino acid side chains react with a substrate. The products are released, and the enzyme is available to bind another substrate molecule.

20.3 Factors Affecting Enzyme Action

LEARNING GOAL: *Describe the effect of temperature, pH, concentration of enzyme, and concentration of substrate on enzyme activity.*

Enzymes are most effective at optimum temperature, usually 37 °C, and optimum pH, usually 7.4. The rate of an enzyme-catalyzed reaction decreases as temperature and pH go above or below the optimum values. An increase in substrate concentration increases the reaction rate of an enzyme-catalyzed reaction. If an enzyme is saturated, adding more substrate will not increase the reaction rate.

20.4 Enzyme Inhibition

LEARNING GOAL: *Describe competitive and noncompetitive inhibition and reversible and irreversible inhibition.*

An inhibitor reduces the activity of an enzyme or makes it inactive. A competitive inhibitor has a structure similar to the substrate and competes for the active site. When the active site is occupied, the enzyme cannot catalyze the reaction of the substrate. A noncompetitive inhibitor attaches elsewhere on the enzyme, changing the shape of both the enzyme and its active site. As long as the noncompetitive inhibitor is attached, the altered active site cannot bind with substrate.

20.5 Regulation of Enzyme Activity

LEARNING GOAL: *Describe the role of zymogens, feedback control, and allosteric enzymes in regulating enzyme activity.*

Insulin and digestive enzymes are produced as inactive forms called zymogens. They are converted to active forms by the removal of a peptide portion from their protein chains. The rate of an enzyme-catalyzed reaction can be increased or decreased by regulator molecules that bind to a regulator site on an allosteric enzyme. The regulator molecule changes the shape of the enzyme and therefore the shape of the active site. A positive regulator increases the rate, whereas a negative regulator decreases the rate. In feedback control, the end product of a reaction sequence binds to a regulator site on the first enzyme, which is an allosteric enzyme, to decrease product formation.

20.6 Enzyme Cofactors and Vitamins

LEARNING GOAL: *Describe the types of cofactors found in enzymes.*

Simple enzymes are biologically active as a protein only, whereas other enzymes require small organic molecules or metal ions called cofactors. A cofactor may be a metal ion, such as Cu^{2+} or Fe^{2+}, or an organic molecule called a coenzyme. A vitamin is a small organic molecule needed for health and normal growth. Vitamins are obtained in small amounts through the foods in the diet. The water-soluble vitamins B and C function as coenzymes. The fat-soluble vitamins are A, D, E, and K. Vitamin A is important in vision, vitamin D for proper bone growth, vitamin E is an antioxidant, and vitamin K is required for proper blood clotting.

KEY TERMS

active site A pocket in a part of the tertiary enzyme structure that binds substrate and catalyzes a reaction.

activity The rate at which an enzyme catalyzes the reaction that converts substrate to product.

allosteric enzyme An enzyme that regulates the rate of a reaction when a regulator molecule attaches to a site other than the active site.

antibiotics Substances usually produced by bacteria, mold, or yeast that inhibit the growth of bacteria.

coenzyme An organic molecule, usually a vitamin, required as a cofactor in enzyme action.

cofactor A metal ion or an organic molecule that is necessary for a biologically functional enzyme.

competitive inhibitor A molecule with a structure similar to the substrate that inhibits enzyme action by competing for the active site.

enzymes Globular proteins, sometimes with cofactors, that catalyze biological reactions.

enzyme–substrate (ES) complex An intermediate consisting of an enzyme that binds to a substrate in an enzyme-catalyzed reaction.

fat-soluble vitamins Vitamins that are not soluble in water and can be stored in the liver and body fat.

feedback control A type of inhibition in which an end product inhibits the first enzyme in a sequence of enzyme-catalyzed reactions.

induced-fit model A model of enzyme action in which the shape of a substrate and the active site of the enzyme adjust to give an optimal fit.

inhibitors Substances that make an enzyme inactive by interfering with its ability to react with a substrate.

irreversible inhibition The loss of enzymatic activity that cannot be reversed.

lock-and-key model A model of enzyme action in which the substrate is like a key that fits the specific shape of the active site (the lock).

noncompetitive inhibitor A type of inhibitor that alters the shape of an enzyme as well as the active site so that the substrate cannot bind properly.

optimum pH The pH at which an enzyme is most active.

optimum temperature The temperature at which an enzyme is most active.

reversible inhibition The loss of enzymatic activity by an inhibitor whose effect can be reversed.

simple enzyme An enzyme that is active as a polypeptide only.

substrate The molecule that reacts in the active site in an enzyme-catalyzed reaction.

vitamins Organic molecules that are essential for normal health and growth and are obtained in small amounts from the diet.

water-soluble vitamins Vitamins that are soluble in water; they cannot be stored in the body, are easily destroyed by heat, ultraviolet light, and oxygen, and function as coenzymes.

zymogen An inactive form of an enzyme that is activated by the removal of a peptide portion from one end of the protein.

UNDERSTANDING THE CONCEPTS

20.47 Ethylene glycol (HO—CH_2—CH_2—OH) is a major component of antifreeze. In the body, it is first converted to $HOOC$—CHO (oxoethanoic acid) and then to $HOOC$—$COOH$ (oxalic acid), which is toxic.

a. What class of enzyme catalyzes both of the reactions of ethylene glycol?

b. The treatment for the ingestion of ethylene glycol is an intravenous solution of ethanol. How might this help prevent toxic levels of oxalic acid in the body?

20.48 Adults who are lactose intolerant cannot break down the disaccharide in milk products. To help digest dairy food, a product known as Lactaid can be added to milk. The milk is then refrigerated for 24 hours.

a. What enzyme is present in Lactaid, and what is the major class of this enzyme?

b. What might happen to the enzyme if the digestion product were stored in a warm area?

20.49 Fresh pineapple contains the enzyme bromelain that degrades proteins.

a. The directions on a gelatin package say not to add fresh pineapple. However, canned pineapple, where pineapple is heated to high temperatures, can be added. Why?

b. Fresh pineapple can be used as a marinade to tenderize tough meat. Why?

20.50 Beano contains an enzyme that breaks down polysaccharides into smaller, more digestible sugars, which diminishes the gas formation that can occur after eating foods such as vegetables and beans.

a. The label says "contains alpha-galactosidase." What class of enzyme is present in beano?

b. What is the substrate for the enzyme?

c. The directions indicate you should not cook with or heat beano. Why?

ADDITIONAL QUESTIONS AND PROBLEMS

For instructor-assigned homework, go to www.masteringchemistry.com.

20.51 Why do the cells in the body have so many enzymes?

20.52 Are all the possible enzymes present at the same time in a cell?

20.53 How are enzymes different from the catalysts used in chemistry laboratories?

20.54 Why do enzymes function only under mild conditions?

20.55 Indicate whether each of the following would be a substrate (S) or an enzyme (E):
a. lactose b. lactase c. urease
d. trypsin e. pyruvate f. transaminase

20.56 Indicate whether each of the following would be a substrate (S) or an enzyme (E):
a. glucose b. hydrolase c. maleate isomerase
d. alanine e. amylose f. amylase

20.57 Give the substrate of each of the following enzymes:
a. urease
b. lactase
c. aspartate transaminase
d. phenylalanine hydroxylase

20.58 Give the substrate of each of the following enzymes:
a. maltase b. fructose oxidase
c. phenolase d. sucrase

20.59 Predict the major class of each of the following enzymes:
a. acyltransferase b. oxidase
c. lipase d. decarboxylase

20.60 Predict the major class for each of the following enzymes:
a. cis–trans isomerase b. reductase
c. carboxylase d. peptidase

20.61 How would the lock-and-key theory explain that sucrase hydrolyses sucrose but not lactose?

20.62 How does the induced-fit model of enzyme action allow an enzyme to catalyze a reaction of a group of substrates?

20.63 If a blood test indicates a high level of LDH and CK, what could be the cause?

20.64 If a blood test indicates a high level of ALT, what could be the cause?

20.65 Indicate whether an enzyme is saturated or unsaturated in each of the following conditions:
a. adding more substrate does not increase the rate of reaction
b. doubling the substrate concentration doubles the rate of reaction

20.66 Indicate whether each of the following enzymes would be functional:
a. pepsin, a digestive enzyme, at pH 2
b. an enzyme at 37 °C, if the enzyme is from a type of thermophilic bacteria that have an optimum temperature of 100 °C

20.67 How does reversible inhibition differ from irreversible inhibition?

20.68 How does competitive reversible inhibition differ from noncompetitive reversible inhibition?

20.69 a. What type of an inhibitor is the antibiotic amoxicillin?
b. Why can amoxicillin be used to treat bacterial infections?

20.70 a. A gardener using Parathion develops a headache, dizziness, nausea, blurred vision, excessive salivation, and muscle twitching. What might be happening to the gardener?
b. Why must humans be careful when using insecticides?

20.71 The zymogen pepsinogen is produced in the gastric mucosa.
a. How and where does pepsinogen become the active form pepsin?
b. Why are proteases such as pepsin produced in inactive forms?

20.72 Thrombin is an enzyme that helps produce blood clotting when an injury and bleeding occur.
a. What would be the name of the zymogen of thrombin?
b. Why would the active form of thrombin be produced only when an injury to tissue occurs?

20.73 What is an allosteric enzyme?

20.74 Why can some regulator molecules speed up a reaction, while others slow it down?

20.75 In feedback control, what type of regulator modifies the catalytic activity of the reaction pathway?

20.76 Why aren't the intermediate products in a reaction sequence used in feedback control?

20.77 Does each of the following statements describe a simple enzyme or an enzyme that requires a cofactor?
a. contains Mg^{2+} in the active site
b. has catalytic activity as a tertiary protein structure
c. requires folic acid for catalytic activity

20.78 Does each of the following statements describe a simple enzyme or an enzyme that requires a cofactor?
a. contains riboflavin or vitamin B_2
b. has four subunits of polypeptide chains
c. requires Fe^{3+} in the active site for catalytic activity

20.79 Match the following vitamins with their coenzymes:
(1) NAD^+ (2) TPP (3) coenzyme A
a. pantothenic acid (B_5)
b. niacin (B_3)
c. thiamine (B_1)

20.80 Match the following vitamins with their coenzymes:
(1) pyridoxal phosphate (2) THF (3) FAD
a. folate
b. riboflavin (B_2)
c. pyridoxine

20.81 Why are only small amounts of vitamins needed in the cells when there are several enzymes that require coenzymes?

20.82 Why is there a daily requirement for vitamins?

20.83 Match each of the following vitamins with their deficiency symptoms or conditions:
(1) night blindness
(2) weak bone structure
(3) pellagra
a. niacin b. vitamin A c. vitamin D

20.84 Match each of the following vitamins with their deficiency symptoms or conditions:
(1) bleeding (2) anemia (3) scurvy
a. cobalamin
b. vitamin C
c. vitamin K

CHALLENGE QUESTIONS

20.85 Lactase is an enzyme that hydrolyzes lactose to glucose and galactose.
    a. What are the reactants and products of the reaction?
    b. Draw an energy diagram for the reaction with and without lactase.
    c. How does lactase make the reaction go faster?

20.86 Maltase is an enzyme that hydrolyzes maltose into two glucose molecules.
    a. What are the reactants and products of the reaction?
    b. Draw an energy diagram for the reaction with and without maltase.
    c. How does maltase make the reaction go faster?

20.87 What is the class of the enzyme that would catalyze each of the following reactions?

    a. $CH_3-\overset{\displaystyle O}{\overset{\|}{C}}-H \longrightarrow CH_3-\overset{\displaystyle O}{\overset{\|}{C}}-OH$

    b. $\overset{+}{N}H_3-CH_2-\overset{\displaystyle O}{\overset{\|}{C}}-NH-\overset{\displaystyle CH_3}{\underset{|}{CH}}-\overset{\displaystyle O}{\overset{\|}{C}}-O^- + H_2O \longrightarrow$

    $\overset{+}{N}H_3-CH_2-\overset{\displaystyle O}{\overset{\|}{C}}-O^- + \overset{+}{N}H_3-\overset{\displaystyle CH_3}{\underset{|}{CH}}-\overset{\displaystyle O}{\overset{\|}{C}}-O^-$

    c. $CH_3-CH=CH-CH_3 + H_2O \longrightarrow$

    $CH_3-CH_2-\overset{\displaystyle OH}{\underset{|}{CH}}-CH_3$

20.88 What is the class of the enzyme that would catalyze each of the following reactions?

    a. $CH_3-\overset{\displaystyle O}{\overset{\|}{C}}-\overset{\displaystyle O}{\overset{\|}{C}}-OH \longrightarrow$

    $CH_3-\overset{\displaystyle O}{\overset{\|}{C}}-OH + CO_2$

    b. $CH_3-\overset{\displaystyle O}{\overset{\|}{C}}-\overset{\displaystyle O}{\overset{\|}{C}}-OH + CO_2 + ATP \longrightarrow$

    $HO-\overset{\displaystyle O}{\overset{\|}{C}}-CH_2-\overset{\displaystyle O}{\overset{\|}{C}}-\overset{\displaystyle O}{\overset{\|}{C}}-OH + ADP + P_i$

    c. glucose-6-phosphate $\longrightarrow$ fructose-6-phosphate

ANSWERS

ANSWERS TO STUDY CHECKS

20.1 hydrolase

20.2 In the lock-and-key model, the shape of a substrate fits the shape of the active site exactly. In the induced-fit model, the substrate and the active site adjust shape to provide the best fit.

20.3 At a pH lower than the optimum pH, denaturation will decrease the activity of urease.

20.4 Pepsin hydrolyzes proteins in the foods we ingest. It is synthesized as a zymogen, pepsinogen, to prevent its digestion of the proteins that make up the organs in the body.

20.5 vitamin B_6

20.6 Water-soluble vitamins are easily destroyed by heat.

ANSWERS TO SELECTED QUESTIONS AND PROBLEMS

20.1 Chemical reactions can occur without enzymes, but the rates are too slow. Catalyzed reactions, which are many times faster, provide the amounts of products needed by the cell at a particular time.

20.3 **a.** oxidation–reduction
    b. transfer of a group from one substance to another
    c. hydrolysis (splitting) of molecules with the addition of water

20.5 **a.** hydrolase   **b.** oxidoreductase
    c. isomerase   **d.** transferase

20.7 **a.** lyase   **b.** transferase

20.9 **a.** succinate oxidase
    b. fumarate hydrase
    c. alcohol dehydrogenase

20.11 **a.** enzyme (2)
    b. enzyme–substrate complex (1)
    c. substrate (3)

20.13 **a.** $E + S \rightleftharpoons ES \longrightarrow E + P$
    b. The active site is a region or pocket within the tertiary structure of an enzyme that accepts the substrate, aligns the substrate for reaction, and catalyzes the reaction.

20.15 Isoenzymes are slightly different forms of an enzyme that catalyze the same reaction in different organs and tissues of the body.

20.17 A doctor might run tests for the enzymes CK, LDH, and AST to determine if the patient had a heart attack.

20.19 **a.** The rate would decrease.
    b. The rate would decrease.
    c. The rate would decrease.
    d. The rate increases as long as there is free substrate to react.

20.21 pepsin, pH 2; sucrase, pH 6; trypsin, pH 8

20.23 **a.** (1) competitive, (2) reversible
    b. (1) noncompetitive, (2) may be either
    c. (1) competitive, (2) reversible
    d. (1) noncompetitive, (2) may be either
    e. (1) competitive, (2) reversible

20.25 a. methanol, CH_3-OH; ethanol, CH_3-CH_2-OH
b. Ethanol has a similar structure to methanol and could compete for the active site.
c. Ethanol is a competitive inhibitor of methanol oxidation.

20.27 Enzymes that act on proteins are proteases and would digest the proteins of the organ where they are produced if they were active immediately upon synthesis.

20.29 In feedback control, the product binds to the first enzyme in a series and changes the shape of the active site. If the active site can no longer bind the substrate effectively, the reaction will stop.

20.31 When a regulator molecule binds to an allosteric site, the shape of the enzyme is altered, which makes the active site more reactive or less reactive and thereby increases or decreases the rate of the reaction.

20.33 a. (3) negative regulator
b. (4) allosteric enzyme
c. (1) zymogen

20.35 a. an enzyme that requires a cofactor
b. an enzyme that requires a cofactor
c. a simple enzyme

20.37 a. THF
b. NAD^+

20.39 a. pantothenic acid (vitamin B_5)
b. folic acid
c. niacin (vitamin B_3)

20.41 a. vitamin D or cholecalciferol
b. ascorbic acid or vitamin C
c. niacin or vitamin B_3

20.43 Vitamin B_6 is a water-soluble vitamin, which means that each day any excess of vitamin B_6 is eliminated from the body.

20.45 The side chain $-CH_2OH$ on the ring is oxidized to $-CHO$, and the other $-CH_2OH$ forms a phosphate ester.

20.47 a. oxidoreductase
b. Ethanol would act as a competitive inhibitor of ethylene glycol, saturate the alcohol dehydrogenase enzyme, and allow ethylene glycol to be removed from the body without producing oxalic acid.

20.49 a. Fresh pineapple contains an enzyme that breaks down protein, which means that the gelatin dessert would not turn solid. The high temperatures used to prepare canned pineapple denature the enzyme so it no longer can break down protein.
b. The enzyme in fresh pineapple juice can be used to tenderize tough meat because the enzyme breaks down proteins.

20.51 The many different reactions that take place in cells require different enzymes because enzymes react with only a certain type of substrate.

20.53 Enzymes are catalysts that are proteins and function only at mild temperature and pH. Catalysts used in chemistry laboratories are usually inorganic materials that can function at high temperatures and in strongly acidic or basic conditions.

20.55 a. S   **b.** E   **c.** E   **d.** E   **e.** S   **f.** E

20.57 a. urea   **b.** lactose
c. aspartate   **d.** phenylalanine

20.59 a. transferase   **b.** oxidoreductase
c. hydrolase   **d.** lyase

20.61 Sucrose fits the shape of the active site in sucrase, but lactose does not.

20.63 A heart attack may be the cause.

20.65 a. saturated   **b.** unsaturated

20.67 In reversible inhibition, the inhibitor can dissociate from the enzyme, whereas in irreversible inhibition, the inhibitor forms a strong covalent bond with the enzyme and does not dissociate. Irreversible inhibitors act as poisons to enzymes.

20.69 a. Antibiotics such as amoxicillin are irreversible inhibitors.
b. Antibiotics inhibit enzymes needed to form cell walls in bacteria, not humans.

20.71 a. When pepsinogen enters the stomach, the low pH cleaves a peptide from its protein chain to form pepsin.
b. An active protease would digest the proteins of the stomach rather than the proteins in foods.

20.73 An allosteric enzyme contains sites for regulators that alter the enzyme and speed up or slow down the rate of the catalyzed reaction.

20.75 This would be feedback control because the end product of the reaction pathway binds to the enzyme to decrease or stop the first reaction in the reaction pathway.

20.77 a. requires a cofactor
b. simple enzyme
c. requires a cofactor (coenzyme)

20.79 a. (3) coenzyme A
b. (1) NAD^+
c. (2) TPP

20.81 A vitamin combines with an enzyme only when the enzyme and coenzyme are needed to catalyze a reaction. When the enzyme is not needed, the vitamin dissociates for use by other enzymes in the cell.

20.83 a. niacin, (3) pellagra
b. vitamin A, (1) night blindness
c. vitamin D, (2) weak bone structure

20.85 a. The reactant is lactose and the products are glucose and galactose.
b.

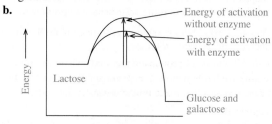

c. By lowering the energy of activation, the enzyme furnishes a lower energy pathway by which the reaction can take place.

20.87 a. oxidoreductase
b. hydrolase
c. lyase

COMBINING IDEAS FROM CHAPTERS 16 TO 20

CI.31 The plastic known as PETE (**poly**ethylene**te**rephthalate) is used to make plastic soft drink bottles and containers for salad dressings, shampoos, and dishwashing liquids. Today, PETE is the most widely recycled of all the plastics. PETE is a polymer of terephthalic acid and ethylene glycol. In a single year, 1.7 billion (10^9) pounds of PETE are recycled. After PETE is separated from other plastics, it can be used in polyester fabric, fill for sleeping bags, doormats, and tennis ball containers. The density of PETE is 1.38 g/mL.

Terephthalic acid   Ethylene glycol

a. Draw the condensed structural formula of the ester formed from one molecule of terephthalic acid and one molecule of ethylene glycol.
b. Draw the condensed structural formula of the product formed when a second molecule of ethylene glycol reacts with the ester you drew for the answer in part **a**.
c. How many kilograms of PETE are recycled in 1 year?
d. What volume, in liters, of PETE is recycled in 1 year?
e. Suppose a landfill with an area of a football field and a depth of 5.0 m holds 2.7×10^7 L of recycled PETE. If all of the PETE that is recycled in a year were placed instead in landfills, how many would it fill?

CI.32 Using the Internet or a reference book such as the *Merck Index* or *Physicians' Desk Reference*, look up the structural formulas of the following medicinal drugs and list the functional groups in the compounds. You may need to refer to the cross-index of names at the back of the reference book.
a. baclofen, a muscle relaxant
b. anethole, a licorice flavoring agent in anise and fennel
c. alibendol, an antispasmodic drug
d. pargyline, an antihypertensive drug
e. naproxen, nonsteroid anti-inflammatory drug

CI.33 The insect repellent DEET is an amide that can be made from 3-methylbenzoic acid and diethylamine. A 6.0-fl-oz can of DEET repellent contains 25% DEET by mass (1 qt = 32 fluid ounces). Assume that the density of DEET solution in a can is 1.0 g/mL.
a. Draw the condensed structural formulas for the reaction that forms DEET.
b. What are the molecular formulas of 3-methylbenzoic acid, diethylamine, and DEET?

c. What are the molar masses of 3-methylbenzoic acid, diethylamine, and DEET?
d. How many grams of DEET are in one spray can?
e. How many molecules of DEET are in one spray can?
f. If 10.0 g of 3-methylbenzoic acid and 10.0 g of diethylamine react and 12.5 g of DEET are produced, what is the percent yield for the reaction?

CI.34 Glyceryl trimyristate (trimyristin) is found in the seeds of the nutmeg (*Myristica fragrans*). The oil known as nutmeg butter contains 75% trimyristin. Ground nutmeg, which is sweet, is used to flavor many foods. It is used as a lubricant and fragrance in soaps and shaving creams. Isopropyl myristate is used to increase absorption of skin creams. Draw the condensed structural formula for each of the following:

a. myristic acid
b. glyceryl trimyristate (trimyristin)
c. isopropyl myristate
d. products of the hydrolysis of glyceryl trimyristate with an acid catalyst
e. products of the saponification of glyceryl trimyristate with KOH
f. reactant and product for oxidation of myristyl alcohol to myristic acid

CI.35 Hyaluronic acid (HA), a polymer of about 25 000 disaccharide units, is a natural component of eye and joint fluid as well as of skin and cartilage. Due to the ability of HA to absorb water, it is used in skin care products and injections to smooth wrinkles and for treatment of arthritis. The repeating disaccharide units in HA consist of D-gluconic acid and D-acetylglucosamine.

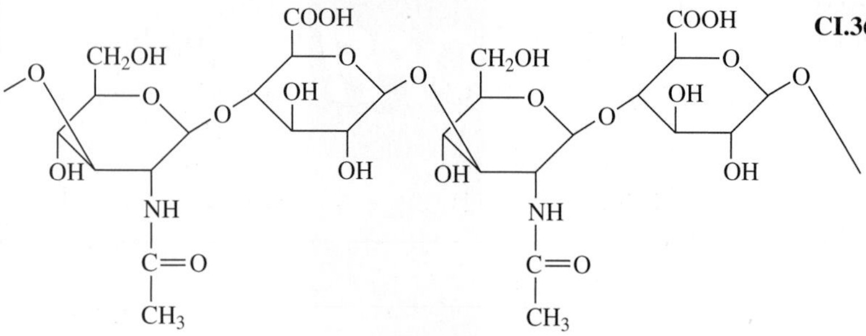

D-Acetylglucosamine is an amide derived from acetic acid and D-glucosamine, in which an amino group ($-NH_2$) replaces the hydroxyl on carbon 2 of D-glucose. Another natural polymer called chitin is found in the shells of lobsters and crabs. Chitin is made of repeating units of D-acetylglucosamine connected by β-1,4-glycosidic bonds.

a. Draw the Haworth structures for the oxidation reaction of the hydroxyl group on carbon 6 in β-D-glucose to form β-gluconic acid.
b. Draw the Haworth structure of β-D-glucosamine.
c. Draw the Haworth structure for the amide product of D-glucosamine and acetic acid.

d. What are the two types of glycosidic bonds that link the monosaccharides?
e. Draw the structure of a section of chitin with three β-D-acetylglucosamine units linked by β-1,4–glycosidic bonds.

CI.36 In response to signals from the nervous system, the hypothalamus secretes a polypeptide hormone known as gonadotropin-releasing factor (GnRF), which stimulates the pituitary gland to release other hormones into the bloodstream. Two of the hormones are known as gonadotropins, which are luteinizing hormone (LH), and follicle-stimulating hormone (FSH). GnRF is a decapeptide with the following primary structure: Glu—His—Tyr—Ser—Tyr—Gly—Leu—Arg—Pro—Gly.

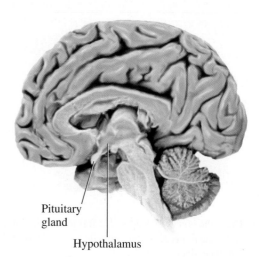

Pituitary gland

Hypothalamus

a. What is the N terminal amino acid?
b. What is the C terminal amino acid?
c. Which amino acids are nonpolar or polar neutral?
d. Write the condensed structural formulas of the acidic or basic amino acids at physiological pH.
e. Write the primary structure of the first three amino acids starting from the N terminal amino acid at physiological pH.
f. When the level of LH or FSH is high in the bloodstream, the hypothalamus stops secreting GnRF. What type of regulation of proteins does this represent?

■ ANSWERS

CI.31 a. 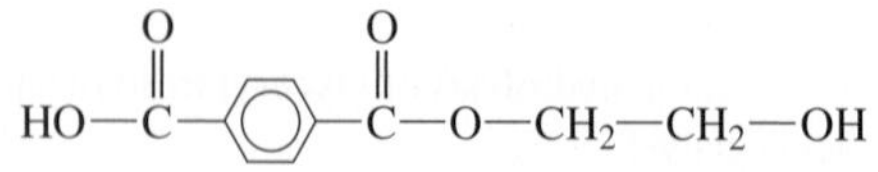 $HO-\overset{O}{\underset{\|}{C}}-\langle\text{benzene}\rangle-\overset{O}{\underset{\|}{C}}-O-CH_2-CH_2-OH$

b. 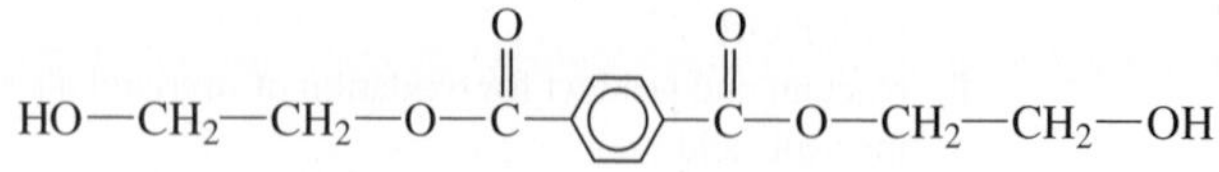 $HO-CH_2-CH_2-O-\overset{O}{\underset{\|}{C}}-\langle\text{benzene}\rangle-\overset{O}{\underset{\|}{C}}-O-CH_2-CH_2-OH$

c. 7.7×10^8 kg of PETE
d. 5.6×10^8 L of PETE
e. 21 landfills

CI.33 a. 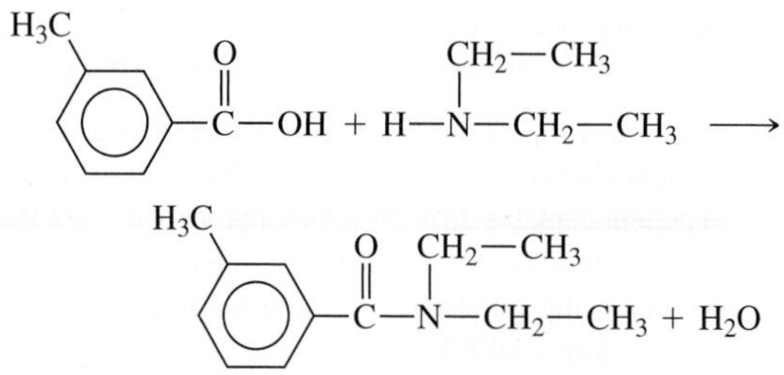 3-methylbenzoic acid + diethylamine reaction:

$H_3C-\langle\text{benzene}\rangle-\overset{O}{\underset{\|}{C}}-OH + H-\overset{CH_2-CH_3}{\underset{|}{N}}-CH_2-CH_3 \longrightarrow$

$H_3C-\langle\text{benzene}\rangle-\overset{O}{\underset{\|}{C}}-\overset{CH_2-CH_3}{\underset{|}{N}}-CH_2-CH_3 + H_2O$

b. $C_8H_8O_2$ (3-methylbenzoic acid), $C_4H_{11}N$ (diethylamine), $C_{12}H_{17}NO$ (DEET)

c. 136 g/mole (3-methylbenzoic acid), 73.0 g/mole
   (diethylamine), 191 g/mole (DEET)

d. 44 g of DEET

e. 1.4×10^{23} molecules

f. 89.3% yield of DEET

CI.35 a.

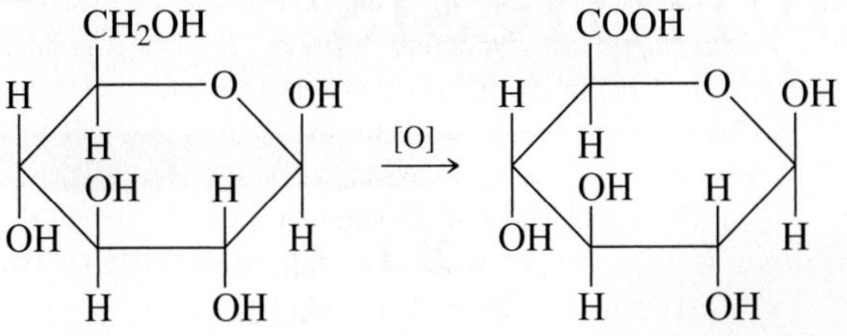

CH$_2$OH ... O, OH ... H ... OH ... H ... OH ... H ... OH ... H ... OH $\xrightarrow{[O]}$ COOH ... O, OH ... H ... OH ... H ... OH ... H ... OH ... H ... OH

b.

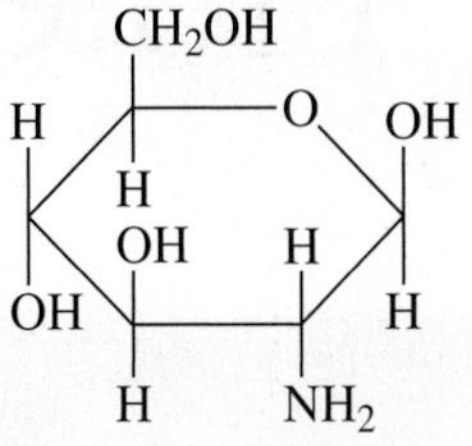

CH$_2$OH ... O, OH ... H ... OH ... H ... OH ... H ... NH$_2$

c.

CH$_2$OH ... O, OH ... H ... OH ... H ... OH ... H ... NH ... C=O ... CH$_3$

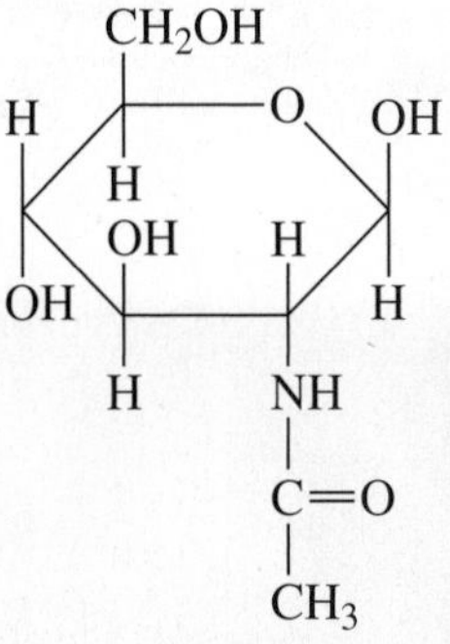

d. They are β-1,4- and β-1,3-glycosidic bonds.

e.

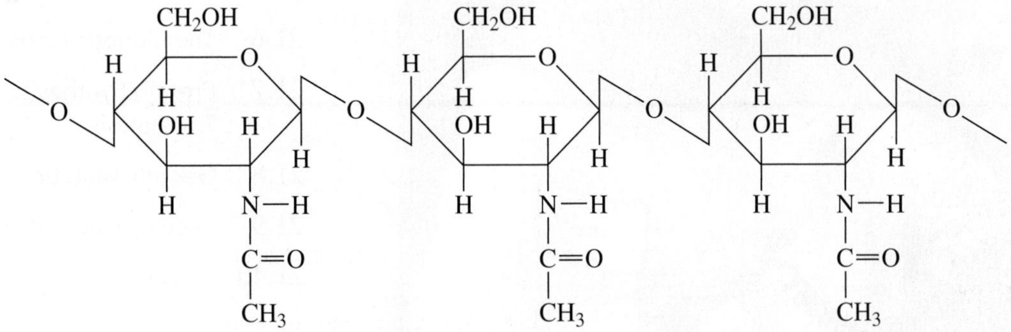

(repeating structure) CH$_2$OH ... O ... H ... OH ... H ... H ... N—H ... C=O ... CH$_3$ (three units linked by O glycosidic bonds)

21 Nucleic Acids and Protein Synthesis

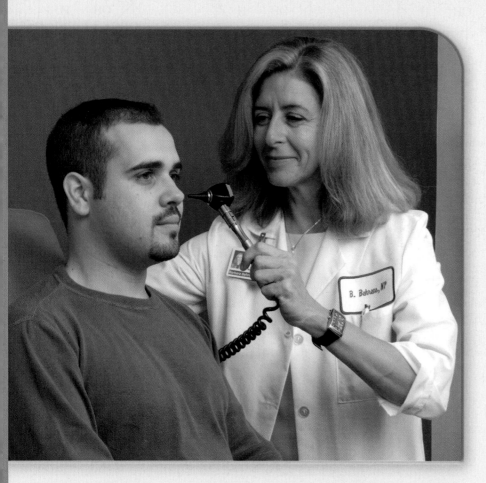

"I run the Hepatitis C Clinic, where patients are often anxious when diagnosed," says Barbara Behrens, nurse practitioner, Hepatitis C Clinic, Kaiser Hospital. "The treatment for hepatitis C can produce significant reactions such as a radical drop in blood count. When this happens, I get help to them within 24 hours. I monitor our patients very closely, and many call me whenever they need to."

Hepatitis C is an RNA virus, or retrovirus, that causes liver inflammation, often resulting in chronic liver disease. Unlike many viruses to which we eventually develop immunity, the hepatitis C virus undergoes mutations so rapidly that scientists have not been able to produce vaccines. People who carry the virus are contagious throughout their lives and are able to pass the virus to other people.

Mastering**CHEMISTRY**™

Visit **www.masteringchemistry.com** for self-study materials and instructor-assigned homework.

Nucleic acids are large molecules found in the nuclei of cells that store information and direct activities for cellular growth and reproduction. Deoxyribonucleic acid (DNA), the genetic material in the nucleus of a cell, contains all the information needed for the development of a complete living organism. The way you grow, your hair, your eyes, your physical appearance, and all the activities of all the cells in your body are determined by a set of directions contained within the DNA of your cells.

All of the genetic information in the cell is called the *genome*. Every time a cell divides, the information in the genome is copied and passed on to the new cells. This replication process must duplicate the genetic instructions exactly. Some sections of DNA called *genes* contain the information to make a particular protein.

As a cell requires protein, another type of nucleic acid, ribonucleic acid (RNA), translates the genetic information in DNA and carries that information to the ribosomes, where the synthesis of protein takes place. However, mistakes may occur that lead to mutations that affect the synthesis of a certain protein.

21.1 | Components of Nucleic Acids

There are two closely related types of nucleic acids: *deoxyribonucleic acid* (**DNA**) and *ribonucleic acid* (**RNA**). Both are unbranched polymers of repeating monomer units known as *nucleotides*. A DNA molecule may contain several million nucleotides; smaller RNA molecules may contain up to several thousand. Each nucleotide has three components: a base, a five-carbon sugar, and a phosphate group. When —PO_3^{2-} is part of a larger molecule, it is called a *phosphoryl group*. (See Figure 21.1.)

LEARNING GOAL

Describe the bases and ribose sugars that make up the nucleic acids DNA and RNA.

Bases

The **bases** in nucleic acids are derivatives of *pyrimidine* or *purine*:

Pyrimidine   Purine

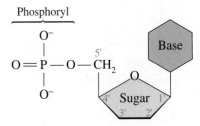

FIGURE 21.1 A diagram of the general structure of a nucleotide found in nucleic acids.

Q In a nucleotide, what types of groups are bonded to a five-carbon sugar?

In DNA, the purine bases with double rings are adenine (A) and guanine (G), and the pyrimidine bases with single rings are cytosine (C) and thymine (T). In RNA, thymine (5-methyluracil) is replaced by uracil (U); adenine (A), guanine (G), and cytosine (C) are the same as in DNA. (See Figure 21.2.)

FIGURE 21.2 DNA contains the bases A, G, C, and T; RNA contains A, G, C, and U.

Q Which bases are found in DNA?

Pyrimidines

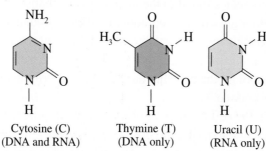

Cytosine (C)   Thymine (T)   Uracil (U)
(DNA and RNA)   (DNA only)   (RNA only)

TUTORIAL
Nucleic Acid Building Blocks

Purines

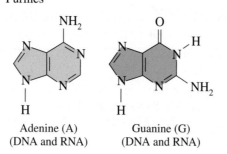

Adenine (A)   Guanine (G)
(DNA and RNA)   (DNA and RNA)

Ribose and Deoxyribose Sugars

In RNA, the five-carbon sugar is *ribose*, which gives the letter R in the abbreviation RNA. The atoms in the pentose sugars are numbered with primes (1′, 2′, 3′, 4′, and 5′) to differentiate them from the atoms in the bases. In DNA, the five-carbon sugar is *deoxyribose*, which is similar to ribose except that there is no hydroxyl group (—OH) on C2′. The *deoxy* prefix means "without oxygen" and provides the D in DNA.

Ribose in RNA

Deoxyribose in DNA

No oxygen is bonded to this carbon

CONCEPT CHECK 21.1

■ **Components of Nucleic Acids**

Identify each of the following bases as a purine or pyrimidine. Indicate if each base is found in RNA, DNA, or both.

a.   **b.**

ANSWER
a. Guanine is a purine found in both RNA and DNA.
b. Uracil is a pyrimidine found only in RNA.

Nucleosides and Nucleotides

A **nucleoside** is produced when a pyrimidine or a purine forms a glycosidic bond to C1′ of a sugar, either ribose or deoxyribose. For example, adenine, a purine, and ribose form a nucleoside called aden**osine**:

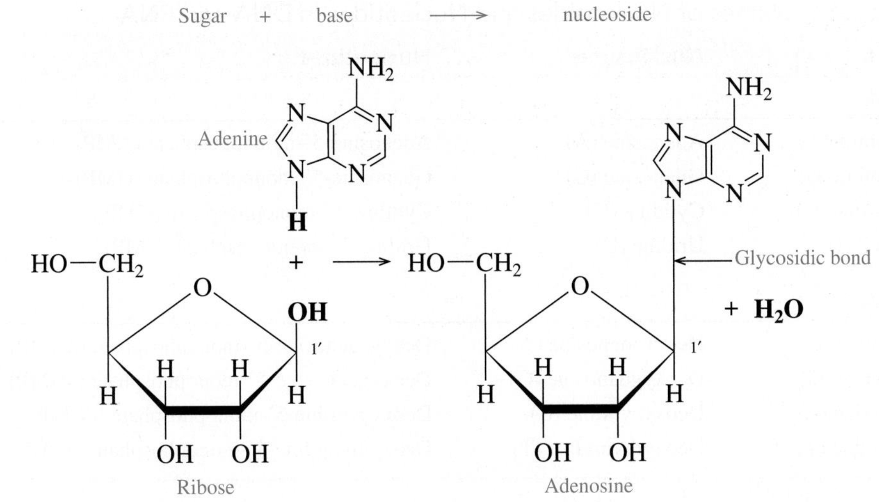

Sugar + base ⟶ nucleoside

Ribose   Adenosine

Nucleotides are formed when the C5′—OH group of ribose or deoxyribose in a nucleoside forms a phosphate ester. Other hydroxyl groups on ribose can also form phosphate esters, but only the 5′-monophosphate nucleotides are found in RNA and DNA. All the nucleotides in RNA and DNA are shown in Figure 21.3.

Naming Nucleosides and Nucleotides

The name of a nucleoside that contains a purine ends with *osine*, whereas a nucleoside that contains a pyrimidine ends with *idine*. The names of nucleosides of DNA add *deoxy* to the beginning of their names. The corresponding nucleotides in RNA and DNA are named by adding *5′-monophosphate*. Although the letters A, G, C, U, and T represent the bases, they are often used in the abbreviations of the respective nucleosides and nucleotides. The

Adenosine-5'-monophosphate (AMP)
Deoxyadenosine-5'-monophosphate (dAMP)

Guanosine-5'-monophosphate (GMP)
Deoxyguanosine-5'-monophosphate (dGMP)

Cytidine-5'-monophosphate (CMP)
Deoxycytidine-5'-monophosphate (dCMP)

Uridine-5'-monophosphate (UMP)

Deoxythymidine-5'-monophosphate (dTMP)

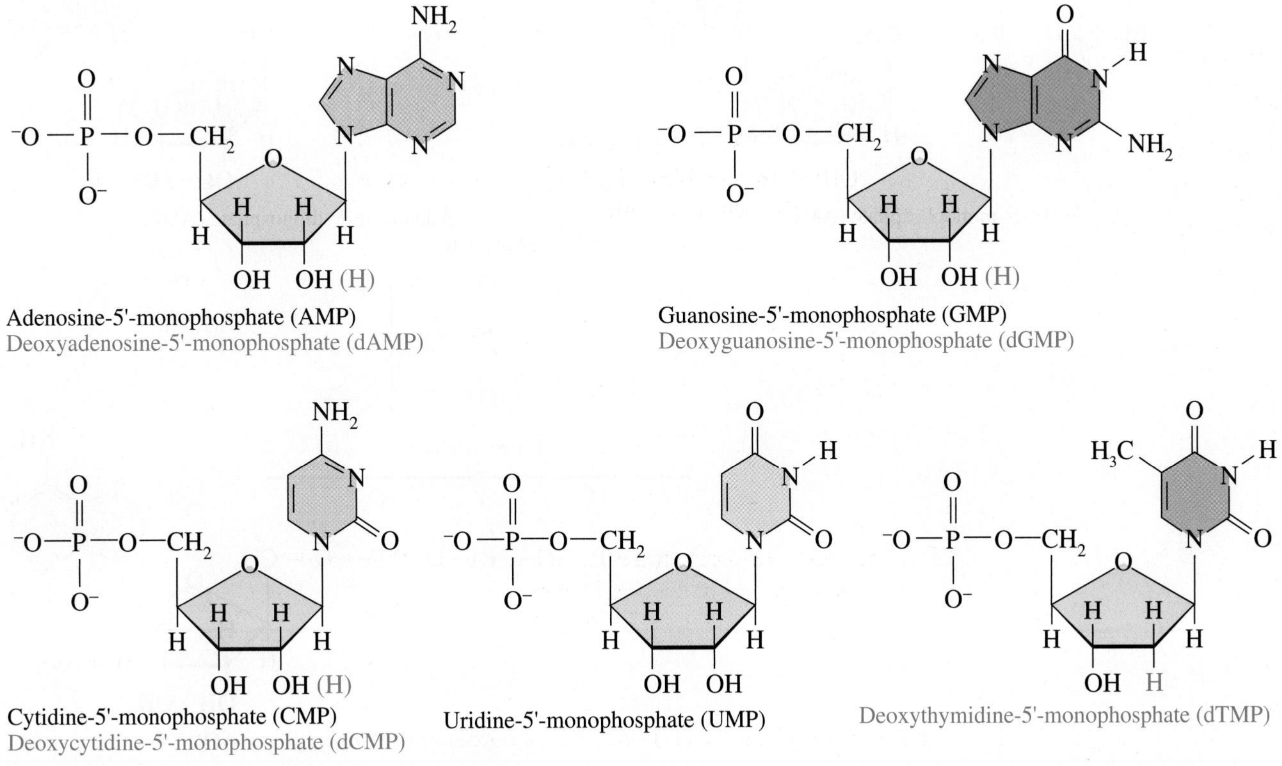

FIGURE 21.3 The nucleotides of RNA are similar to those of DNA, except in DNA (shown in magenta) the sugar is deoxyribose and deoxythymidine replaces uridine.

Q What are two differences in the nucleotides of RNA and DNA?

TABLE 21.1 Names of Nucleosides and Nucleotides in DNA and RNA

Base	Nucleosides	Nucleotides
RNA		
Adenine (A)	Adenosine (A)	Adenosine-5′-monophosphate (AMP)
Guanine (G)	Guanosine (G)	Guanosine-5′-monophosphate (GMP)
Cytosine (C)	Cytidine (C)	Cytidine-5′-monophosphate (CMP)
Uracil (U)	Uridine (U)	Uridine-5′-monophosphate (UMP)
DNA		
Adenine (A)	Deoxyadenosine (A)	Deoxyadenosine-5′-monophosphate (dAMP)
Guanine (G)	Deoxyguanosine (G)	Deoxyguanosine-5′-monophosphate (dGMP)
Cytosine (C)	Deoxycytidine (C)	Deoxycytidine-5′-monophosphate (dCMP)
Thymine (T)	Deoxythymidine (T)	Deoxythymidine-5′-monophosphate (dTMP)

names of the bases, nucleosides, and nucleotides in DNA and RNA and their abbreviations are listed in Table 21.1.

Formation of Nucleoside Di- and Triphosphates

The phosphoryl in any nucleoside 5′-monophosphate can bond to one or two additional phosphate groups to form di- and triphosphates. For example, adding one phosphate to AMP gives ADP (*adenosine-5′-diphosphate*). Adding another phosphate to ADP gives ATP (*adenosine-5′-triphosphate*). (See Figure 21.4.) Of the triphosphates, ATP is of particular

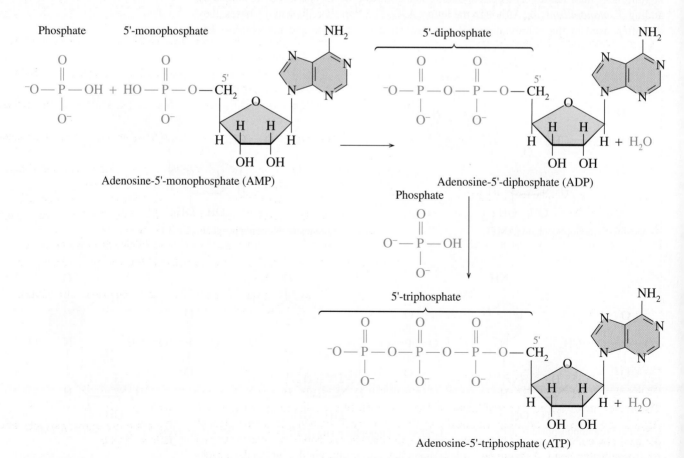

FIGURE 21.4 The addition of one or two phosphate groups to AMP forms adenosine-5′-diphosphate (ADP) and adenosine-5′-triphosphate (ATP).

Q How does the structure of deoxyguanosine triphosphate (dGTP) differ from ATP?

interest because it is the major source of energy for most energy-requiring activities in the cell. In other examples, phosphate is added to GMP to yield GDP and GTP, and to dCMP to form dCDP and dCTP. GTP is an energy source for protein synthesis, and CTP is an intermediate in phospholipid synthesis.

SAMPLE PROBLEM **21.1**

■ Nucleotides

For each of the following nucleotides, identify the components and whether the nucleotide is found in DNA, RNA, or both:

a. deoxyguanosine-5′-monophosphate (dGMP)
b. adenosine-5′-monophosphate (AMP)

SOLUTION

a. This nucleotide of deoxyribose, guanine, and a phosphoryl group is found in DNA.
b. This nucleotide of ribose, adenine, and a phosphoryl group is found in RNA.

STUDY CHECK

What is the name and abbreviation of the DNA nucleotide of cytosine?

QUESTIONS AND PROBLEMS

Components of Nucleic Acids

21.1 Identify each of the following bases as a purine or pyrimidine:
a. thymine
b.

NH$_2$

N

O

H

21.2 Identify each of the following bases as a purine or pyrimidine:
a. guanine
b.

NH$_2$

N

N

N

N

H

21.3 Identify the bases in problem 21.1 as components of RNA, DNA, or both.

21.4 Identify the bases in problem 21.2 as components of RNA, DNA, or both.

21.5 What are the names and abbreviations of the four nucleotides in DNA?

21.6 What are the names and abbreviations of the four nucleotides in RNA?

21.7 Identify each of the following as a nucleoside or nucleotide:
a. adenosine
b. deoxycytidine
c. uridine
d. cytidine-5′-monophosphate

21.8 Identify each of the following as a nucleoside or nucleotide:
a. deoxythymidine
b. guanosine
c. adenosine
d. uridine-5′-monophosphate

21.9 Draw the structure of deoxyadenosine-5′-monophosphate (dAMP).

21.10 Draw the structure of uridine-5′-monophosphate (UMP).

21.2 Primary Structure of Nucleic Acids

The **nucleic acids** are polymers of many nucleotides in which the 3′-hydroxyl group of the sugar in one nucleotide bonds to the phosphoryl group on the 5′-carbon atom in the sugar of the next nucleotide. This link between the sugars in adjacent nucleotides is referred to as a **phosphodiester bond**. As more nucleotides are added using phosphodiester bonds, a backbone forms that consists of alternating sugar and phosphate groups. The bases, which are attached to each sugar, extend out from the sugar-phosphate backbone. Each nucleic acid has its own unique sequence of bases, which is known as its **primary structure**.

LEARNING GOAL

Describe the primary structures of RNA and DNA.

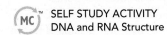

SELF STUDY ACTIVITY
DNA and RNA Structure

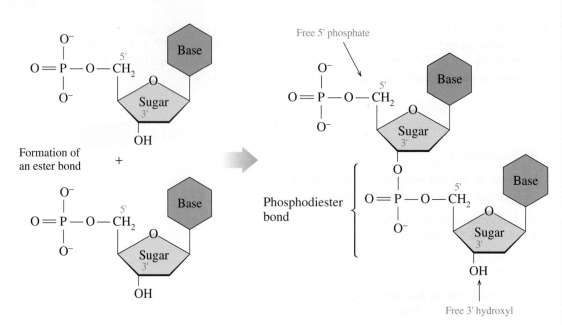

In any nucleic acid, the sugar at one end has an unreacted, or free, 5′-phosphate terminal end, and the sugar at the other end has a free 3′-hydroxyl group. A nucleic acid sequence is read from the sugar with the free 5′-phosphate to the sugar with the free 3′-hydroxyl group. The order of nucleotides is often written using only the letters of the bases. For example, the nucleotide sequence starting with adenine (free 5′-phosphate end) in the section of RNA shown in Figure 21.5 is 5′—A—C—G—U—3′.

RNA (ribonucleic acid)

FIGURE 21.5 In the primary structure of an RNA, A, C, G, and U are linked by 3′–5′ phosphodiester bonds.

Q Where are the free 5′-phosphate and 3′-hydroxyl groups of ribose?

SAMPLE PROBLEM 21.2

■ **Bonding of Nucleotides**

Draw the structure of an RNA dinucleotide formed by two CMP.

SOLUTION

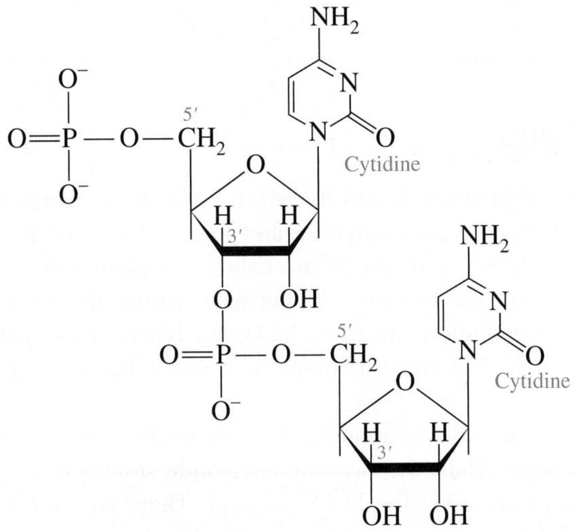

STUDY CHECK

In the dinucleotide of cytidine shown in the solution to Sample Problem 21.2, identify the free 5′-phosphate group and the free 3′-hydroxyl (—OH) group.

QUESTIONS AND PROBLEMS

Primary Structure of Nucleic Acids

21.11 How are the nucleotides held together in a nucleic acid chain?

21.12 How do the ends of a nucleic acid polymer differ?

21.13 Write the structure of the dinucleotide GC that would be in RNA.

21.14 Write the structure of the dinucleotide AT that would be in DNA.

21.3 DNA Double Helix

During the 1940s, biologists determined that DNA in a variety of organisms had a specific relationship between bases: the amount of adenine (A) was equal to the amount of thymine (T), and the amount of guanine (G) was equal to the amount of cytosine (C). Eventually, biologists determined that adenine is always paired (1:1) with thymine, and guanine is always paired (1:1) with cytosine. (See Table 21.2.) This relationship, known as *Chargaff's rules*, can be summarized as follows:

Number of purine molecules = Number of pyrimidine molecules

$$A = T$$
$$G = C$$

In 1953, James Watson and Francis Crick proposed that DNA was a **double helix** that consists of two polynucleotide strands winding about each other like a spiral staircase. (See Figure 21.6.) The sugar-phosphate backbones are analogous to the outside railings with the bases arranged like steps along the inside. One strand goes in the 5′–3′ direction, and the other strand goes in the 3′–5′ direction.

LEARNING GOAL

Describe the double helix of DNA.

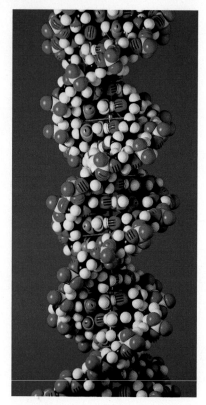

FIGURE 21.6 This space-filling model shows the double helix that is the characteristic shape of DNA molecules.

Q What is meant by the term *double helix*?

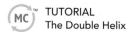 TUTORIAL
The Double Helix

TABLE 21.2 Percentages of Bases in the DNAs of Selected Organisms

Organism	%A	%T	%G	%C
Human	30	30	20	20
Chicken	28	28	22	22
Salmon	28	28	22	22
Corn (maize)	27	27	23	23
Neurospora	23	23	27	27

Complementary Base Pairs

Each of the bases along a polynucleotide strand forms hydrogen bonds to a specific base on the opposite DNA strand. Adenine bonds only to thymine and guanine bonds only to cytosine. (See Figure 21.7.) The pairs A—T and G—C are called **complementary base pairs**. The specific pairing of the bases occurs because adenine and thymine form only two hydrogen bonds, while cytosine and guanine form three hydrogen bonds. This specific pairing of the bases explains why DNA has equal amounts of A and T bases and equal amounts of G and C.

Since each base pair contains a purine and a pyrimidine, the total width of the two pairs of bases A—T and G—C is the same. Thus, the two polynucleotide strands of a DNA molecule are the same distance apart all along the DNA polymer. There are no C—T, C—A, G—T, or G—A pairs in DNA because such base-pair combinations cannot form as many hydrogen bonds or maintain a constant distance between the two DNA backbones. (See Figure 21.8.)

SAMPLE PROBLEM   21.3

■ Complementary Base Pairs

Write the complementary base sequence for the following segment of a strand of DNA:

    5′—A—C—G—A—T—C—T—3′

SOLUTION

In the complementary segment of DNA, A pairs with T, and G pairs with C:

    Given segment of DNA: 5′—A—C—G—A—T—C—T—3′
                             :   :   :   :   :   :   :
    Complementary segment: 3′—T—G—C—T—A—G—A—5′

STUDY CHECK

What sequence of bases is complementary to a DNA segment with the base sequence of 5′—G—G—T—T—A—A—C—C—3′?

QUESTIONS AND PROBLEMS

DNA Double Helix

21.15 How are the two strands of nucleic acid in DNA held together?

21.16 What is meant by complementary base pairing?

21.17 Write the base sequence in a new DNA segment if the original segment has the following base sequence:
   a. 5′—A—A—A—A—A—A—3′
   b. 5′—G—G—G—G—G—G—3′
   c. 5′—A—G—T—C—C—A—G—G—T—3′
   d. 5′—C—T—G—T—A—T—A—C—G—T—T—A—3′

21.18 Write the base sequence in a new DNA segment if the original segment has the following base sequence:
   a. 5′—T—T—T—T—T—T—3′
   b. 5′—C—C—C—C—C—C—C—C—C—C—3′
   c. 5′—A—T—G—G—C—A—3′
   d. 5′—A—T—A—T—G—C—G—C—T—A—A—A—3′

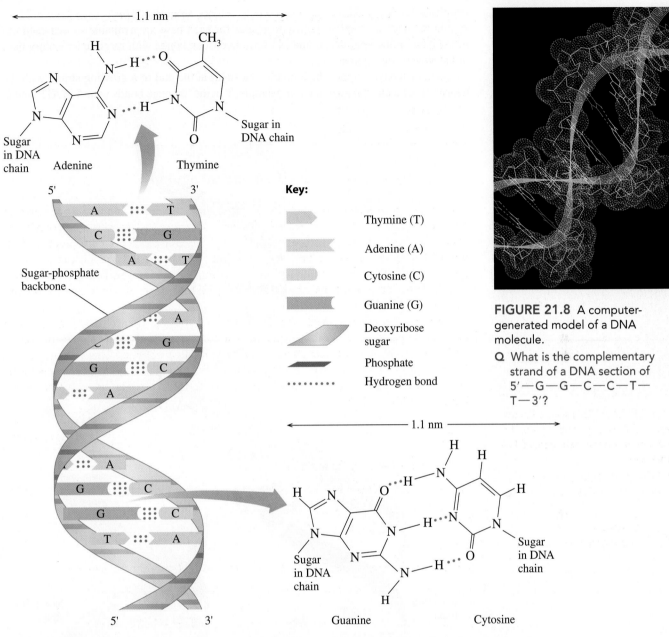

Key:

Thymine (T)

Adenine (A)

Cytosine (C)

Guanine (G)

Deoxyribose sugar

Phosphate

.... Hydrogen bond

FIGURE 21.8 A computer-generated model of a DNA molecule.

Q What is the complementary strand of a DNA section of 5'—G—G—C—C—T—T—3'?

FIGURE 21.7 Hydrogen bonds between complementary base pairs hold the polynucleotide strands together in the double helix of DNA.

Q Why are G—C base pairs more stable than A—T base pairs?

21.4 DNA Replication

DNA found in the cells of animals, plants, and bacteria is chemically similar and has the same function, which is to preserve genetic information. As cells divide, copies of DNA are produced that transfer genetic information to the new cells.

Replication and Energy

In DNA **replication**, the strands in the parent DNA molecule separate, which allows the synthesis of complementary strands of DNA. The replication process begins when an enzyme called *helicase* catalyzes the unwinding of a portion of the double helix by breaking the hydrogen bonds between the complementary bases. These single strands now act as

LEARNING GOAL

Describe the process of DNA replication.

 TUTORIAL
DNA Replication

MC SELF STUDY ACTIVITY
DNA Replication

templates for the synthesis of new complementary strands of DNA. (See Figure 21.9.) Within the nucleus, nucleoside triphosphates for each base are available so that each exposed base on the template strand can form hydrogen bonds with its complementary base in the nucleoside triphosphate.

Each nucleoside triphosphate bonds to a sugar at the end of a growing strand with the hydrolysis of a phosphate bond. For example, T in the template bonds with A in ATP, and G

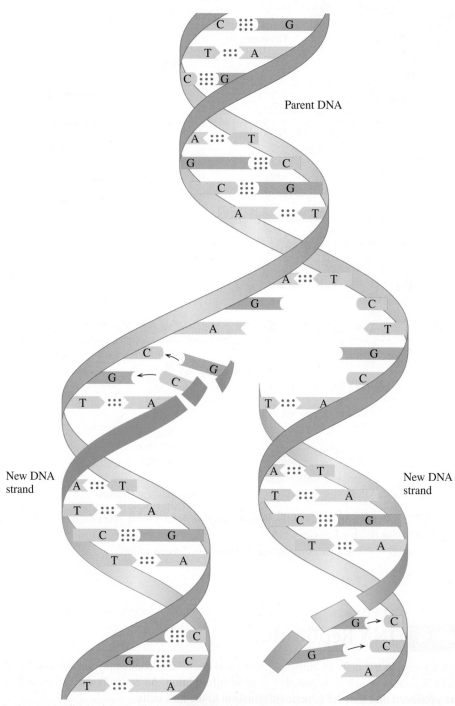

FIGURE 21.9 In DNA replication, the separate strands of the parent DNA are the templates for the synthesis of complementary strands, which produce two exact copies of DNA.

Q How many strands of the parent DNA are contained in each of the daughter DNAs?

on the template strand bonds with CTP. As the base pairs form, *DNA polymerase* catalyzes the formation of phosphodiester bonds between the nucleotides. The hydrolysis of pyrophosphate releases energy for the new bonds. In this way, energy is provided to join each new nucleotide to the backbone of a growing DNA strand. (See Figure 21.10.)

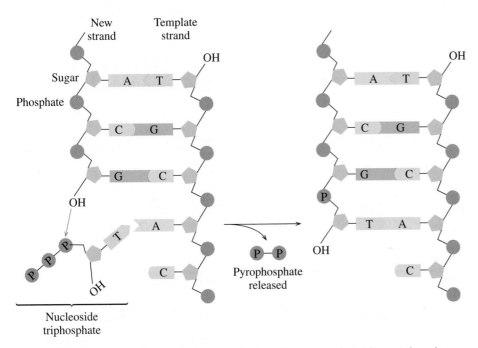

FIGURE 21.10 Energy for the formation of a bond between thymidine triphosphate and the 3′—OH of the preceding sugar is provided by the removal of two phosphates (as pyrophosphate).

Q Why are nucleoside triphosphates used to provide the complementary bases instead of nucleoside monophosphates?

CAREER FOCUS

Occupational Therapist

"Occupational therapists teach children and adults the skills they need for the job of living," says occupational therapist Leslie Wakasa. "When working with the pediatric population, we are crucial in educating children with disabilities, their families, caregivers, and school staff in ways to help them be as independent as they can be in all aspects of their daily lives. It's rewarding when you can show children how to feed themselves, which is a huge self-esteem issue for them. The opportunity to help people become more independent is very rewarding."

A combination of technology and occupational therapy helps children who are nonverbal to communicate and interact with their environment. By leaning on a red switch, Alex is learning to use a computer.

SELF STUDY ACTIVITY
DNA Replication

Eventually the entire double helix of the parent DNA is copied. In each new DNA molecule, one strand of the double helix is from the original DNA, and one is a newly synthesized strand. This process, called *semi-conservative replication*, produces two new DNAs called *daughter DNAs* that are identical to each other and exact copies of the original parent DNA. In the process of DNA replication, complementary base pairing ensures the correct placements of bases in the new DNA strands.

Direction of Replication

Now that we have seen the overall process, we can take a look at some of the details that are important in understanding DNA replication. The unwinding of DNA by *helicase* occurs simultaneously in several sections along the parent DNA molecule. As a result, *DNA polymerase* can catalyze the replication process at each of these open DNA sections called **replication forks**. However, DNA polymerase catalyzes only phosphodiester bonds between the 5′-phosphate of one nucleotide and the 3′-hydroxyl of the next, which means that DNA polymerases have to move in opposite directions along the separated strands of DNA. The new DNA strand that grows in the 5′–3′ direction, the *leading strand*, is synthesized continuously. The other new DNA, the *lagging strand*, is synthesized in the opposite direction, which is in the reverse 3′–5′ direction. In this lagging strand, short sections called **Okazaki fragments** are synthesized at the same time by several *DNA polymerases* and connected to form a continuous strand by *DNA ligases* to give a single 3′–5′ DNA strand. (See Figure 21.11.)

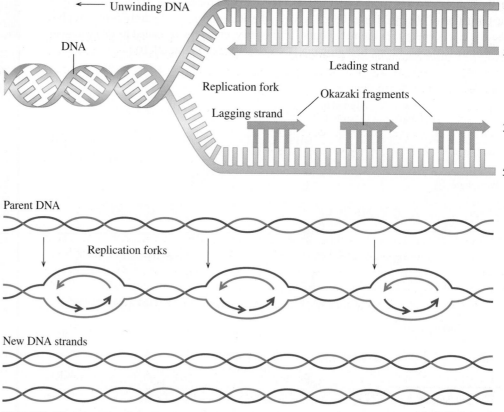

FIGURE 21.11 At each replication fork, DNA polymerase synthesizes a continuous DNA strand in the 5′ to 3′ direction. In the new 3′ to 5′ DNA strand, small Okazaki fragments are produced that are joined by DNA ligase.

Q Why is only one of the new DNA strands synthesized in a continuous direction?

CONCEPT CHECK 21.2

■ DNA Replication

In an original DNA strand, a segment has the base sequence 5′—A—G—T—3′.

a. What is the sequence of nucleotides in the daughter DNA strand that is complementary to this segment?

b. Why would the complementary sequence in the daughter DNA strand be synthesized as Okazaki fragments that require a DNA ligase?

ANSWER

a. Only one possible nucleotide can pair with each base in the original segment. Thymine will pair only with adenine, cytosine only with guanine, and adenine only with thymine to give the complementary base sequence: 3′—T—C—A—5′.

b. The DNA produced in the 3′–5′ direction, called the lagging strand, is synthesized as short sections, which are joined by DNA ligase.

QUESTIONS AND PROBLEMS

DNA Replication

21.19 What is the function of the enzyme helicase in DNA replication?

21.20 What is the function of the enzyme DNA polymerase in DNA replication?

21.21 What process ensures that the replication of DNA produces identical copies?

21.22 Why are Okazaki fragments needed in the synthesis of the lagging strand?

21.5 RNA and Transcription

Ribonucleic acid, RNA, which makes up most of the nucleic acid found in the cell, is involved with transmitting the genetic information needed to operate the cell. Similar to DNA, RNA molecules are unbranched polymers of nucleotides. However, RNA differs from DNA in several important ways:

1. The sugar in RNA is ribose rather than the deoxyribose found in DNA.
2. In RNA, the base uracil replaces thymine.
3. RNA molecules are single-stranded nucleic acids.
4. RNA molecules are much smaller than DNA molecules.

LEARNING GOAL

Identify the different types of RNA; describe the synthesis of mRNA.

Types of RNA

There are three major types of RNA in the cells: *messenger RNA*, *ribosomal RNA*, and *transfer RNA*. (See Table 21.3.) Ribosomal RNA (**rRNA**), the most abundant type of RNA, is combined with proteins in the ribosomes. Ribosomes, which are the sites within the cells where protein synthesis occurs, consist of two subunits: a large subunit and a small subunit. (See Figure 21.12.) Cells that synthesize large numbers of proteins have thousands of ribosomes.

TUTORIAL
Types of RNA

TABLE 21.3 Types of RNA Molecules in Humans

Type	Abbreviation	Percentage of Total RNA	Function in the Cell
Ribosomal RNA	rRNA	80	Major component of the ribosomes
Messenger RNA	mRNA	5	Carries information for protein synthesis from the DNA in the nucleus to the ribosomes
Transfer RNA	tRNA	15	Brings amino acids to the ribosomes for protein synthesis

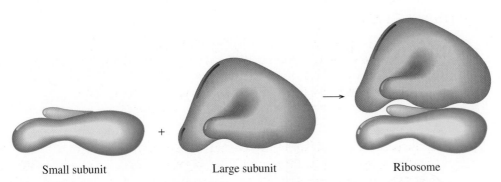

Small subunit + Large subunit → Ribosome

FIGURE 21.12 A typical prokaryotic ribosome consists of a small subunit and a large subunit.

Q Why would there be many thousands of ribosomes in a cell?

Messenger RNA (**mRNA**) carries genetic information from the DNA, located in the nucleus of the cell, to the ribosomes, located in the cytoplasm of the cell. Each gene segment of DNA produces a specific mRNA for a particular protein that is needed in the cell. The size of an mRNA depends on the number of nucleotides in that gene.

Transfer RNA (**tRNA**), the smallest of the RNA molecules, interprets the genetic information in mRNA and brings specific amino acids to the ribosome for protein synthesis. Only the tRNA molecules can translate the genetic information into amino acids for proteins. Each of the 20 amino acids has one or more different tRNA molecules. The structures of the tRNAs are similar, consisting of 70–90 nucleotides. Hydrogen bonds between some of the complementary bases in the chain produce loops that give some double-stranded regions.

Although the structure of tRNA is complex, we draw tRNA as a cloverleaf to illustrate its features. All tRNA molecules have a 3′ end with the nucleotide sequence ACC—, which is known as the *acceptor stem*. An enzyme attaches an amino acid by forming an ester bond with the free —OH of the acceptor stem. Each tRNA contains an **anticodon**, which is a series of three bases that complements three bases on an mRNA. (See Figure 21.13.)

FIGURE 21.13 (a) In the L shape of a transfer RNA, some sections of the ribose–phosphate backbone form regions of complementary base bonding. **(b)** A typical tRNA molecule has an acceptor stem that attaches to an amino acid and an anticodon loop that complements a codon on mRNA.

Q Why will different tRNAs have different bases in the anticodon loop?

(a.)

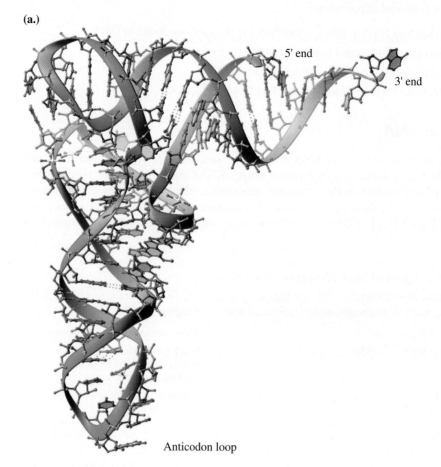

5′ end

3′ end

Anticodon loop

(b.)

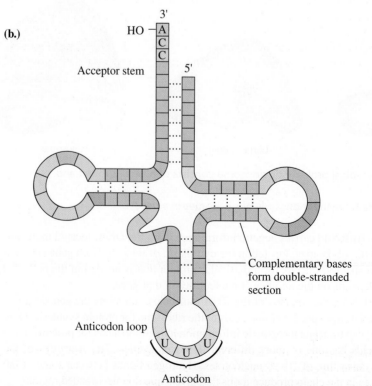

3′

HO—A C C

Acceptor stem

5′

Complementary bases form double-stranded section

Anticodon loop

U U U

Anticodon

SAMPLE PROBLEM 21.4

■ Types of RNA

What is the function of mRNA in a cell?

SOLUTION

The mRNA molecules carry instructions for the synthesis of a protein from the DNA in the nucleus to the ribosomes in the cytoplasm.

STUDY CHECK

What is the function of tRNA in a cell?

RNA and Protein Synthesis

We now look at the overall processes involved in transferring genetic information encoded in the DNA to the production of proteins. In the nucleus, the genetic information for the synthesis of a protein is copied from a gene in DNA to make a messenger RNA (mRNA), a process called **transcription**. The mRNA molecules move out of the nucleus into the cytoplasm, where they combine with the ribosomes. Then in a process called **translation**, tRNA molecules convert the mRNA information into amino acids, which are placed in the proper sequence to synthesize a protein. (See Figure 21.14.)

 **SELF STUDY ACTIVITY**
Transcription

$$DNA \xrightarrow{\text{Transcription}} mRNA \xrightarrow{\text{Translation}} protein$$

Transcription: Synthesis of mRNA

Transcription begins when the section of a DNA molecule that contains the gene to be copied unwinds. Within this unwound portion of DNA called a *transcription bubble*, RNA polymerase moves along the template strand in a 3′ to 5′ direction. The mRNA forms with bases that are complementary to the DNA template. In mRNA synthesis, C and G form pairs, T (in DNA) pairs with A (in mRNA), and A (in DNA) pairs with U (in mRNA). When RNA polymerase reaches the termination site, transcription ends, and the new mRNA is released. The unwound portion of the DNA returns to its double helix structure. (See Figure 21.15.)

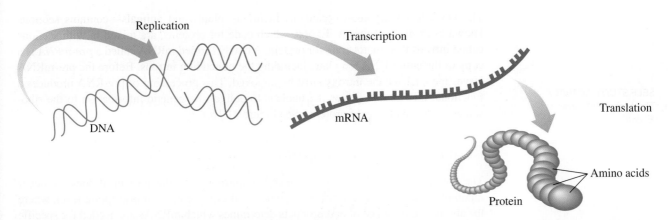

FIGURE 21.14 The genetic information in DNA is replicated in cell division and is used to produce messenger RNAs that code for amino acids needed for protein synthesis.

Q What is the difference between transcription and translation?

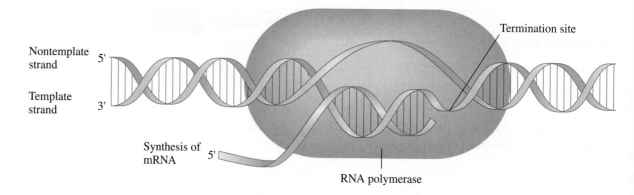

FIGURE 21.15 DNA undergoes transcription when RNA polymerase makes a complementary copy of a gene using the 3′ to 5′ strand as the template.

Q Why is the mRNA connected in a 5′ to 3′ direction?

RNA polymerase

Section of bases on DNA template: 3′—G—A—A—C—T—5′
                                                              ↓   ↓   ↓   ↓   ↓
Complementary base sequence in mRNA: 5′—C—U—U—G—A—3′

SAMPLE PROBLEM 21.5

■ RNA Synthesis

The sequence of bases in a part of the DNA template for mRNA is 3′—C—G—A—T—C—A—5′. What is the corresponding mRNA produced?

SOLUTION

To form the mRNA, the bases in the DNA template are paired with their complementary bases: G with C, C with G, T with A, and A with U.

Portion of DNA template: 3′—C—G—A—T—C—A—5′
Complementary bases in mRNA: 5′—G—C—U—A—G—U—3′

STUDY CHECK

What is the DNA template that codes for the mRNA segment with the nucleotide sequence 5′—G—G—G—U—U—U—A—A—A—3′?

Processing of mRNA

The DNA in eukaryotes—organisms including plants and animals—contains sections known as *exons* and *introns*. **Exons**, which code for proteins, are mixed in with sections called **introns** that do not code for protein. A newly formed mRNA called a *pre-mRNA* is a copy of the entire DNA template, including the noncoding introns. Before the pre-mRNA leaves the nucleus, the introns must be removed. This processing of pre-RNA produces a functional mRNA that leaves the nucleus to deliver the genetic information to the ribosomes for the synthesis of protein. (See Figure 21.16.)

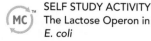

SELF STUDY ACTIVITY
The Lactose Operon in *E. coli*

Regulation of Transcription

The synthesis of mRNA occurs when cells require a particular protein; it does not occur randomly. The regulation of mRNA synthesis takes place at the transcription level, where the absence or presence of end products determines which mRNAs are needed for specific proteins. For example, *E. coli* bacteria that grow on lactose need β-galactosidase to hydrolyze lactose to glucose and galactose. When the lactose level is low, β-galactosidase is not needed; the transcription of its mRNA is turned off. When lactose enters the cell and

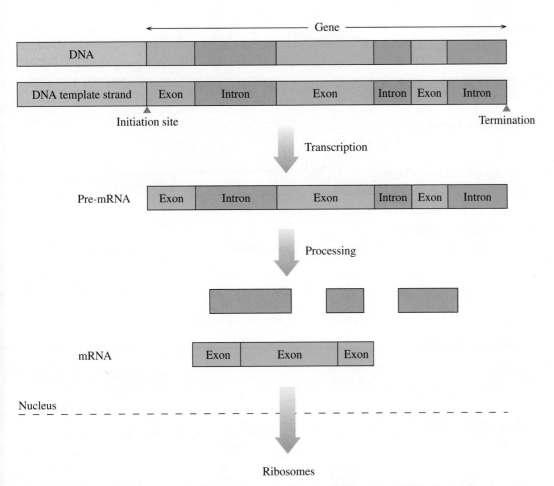

FIGURE 21.16 A pre-RNA, containing copies of the exons and introns from the gene, is processed to remove the introns and form mRNA that codes for a protein.

Q What is the difference between exons and introns?

β-galactosidase is required, lactose initiates the synthesis of mRNA for the enzyme. This process, known as **enzyme induction**, occurs when high levels of a substrate turn on the transcription of the genes that produce the mRNAs that code for specific enzymes.

Within a gene, sections of DNA called **operons** regulate the synthesis of related proteins. Each operon has a **control site** followed by the **structural genes** that produce the mRNAs for specific proteins. (See Figure 21.17.)

In front of the lactose operon, there is a **regulatory gene** that produces an mRNA for the synthesis of a **repressor** protein that blocks the synthesis of β-galactosidase by RNA polymerase. When lactose enters the cell, it combines with the repressor and removes it from the control site. Without a repressor, RNA polymerase proceeds to the structural genes, which now produces the mRNAs needed for the synthesis of the lactose enzymes.

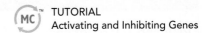

TUTORIAL
Activating and Inhibiting Genes

CONCEPT CHECK 21.3

■ **Transcription**

Describe why transcription will or will not take place in each of the following conditions:

a. A repressor binds to the control site.
b. An inducer binds to the repressor protein.

ANSWER

a. Transcription will not take place as long as a repressor is attached to the control site, which blocks the synthesis of mRNA by RNA polymerase.
b. Transcription will take place when an inducer attaches to the repressor, which removes it from the control site.

(a) The lactose operon

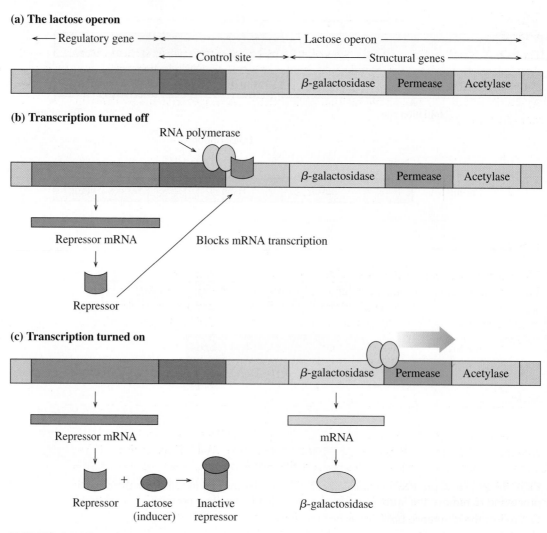

(b) Transcription turned off

(c) Transcription turned on

FIGURE 21.17 **(a)** The lactose operon consists of a control site and structural genes. **(b)** Without lactose, a repressor protein blocks the transcription of enzymes for lactose. **(c)** Lactose, an inducer, removes the repressor to allow the transcription of enzymes for lactose hydrolysis.

Q Why is transcription blocked when no lactose is present in the cell?

QUESTIONS AND PROBLEMS

RNA and Transcription

21.23 What are the three different types of RNA?

21.24 What is the function of each type of RNA?

21.25 What is the composition of a ribosome?

21.26 What is the smallest RNA?

21.27 What is meant by the term "transcription"?

21.28 What bases in mRNA are used to complement the bases A, T, G, and C in DNA?

21.29 Write the corresponding section of mRNA produced from the following section of DNA template:

3′—C—C—G—A—A—G—G—T—T—C—A—C—5′

21.30 Write the corresponding section of mRNA produced from the following section of DNA template:

3′—T—A—C—G—G—C—A—A—G—C—T—A—5′

21.31 What are introns and exons?

21.32 What kind of processing do mRNA molecules undergo before they leave the nucleus?

21.33 What is an operon?

21.34 Why does the operon model control protein synthesis at the transcription level?

21.35 How is the lactose operon turned off in *E. coli* that grow on lactose?

21.36 How is the lactose operon activated in *E. coli* that grow on lactose?

21.6 The Genetic Code

The overall function of the different types of RNA in the cell is to facilitate the task of synthesizing proteins. After the genetic information encoded in DNA is transcribed into mRNA molecules, the mRNAs move out of the nucleus to the ribosomes in the cytoplasm. At the ribosomes, the genetic information in the mRNAs is converted into a sequence of amino acids in protein:

LEARNING GOAL

Describe the function of the codons in the genetic code.

$$\text{mRNA} \xrightarrow{\substack{\text{Translation at the} \\ \text{ribosomes in the cytoplasm}}} \text{protein}$$

Codons

The **genetic code** consists of a series of three nucleotides (triplet) in mRNA called a **codon**. Each codon specifies an amino acid and its sequence in a protein. Early work on protein synthesis showed that repeating triplets of uracil, UUU, produced a polypeptide that contained only phenylalanine. Therefore, a sequence of $5'-\text{UUU}-\text{UUU}-\text{UUU}-3'$ codes for three phenylalanines:

MC™ TUTORIAL
Genetic Code

Codons in mRNA	$5'-\text{UUU}-\text{UUU}-\text{UUU}-3'$
Translation	↓ ↓ ↓
Amino acid sequence	—Phe — Phe — Phe—

Codons have been determined for all 20 amino acids. A total of 64 codons are possible from the triplet combinations of A, G, C, and U. (See Table 21.4.) Three of these, UGA, UAA, and UAG, are stop signals that code for the termination of protein synthesis. All the other three-base codons specify amino acids; one amino acid can have several codons. For example, glycine has four codons: GGU, GGC, GGA, and GGG. The triplet AUG has two roles in protein synthesis. At the beginning of an mRNA, the codon AUG signals the start of protein synthesis. In the middle of a series of codons, the AUG codon specifies the amino acid methionine.

TABLE 21.4 mRNA Codons: The Genetic Code for Amino Acids

First Letter	Second Letter				Third Letter
	U	C	A	G	
U	UUU UUC } Phe UUA UUG } Leu	UCU UCC UCA UCG } Ser	UAU UAC } Tyr UAA STOP UAG STOP	UGU UGC } Cys UGA STOP UGG Trp	U C A G
C	CUU CUC CUA CUG } Leu	CCU CCC CCA CCG } Pro	CAU CAC } His CAA CAG } Gln	CGU CGC CGA CGG } Arg	U C A G
A	AUU AUC } Ile AUA ᵃAUG START/Met	ACU ACC ACA ACG } Thr	AAU AAC } Asn AAA AAG } Lys	AGU AGC } Ser AGA AGG } Arg	U C A G
G	GUU GUC GUA GUG } Val	GCU GCC GCA GCG } Ala	GAU GAC } Asp GAA GAG } Glu	GGU GGC GGA GGG } Gly	U C A G

ᵃSTART codon signals the initiation of a peptide chain.
STOP codons signal the end of a peptide chain.

■ The Genetic Code

Indicate the nucleotides in mRNA that code for the following:

a. the amino acid phenylalanine
b. the amino acid proline
c. the start of a polypeptide

ANSWER

a. In mRNA, the codons UUU and UUC would place the amino acid phenylalanine (Phe) in a polypeptide.
b. In mRNA, the codons CCU, CCC, CCA, and CCG would place the amino acid proline (Pro) in a polypeptide.
c. The codon AUG in mRNA signals the start of the synthesis of a polypeptide.

SAMPLE PROBLEM 21.6

■ Codons

What is the sequence of amino acids coded by the following codons in mRNA?

$$5' - GUC - AGC - CCA - 3'$$

SOLUTION

According to Table 21.4, GUC codes for valine, AGC for serine, and CCA for proline. The sequence of amino acids is Val-Ser-Pro.

STUDY CHECK

What tripeptide is coded for by the following codons in mRNA?

$$5' - AAU - GCU - UGU - 3'$$

QUESTIONS AND PROBLEMS

The Genetic Code

21.37 What is a codon?

21.38 What is the genetic code?

21.39 What amino acid is coded for by each of the following codons?
  a. CUU   **b.** UCA
  c. GGU   **d.** AGG

21.40 What amino acid is coded for by each of the following codons?
  a. AAA   **b.** GUC
  c. CGG   **d.** GCA

21.41 When does the codon AUG signal the start of a protein? When does it code for the amino acid methionine?

21.42 The codons UAA and UAG do not code for amino acids. What is their role as codons in mRNA?

21.7 Protein Synthesis: Translation

LEARNING GOAL

Describe the process of protein synthesis from mRNA.

Once a molecule of mRNA is synthesized, it migrates out of the nucleus into the cytoplasm to the ribosomes. In the *translation* process, tRNA molecules, amino acids, and enzymes convert the codons on mRNA into amino acids to build a protein.

MC™ SELF STUDY ACTIVITY
Translation

Activation of tRNA

Molecules of tRNA read the codons of mRNA and pick up the corresponding amino acids. Each tRNA molecule contains a loop called the *anticodon*, which is a triplet of bases that

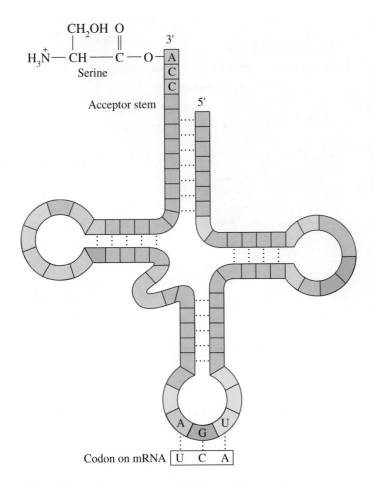

FIGURE 21.18 An activated tRNA with anticodon AGU bonds to serine at the acceptor stem.

Q What is the codon for serine for this tRNA?

HEALTH NOTE

Many Antibiotics Inhibit Protein Synthesis

Several antibiotics stop bacterial infections by interfering with the synthesis of proteins needed by the bacteria. Some antibiotics act only on bacterial cells, binding to the ribosomes in bacteria but not those in human cells. A description of some of these antibiotics is given in Table 21.5.

TABLE 21.5 Antibiotics That Inhibit Protein Synthesis in Bacterial Cells

Antibiotic	Effect on Ribosomes to Inhibit Protein Synthesis
Chloramphenicol	Inhibits peptide bond formation and prevents the binding of tRNA
Erythromycin	Inhibits peptide chain growth by preventing the translocation of the ribosome along the mRNA
Puromycin	Causes release of an incomplete protein by ending the growth of the polypeptide early
Streptomycin	Prevents the proper attachment of the initial tRNA
Tetracycline	Prevents the binding of tRNAs

complements a codon in an mRNA. An amino acid is attached to the acceptor stem of each tRNA by an enzyme called *aminoacyl–tRNA synthetase*. Each amino acid has a different synthetase. (See Figure 21.18.) Activation takes place when a *tRNA synthetase* uses the anticodon of a tRNA to form an ester bond between the carboxylate group of its amino acid and the hydroxyl group on the acceptor stem. Each synthetase then checks the tRNA–amino acid combination and hydrolyzes any incorrect combinations.

Initiation and Chain Elongation

Protein synthesis begins when an mRNA combines with the ribosome. The first codon in an mRNA is a *start* codon, AUG. Therefore, a tRNA with an anticodon of UAC and the amino acid methionine forms hydrogen bonds with the AUG codon. (See Figure 21.19.) In *chain elongation*, another tRNA carries a second amino acid to the adjacent codon on the mRNA. With two amino acids close together, a peptide bond forms. Then the first tRNA detaches from the ribosome, and the ribosome shifts to the next codon on the mRNA, a process called *translocation*. As the next tRNA attaches to the open binding site, its amino acid attaches to the growing peptide chain. As another tRNA detaches, the ribosome moves along the mRNA to read the next codon. Sometimes several ribosomes, called a *polysome*, translate a single strand of mRNA simultaneously to produce several copies of the peptide chain at the same time.

Chain Termination

Eventually, a ribosome encounters a stop codon—UAA, UGA, or UAG—that signals the termination of polypeptide synthesis. The stop codons have no corresponding tRNAs but are recognized by proteins called *release factor*s, which release the completed polypeptide chain from the ribosome. The initial amino acid methionine is usually removed from the beginning of the polypeptide chain. The R groups of the amino acids along the polypeptide chain interact to give the tertiary structure of a biologically active protein.

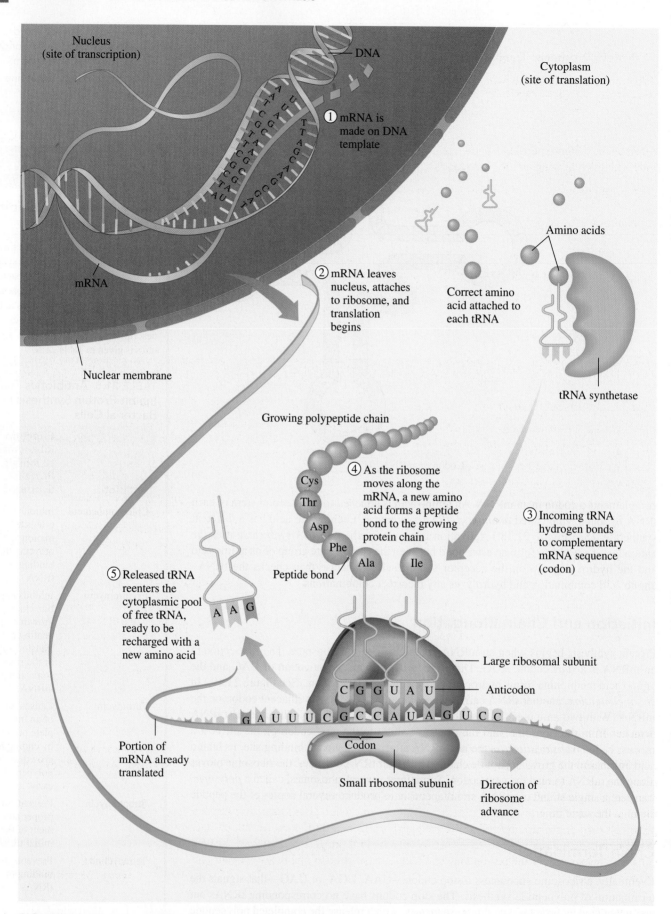

FIGURE 21.19 In the translation process, the mRNA synthesized by transcription attaches to a ribosome, and tRNAs pick up their amino acids and place them in a growing peptide chain.

Q How is the correct amino acid placed in the peptide chain?

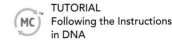

SAMPLE PROBLEM 21.7

TUTORIAL
Following the Instructions in DNA

■ **Protein Synthesis: Translation**

What order of amino acids would you expect in a peptide for the mRNA sequence of 5′—UCA—AAA—GCC—CUU—3′?

SOLUTION

Each of the codons specifies a particular amino acid. Using Table 21.4, we write a peptide with the following amino acid sequence:

mRNA codons: 5′—UCA—AAA—GCC—CUU—3′
                            ↓   ↓   ↓   ↓

Amino acid sequence: — Ser — Lys — Ala — Leu —

STUDY CHECK

Where would protein synthesis stop in the following series of bases in an mRNA?

5′—GGG—AGC—AGU—UAG—GUU—3′

SELF STUDY ACTIVITY
Overview of Protein Synthesis

QUESTIONS AND PROBLEMS

Protein Synthesis: Translation

21.43 What is the difference between a *codon* and an *anticodon*?

21.44 Why are there at least 20 different tRNAs?

21.45 What are the three steps of translation?

21.46 Where does protein synthesis take place?

21.47 What amino acid sequence would you expect from each of the following mRNA segments?
   a. 5′—AAA—AAA—AAA—3′
   b. 5′—UUU—CCC—UUU—CCC—3′
   c. 5′—UAC—GGG—AGA—UGU—3′

21.48 What amino acid sequence would you expect from each of the following mRNA segments?
   a. 5′—AAA—CCC—UUG—GCC—3′
   b. 5′—CCU—CGA—AGC—CCA—UGA—3′
   c. 5′—AUG—CAC—AAA—GAA—GUA—CUU—3′

21.49 How is a peptide chain extended?

21.50 What is meant by "translocation"?

21.51 The following is a portion of DNA is in the template DNA strand:

    3′—GCT—TTT—CAA—AAA—5′

   a. What is the corresponding mRNA section?
   b. What are the anticodons of the tRNAs?
   c. What amino acids will be placed in the peptide chain?

21.52 The following is a portion of DNA is in the template DNA strand:

    3′—TGT—GGG—GTT—ATT—5′

   a. What is the corresponding mRNA section?
   b. What are the anticodons of the tRNAs?
   c. What amino acids will be placed in the peptide chain?

21.8 Genetic Mutations

A **mutation** is a change in the nucleotide sequence of DNA. Such a change may alter the sequence of amino acids, affecting the structure and function of a protein in a cell. Mutations result from X-rays, overexposure to sun (ultraviolet or UV light), chemicals called *mutagens*, and possibly some viruses. If a mutation occurs in a somatic cell (a cell other than a reproductive cell), the altered DNA is limited to that cell and its daughter cells. If there is uncontrolled growth, the mutation could lead to cancer. If a mutation occurs in a germ cell (egg or sperm), then all DNA produced will contain the same genetic change. When a mutation severely alters the function of structural proteins or enzymes, the new cells may not survive or the person may exhibit a disease or condition that is a result of a genetic defect.

LEARNING GOAL
Describe some ways in which DNA is altered to cause mutations.

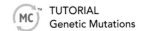

TUTORIAL
Genetic Mutations

Types of Mutations

Consider a triplet of bases CCG in the coding strand of DNA, which produces the codon GGC in mRNA. At the ribosome, tRNA would place the amino acid glycine in the peptide

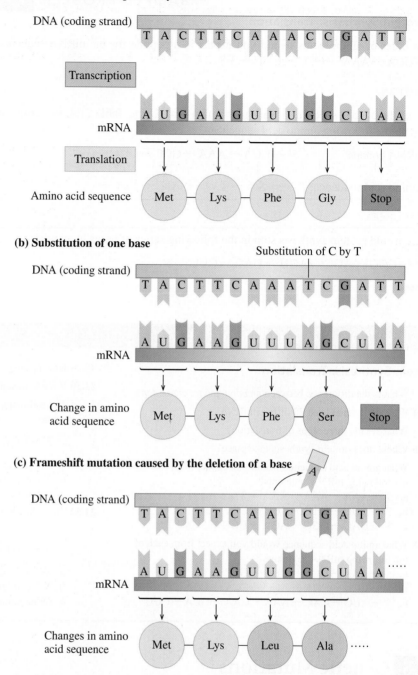

FIGURE 21.20 An alteration in the DNA coding strand (template) produces a change in the sequence of amino acids in the protein, which may lead to a mutation. **(a)** A normal DNA leads to the correct amino acid order in a protein. **(b)** The substitution of a base in DNA leads to a change in the mRNA codon and a change in the amino acid. **(c)** The deletion of a base causes a frameshift mutation, which changes the amino acid order that follows the mutation.

Q When would a substitution mutation cause protein synthesis to stop?

chain. (See Figure 21.20a.) Now, suppose that T replaces the first C in the DNA triplet, which gives TCG as the triplet. Then the codon produced in the mRNA is AGC, which brings the tRNA with the amino acid serine to add to the peptide chain. The replacement of one base in the coding strand of DNA with another is called a **substitution mutation**. With a change of nucleotides in the codon, a different amino acid may be inserted into the polypeptide. Substitution is the most common way in which mutations occur. (See Figure 21.20b.)

In a **frameshift mutation**, a base is added to or deleted from the normal order of bases in the coding strand of DNA. Suppose now an A is deleted from the triplet AAA, which gives a new triplet of AAC. The next triplet becomes CGA rather than CCG, and so on. All the triplets shift over by one base, which changes all the codons that follow and leads to a different sequence of amino acids from that point. Figure 21.20c illustrates a frameshift mutation by deletion.

Effect of Mutations

When a mutation causes a change in the amino acid sequence, the structure of the resulting protein can be altered severely and may lose biological activity. If the protein is an enzyme, it may no longer bind to its substrate or react with the substrate at the active site. When an altered enzyme cannot catalyze a reaction, certain substances may accumulate until they act as poisons in the cell, or substances vital to survival may not be synthesized. If a defective enzyme occurs in a major metabolic pathway or in the building of a cell membrane, the mutation can be lethal. When a protein deficiency is hereditary, the condition is called a **genetic disease**.

X-rays,
UV sunlight,
mutagens,
viruses

DNA $\longrightarrow$ alteration of $\longrightarrow$ defective $\longrightarrow$ genetic disease (germ cells)
DNA   protein   or cancer (somatic cells)

SAMPLE PROBLEM 21.8

■ Mutations

An mRNA has the sequence of codons 5′—CCC—AGA—GCC—3′. If a base substitution in the DNA changes the mRNA codon of AGA to GGA, how is the amino acid sequence affected in the resulting protein?

SOLUTION

The mRNA sequence —CCC—AGA—GCC— codes for the following amino acids: proline, arginine, and alanine. When the mutation occurs, the new sequence of the mRNA codons is —CCC—GGA—GCC—, which codes for proline, glycine, and alanine. The basic amino acid arginine is replaced by nonpolar glycine.

	Normal		*After Mutation*	
mRNA codons	—CCC— AGA —GCC—		—CCC— GGA —GCC—	
Amino acids	— Pro — Arg — Ala —		— Pro — Gly — Ala —	

STUDY CHECK

How might the protein made from this mRNA be affected by this mutation?

Genetic Diseases

A genetic disease is the result of a defective enzyme caused by a mutation in its genetic code. For example, phenylketonuria (PKU) results when DNA cannot direct the synthesis of the enzyme phenylalanine hydroxylase, required for the conversion of phenylalanine to

---

EXPLORE YOUR WORLD

A Model for DNA Replication and Mutation

1. Cut out 16 rectangular pieces of paper. Using 8 rectangular pieces for DNA strand 1, write two each of the following nucleotide symbols: A══, T══, G≡≡, and C≡≡.

2. Using the other 8 rectangular pieces for DNA strand 2, write two of each of the following nucleotide symbols: ══A, ══T, ≡≡G, and ≡≡C.

3. Place the pieces for strand 1 in random order.

4. Using the DNA segment strand 1 you made in part 3, select the correct bases to build the complementary segment of DNA strand 2.

5. Using the rectangular pieces for nucleotides, put together a DNA segment using a template strand of —A—T—T—G—C—C—. What is the mRNA from this segment of DNA? What is the dipeptide that would form from this mRNA?

6. In the DNA segment of part 5, change the G to an A. What is the mRNA from this segment of DNA? What is the dipeptide that forms? How could this change in codons lead to a mutation?

tyrosine. In an attempt to break down the phenylalanine, other enzymes in the cells convert it to phenylpyruvate. The accumulation of phenylalanine and phenylpyruvate in the blood can lead to severe brain damage and mental retardation. If PKU is detected in a newborn baby, a diet is prescribed that eliminates all the foods that contain phenylalanine. Preventing the buildup of the phenylpyruvate ensures normal growth and development.

The amino acid tyrosine is needed in the formation of melanin, the pigment that gives the color to our skin and hair. If the enzyme that converts tyrosine to melanin is defective, no melanin is produced, a genetic disease known as albinism. Persons and animals with no melanin have no skin or hair pigment. (See Figure 21.21.) Table 21.6 lists some other common genetic diseases and the type of metabolism or area affected.

FIGURE 21.21 A peacock with albinism does not produce the melanin needed to the make bright colors of its feathers.

Q Why are traits such as albinism related to the gene?

TABLE 21.6 Some Genetic Diseases

Genetic Disease	Result
Galactosemia	The transferase enzyme required for the metabolism of galactose-1-phosphate is absent. Accumulation of Gal-1-P leads to cataracts and mental retardation. It occurs in about 1 in every 50 000 births.
Cystic fibrosis	One of the most common inherited diseases in children. Thick mucus secretions make breathing difficult and block pancreatic function.
Down syndrome	The leading cause of mental retardation, occurring in about 1 of every 800 live births although mother's age strongly influences its occurence. Mental and physical problems including heart and eye defects are the result of the formation of three chromosomes, usually chromosome 21, instead of a pair.
Familial hypercholesterolemia	A mutation of a gene on chromosome 19 results in high cholesterol levels that lead to early coronary heart disease in people 30–40 years old.
Muscular dystrophy (MD) (Duchenne)	One of 10 forms of MD. A mutation in the X chromosome results in the low or abnormal production of *dystrophin*. This muscle-destroying disease appears at about age 5 with death by age 20 and occurs in about 1 of 10,000 males.
Huntington's disease (HD)	Appearing in middle age, HD affects the nervous system, leading to total physical impairment. It is the result of a mutation in a gene on chromosome 4, which can now be mapped to test people in families with HD. There are about 30 000 people with Huntington's disease in the United States.
Sickle-cell anemia	A defective hemoglobin from a mutation in a gene on chromosome 11 decreases the oxygen-carrying ability of red blood cells, which take on a sickled shape, causing anemia and plugged capillaries from red blood cell aggregation. In the United States, about 72 000 people are affected by sickle cell anemia.
Hemophilia	One or more defective blood-clotting factors lead to poor coagulation, excessive bleeding, and internal hemorrhages. There are about 20 000 hemophilia patients in the United States.
Tay-Sachs disease	Hexosaminidase A is defective, causing an accumulation of gangliosides resulting in mental retardation, loss of motor control, and early death.

QUESTIONS AND PROBLEMS

Genetic Mutations

21.53 What is a substitution mutation?

21.54 How does a substitution mutation in the genetic code for an enzyme affect the order of amino acids in that protein?

21.55 What is the effect of a frameshift mutation on the amino acid sequence in the polypeptide?

21.56 How can a mutation decrease the activity of a protein?

21.57 How is protein synthesis affected if the normal base sequence TTT in the DNA template is changed to TTC?

21.58 How is protein synthesis affected if the normal base sequence CCC is changed to ACC?

21.59 Consider the following portion of mRNA produced by the normal order of DNA nucleotides:

$$5'—ACA—UCA—CGG—GUA—3'$$

   a. What is the amino acid order produced for normal DNA?

   b. What is the amino acid order if a mutation changes UCA to ACA?

   c. What is the amino acid order if a mutation changes CGG to GGG?

   d. What happens to protein synthesis if a mutation changes UCA to UAA?

   e. What happens if a G is added to the beginning of the mRNA segment?

   f. What happens if the A is removed from the beginning of the mRNA segment?

21.60 Consider the following portion of mRNA produced by the normal order of DNA nucleotides:

$$5'—CUU—AAA—CGA—GUU—3'$$

   a. What is the amino acid order produced for normal DNA?

   b. What is the amino acid order if a mutation changes CUU to CCU?

   c. What is the amino acid order if a mutation changes CGA to AGA?

   d. What happens to protein synthesis if a mutation changes AAA to UAA?

   e. What happens if a G is added to the beginning of the mRNA segment?

   f. What happens if the C is removed from the beginning of the mRNA segment?

21.61 a. A base substitution changes a codon for an enzyme from GCC to GCA. Why is there no change in the amino acid order in the protein?

   b. In sickle-cell anemia, a base substitution in hemoglobin replaces glutamic acid (a polar acidic amino acid) with valine. Why does the replacement of one amino acid cause such a drastic change in biological function?

21.62 a. A base substitution for an enzyme replaces leucine (a nonpolar amino acid) with alanine. Why does this change in amino acids have little effect on the biological activity of the enzyme?

   b. A base substitution replaces cytosine in the codon UCA with adenine. How would this substitution affect the amino acids in the protein?

21.9   Recombinant DNA

Techniques in the field of genetic engineering permit scientists to cut and recombine DNA fragments to form **recombinant DNA**. The technology of recombinant DNA is used to produce human insulin for diabetics, the antiviral substance interferon, blood clotting factor VIII, and human growth hormone.

Preparing Recombinant DNA

Most of the work in recombinant DNA is done with *Escherichia coli (E. coli)* bacteria. The DNA in bacterial cells exists as small circular molecules called *plasmids*, which are easy to isolate and capable of replication. Initially, *E. coli* cells are soaked in a detergent solution to dissolve the plasma membrane. The contents of the cells, including the plasmids, are released and collected. A *restriction enzyme*, which breaks phosphodiester bonds in DNA between specific nucleotides, is used to cut open the circular DNA strands in the plasmids. (See Figure 21.22.)

The same enzymes are also used to cut out a piece of DNA from a different organism, such as the gene that produces insulin or growth hormone. The cut-out genes are then mixed with the plasmids that were cut open. The ends of the foreign DNA piece and the ends of the opened plasmids are joined by a DNA ligase. Then the altered plasmids containing the recombined DNA are placed in a fresh culture of *E. coli* bacteria, where they can be reabsorbed into the bacterial cells.

The new gene that was inserted in the plasmids is copied as the genetically engineered *E. coli* cells start to replicate. In a single day, one *E. coli* bacterium is capable of producing a million copies of itself including the foreign DNA, a process known as gene cloning. If

LEARNING GOAL

Describe the preparation and uses of recombinant DNA.

SELF STUDY ACTIVITIES
Applications of DNA Technology
Restriction Enzymes

SELF STUDY ACTIVITIES
Cloning a Gene in Bacteria
Gel Electrophoresis of DNA

FIGURE 21.22 Recombinant DNA is formed by placing a gene from another organism in a plasmid DNA of the bacterium, which causes the bacterium to produce a non-bacterial protein such as insulin or growth hormone.

Q How can recombinant DNA help a person with a genetic disease?

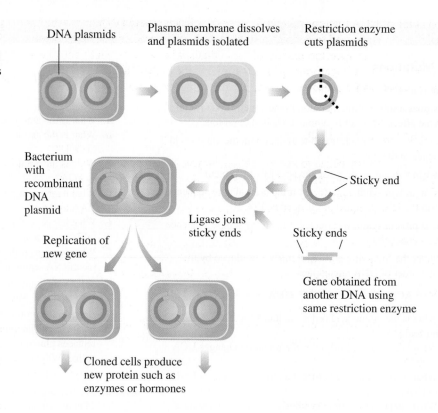

TABLE 21.7 Therapeutic Products of Recombinant DNA

Product	Therapeutic Use
Human insulin	Treat diabetes
Erythropoietin (EPO)	Treat anemia; stimulate production of erythrocytes
Human growth hormone (HGH)	Stimulate growth
Interferon	Treat cancer and viral disease
Tumor necrosis factor (TNF)	Destroy tumor cells
Monoclonal antibodies	Transport drugs needed to treat cancer and transplant rejection
Epidermal growth factor (EGF)	Stimulate healing of wounds and burns
Human blood clotting factor VIII	Treat hemophilia; allows blood to clot normally
Interleukins	Stimulate immune system; treat cancer
Prourokinase	Destroy blood clots; treat myocardial infarctions

the inserted DNA codes for the human insulin protein, the altered plasmids begin to synthesize human insulin. Eventually, a large number of cells with the new DNA produce the insulin protein. Table 21.7 lists some of the products developed through recombinant DNA technology that are now used therapeutically.

DNA Fingerprinting

SELF STUDY ACTIVITY
DNA Fingerprinting

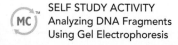

SELF STUDY ACTIVITY
Analyzing DNA Fragments
Using Gel Electrophoresis

In a process called DNA fingerprinting, restriction enzymes are used to cut DNA into smaller fragments called RFLPs (restriction fragment length polymorphisms). The RFLPs are separated by size by placing them on a gel. The gel is treated with a radioactive isotope that adheres to specific base sequences in the RFLPs. A piece of X-ray film placed over the gel is exposed by the radiation from the RFLPs. The pattern of dark and light bands on the film is known as a DNA fingerprint, which represents the order of nucleotides. (See Figure 21.23.) Scientists estimate that the odds of two people who are not identical twins producing the same DNA fingerprint are less than one in a billion.

One application of DNA fingerprinting is in forensic science, where DNA from samples of blood, hair, or semen is used to connect a suspect with a crime. Recently, DNA fingerprinting has been used to gain the release of individuals who were wrongly convicted. Other applications of DNA fingerprinting are determining the biological parents of a child, establishing the identity of a deceased person, and matching recipients with organ donors.

Human Genome Project

During the 1970s, scientists began to use restriction enzymes to map the location of genes within the DNA of the genome, which contains the hereditary information of an organism. By 1987, the genome of *E. coli* was determined. More recently, these techniques combined with new computer programs have compiled the map of the human genome, which contains about 30 000 genes.

Scientists think that most of the genome is not functional and has perhaps been carried from generation to generation for millions of years. Large blocks of genes are copied from one human chromosome to another even though they no longer code for needed proteins. Thus, the coding portions of the genes seem to make up only about 1% of the total genome. The results of the genome project will help us identify defective genes that lead to genetic disease. Today, DNA fingerprinting is used to screen for genes responsible for genetic diseases such as sickle-cell anemia, cystic fibrosis, breast cancer, colon cancer, Huntington's disease, and Lou Gehrig's disease.

Polymerase Chain Reaction

The process of gene cloning using recombinant DNA requires living cells such as *E. coli*. In 1987, a process called **polymerase chain reaction (PCR)** made it possible to produce multiple copies of (amplify) the DNA in a short time. In the PCR technique, a sequence of a DNA molecule is selected to copy, and the DNA is heated to separate the strands. Primers that are complementary to a small group of nucleotides on each side of the sequence to be copied are added to the ends of the templates. The DNA strands with their primers are mixed with DNA polymerase and a mixture of deoxyribonucleotides to produce complementary strands for the DNA section. Then the process is repeated with the new batch of DNA. After several cycles of the PCR process, millions of copies of the initial DNA section are produced. (See Figure 21.24.)

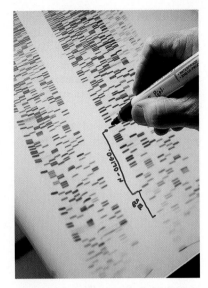

FIGURE 21.23 A scientist analyzes a nucleotide sequence in DNA from a human gene. Dark and light bands on the film represent the order of nucleotides. The marked sequences are involved in the growth of melanoma cancer cells.

Q What causes DNA fragments to appear on X-ray film?

 SELF STUDY ACTIVITY
The Human Genome Project: Human Chromosome 17

CONCEPT CHECK 21.5

■ Recombinant DNA

What is the function of restriction enzymes in recombinant DNA?

ANSWER
Restriction enzymes are used to cut out a particular piece of DNA from a gene and to cut open the circular plasmids in a bacterium where the foreign DNA attaches.

QUESTIONS AND PROBLEMS

Recombinant DNA

21.63 Why are *E. coli* bacteria used in recombinant DNA procedures?

21.64 What is a plasmid?

21.65 How are plasmids obtained from *E. coli*?

21.66 Why are restriction enzymes mixed with the plasmids?

21.67 How is a gene for a particular protein inserted into a plasmid?

21.68 Why is DNA polymerase useful in criminal investigations?

21.69 What is a DNA fingerprint?

20.70 What beneficial proteins are produced from recombinant DNA technology?

FIGURE 21.24 Each cycle of the polymerase chain reaction doubles the number of copies of the DNA section.

Q Why are the DNA strands heated at the start of each cycle?

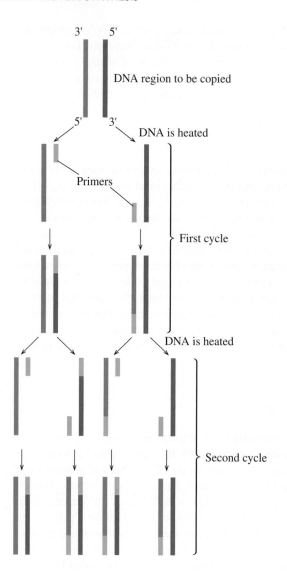

TABLE 21.8 Some Diseases Caused by Viral Infection

Disease	Virus
Common cold	Coronavirus (over 100 types)
Influenza	Orthomyxovirus
Warts	Papovavirus
Herpes	Herpesvirus
HPV	Human papillomavirus
Leukemia, cancers, AIDS	Retrovirus
Hepatitis	Hepatitis A virus (HAV), hepatitis B virus (HBV), hepatitis C virus (HCV)
Mumps	Paramyxovirus
Mononucleosis	Epstein–Barr virus (EBV)
Chicken pox (shingles)	Varicella zoster virus (VZV)

LEARNING GOAL

Describe the methods by which a virus infects a cell.

21.10 Viruses

Viruses are small particles of 3 to 200 genes that cannot replicate without a host cell. A typical virus contains a nucleic acid, DNA or RNA, but not both, inside a protein coat. A virus does not have the necessary materials such as nucleotides and enzymes to synthesize proteins and to grow. The only way a virus can replicate (make additional copies of itself) is to invade a host cell and take over the materials necessary for protein synthesis and growth. Some infections caused by viruses invading human cells are listed in Table 21.8. There are also viruses that attack bacteria, plants, and animals.

A viral infection begins when an enzyme in the protein coat of the virus makes a hole in the host cell, allowing the viral nucleic acid to enter and mix with the materials in the host cell. (See Figure 21.25.) If the virus contains DNA, the host cell begins to replicate the viral DNA in the same way it would replicate normal DNA. Viral DNA produces viral RNA, and a protease produces a protein coat to form a viral particle that leaves the cell. (See Figure 21.26.) The cell synthesizes so many virus particles, the cell eventually bursts and releases new viruses to infect more cells.

Vaccines are inactive forms of viruses that boost the immune response by causing the body to produce antibodies to the virus. Several childhood diseases, such as polio, mumps, chicken pox, and measles, can be prevented through the use of vaccines.

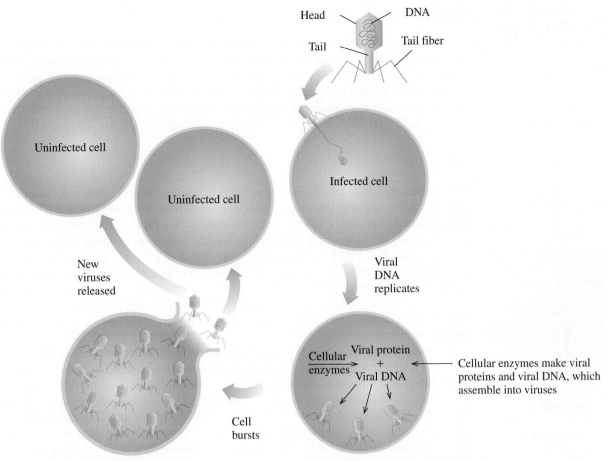

FIGURE 21.25 After a virus attaches to the host cell, it injects its viral DNA and uses the host cell's amino acids to synthesize viral protein, nucleic acids, enzymes, and ribosomes to make viral RNA. When the cell bursts, the new viruses are released to infect other cells.

Q Why does a virus need a host cell for replication?

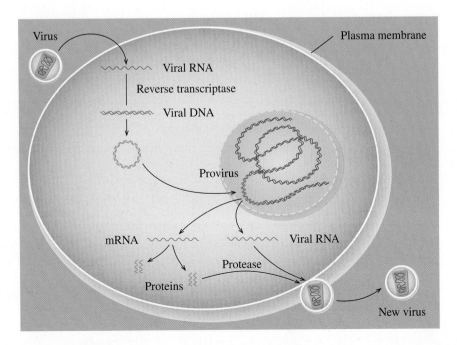

FIGURE 21.26 After a retrovirus injects its viral RNA into a cell, it forms a DNA strand by reverse transcription. The DNA forms a double-stranded DNA called a provirus, which joins the host cell DNA. When the cell replicates, the provirus produces the viral RNA needed to produce more virus particles.

Q What is reverse transcription?

Reverse Transcription

A virus that contains RNA as its genetic material is a **retrovirus**. Once inside the host cell, the retrovirus must first make viral DNA using a process known as *reverse transcription*. A retrovirus contains a polymerase enzyme called *reverse transcriptase* that uses the viral RNA template to synthesize complementary strands of DNA. Once produced, the DNA strands form double-stranded DNA using the nucleotides present in the host cell. This newly formed viral DNA, called a *provirus*, integrates with the DNA of the host cell.

AIDS

During the early 1980s, a disease called acquired immune deficiency syndrome, commonly known as AIDS, began to claim an alarming number of lives. We now know that HIV virus (human immunodeficiency virus) causes the disease. (See Figure 21.27.) HIV is a retrovirus that infects and destroys T4 lymphocyte cells, which are involved in the immune response. After the HIV binds to receptors on the surface of a T4 cell, the virus injects viral RNA into the host cell. As a retrovirus, the genes of the viral RNA direct the formation of viral DNA. The gradual depletion of T4 cells reduces the ability of the immune system to destroy harmful organisms. The AIDS syndrome is characterized by opportunistic infections such as *Pneumocystis carinii*, which causes pneumonia, and *Kaposi's sarcoma*, a skin cancer.

Treatment for AIDS is based on attacking the HIV at different points in its life cycle, including reverse transcription and protein synthesis. Nucleoside analogs mimic the structures of the nucleosides used for DNA synthesis. For example, the drug AZT (3'-azido-3'-deoxythymidine) is similar to thymidine, and ddI (2',3'-dideoxyinosine) is similar to guanosine. Two other drugs are 2',3'-dideoxycytidine (ddC) and 2',3'-didehydro-3'-deoxythymidine (d4T). Such compounds are found in the "cocktails" that are providing extended remission of HIV infections. When a nucleoside analog is incorporated into viral DNA, the lack of a hydroxyl group on the 3'-carbon in the sugar prevents the formation of the sugar–phosphate bonds and stops the replication of the virus.

(MC) SELF STUDY ACTIVITY
HIV Reproductive Cycle

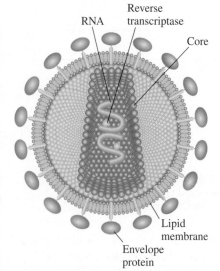

FIGURE 21.27 HIV virus causes AIDS, which destroys the immune system in the body.

Q Is HIV a DNA virus or an RNA retrovirus?

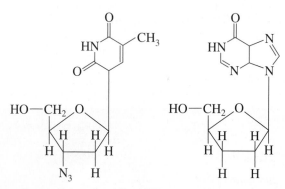

3'-azido-3'-deoxythymidine (AZT)

2',3'-Dideoxyinosine (ddI)

2',3'-Dideoxycytidine (ddC)

2',3'-Didehydro-3'-deoxythymidine (d4T)

The newest and most powerful anti-HIV drugs are the protease inhibitors such as saquinavir (Invirase), indinavir, and ritonavir. The inhibition of protease prevents the synthesis of proteins needed to make more copies of the virus. Researchers are not yet certain how long protease inhibitors will be beneficial for a person with AIDS.

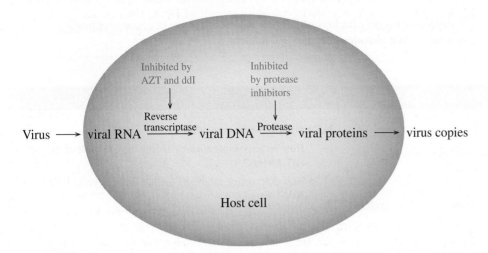

HEALTH NOTE

Cancer

In an adult body, many cells do not continue to reproduce. When cells in the body begin to grow and multiply inappropriately, they are called a tumor. If the effect of these tumors is limited, they are benign. When they invade other tissues and interfere with normal functions of the body, the tumors are cancerous. Cancer can be caused by chemical and environmental substances, by radiation, or by oncogenic viruses, which are viruses associated with human cancers. (See Table 21.9.)

Some reports estimate that chemical and environmental substances initiate 70–80% of all human cancers. A carcinogen is any substance that increases the chance of inducing a tumor. Known carcinogens include dyes, cigarette smoke, and asbestos. More than

90% of all persons with lung cancer are smokers. A carcinogen causes cancer by reacting with the DNA molecules in a cell, which alters the growth of that cell. Some known carcinogens are listed in Table 21.10.

Radiant energy from sunlight or medical radiation is another type of environmental factor. Skin cancer has become one of the most prevalent forms of cancer. The DNA damage in the exposed areas of the skin may eventually cause mutations. The cells lose their ability to control protein synthesis. This type of uncontrolled cell division becomes skin cancer. The incidence of malignant melanoma, one of the most serious skin cancers, has been rapidly increasing. Some possible factors for this increase may be the popularity of sun tanning as well as the reduction of the ozone layer, which absorbs much of the harmful radiation from sunlight.

Some cancers such as retinoblastoma and breast cancer appear to occur more frequently in families. Research indicates that a missing or defective gene is responsible.

TABLE 21.9 Human Cancers Caused by Oncogenic Viruses

Virus	Disease
RNA viruses	
Human T-cell lymphotropic virus-type I (HTLV-I)	Leukemia
DNA viruses	
Epstein–Barr virus (EBV)	Burkitt's lymphoma (cancer of white blood B cells)
	Nasopharyngeal carcinoma
	Hodgkin's disease
Hepatitis B virus (HBV)	Liver cancer
Herpes simplex virus (type 2)	Cervical and uterine cancer
Papilloma virus	Cervical and colon cancer, genital warts

TABLE 21.10 Some Chemical and Environmental Carcinogens

Carcinogen	Tumor Site
Asbestos	Lung, respiratory tract
Arsenic	Skin, lung
Cadmium	Prostate, kidneys
Chromium	Lung
Nickel	Lung, sinuses
Aflatoxin	Liver
Nitrites	Stomach
Aniline dyes	Bladder
Vinyl chloride	Liver

CONCEPT CHECK 21.6

■ Viruses

Why are viruses unable to replicate on their own?

ANSWER

Viruses contain only packets of DNA or RNA but not the necessary replication machinery that includes enzymes and nucleosides.

QUESTIONS AND PROBLEMS

Viruses

21.71 What type of genetic information is found in a virus?

21.72 Why do viruses need to invade a host cell?

21.73 A virus contains viral RNA.
   a. Why would reverse transcription be used in the life cycle of this type of virus?
   b. What is the name of this type of virus?

21.74 What is the purpose of a vaccine?

21.75 How do nucleoside analogs disrupt the life cycle of the HIV-1 virus?

21.76 How do protease inhibitors disrupt the life cycle of the HIV-1 virus?

CONCEPT MAP

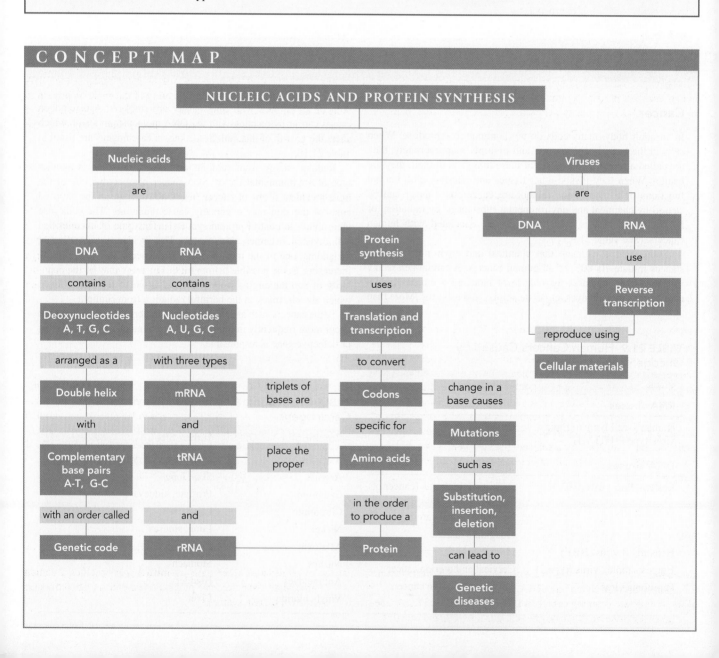

NUCLEIC ACIDS AND PROTEIN SYNTHESIS

CHAPTER REVIEW

21.1 Components of Nucleic Acids
LEARNING GOAL: *Describe the bases and ribose sugars that make up the nucleic acids DNA and RNA.*
Nucleic acids, such as deoxyribonucleic acid (DNA) and ribonucleic acid (RNA), are polymers of nucleotides. A nucleoside is a combination of a pentose sugar and a base. A nucleotide is composed of three parts: a pentose sugar, a base, and a phosphoryl group. In DNA, the sugar is deoxyribose and the base can be adenine, thymine, guanine, or cytosine. In RNA, the sugar is ribose, and uracil replaces thymine.

21.2 Primary Structure of Nucleic Acids
LEARNING GOAL: *Describe the primary structures of RNA and DNA.*
Each nucleic acid has its own unique sequence of bases known as its primary structure. In a nucleic acid polymer, the $3'$ — OH of each ribose sugar in RNA or deoxyribose sugar in DNA forms a phosphodiester bond to the phosphate group of the $5'$-carbon atom group of the sugar in the next nucleotide to give a backbone of alternating sugar and phosphate groups. There is a free $5'$-phosphate at one end of the polymer and a free $3'$ — OH group at the other end.

21.3 DNA Double Helix
LEARNING GOAL: *Describe the double helix of DNA.*
A DNA molecule consists of two strands of nucleotides that are wound around each other like a spiral staircase. The two strands are held together by hydrogen bonds between complementary base pairs, A with T, and G with C.

21.4 DNA Replication
LEARNING GOAL: *Describe the process of DNA replication.*
During DNA replication, DNA polymerase makes new DNA strands along each of the original DNA strands that serve as templates. Complementary base pairing ensures the correct pairing of bases to give identical copies of the original DNA.

21.5 RNA and Transcription
LEARNING GOAL: *Identify the different types of RNA; describe the synthesis of mRNA.*
The three types of RNA differ by function in the cell: ribosomal RNA makes up most of the structure of the ribosomes, messenger RNA carries genetic information from the DNA to the ribosomes, and transfer RNA places the correct amino acids in a growing peptide chain. Transcription is the process by which RNA polymerase produces mRNA from one strand of DNA. The bases in the mRNA are complementary to the DNA, except U is paired with A in RNA. The production of mRNA occurs when certain proteins are needed in the cell. In enzyme induction, the appearance of a substrate in a cell removes a repressor from the control site, which allows RNA polymerase to produce mRNA at the structural genes.

21.6 The Genetic Code
LEARNING GOAL: *Describe the function of the codons in the genetic code.*
The genetic code consists of a series of codons, which are sequences of three bases that specify the order for the amino acids in a protein. There are 64 codons for the 20 amino acids, which means there are multiple codons for most amino acids. The codon AUG signals the start of transcription, and codons UAG, UGA, and UAA signal it to stop.

21.7 Protein Synthesis: Translation
LEARNING GOAL: *Describe the process of protein synthesis from mRNA.*
Proteins are synthesized at the ribosomes in a translation process that includes three steps: initiation, translocation, and termination. During translation, tRNAs bring the appropriate amino acids to the ribosome, and peptide bonds form. When the polypeptide is released, it takes on its secondary and tertiary structures and becomes a functional protein in the cell.

21.8 Genetic Mutations
LEARNING GOAL: *Describe some ways in which DNA is altered to cause mutations.*
A genetic mutation is a change of one or more bases in the DNA sequence that alters the structure and ability of the resulting protein to function properly. In a substitution, one codon is altered, and a frameshift mutation inserts or deletes a base, which changes all the codons after the base change.

21.9 Recombinant DNA
LEARNING GOAL: *Describe the preparation and uses of recombinant DNA.*
A recombinant DNA is prepared by inserting a DNA segment—a gene—into the DNA present in plasmids of *E. coli* bacteria. As the altered bacterial cells replicate, the protein expressed by the foreign DNA segment is produced. In criminal investigation, large quantities of DNA are obtained from smaller amounts by DNA polymerase chain reactions.

21.10 Viruses
LEARNING GOAL: *Describe the methods by which a virus infects a cell.*
Viruses containing DNA or RNA must invade host cells to use the machinery within the cell for the synthesis of more viruses. For a retrovirus containing RNA, a viral DNA is synthesized by reverse transcription using the nucleotides and enzymes in the host cell. In the treatment of AIDS, nucleoside analogs inhibit the reverse transcriptase of the HIV-1 virus, and protease inhibitors disrupt the catalytic activity of protease needed to produce proteins for the synthesis of more viruses.

KEY TERMS

anticodon The triplet of bases in the center loop of tRNA that is complementary to a codon on mRNA.

bases Nitrogen-containing compounds found in DNA and RNA: adenine (A), thymine (T), cytosine (C), guanine (G), and uracil (U).

codon A sequence of three bases in mRNA that specifies a certain amino acid to be placed in a protein. A few codons signal the start or stop of protein synthesis.

complementary base pairs In DNA, adenine is always paired with thymine (A—T or T—A), and guanine is always paired with cytosine (G—C or C—G). In forming RNA, adenine is paired with uracil (A—U).

control site A section of DNA that regulates protein synthesis.

DNA Deoxyribonucleic acid; the genetic material of all cells containing nucleotides with deoxyribose sugar, phosphate, and the four bases adenine, thymine, guanine, and cytosine.

double helix The helical shape of the double chain of DNA that is like a spiral staircase with a sugar–phosphate backbone on the outside and base pairs like stair steps on the inside.

enzyme induction A model of cellular regulation in which protein synthesis is induced by a substrate.

exons The sections in a DNA template that code for proteins.

frameshift mutation A mutation that inserts or deletes a base in a DNA sequence.

genetic code The sequence of codons in mRNA that specifies the amino acid order for the synthesis of protein.

genetic disease A physical malformation or metabolic dysfunction caused by a mutation in the base sequence of DNA.

introns The sections in DNA that do not code for proteins.

mRNA Messenger RNA; produced in the nucleus from DNA to carry the genetic information to the ribosomes for the construction of a protein.

mutation A change in the DNA base sequence that alters the formation of a protein in the cell.

nucleic acids Large molecules composed of nucleotides; found as a double helix in DNA and as the single strands of RNA.

nucleoside The combination of a pentose sugar and a base.

nucleotides Building blocks of a nucleic acid consisting of a base, a pentose sugar (ribose or deoxyribose), and a phosphoryl group.

Okazaki fragments The short segments formed by DNA polymerase in the daughter DNA strand that runs in the 3′ to 5′ direction.

operon A group of genes, including a control site and structural genes, whose transcription is controlled by the same regulatory gene.

phosphodiester bond The phosphate link that joins the 3′-hydroxyl group in one nucleotide to the phosphate group on the 5′-carbon atom in the next nucleotide.

polymerase chain reaction (PCR) A procedure in which a strand of DNA is copied many times by mixing it with DNA polymerase and a mixture of deoxyribonucleotides.

primary structure The sequences of nucleotides in nucleic acids.

recombinant DNA DNA combined from different organisms to form new, synthetic DNA.

regulatory gene A gene in front of the control site that produces a repressor.

replication The process of duplicating DNA by pairing the bases on each parent strand with their complementary base.

replication forks The open sections in unwound DNA strands where DNA polymerase begins the replication process.

repressor A protein that interacts with the control site in an operon to prevent the transcription of mRNA.

retrovirus A virus that contains RNA as its genetic material and that synthesizes a complementary DNA strand inside a cell.

RNA Ribonucleic acid; a type of nucleic acid that is a single strand of nucleotides containing adenine, cytosine, guanine, and uracil.

rRNA Ribosomal RNA; the most prevalent type of RNA and a major component of the ribosomes.

structural genes The sections of DNA that code for the synthesis of proteins.

substitution mutation A mutation that replaces one base in a DNA with a different base.

transcription The transfer of genetic information from DNA by the formation of mRNA.

translation The interpretation of the codons in mRNA as amino acids in a peptide.

tRNA Transfer RNA; an RNA that places a specific amino acid into a peptide chain at the ribosome. There is one or more tRNA for each of the 20 different amino acids.

virus Small particles containing DNA or RNA in a protein coat that require a host cell for replication.

UNDERSTANDING THE CONCEPTS

21.77 Answer the following questions for the given section of DNA:
   a. Complete the bases in the parent and template strands.

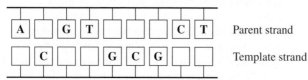

   b. Using the template strand, write the mRNA sequence.

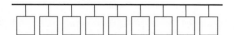

   c. Write the 3-letter symbols of the amino acids that would go into the peptide from the mRNA you wrote in part **b**.

21.78 Suppose a mutation occurs in the DNA section in problem 21.77, and the first base in the parent chain, adenine, is replaced by guanine.
   a. What type of mutation has occurred?
   b. Using the template strand that results from this mutation, write the order of bases in the altered mRNA.

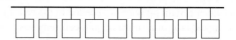

   c. Write the 3-letter symbols of the amino acids that would go into the peptide from the mRNA you wrote in part **b**.

   d. What effect, if any, might this mutation have on the structure and/or function of the resulting protein?

ADDITIONAL QUESTIONS AND PROBLEMS

For instructor-assigned homework, go to www.masteringchemistry.com.

21.79 Identify each of the following bases as a pyrimidine or a purine:
    a. cytosine   **b.** adenine   **c.** uracil
    d. thymine   **e.** guanine

21.80 Indicate if each of the bases in problem 21.79 are found in DNA only, RNA only, or both DNA and RNA.

21.81 Identify the base and sugar in each of the following nucleosides:
    a. deoxythymidine   **b.** adenosine
    c. cytidine   **d.** deoxyguanosine

21.82 Identify the base and sugar in each of the following nucleotides:
    a. CMP   **b.** dAMP
    c. dGMP   **d.** UMP

21.83 How do the bases thymine and uracil differ?

21.84 How do the bases cytosine and uracil differ?

21.85 Draw the structure of CMP.

21.86 Draw the structure of dGMP.

21.87 What is similar about the primary structure of RNA and DNA?

21.88 What is different about the primary structure of RNA and DNA?

21.89 If the DNA double helix in salmon contains 28% adenine, what is the percentage of thymine, guanine, and cytosine?

21.90 If the DNA double helix in humans contains 20% cytosine, what is the percentage of guanine, adenine, and thymine?

21.91 In DNA, how many hydrogen bonds form between each of the following:
    a. adenine and thymine   **b.** guanine and cytosine

21.92 How does polymerase chain reaction (PCR) produce many copies of a DNA section?

21.93 Write the complementary base sequence for each of the following DNA segments:
    a. 5′—G—A—C—T—T—A—G—G—C—3′
    b. 3′—T—G—C—A—A—A—C—T—A—G—C—T—5′
    c. 5′—A—T—C—G—A—T—C—G—A—T—C—G—3′

21.94 Write the complementary base sequence for each of the following DNA segments:
    a. 5′—T—T—A—C—G—G—A—C—C—G—C—3′
    b. 5′—A—T—A—G—C—C—C—T—T—A—C—T—G—G—3′
    c. 3′—G—G—C—C—T—A—C—C—T—T—A—A—C—G—A—C—G—5′

21.95 In DNA replication, what is the difference in the synthesis of the leading strand and the lagging strand?

21.96 How are the Okazaki fragments joined to the growing DNA strand?

21.97 Where are the DNA strands of the original DNA found in the double helix of each of the daughter DNA molecules?

21.98 How can replication occur at several places along a DNA double helix?

21.99 Match the following statements with rRNA, mRNA, or tRNA:
    a. is the smallest type of RNA
    b. makes up the highest percentage of RNA in the cell
    c. carries genetic information from the nucleus to the ribosomes

21.100 Match the following statements with rRNA, mRNA, or tRNA:
    a. combines with proteins to form ribosomes
    b. brings amino acids to the ribosomes for protein synthesis
    c. acts as a template for protein synthesis

21.101 What are the possible codons for each of the following amino acids?
    a. threonine   **b.** serine   **c.** cysteine

21.102 What are the possible codons for each of the following amino acids?
    a. valine   **b.** proline   **c.** histidine

21.103 What is the amino acid for each of the following codons?
    a. AAG   **b.** AUU   **c.** CGU

21.104 What is the amino acid for each of the following codons?
    a. CAA   **b.** GGC   **c.** AAC

21.105 Endorphins are polypeptides that reduce pain. What is the amino acid order for the following mRNA that codes for a pentapeptide that is an endorphin called leucine enkephalin?

    5′—AUG—UAC—GGU—GGA—UUU—CUA—UAA—3′

21.106 Endorphins are polypeptides that reduce pain. What is the amino acid order for the following mRNA that codes for a pentapeptide that is an endorphin called methionine enkephalin?

    5′—AUG—UAC—GGU—GGA—UUU—AUG—UAA—3′

21.107 What is the anticodon on tRNA for each of the following codons in an mRNA?
    a. AGC   **b.** UAU   **c.** CCA

21.108 What is the anticodon on tRNA for each of the following codons in an mRNA?
    a. GUG   **b.** CCC   **c.** GAA

CHALLENGE QUESTIONS

21.109 Oxytocin is a nonapeptide with nine amino acids. How many nucleotides would be found in the mRNA for this protein?

21.110 Why are there no base pairs in DNA between adenine and guanine or thymine and cytosine?

21.111 What is the difference between a DNA virus and a retrovirus?

21.112 A protein contains 35 amino acids. How many nucleotides would be found in the mRNA for this protein?

ANSWERS

ANSWERS TO STUDY CHECKS

21.1 deoxycytidine-5′-monophosphate (dCMP)

21.2

Free 5′ phosphate

Cytidine

Cytidine

Free 3′ OH ⟶ OH   OH

21.3 3′—C—C—A—A—T—T—G—G—5′

21.4 Each type of tRNA matches a specific codon to a specific amino acid and brings the amino acids to the ribosomes for protein synthesis.

21.5 3′—C—C—C—A—A—A—T—T—T—5′

21.6 Asn—Ala—Cys

21.7 at UAG

21.8 If the substitution of an amino acid in the polypeptide affects an interaction essential to functional structure on the binding of a substrate, the resulting protein could be less effective or nonfunctional.

ANSWERS TO SELECTED QUESTIONS AND PROBLEMS

21.1 a. pyrimidine   **b.** pyrimidine

21.3 a. DNA   **b.** both DNA and RNA

21.5 deoxyadenosine-5′-monophosphate (dAMP), deoxy-thymidine-5′-monophosphate (dTMP), deoxycytidine-5′-monophosphate (dCMP), and deoxyguanosine-5′-monophosphate (dGMP)

21.7 a. nucleoside   **b.** nucleoside
c. nucleoside   **d.** nucleotide

21.9

21.11 The nucleotides in nucleic acids are held together by phospho-diester bonds between the 3′—OH of a sugar (ribose or deoxyribose) and a phosphate group on the 5′-carbon of another sugar.

21.13

Guanine (G)

Cytidine (C)

21.15 The two DNA strands are held together by hydrogen bonds between the bases in each strand.

21.17 a. 3′—T—T—T—T—T—T—5′
b. 3′—C—C—C—C—C—C—5′
c. 3′—T—C—A—G—G—T—C—C—A—5′
d. 3′—G—A—C—A—T—A—T—G—C—A—A—T—5′

21.19 The enzyme helicase unwinds the DNA helix to prepare the parent DNA strands for the synthesis of daughter DNA strands.

21.21 Once the DNA strands separate, the DNA polymerase pairs each of the bases with its complementary base and produces two exact copies of the original DNA.

21.23 ribosomal RNA, messenger RNA, and transfer RNA

21.25 A ribosome consists of a small subunit and a large subunit.

21.27 In transcription, the sequence of nucleotides on a DNA template (one strand) is used to produce the base sequences of a messenger RNA.

21.29 5′—G—G—C—U—U—C—C—A—A—G—U—G—3′

21.31 In eukaryotic cells, genes contain sections called exons that code for proteins and sections called introns that do not code for protein.

21.33 An operon is a section of DNA that regulates the synthesis of one or more proteins.

21.35 When the lactose level is low in *E. coli*, a repressor produced by the mRNA from the regulatory gene binds to the control site, which blocks the synthesis of mRNA from the genes preventing the synthesis of protein.

21.37 A codon is a three-base sequence in mRNA that codes for a specific amino acid in a protein.

21.39 a. leucine (Leu)   **b.** serine (Ser)
c. glycine (Gly)   **d.** arginine (Arg)

21.41 When AUG is the first codon, it signals the start of protein synthesis. Thereafter, AUG codes for methionine.

21.43 A codon is a base triplet in the mRNA. An anticodon is the complementary triplet on a tRNA for a specific amino acid.

21.45 initiation, chain elongation, and termination

21.47 a. —Lys—Lys—Lys—
b. —Phe—Pro—Phe—Pro—
c. —Tyr—Gly—Arg—Cys—

21.49 The new amino acid is joined by a peptide bond to the peptide chain. The ribosome moves to the next codon, which attaches to a tRNA carrying the next amino acid.

21.51 a. 5′—CGA—AAA—GUU—UUU—3′
b. GCU, UUU, CAA, AAA
c. using codons in mRNA: —Arg—Lys—Val—Phe—

21.53 A base in DNA is replaced by a different base.

21.55 In a frameshift mutation caused by a deletion or an addition, all the codons from the mutation onward are changed, which changes the order of amino acids in the rest of the polypeptide chain.

21.57 The normal triplet TTT forms a codon AAA, which codes for lysine. The mutation TTC forms a codon AAG, which also codes for lysine. There is no effect on the amino acid sequence.

21.59 a. —Thr—Ser—Arg—Val—
b. —Thr—Thr—Arg—Val—
c. —Thr—Ser—Gly—Val—
d. —Thr—STOP. Protein synthesis would terminate early. If this occurs early in the formation of the polypeptide, the resulting protein will probably be nonfunctional.
e. The new protein will contain the sequence —Asp—Ile—Thr—Gly—.
f. The new protein will contain the sequence —His—His—Gly—.

21.61 a. GCC and GCA both code for alanine.
b. A vital ionic cross-link in the tertiary structure of hemoglobin cannot be formed when the polar glutamic acid is replaced by valine, which is nonpolar. The resulting hemoglobin is malformed and less capable of carrying oxygen.

21.63 *E. coli* bacterial cells contain several small circular plasmids of DNA that can be isolated easily. After the recombinant DNA is formed, *E. coli* multiply rapidly, producing many copies of the recombinant DNA in a relatively short time.

21.65 *E. coli* are soaked in a detergent solution that dissolves the plasma membrane and releases the cell contents including the plasmids, which are collected.

21.67 When a gene has been obtained using restriction enzymes, it is mixed with the plasmids that have been opened by the same enzymes. When mixed together in a fresh *E. coli* culture, the sticky ends of the DNA fragments bond with the sticky ends of the plasmid DNA to form a recombinant DNA.

21.69 In DNA fingerprinting, restriction enzymes cut a sample DNA into fragments, which are sorted by size by gel electrophoresis. After tagging the DNA fragments with a radioactive isotope, a piece of X-ray film placed over the gel is exposed by the radioactivity to give a pattern of dark and light bands known as a DNA fingerprint.

21.71 DNA or RNA, but not both

21.73 a. A viral RNA is used to synthesize a viral DNA to produce the proteins for the protein coat, which allows the virus to replicate and leave the cell.
b. retrovirus

21.75 Nucleoside analogs such as AZT and ddI are similar to the nucleosides required to make viral DNA in reverse transcription. However, they interfere with the ability of the DNA to form and thereby disrupt the life cycle of the HIV-1 virus.

21.77

a.

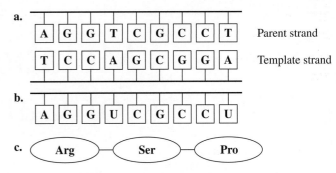

| A | G | G | T | C | G | C | C | T | Parent strand |

| T | C | C | A | G | C | G | G | A | Template strand |

b.

| A | G | G | U | C | G | C | C | U |

c. Arg — Ser — Pro

21.79 a. pyrimidine   **b.** purine   **c.** pyrimidine
d. pyrimidine   **e.** purine

21.81 a. thymine and deoxyribose   **b.** adenine and ribose
c. cytosine and ribose   **d.** guanine and deoxyribose

21.83 They are both pyrimidines, but thymine has a methyl group.

21.85

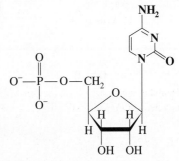

21.87 They are both polymers of nucleotides connected through phosphodiester bonds between alternating sugar and phosphate groups with bases extending out from each sugar.

21.89 28% T, 22% G, and 22% C

21.91 a. two   **b.** three

21.93 a. 3′—C—T—G—A—A—T—C—C—G—5′
b. 5′—A—C—G—T—T—T—G—A—T—C—G—A—3′
c. 3′—T—A—G—C—T—A—G—C—T—A—G—C—5′

21.95 DNA polymerase synthesizes the leading strand continuously in the 5′ to 3′ direction. The lagging strand is synthesized in small segments called Okazaki fragments because it must grow in the 3′ to 5′ direction.

21.97 One strand of the parent DNA is found in each of the two copies of the daughter DNA molecule.

21.99 a. tRNA   **b.** rRNA   **c.** mRNA

21.101 a. ACU, ACC, ACA, and ACG
b. UCU, UCC, UCA, UCG, AGU, and AGC
c. UGU and UGC

21.103 a. lysine   **b.** isoleucine   **c.** arginine

21.105 START—Tyr—Gly—Gly—Phe—Leu—STOP

21.107 a. UCG   **b.** AUA   **c.** GGU

21.109 Three nucleotides are needed to code for each amino acid plus the start and stop codons of three nucleotides each, which makes a minimum total of 33 nucleotides.

21.111 A DNA virus attaches to a cell and injects viral DNA that uses the host cell to produce copies of the DNA to make viral RNA. A retrovirus injects viral RNA from which complementary DNA is produced by reverse transcription.

22 Metabolic Pathways for Carbohydrates

"I was checking this dog's ears for foxtails and her eyes for signs of conjunctivitis," says Joyce Rhodes, veterinary assistant at the Sonoma Animal Hospital. "We always check a dog's teeth for tartar, because dental care is very important to the well-being of the animal. When I do need to give a medication to an animal, I use my chemistry to prepare the proper dose that the pet should take. Dosages may be in milligrams, kilograms, or milliliters."

As a member of the veterinary health care team, a veterinary technician (VT) assists a veterinarian in the care and handling of animals. A VT takes medical histories, collects specimens, performs laboratory procedures, prepares an animal for surgery, assists in surgical procedures, takes X-rays, talks with animal owners, and cleans teeth.

MasteringCHEMISTRY™

Visit www.masteringchemistry.com for self-study materials and instructor-assigned homework.

CREDITS

GLOSSARY/INDEX

t = table;

Italic number = figure

A

Abbreviated configuration, 120

Absolute zero, 62, 62*t*

Acceptor stem, 752, *752*, 759

Acetal The product of the addition of two alcohols to an aldehyde or ketone. 522, 534

Acetaldehyde

    from alcohol oxidation, 496, 498

    ball-and-stick model, *511*

    oxidization of, 502, 862

    produced in liver, 498

    from threonine degradation, 862

Acetaminophen (Tylenol), 645, 662

Acetic acid, 438, 577, 577*t*

    buffers, 402–403, *402*

Acetoacetate, 849, *849*

    from amino acid degradation, 862

Acetoacetyl CoA, 861–862, *861*

Acetone, 438, 513

    ketosis and, 849, *849*, 850

Acetyl-ACP, *852*

Acetylcholinesterase, inhibitors, 715

Acetyl CoA The compound that is formed when a two-carbon acetyl unit bonds to coenzyme A. 779, *780*, 787–788

    accumulation in liver, ketone bodies and, 849

    from acetaldehyde, 862

    from amino acid degradation, 862

    beta oxidation and, 842, 843–844

    citric acid cycle and, 818, *818*, 867

    cleavage of, 843

    ketogenesis and, 849, *849*, 850

    ketogenic amino acid and, 861–862, *861*

    lipogenesis and, 851

    from pyruvate, 9, 796, *797*, 805

Acetylene (ethyne), 447–448, *447*

Acetylsalicylic acid (aspirin), 2, 36*t*, 438, 586, 610

Achiral Molecules with mirror images that are superimposable. 526–527, *526*

Achiral compound, *528*

Acid A substance that dissolves in water and produces hydrogen ions (H^+), according to the Arrhenius theory. All acids are proton donors, according to the Brønsted-Lowry theory. 371–414

    amphoteric, 383–384

    bases and (neutralization), 394–396

    Brønsted-Lowry, 374, 375*t*

    characteristics of, 375*t*, 382*t*

    conjugate acid-base pair, 375–377, 387*t*

    denaturing protein, 694, *694*

    naming, 372, 373*t*

    reactions of, 393–398

    salts forming acidic solutions, 399–401, 400*t*

    stomach, 388

    strength of, 377–383

    strong, 378–379, 378*t*, *379*, 382*t*

    titration, 396–398, *396*

    weak, 378–382, 378*t*, *379*

Acid-base properties of salt solutions, 399–401, 400*t*

Acid-base titration, 396–398, *396*

Acid dissociation constant (K_a) The product of the concentrations of the ions from the dissociation of a weak acid divided by the concentration of the weak acid. 381–382, 382*t*

Acidic amino acid An amino acid that has an R group with a carboxylate (—COO⁻). 674

Acidic solution, 374, 384, *384*

    cation and anion of salt, 400*t*

    examples of, 384*t*

    forming from salt, 399

    pH of, 386

    stomach acid, 388

Acidosis Low blood pH resulting from the formation of acidic ketone bodies. 405, 405*t*, 849

Acid rain, 394

Aconitase, 814

ACP (acyl carrier protein), 851, *852*, 853

Acquired immune deficiency syndrome (AIDS), 770–771

Actin, 784

Actinides, *99*, 100

Activation energy The energy needed to break the bonds of reacting molecules. 338–339, *338*

Active learning, 9, 10*t*

Active site A pocket in a part of the tertiary enzyme structure that binds substrate and catalyzes a reaction. 706–707, *706*

Active transport, 635, *635*

Activity The rate at which an enzyme catalyzes the reaction that converts substrate to product. 710–713

Actron, 609

Actual yield The actual amount of product produced by a reaction. 240–241

Acyl carrier protein (ACP), 851, *852*, 853

Acyl CoA synthetase, 842

Addition A reaction in which atoms or groups of atoms bond to a double bond. Addition reactions include the addition of hydrogen (hydrogenation), halogens (halogenation), hydrogen halides (hydrohalogenation), or water (hydration). 455–462, 456*t*

Addition (mathematical), significant figures and, 25–27

Adenine (A), 739–740, *740*, 742*t*

Adenosine 5'-diphosphate (ADP), 742, 742*t*, *742*

Adenosine 5'-monophosphate (AMP), *741*, 742, 742, 742*t*

Adenosine 5'-triphosphate (ATP), 742, *742*

Adenosine diphosphate. *See* ADP

Adenosine triphosphate. *See* ATP

Adipocytes, 839, *839*

Adipose tissue, 48

ADP Adenosine diphosphate, formed by the hydrolysis of ATP; consists of adenine, a ribose sugar, and two phosphate groups. 782–783, *783*

    activating enzymes in citric acid cycle, 818, *818*

    metabolism and, 867

    as nucleotide, 742, *742*

Adrenal corticosteroid, 632

Adrenal gland, 632

Adrenaline (epinephrine), 530, 647

Aerobic An oxygen-containing environment in the cells. 796

Agent Orange, 490

Agitation, 695

Agricultural technologist, 672

AIDS (acquired immune deficiency syndrome), 770–771

Air

    as gas mixture, 286, 296

    typical composition, 286*t*

Alanine, 675*t*

    from conversion of tryptophan, 862

    converting to pyruvate, 862

    as nonessential amino acid, 863*t*

    synthesis, *863*, 864

Albinism, 764, *764*

Alchemists, 4

Alcohol An organic compound that contains the hydroxyl (—OH) functional group attached to a carbon chain. 435, 437*t*, 480–486

    abuse of, 498

    ball-and-stick model, 480, *480*

    blood alcohol content, 498

    boiling point, 491–492, 492*t*

    breathalyzer test, 498

    classifying, 437*t*, 480–481

    combustion, *494*

    dehydrating to form alkene, 494–495

    disinfectant, 695

    fermentation, 787, 798

    functional group, 437*t*

    heats of fusion and vaporization, 82*t*

    household products, 482

    hydroxyl groups in, 436, 480, 481

    important, 483

    isomers, 488–489

    naming, 481–482, 501

    oxidation, 496–498

    oxidation in body, 488*t*, 498

    oxidation to acetaldehyde, 496

    reactions of, 494–500

    solubility in water, 492–493, 492*t*

    sugar, 556, 560*t*

Wine making, 798
Wintergreen oil, 584
Wood alcohol (methanol), 496
Work An activity that requires energy. 56

X

X-ray, 114, *114*
 radiation from, 152*t*
Xylitol, 556, 560*t*
Xylocaine, 654
Xylose, 556

Y

Yard (length measurement), 15
Yeast fermentation, 798
Yield, 240–241
Yogurt, 694

Z

Zeros, significant, 22, 22*t*
 adding, 25–26
Zinc ion (cofactor), 721–722, *722*

Zwitterion The dipolar form of an amino acid consisting of two oppositely charged ionic regions, $-NH_3^+$ and $-COO^-$. 677–680
Zymogen An inactive form of an enzyme that is activated by removing a peptide portion from one end of the protein. 717–719, 718*t*

METRIC AND SI UNITS AND SOME USEFUL CONVERSION FACTORS

Length SI unit meter (m)	Volume SI unit cubic meter (m³)	Mass SI unit kilogram (kg)
1 meter (m) = 100 centimeters (cm)	1 liter (L) = 1000 milliliters (mL)	1 kilogram (kg) = 1000 grams (g)
1 meter (m) = 1000 millimeters (mm)	1 mL = 1 cm³	1 g = 1000 milligrams (mg)
1 cm = 10 mm	1 L = 1.06 quart (qt)	1 kg = 2.20 lb
1 kilometer (km) = 0.6214 mile (mi)	1 qt = 946 mL	1 lb = 454 g
1 inch (in.) = 2.54 cm (exact)		1 mole = 6.02×10^{23} particles
		Water
		density = 1.00 g/mL

Temperature SI unit kelvin (K)	Pressure SI unit pascal (Pa)	Energy SI unit joule (J)
°F = 1.8(°C) + 32	1 atm = 760 mmHg	1 calorie (cal) = 4.184 J
$°C = \dfrac{(°F - 32)}{1.8}$	1 atm = 760 torr	1 kcal = 1000 cal
	1 mole (STP) = 22.4 L	**Water**
K = °C + 273	R = 0.0821 L · atm/mole · K	Heat of fusion = 80. cal/g; 334 J/g
	R = 62.4 L · mmHg/mole · K	Heat of vaporization = 540 cal/g; 2260 J/g
		Specific heat = 4.184 J/g°C; 1 cal/g°C

PREFIXES FOR METRIC (SI) UNITS

Prefix	Symbol	Power of Ten
Values greater than 1		
peta	P	10^{15}
tera	T	10^{12}
giga	G	10^{9}
mega	M	10^{6}
kilo	k	10^{3}
Values less than 1		
deci	d	10^{-1}
centi	c	10^{-2}
milli	m	10^{-3}
micro	μ	10^{-6}
nano	n	10^{-9}
pico	p	10^{-12}
femto	f	10^{-15}

FORMULAS AND MOLAR MASSES OF SOME TYPICAL COMPOUNDS

Name	Formula	Molar Mass (g/mole)	Name	Formula	Molar Mass (g/mole)
Ammonia	NH_3	17.0	Hydrogen chloride	HCl	36.5
Ammonium chloride	NH_4Cl	53.5	Iron(III) oxide	Fe_2O_3	159.8
Ammonium sulfate	$(NH_4)_2SO_4$	132.1	Magnesium oxide	MgO	40.3
Bromine	Br_2	159.8	Methane	CH_4	16.0
Butane	C_4H_{10}	58.0	Nitrogen	N_2	28.0
Calcium carbonate	$CaCO_3$	100.1	Oxygen	O_2	32.0
Calcium chloride	$CaCl_2$	111.1	Potassium carbonate	K_2CO_3	138.2
Calcium oxide	CaO	56.1	Propane	C_3H_8	44.0
Carbon dioxide	CO_2	44.0	Sodium chloride	$NaCl$	58.5
Chlorine	Cl_2	71.0	Sodium hydroxide	$NaOH$	40.0
Copper(II) sulfide	CuS	95.7	Sulfur dioxide	SO_2	64.1
Hydrogen	H_2	2.0	Water	H_2O	18.0